Virginia Life Science

interactive SCIENCE

Go to MyScienceOnline.co[m to]
experience science in a whole ne[w w]ay.

Interactive tools such as My Planet Diary connect you to the latest science happenings.

MY PLANET DIARY

- Search Earth's Journal for important science news from around the world.
- Use Earth's Calendar to find out when cool scientific events occur.
- Explore science Links to find even more exciting information about our planet.
- Visit Jack's Blog to be the first to know about what is going on in science!

PEARSON

Glenview, Illinois • Boston, Massachusetts • Chandler, Arizona • Upper Saddle River, New Jersey

Virginia • Science • Virginia • Science • Virginia • Science • Virginia • Science

You're an author!

As you write in this science book, your answers and personal discoveries will be recorded for you to keep, making this book unique to you. That is why you are one of the primary authors of this book.

In the space below, print your name, school, town, and state. Then write a short autobiography that includes your interests and accomplishments.

Your Photo

YOUR NAME

SCHOOL

TOWN, STATE

AUTOBIOGRAPHY

Acknowledgments appear on pages 553–557, which constitute an extension of this copyright page.

ISBN-13: 978-0-13-319782-2
ISBN-10: 0-13-319782-4
9 18

ON THE COVER
Northern Cardinal
The Northern Cardinal is the state bird of Virginia. The male is bright red and the female is brown with a dull red crest, wings, and tail. Cardinals do not migrate, so look for them year-round. Listen for their distinctive cheer-cheer-cheer or purty-purty-purty song.

Program Authors

KATHRYN THORNTON, Ph.D.
Professor and Associate Dean, School of Engineering and Applied Science, University of Virginia, Charlottesville, Virginia
Selected by NASA in May 1984, Dr. Kathryn Thornton is a veteran of four space flights. She has logged more than 975 hours in space, including more than 21 hours of extravehicular activity. As an author on the *Scott Foresman Science* series, Dr. Thornton's enthusiasm for science has inspired teachers around the globe.

DON BUCKLEY, M.Sc.
Information and Communications Technology Director, The School at Columbia University, New York, New York
A founder of New York City Independent School Technologists (NYCIST) and long-time chair of New York Association of Independent Schools' annual IT conference, Mr. Buckley has taught students on two continents and created multimedia and Internet-based instructional systems for schools worldwide.

ZIPPORAH MILLER, M.A.Ed.
Associate Executive Director for Professional Programs and Conferences, National Science Teachers Association, Arlington, Virginia
Ms. Zipporah Miller is a former K–12 science supervisor and STEM coordinator for the Prince George's County Public School District in Maryland. She is a science education consultant who has overseen curriculum development and staff training for more than 150 district science coordinators.

MICHAEL J. PADILLA, Ph.D.
Associate Dean and Director, Eugene P. Moore School of Education, Clemson University, Clemson, South Carolina
A former middle school teacher and a leader in middle school science education, Dr. Michael Padilla has served as president of the National Science Teachers Association and as a writer of the National Science Education Standards. He is professor of science education at Clemson University.

MICHAEL E. WYSESSION, Ph.D.
Associate Professor of Earth and Planetary Science, Washington University, St. Louis, Missouri
An author on more than 50 scientific publications, Dr. Wysession was awarded the prestigious Packard Foundation Fellowship and Presidential Faculty Fellowship for his research in geophysics. Dr. Wysession is an expert on Earth's inner structure and has mapped various regions of Earth using seismic tomography. He is known internationally for his work in geoscience education and outreach.

Instructional Design Author

GRANT WIGGINS, Ed.D.
President, Authentic Education, Hopewell, New Jersey
Dr. Wiggins is a co-author with Jay McTighe of *Understanding by Design, 2nd Edition* (ASCD 2005). His approach to instructional design provides teachers with a disciplined way of thinking about curriculum design, assessment, and instruction that moves teaching from covering content to ensuring understanding.

Planet Diary Author

JACK HANKIN
Science/Mathematics Teacher, The Hilldale School, Daly City, California, Founder, Planet Diary Web site
Mr. Hankin is the creator and writer of Planet Diary, a science current events Web site. He is passionate about bringing science news and environmental awareness into classrooms and offers numerous Planet Diary workshops at NSTA and other events to train middle and high school teachers.

ELL Consultant

JIM CUMMINS, Ph.D.
Professor and Canada Research Chair, Curriculum, Teaching and Learning department at the University of Toronto
Dr. Cummins focuses on literacy development in multilingual schools and the role of technology in promoting student learning across the curriculum. *Interactive Science* incorporates essential research-based principles for integrating language with the teaching of academic content based on his instructional framework.

Reading Consultant

HARVEY DANIELS, Ph.D.
Professor of Secondary Education, University of New Mexico, Albuquerque, New Mexico
Dr. Daniels is an international consultant to schools, districts, and educational agencies. He has authored or coauthored 13 books on language, literacy, and education. His most recent works are *Comprehension and Collaboration: Inquiry Circles in Action* and *Subjects Matter: Every Teacher's Guide to Content-Area Reading*.

Contributing Writers

Edward Aguado, Ph.D.
Professor, Department of Geography
San Diego State University
San Diego, California

Elizabeth Coolidge-Stolz, M.D.
Medical Writer
North Reading, Massachusetts

Donald L. Cronkite, Ph.D.
Professor of Biology
Hope College
Holland, Michigan

Jan Jenner, Ph.D.
Science Writer
Talladega, Alabama

Linda Cronin Jones, Ph.D.
Associate Professor of Science and Environmental Education
University of Florida
Gainesville, Florida

T. Griffith Jones, Ph.D.
Clinical Associate Professor of Science Education
College of Education
University of Florida
Gainesville, Florida

Andrew C. Kemp, Ph.D.
Teacher
Jefferson County Public Schools
Louisville, Kentucky

Matthew Stoneking, Ph.D.
Associate Professor of Physics
Lawrence University
Appleton, Wisconsin

R. Bruce Ward, Ed.D.
Senior Research Associate
Science Education Department
Harvard-Smithsonian Center for Astrophysics
Cambridge, Massachusetts

Content Reviewers

Paul D. Beale, Ph.D.
Department of Physics
University of Colorado at Boulder
Boulder, Colorado

Jeff R. Bodart, Ph.D.
Professor of Physical Sciences
Chipola College
Marianna, Florida

Joy Branlund, Ph.D.
Department of Earth Science
Southwestern Illinois College
Granite City, Illinois

Marguerite Brickman, Ph.D.
Division of Biological Sciences
University of Georgia
Athens, Georgia

Bonnie J. Brunkhorst, Ph.D.
Science Education and Geological Sciences
California State University
San Bernardino, California

Michael Castellani, Ph.D.
Department of Chemistry
Marshall University
Huntington, West Virginia

Charles C. Curtis, Ph.D.
Research Associate Professor of Physics
University of Arizona
Tucson, Arizona

Diane I. Doser, Ph.D.
Department of Geological Sciences
University of Texas
El Paso, Texas

Rick Duhrkopf, Ph.D.
Department of Biology
Baylor University
Waco, Texas

Alice K. Hankla, Ph.D.
The Galloway School
Atlanta, Georgia

Mark Henriksen, Ph.D.
Physics Department
University of Maryland
Baltimore, Maryland

Chad Hershock, Ph.D.
Center for Research on Learning and Teaching
University of Michigan
Ann Arbor, Michigan

Jeremiah N. Jarrett, Ph.D.
Department of Biology
Central Connecticut State University
New Britain, Connecticut

Scott L. Kight, Ph.D.
Department of Biology
Montclair State University
Montclair, New Jersey

Jennifer O. Liang, Ph.D.
Department of Biology
University of Minnesota–Duluth
Duluth, Minnesota

Joseph F. McCullough, Ph.D.
Physics Program Chair
Cabrillo College
Aptos, California

Heather Mernitz, Ph.D.
Department of Physical Science
Alverno College
Milwaukee, Wisconsin

Sadredin C. Moosavi, Ph.D.
Department of Earth and Environmental Sciences
Tulane University
New Orleans, Louisiana

David L. Reid, Ph.D.
Department of Biology
Blackburn College
Carlinville, Illinois

Scott M. Rochette, Ph.D.
Department of the Earth Sciences
SUNY College at Brockport
Brockport, New York

Karyn L. Rogers, Ph.D.
Department of Geological Sciences
University of Missouri
Columbia, Missouri

Laurence Rosenhein, Ph.D.
Department of Chemistry
Indiana State University
Terre Haute, Indiana

Sara Seager, Ph.D.
Department of Planetary Sciences and Physics
Massachusetts Institute of Technology
Cambridge, Massachusetts

Tom Shoberg, Ph.D.
Missouri University of Science and Technology
Rolla, Missouri

Patricia Simmons, Ph.D.
North Carolina State University
Raleigh, North Carolina

William H. Steinecker, Ph.D.
Research Scholar
Miami University
Oxford, Ohio

Paul R. Stoddard, Ph.D.
Department of Geology and Environmental Geosciences
Northern Illinois University
DeKalb, Illinois

John R. Villarreal, Ph.D.
Department of Chemistry
The University of Texas–Pan American
Edinburg, Texas

John R. Wagner, Ph.D.
Department of Geology
Clemson University
Clemson, South Carolina

Jerry Waldvogel, Ph.D.
Department of Biological Sciences
Clemson University
Clemson, South Carolina

Donna L. Witter, Ph.D.
Department of Geology
Kent State University
Kent, Ohio

Edward J. Zalisko, Ph.D.
Department of Biology
Blackburn College
Carlinville, Illinois

Special thanks to the Museum of Science, Boston, Massachusetts, and Ioannis Miaoulis, the Museum's president and director, for serving as content advisors for the technology and design strand in this program.

Content Reviewers

Karen Brewer, Ph.D.
Virginia Polytechnic Institute
Blacksburg, Virginia

John T. Haynes, Ph.D.
James Madison University
Harrisonburg, Virginia

Candace Lutzow-Felling, Ph.D.
Director of Education
The State Arboretum of Virginia
University of Virginia
Boyce, Virginia

Cortney V. Martin, Ph.D.
Virginia Polytechnic Institute
Blacksburg, Virginia

Teacher Reviewers

Julian G. Barnes
Coordinator of Science
Roanoke County Public Schools
Roanoke, Virginia

Patricia Colot
Taylor Middle School
Warrenton, Virginia

Veronica E. Haynes, Ph.D.
Senior Coordinator of Science
Norfolk Public Schools
Norfolk, Virginia

Sandra G. Robinson
Matoaca Middle School
Chesterfield, Virginia

Teacher Note Writers

Beth Evans
Sutherland Middle School
Charlottesville, Virginia

Asante Johnson, M.A.
George Washington Middle School #2
Alexandria, Virginia

Teacher Reviewers

Herb Bergamini
The Northwest School
Seattle, Washington

David R. Blakely
Arlington High School
Arlington, Massachusetts

Jane E. Callery
Capital Region Education Council
Hartford, Connecticut

Jeffrey C. Callister
Former Earth Science Instructor
Newburgh Free Academy
Newburgh, New York

Colleen Campos
Cherry Creek Schools
Aurora, Colorado

Scott Cordell
Amarillo Independent School District
Amarillo, Texas

Dan Gabel
Consulting Teacher, Science
Montgomery County Public Schools
Montgomery County, Maryland

Wayne Goates
Kansas Polymer Ambassador
Intersociety Polymer Education Council (IPEC)
Wichita, Kansas

Katherine Bobay Graser
Mint Hill Middle School
Charlotte, North Carolina

Darcy Hampton
Science Department Chair
Deal Middle School
Washington, D.C.

Sean S. Houseknecht
Elizabethtown Area Middle School
Elizabethtown, Pennsylvania

Tanisha L. Johnson
Prince George's County Public Schools
Lanham, Maryland

Karen E. Kelly
Pierce Middle School
Waterford, Michigan

Dave J. Kelso
Manchester Central High School
Manchester, New Hampshire

Beverly Crouch Lyons
Career Center High School
Winston-Salem, North Carolina

Angie L. Matamoros, Ed.D.
ALM Consulting
Weston, Florida

Corey Mayle
Durham Public Schools
Durham, North Carolina

Keith W. McCarthy
George Washington Middle School
Wayne, New Jersey

Timothy McCollum
Charleston Middle School
Charleston, Illinois

Bruce A. Mellin
Cambridge College
Cambridge, Massachusetts

John Thomas Miller
Thornapple Kellogg High School
Middleville, Michigan

Randy Mousley
Dean Ray Stucky Middle School
Wichita, Kansas

Yolanda O. Peña
John F. Kennedy Junior High School
West Valley, Utah

Kathleen M. Poe
Fletcher Middle School
Jacksonville Beach, Florida

Judy Pouncey
Thomasville Middle School
Thomasville, North Carolina

Vickki Lynne Reese
Mad River Middle School
Dayton, Ohio

Bronwyn W. Robinson
Director of Curriculum
Algiers Charter Schools Association
New Orleans, Louisiana

Shirley Rose
Lewis and Clark Middle School
Tulsa, Oklahoma

Linda Sandersen
Sally Ride Academy
Whitefish Bay, Wisconsin

Roxanne Scala
Schuyler-Colfax Middle School
Wayne, New Jersey

Patricia M. Shane, Ph.D.
Associate Director
Center for Mathematics & Science Education
University of North Carolina at Chapel Hill
Chapel Hill, North Carolina

Bradd A. Smithson
Science Curriculum Coordinator
John Glenn Middle School
Bedford, Massachusetts

Sharon Stroud
Consultant
Colorado Springs, Colorado

Master Teacher Board

Emily Compton
Park Forest Middle School
Baton Rouge, Louisiana

Georgi Delgadillo
East Valley School District
Spokane Valley, Washington

Treva Jeffries
Toledo Public Schools
Toledo, Ohio

James W. Kuhl
Central Square Middle School
Central Square, New York

Bonnie Mizell
Howard Middle School
Orlando, Florida

Joel Palmer, Ed.D.
Mesquite Independent School District
Mesquite, Texas

Leslie Pohley
Largo Middle School
Largo, Florida

Susan M. Pritchard, Ph.D.
Washington Middle School
La Habra, California

Anne Rice
Woodland Middle School
Gurnee, Illinois

Richard Towle
Noblesville Middle School
Noblesville, Indiana

Virginia Table of Contents

CHAPTER 1

What Is Science?

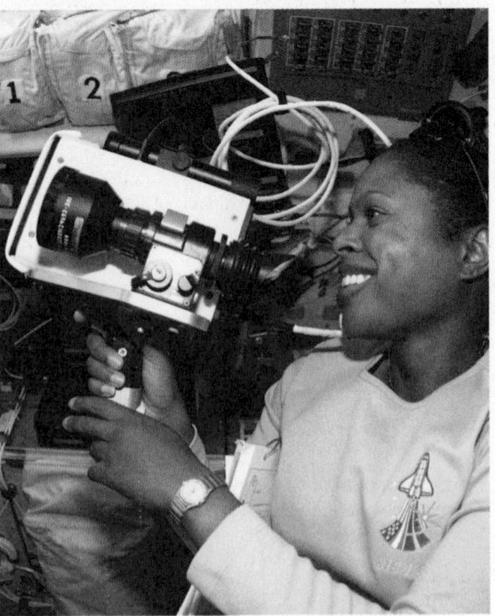

Enter the Lab zone for hands-on inquiry.

my science online.com

Go to MyScienceOnline.com to interact with this chapter's content. Keyword: What Is Science?

CHAPTER 2

The Tools of Science

Enter the Lab zone for hands-on inquiry.

my science online.com

Go to MyScienceOnline.com to interact with this chapter's content. Keyword: The Tools of Science

CHAPTER 3

Introduction to Living Things

Enter the Lab zone for hands-on inquiry.

Chapter Lab Investigation:
• Directed Inquiry: Please Pass the Bread
• Open Inquiry: Please Pass the Bread

Inquiry Warm-Ups: • Is It Living or Nonliving? • Can You Organize a Junk Drawer? • Which Organism Goes Where? • Observing Similarities

Quick Labs: • React! • Compare Broth Samples • Classifying Seeds • Make a Classification Chart • Living Mysteries • Staining Leaves • Common Ancestors

my science online.com

Go to MyScienceOnline.com to interact with this chapter's content. Keyword: Introduction to Living Things

UNTAMED SCIENCE
• What Can You Explore in a Swamp?

PLANET DIARY
• Introduction to Living Things

INTERACTIVE ART
• Redi's and Pasteur's Experiments
• Taxonomic Key

ART IN MOTION
• Finding a Common Ancestor

VIRTUAL LAB
• Classifying Life

CHAPTER 4

Introduction to Cells

Enter the Lab zone for hands-on inquiry.

Chapter Lab Investigation:
• Directed Inquiry: Design and Build a Microscope
• Open Inquiry: Design and Build a Microscope

Inquiry Warm-Ups: • What Can You See? • How Large Are Cells? • Detecting Starch • Diffusion in Action

Quick Labs: • Comparing Cells • Observing Cells • Gelatin Cell Model • Tissues, Organs, Systems • What Is a Compound? • What's That Taste? • Effect of Concentration on Diffusion

MY SCIENCE ONLINE.com

Go to MyScienceOnline.com to interact with this chapter's content. Keyword: Introduction to Cells

UNTAMED SCIENCE
• Touring Hooke's Crib!

PLANET DIARY
• Introduction to Cells

INTERACTIVE ART
• Plant and Animal Cells • Specialized Cells

ART IN MOTION
• Passive and Active Transport

VIRTUAL LAB
• How Can You Observe Cells?

CHAPTER 5 Cell Processes and Energy

Enter the Lab zone for hands-on inquiry.

Chapter Lab Investigation:
- Directed Inquiry: Exhaling Carbon Dioxide
- Open Inquiry: Exhaling Carbon Dioxide

Inquiry Warm-Ups: • Where Does the Energy Come From? • Cellular Respiration • What Are the Yeast Cells Doing?

Quick Labs: • Energy From the Sun • Looking at Pigments • Observing Fermentation • Observing Mitosis • Modeling Mitosis

my science online.com

Go to MyScienceOnline.com to interact with this chapter's content. Keyword: Cell Processes and Energy

UNTAMED SCIENCE
- Yum...Eating Solar Energy

PLANET DIARY
- Cell Processes and Energy

INTERACTIVE ART
- Photosynthesis • Cellular Respiration
- Cell Growth and Division

ART IN MOTION
- Opposite Processes

VIRTUAL LAB • The Inner Workings of Photosynthesis

CHAPTER 6

Genetics: The Science of Heredity

Enter the Lab zone for hands-on inquiry.

Chapter Lab Investigation:
• Directed Inquiry: Make the Right Call!
• Open Inquiry: Make the Right Call!

Inquiry Warm-Ups: • What Does the Father Look Like? • What's the Chance? • Observing Traits • Which Chromosome Is Which?

Quick Labs: • Observing Pistils and Stamens • Inferring the Parent Generation • Coin Crosses • Patterns of Inheritance • Is It All in the Genes? • Chromosomes and Inheritance • Modeling Meiosis

my science online.com

Go to MyScienceOnline.com to interact with this chapter's content. Keyword: Genetics: The Science of Heredity

UNTAMED SCIENCE
• Where'd You Get Those Genes?

PLANET DIARY
• Genetics: The Science of Heredity

INTERACTIVE ART
• Punnett Squares • Effects of Environment on Genetic Traits

ART IN MOTION
• Meiosis

CHAPTER 7

DNA: The Code of Life

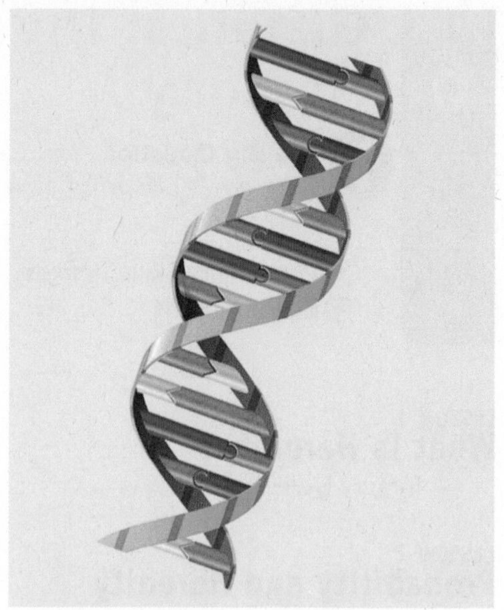

Enter the Lab zone for hands-on inquiry.

Chapter Lab Investigation:
- Directed Inquiry: Guilty or Innocent?
- Open Inquiry: Guilty or Innocent?

Inquiry Warm-Ups: • Can You Crack the Code? • What Is RNA? • Oops!

Quick Labs: • Modeling the Genetic Code • Modeling Protein Synthesis • Effects of Mutations • What Happens When There Are Too Many Cells?

my science online.com

Go to MyScienceOnline.com to interact with this chapter's content. Keyword: DNA: The Code of Life

UNTAMED SCIENCE
- Why Is This Lobster Blue?

PLANET DIARY
- DNA: The Code of Life

INTERACTIVE ART
- Copying DNA • Making Proteins

ART IN MOTION
- Understanding DNA

VIRTUAL LAB
- Track Down the Genetic Mutation

CHAPTER 8

Human Genetics and Genetic Technology

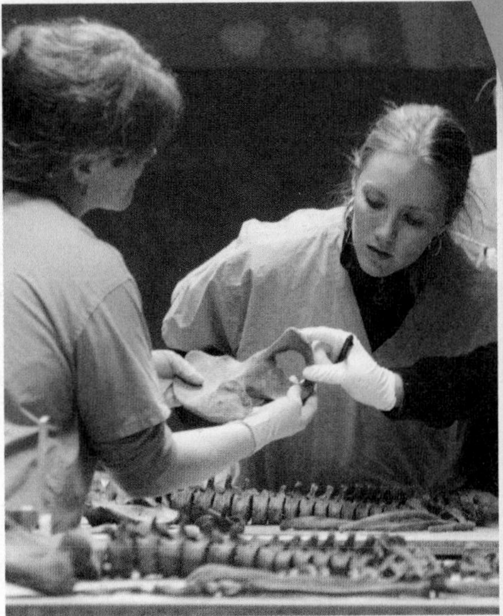

Enter the Lab zone for hands-on inquiry.

Chapter Lab Investigation:
• Directed Inquiry: How Are Genes on the Sex Chromosomes Inherited?
• Open Inquiry: How Are Genes on the Sex Chromosomes Inherited?

Inquiry Warm-Ups: • How Tall Is Tall? • How Many Chromosomes? • What Do Fingerprints Reveal? • Using Genetic Information

Quick Labs: • The Eyes Have It • What Went Wrong? • Family Puzzle • Selective Breeding • Extraction in Action

my science online.com

Go to MyScienceOnline.com to interact with this chapter's content. Keyword: Human Genetics and Genetic Technology

UNTAMED SCIENCE
• The Case of the X-Linked Gene

PLANET DIARY
• Human Genetics and Genetic Technology

INTERACTIVE ART
• Pedigree • DNA Fingerprinting

ART IN MOTION
• Understanding Genetic Engineering

VIRTUAL LAB
• Why Does My Brother Have It and I Don't?

CHAPTER 9

Change Over Time

Enter the Lab zone for hands-on inquiry.

Chapter Lab Investigation:
- Directed Inquiry: Nature at Work
- Open Inquiry: Nature at Work

Inquiry Warm-Ups: • How Do Living Things Vary? • How Can You Classify a Species? • Making a Timeline

Quick Labs: • Bird Beak Adaptations • Finding Proof • Large-Scale Isolation • Slow or Fast?

my science online.com

Go to MyScienceOnline.com to interact with this chapter's content. Keyword: Change Over Time

UNTAMED SCIENCE
- Why Would a Fish Have Red Lips?

PLANET DIARY
- Change Over Time

INTERACTIVE ART
- What Is It Adapted To?
- Homologous Structures

ART IN MOTION
- Rate of Evolution

REAL-WORLD INQUIRY
- What Affects Natural Selection?

CHAPTER 10

Plants

Enter the Lab zone for hands-on inquiry.

Chapter Lab Investigation:
• Directed Inquiry: Investigating Stomata
• Open Inquiry: Investigating Stomata

Inquiry Warm-Ups: • What Do Leaves Reveal About Plants? • Will Mosses Absorb Water? • Which Plant Part Is It? • Make the Pollen Stick • Can a Plant Respond To Touch? • Feeding the World

Quick Labs: • Algae and Other Plants • Local Plant Diversity • Masses of Mosses • Examining a Fern • Common Characteristics • The In-Seed Story • Modeling Flowers • Plant Life Cycles • Where Are the Seeds? • Watching Roots Grow • Seasonal Changes • Everyday Plants

my science online.com

Go to MyScienceOnline.com to interact with this chapter's content. Keyword: Plants

PLANET DIARY
• Plants

INTERACTIVE ART
• Plant Cell Structures • The Structure of a Flower • Seed Dispersal

ART IN MOTION
• Plant Tropisms

VIRTUAL LAB
• Classifying Plants

Introduction to Animals

Enter the Lab zone for hands-on inquiry.

Chapter Lab Investigations:
Open Inquiry: • Earthworm Responses • One for All
Directed Inquiry: • Earthworm Responses • One for All

Inquiry Warm-Ups: • Is It an Animal? • How Many Ways Can You Fold It? • How Do Natural and Synthetic Sponges Compare? • How Is an Umbrella Like a Skeleton? • Exploring Vertebrates • Communicating Without Words

Quick Labs: • Get Moving • Classifying Animals • Organizing Animal Bodies • Front-End Advantages • Characteristics of Vertebrates • Keeping Warm • It's Plane to See • Animal Communication • Behavior Cycles

my science online.com

Go to MyScienceOnline.com to interact with this chapter's content. Keyword: Introduction to Animals

PLANET DIARY
• Introduction to Animals

INTERACTIVE ART
• Structure of a Sponge • Where Could They Live?

ART IN MOTION
• Invertebrate Diversity

REAL-WORLD INQUIRY
• Cyclic Behavior

VIRTUAL LAB
• Classifying Animals

CHAPTER 12

Populations and Communities

Enter the Lab zone for hands-on inquiry.

Chapter Lab Investigation:
• Directed Inquiry: World in a Bottle
• Open Inquiry: World in a Bottle

Inquiry Warm-Ups: • What's in the Scene? • Populations • Can You Hide a Butterfly? • How Communities Change

Quick Labs: • Organisms and Their Habitats • Organizing an Ecosystem • Growing and Shrinking • Elbow Room • Adaptations for Survival • Competition and Predation • Type of Symbiosis • Primary or Secondary

my science online.com

Go to MyScienceOnline.com to interact with this chapter's content. Keyword: Populations and Communities

UNTAMED SCIENCE
• Clown(fish)ing Around

PLANET DIARY
• Populations and Communities

INTERACTIVE ART
• Changes in Population • Animal Defense Strategies

ART IN MOTION
• Primary and Secondary Succession

REAL-WORLD INQUIRY
• An Ecological Mystery

CHAPTER 13

Ecosystems and Biomes

Enter the Lab zone for hands-on inquiry.

Chapter Lab Investigation:
• Directed Inquiry: Ecosystem Food Chains
• Open Inquiry: Ecosystem Food Chains

Inquiry Warm-Ups: • Where Did Your Dinner Come From? • Are You Part of a Cycle? • How Much Rain Is That? • Where Does It Live? • How Can You Move a Seed?

Quick Labs: • Observing Decomposition • Following Water • Carbon and Oxygen Blues • Playing Nitrogen Cycle Roles • Inferring Forest Climates • Dissolved Oxygen • Relating Continental Drift to Dispersal

my science online.com

Go to MyScienceOnline.com to interact with this chapter's content. Keyword: Ecosystems and Biomes

UNTAMED SCIENCE
• Give Me That Carbon!

PLANET DIARY
• Ecosystems and Biomes

INTERACTIVE ART
• Ocean Food Web • Water Cycle • Cycles of Matter • Earth's Biomes • Continental Drift • Seed Dispersal

VIRTUAL LAB
• Where's All the Food?

CHAPTER 14

Ecosystems and Human Activity

Enter the Lab zone for hands-on inquiry.

Chapter Lab Investigation:
• Directed Inquiry: Investigating Soils and Drainage
• Open Inquiry: Investigating Soils and Drainage

Inquiry Warm-Ups: • What Can You Do to Protect Land and Soil Near Your School? • How Can You Keep Soil From Washing Away? • How Much Variety Is There?

Quick Labs: • Which Type of Pollution Is Worst? • What Can You Do to Reduce Land Pollution? • Soil Conservation • Modeling Keystone Species • Grocery Gene Pool • Humans and Biodiversity

my science online.com

Go to MyScienceOnline.com to interact with this chapter's content. Keyword: Ecosystems and Human Activity

UNTAMED SCIENCE
• The Great Macaw Debate

PLANET DIARY
• Value of Biodiversity

INTERACTIVE ART
• Reducing Land Pollution

REAL-WORLD INQUIRY
• Soil Conservation

VIRTUAL LAB
• Human Impact on Biodiversity

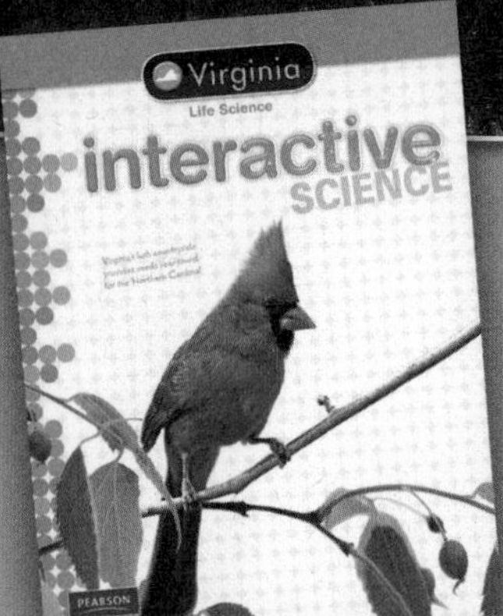

Virginia

interactive SCIENCE

Interactive Science

Virginia Interactive Science is a program that features 3 pathways to match the way you learn.

- The write-in student edition enables you to become an active participant as you read about science.
- A variety of hands-on activities will not only engage you but also provide you with a deep understanding of the Virginia Standards of Learning.
- Go to MyScienceOnline.com to access a wide array of digital resources built especially for Virginia students like you!

Interact with your textbook.

Interact with inquiry.

Interact online.

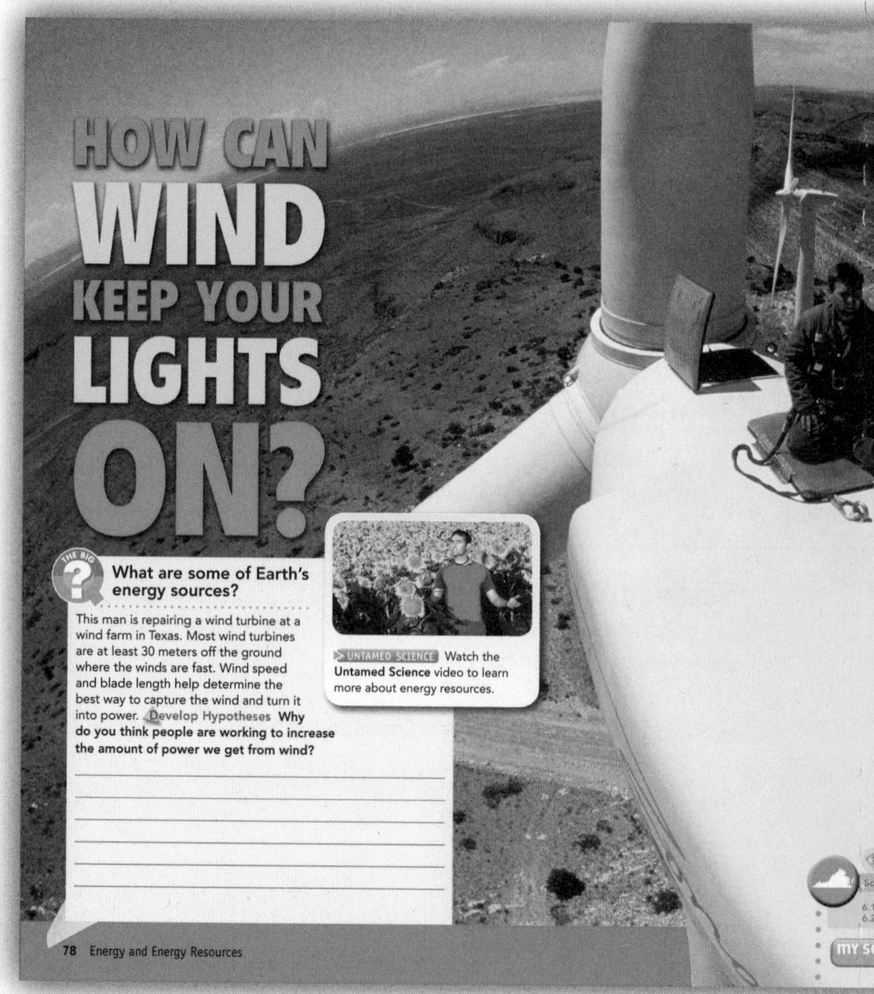

Focus on the Virginia Standards

Each chapter begins with a Big Question. This Big Question sets a clear learning target and helps you develop a deeper understanding of the Virginia Standards of Learning.

Built for Virginia

Fully aligned to the Virginia Standards of Learning, Virginia Interactive Science provides comprehensive support to prepare you for the SOL test!

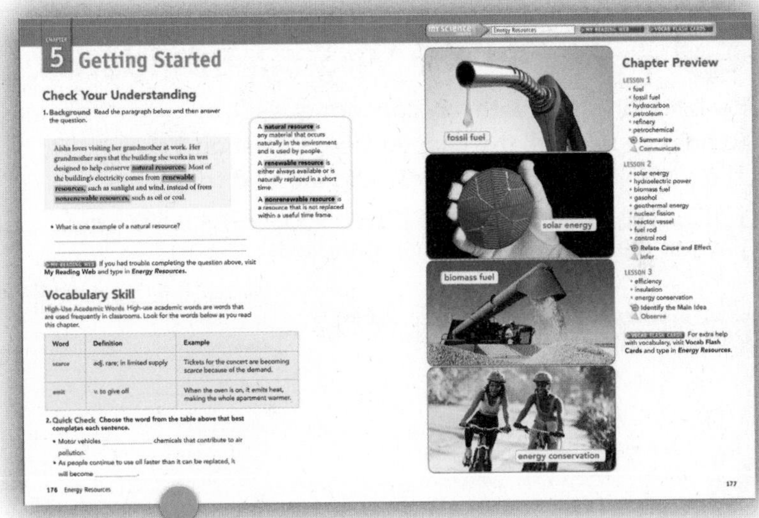

Build Reading, Inquiry, and Vocabulary Skills

- In every lesson you will learn new Reading and Inquiry skills to help you read and think like a scientist.
- Go online to MyScienceOnline.com and click on My Reading Web to get additional reading at your level.

my science online .com

Go Online!

At MyScienceOnline.com, you will find a variety of engaging digital resources such as the Untamed Science videos. Follow the Untamed Science video crew as they travel the globe exploring the Big Ideas of Science.

Unlocking the Virginia Standards

my science online .com

Go to MyScienceOnline.com to access a wide array of digital resources such as Virtual Labs, additional My Planet Diary activities, and Got It? assessments with instant feedback.

Focus on the Virginia Standards

Each lesson starts with key concept questions to help you unlock the chapter's Big Question. The Virginia Standards of Learning are tied to the key concept questions. That means when you see a key, you are learning your Virginia Standards.

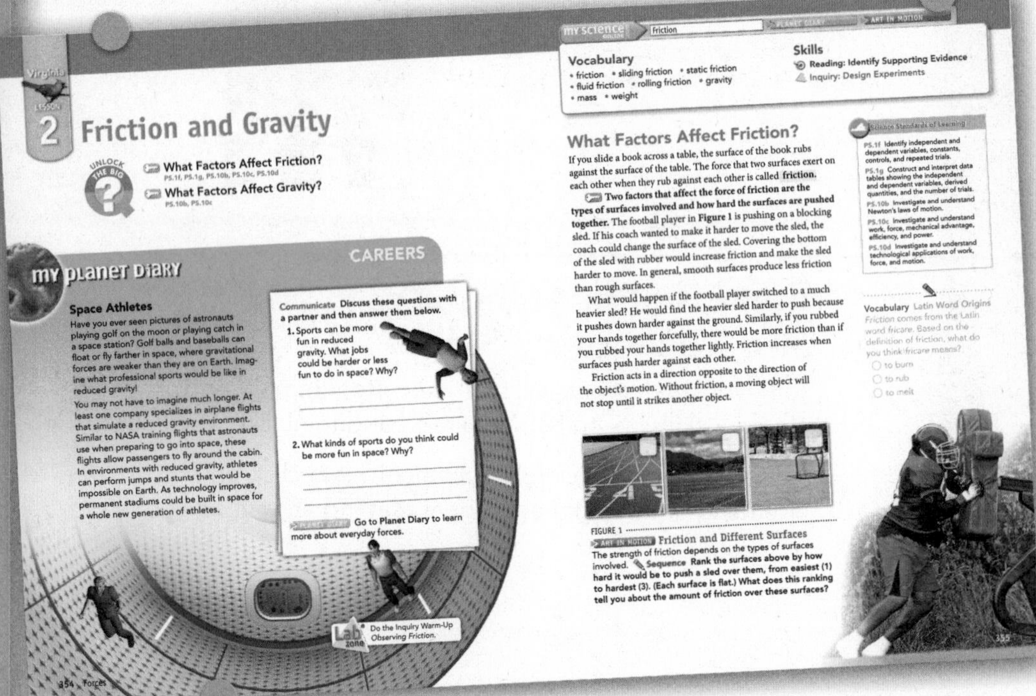

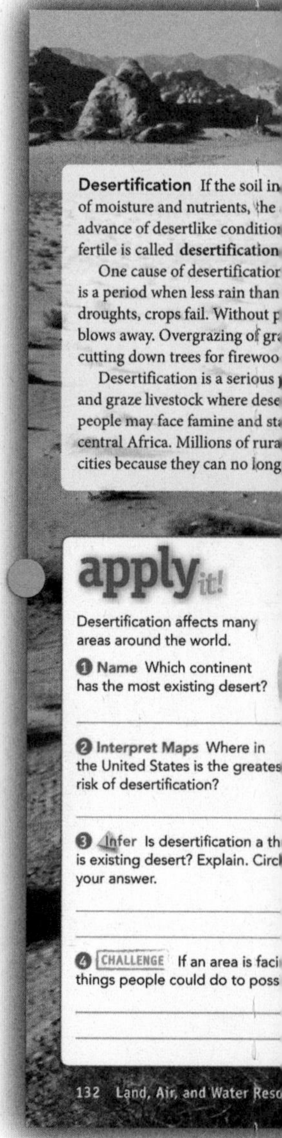

my planet Diary

At the start of each lesson, My Planet Diary will introduce you to amazing events, significant people, and important discoveries in science or help you to overcome common misconceptions about science concepts.

apply it!

Elaborate further with the Apply It activities. This is your opportunity to take what you've learned and apply those skills to new situations.

Explore the Virginia Standards Through Inquiry

Look for the Lab Zone triangle throughout your lesson. This means that it's time to do a hands-on inquiry lab. There's a Lab Zone activity for each key question—that means you can learn each Virginia content standard as well as the process standards through hands-on inquiry!

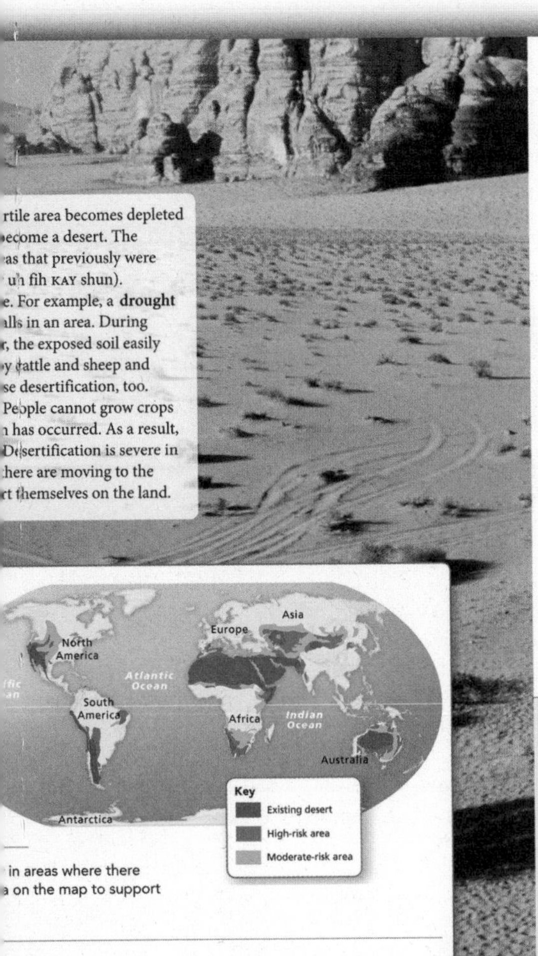
rtile area becomes depleted
ecome a desert. The
as that previously were
uh fih KAY shun).
e. For example, a **drought**
alls in an area. During
r, the exposed soil easily
y cattle and sheep and
se desertification, too.
People cannot grow crops
n has occurred. As a result,
Desertification is severe in
here are moving to the
rt themselves on the land.

in areas where there
a on the map to support

tification, what are some
its effects?

Land Reclamation Fortunately, it is possible to replace land damaged by erosion or mining. The process of restoring an area of land to a more productive state is called **land reclamation.** In addition to restoring land for agriculture, land reclamation can restore habitats for wildlife. Many different types of land reclamation projects are currently underway all over the world. But it is generally more difficult and expensive to restore damaged land and soil than it is to protect those resources in the first place. In some cases, the land may not return to its original state.

FIGURE 4
Land Reclamation
These pictures show land before and after it was mined.
Communicate Below the pictures, write a story about what happened to the land.

Do the Quick Lab *Modeling Soil Conservation.*

Assess Your Understanding

1a. Review Subsoil has (less/more) plant and animal matter than topsoil.

b. Explain What can happen to soil if plants are removed?

c. Apply Concepts Wha... that could prevent ... land reclamation?

got it? ....

○ I get it! Now I know that soil management is important because

○ I need extra help with

Go to MY SCIENCE COACH online for help with this subject.

got it?

Evaluate Your Progress

After answering the Got It question, think about how you're doing. Did you get it or do you need a little help? Remember, **MY SCIENCE COACH** is there for you if you need extra help.

Assessing the Virginia Standards

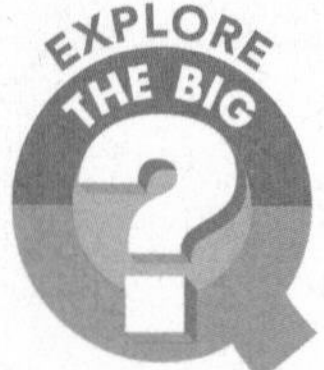

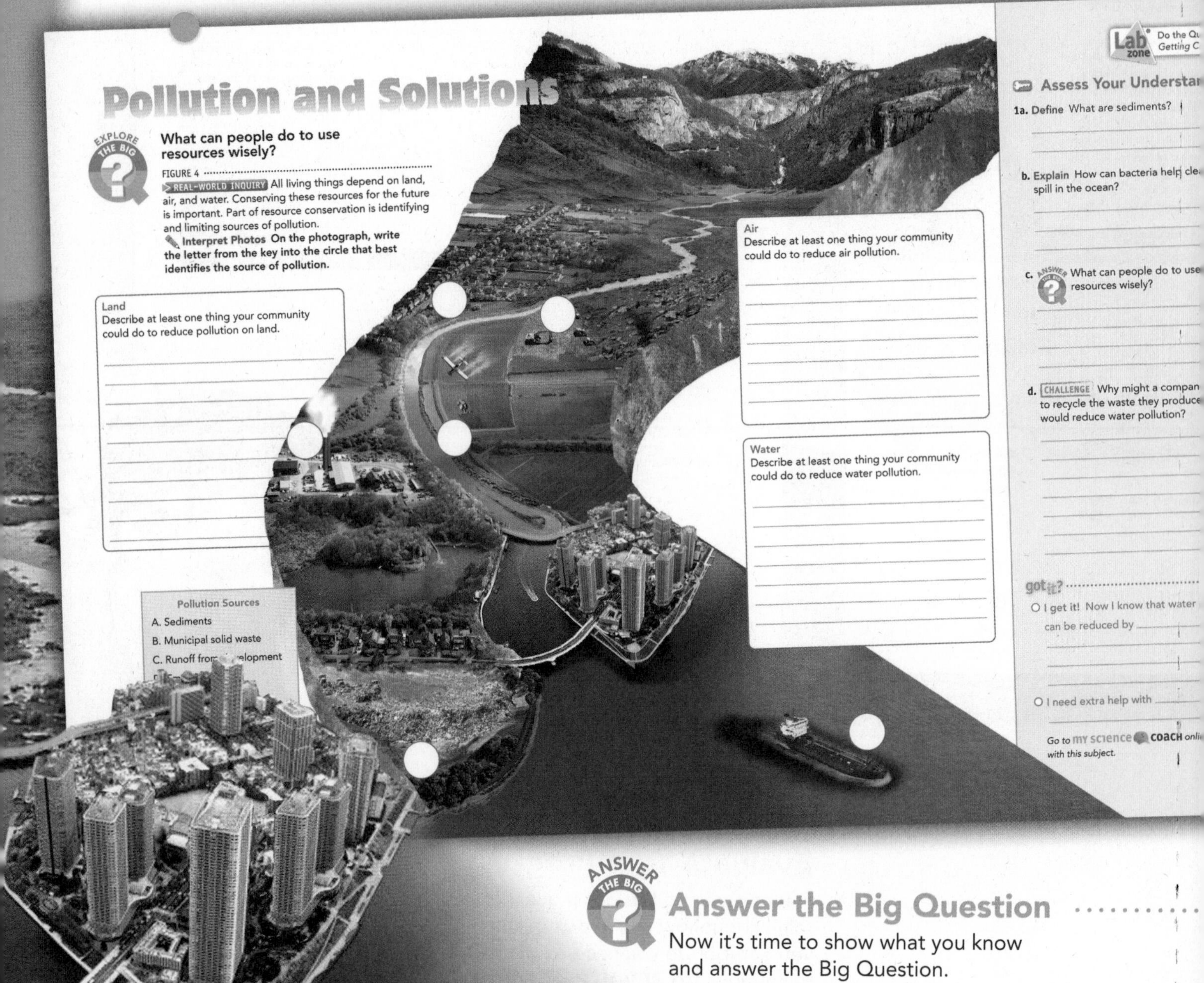

Explore the Big Question

At one point in the chapter, you'll have the opportunity to take all that you've learned to further explore the Big Question.

Answer the Big Question

Now it's time to show what you know and answer the Big Question.

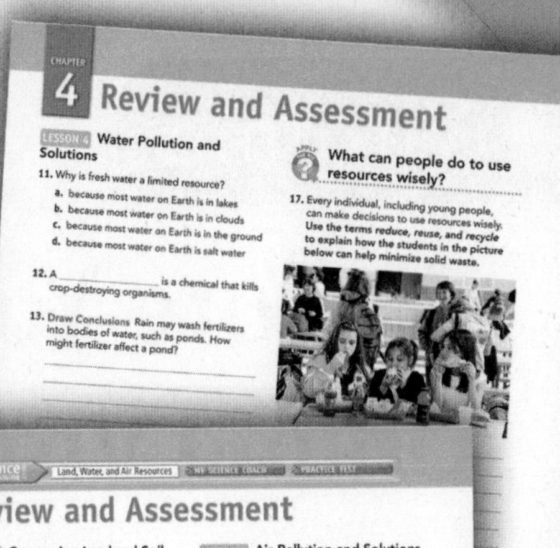

Review What You've Learned

Use the Chapter Study Guide to review the Big Question and prepare for the test.

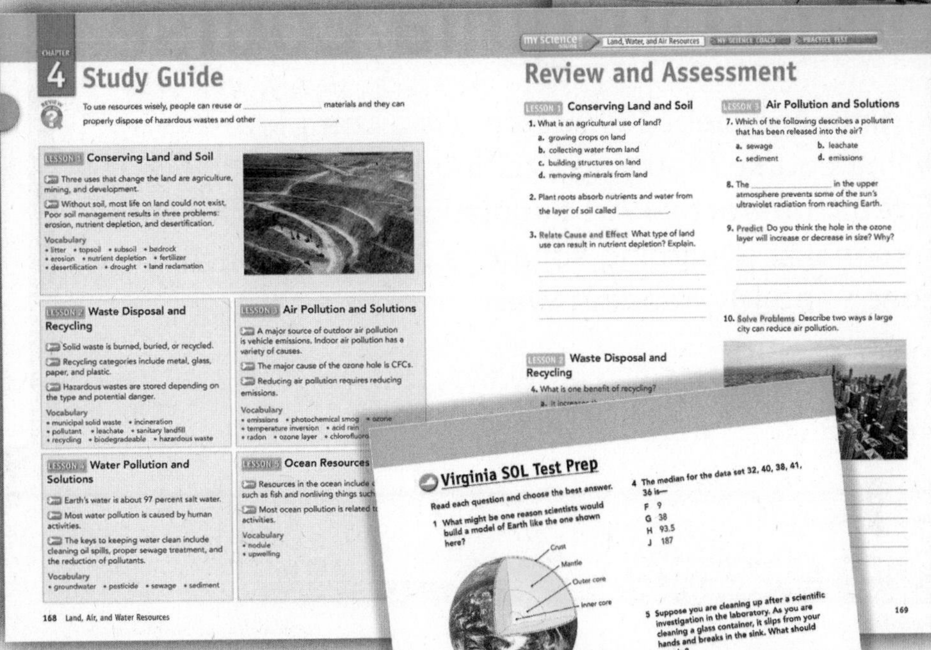

Virginia SOL Test Prep

Read each question and choose the best answer.

1 What might be one reason scientists would build a model of Earth like the one shown here?

Crust
Mantle
Outer core
Inner core

A to show the color of the continents
B to show the depths of Earth's oceans
C to show the layers of Earth
D to show pressure inside Earth

2 Nicole measured the height of her locker as 39.8 cm, 42.3 cm, 42.0 cm, and 43.1 cm. The locker is actually 45.5 cm. Which best describes Nicole's measurements?

F They were accurate.
G They were precise.
H They were both accurate and precise.
J They were neither accurate nor precise.

3 Which SI unit would you use to measure the volume of a tomato?

A gram
B grams per cubic meter
C cubic centimeter
D newton

4 The median for the data set 32, 40, 38, 41, 36 is—

F 9
G 38
H 93.5
J 187

5 Suppose you are cleaning up after a scientific investigation in the laboratory. As you are cleaning a glass container, it slips from your hands and breaks in the sink. What should you do?

A Pick up the broken glass.
B Leave the broken glass in the sink.
C Tell your teacher or another adult in the room.
D Recycle the broken glass.

6 What kind of trend do the data show?

Ant Population
Days

F linear
G positive
H no trend
J nonlinear

85

Practice the Virginia Standards

Practice key concepts at the end of each chapter in the SOL test format to prepare you for the "big test."

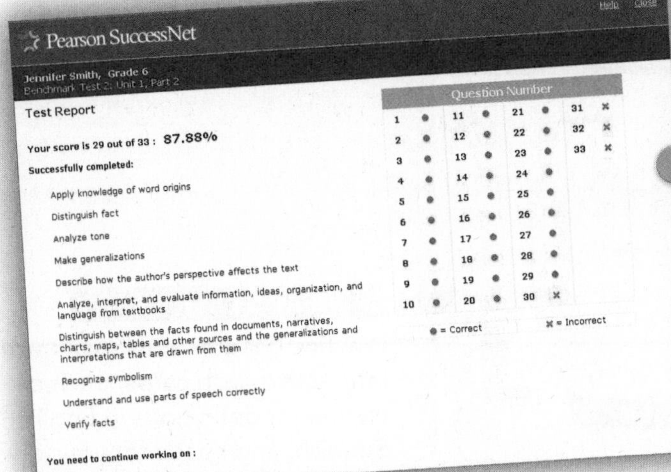

MY SCIENCE ONLINE.com

Assess the Virginia Standards Online

Go to MyScienceOnline.com to show what you know and get extra help. Through Pearson SuccessNet™, you can take benchmark assessments online. Activities are assigned to you immediately based on your performance on each Virginia Standard of Learning.

Explore Your Complete Online Virginia Course

Virginia *MyScienceOnline.com* is a complete online course featuring exciting Untamed Science Videos, Interactive Art Simulations, and innovative personalized learning solutions like My Science Coach and My Reading Web.

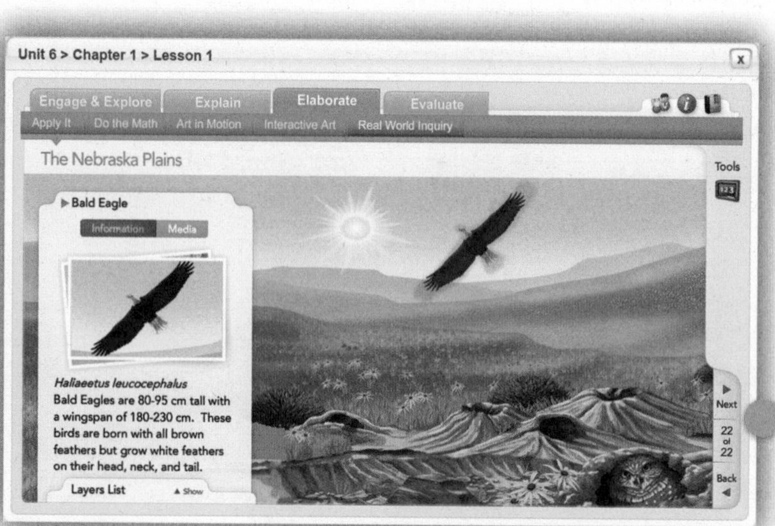

INTERACTIVE ART

At MyScienceOnline.com, many of the beautiful visuals in your book become interactive so you can extend your learning.

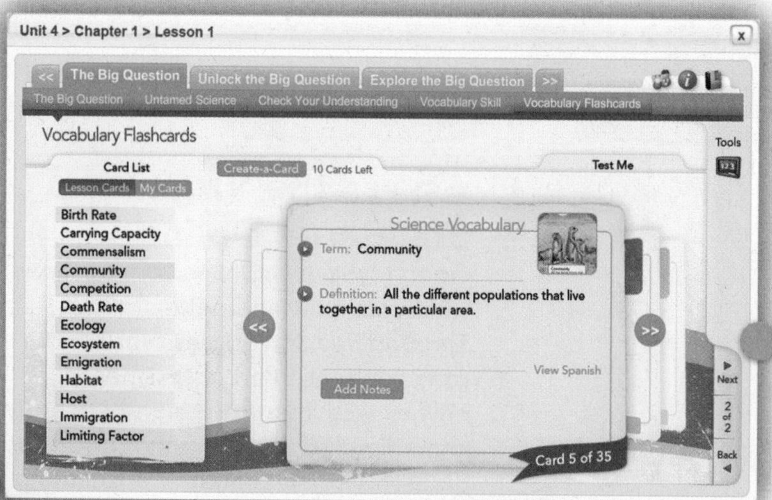

VOCAB FLASH CARDS

Practice chapter vocabulary with interactive flash cards. Each card has an image, definitions in English and Spanish, and space for your own notes.

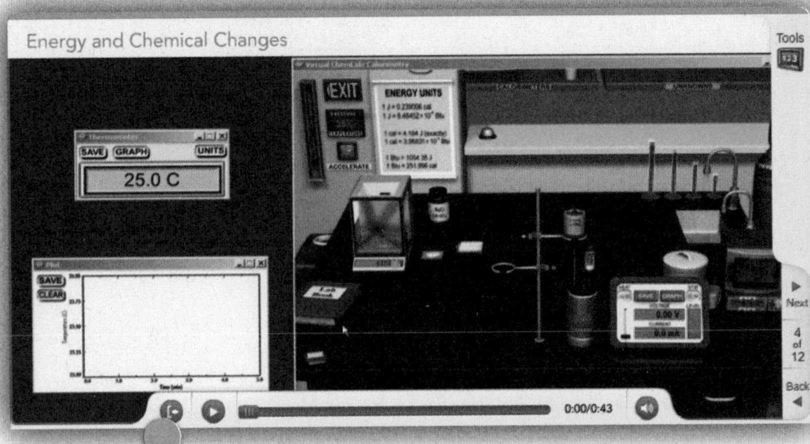

VIRTUAL LAB

Get more practice with realistic virtual labs. Interact with on-line labs without costly equipment or clean-up.

Your Virginia Online Student Edition

Create an online notebook! Highlighted important information and post-it notes are saved in your profile.

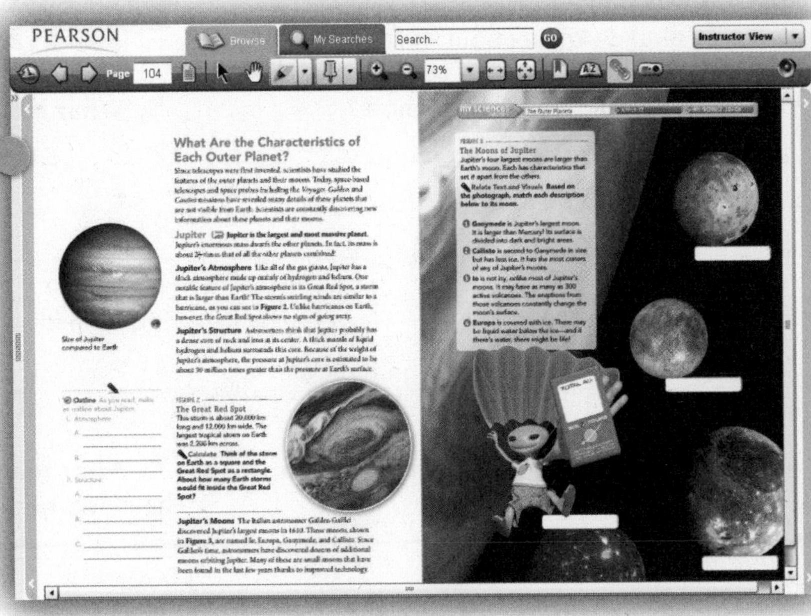

BIG IDEAS OF SCIENCE

Have you ever worked on a jigsaw puzzle? Usually a puzzle has a theme that leads you to group the pieces by what they have in common. But until you put all the pieces together you can't solve the puzzle. Studying science is similar to solving a puzzle. The big ideas of science are like puzzle themes. To understand big ideas, scientists ask questions. The answers to those questions are like pieces of a puzzle. Each chapter in this book asks a big question to help you think about a big idea of science. By answering the big questions, you will get closer to understanding the big idea.

Before you read each chapter, write about what you know and what more you'd like to know.

BIGIDEA

Scientists use scientific inquiry to explain the natural world.

Scientific inquiry requires a logical way of thinking based on gathering and evaluating evidence.

What do you already know about how scientists investigate the natural world?

What more would you like to know?

Big Question:

How do scientists investigate the natural world? Chapter 1

After reading the chapter, write what you have learned about the Big Idea.

BIGIDEA

Scientists use mathematics in many ways.

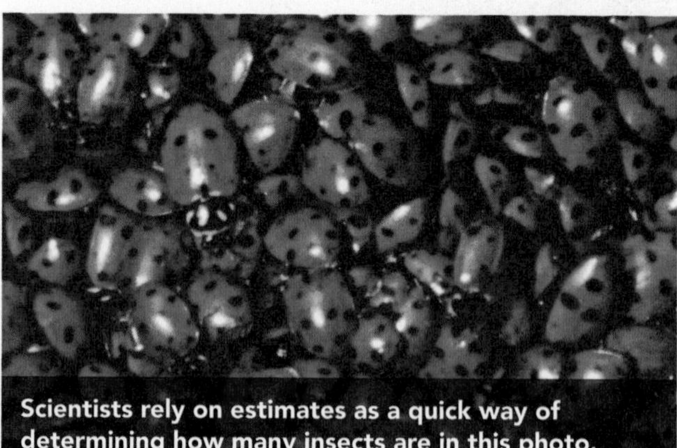

Scientists rely on estimates as a quick way of determining how many insects are in this photo.

Which tools have you used to study science?

What more would you like to know?

Big Question:

How important is mathematics to the work of scientists? Chapter 2

After reading the chapter, write what you have learned about the Big Idea.

BIGIDEA

Living things are made of cells.

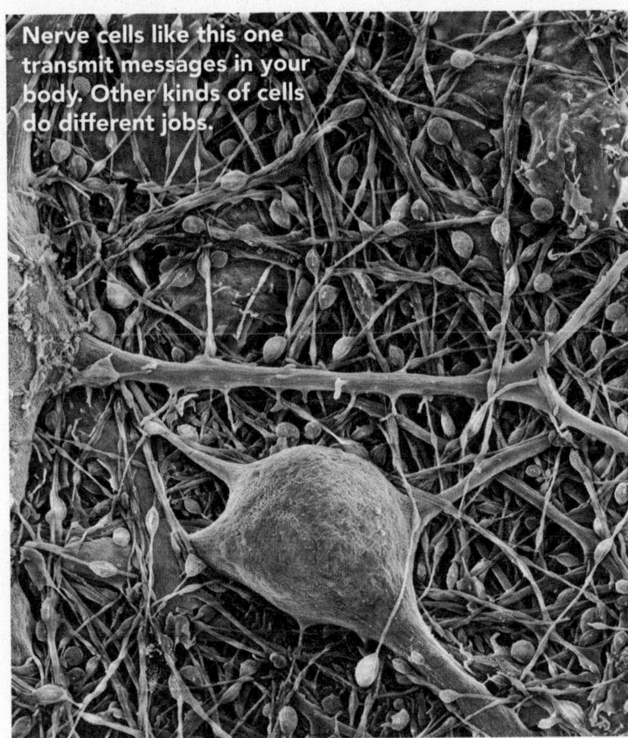

Nerve cells like this one transmit messages in your body. Other kinds of cells do different jobs.

What do you already know about what a cell does? What more would you like to know?

Big Questions:

How are living things alike yet different? Chapter 3

What are cells made of? Chapter 4

After reading the chapter, write what you have learned about the Big Idea.

BIGIDEA

Living things get and use energy.

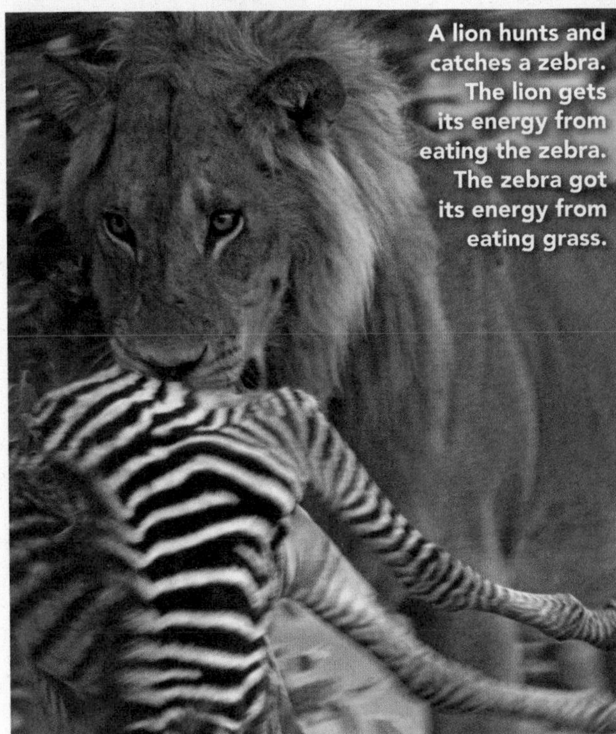

A lion hunts and catches a zebra. The lion gets its energy from eating the zebra. The zebra got its energy from eating grass.

What do you already know about how animals and plants get food and energy? What more would you like to know?

Big Question:

How do living things get energy? Chapter 5

After reading the chapter, write what you have learned about the Big Idea.

BIGIDEA

Genetic information passes from parents to offspring.

Once in a while, a koala joey is born with white fur instead of the usual gray fur. Even with such a striking difference, you can tell the joey is related to its mother.

What do you already know about how offspring resemble their parents? What more would you like to know?

Big Questions:

- Why don't offspring always look like their parents? Chapter 6
- What does DNA do? Chapter 7
- How can genetic information be used? Chapter 8

After reading the chapters, write what you have learned about the Big Idea.

BIGIDEA

Living things change over time.

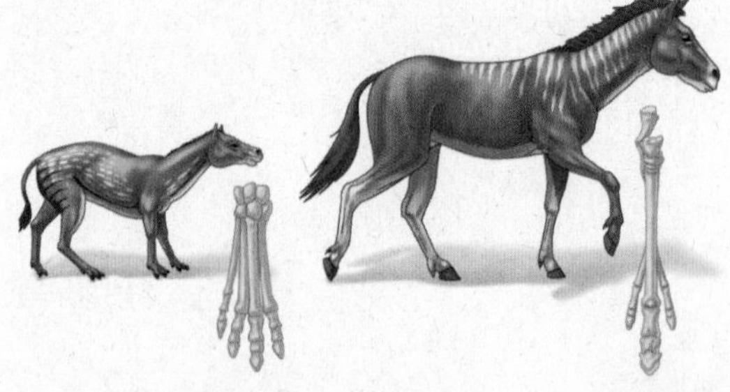

Modern horses are descended from much smaller animals with toes instead of hooves.

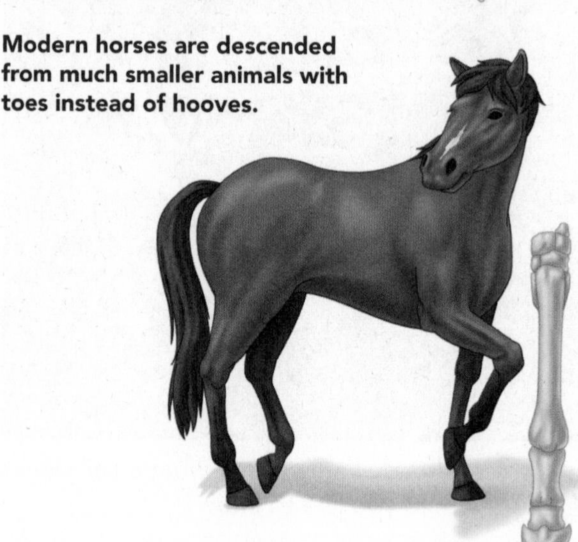

What do you already know about how life forms change? What more would you like to know?

Big Question:

- How do life forms change over time? Chapter 9

After reading the chapter, write what you have learned about the Big Idea.

BIGIDEA

Living things are alike yet different.

Grasses and wildflowers look different, but they all grow in soil and need sunlight and water.

What do you already know about how all living things are alike yet different? **What more would you like to know?**

Big Questions:

- How do you know a plant when you see it? Chapter 10
- How do you know an animal when you see it? Chapter 11

After reading the chapters, write what you have learned about the Big Idea.

BIGIDEA

Living things interact with their environment.

People depend on the ocean's living resources, such as codfish, for food.

What do you already know about how you get food, water, and shelter from your surroundings? **What more would you like to know?**

Big Questions:

- How do living things affect one another? Chapter 12
- How do energy and matter move through ecosystems? Chapter 13
- How do natural and human activities change ecosystems? Chapter 14

After reading the chapters, write what you have learned about the Big Idea.

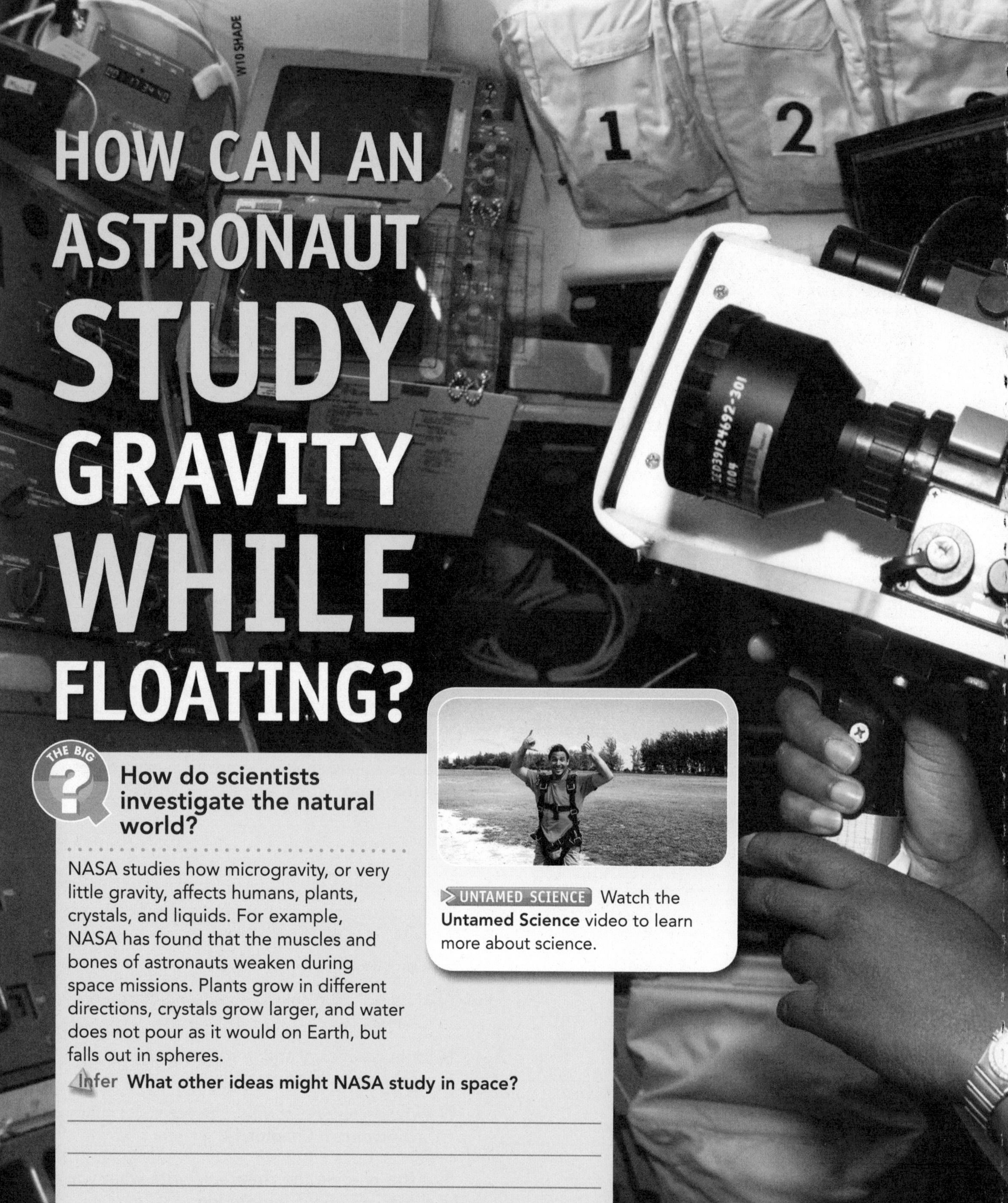

HOW CAN AN ASTRONAUT STUDY GRAVITY WHILE FLOATING?

THE BIG Q

How do scientists investigate the natural world?

NASA studies how microgravity, or very little gravity, affects humans, plants, crystals, and liquids. For example, NASA has found that the muscles and bones of astronauts weaken during space missions. Plants grow in different directions, crystals grow larger, and water does not pour as it would on Earth, but falls out in spheres.

Infer What other ideas might NASA study in space?

UNTAMED SCIENCE Watch the **Untamed Science** video to learn more about science.

Virginia

CHAPTER 1

What Is Science?

Science Standards of Learning

LS.1a, LS.1d, LS.1e, LS.1f, LS.1g, LS.1h, LS.1i, LS.1j, LS.4d

CHAPTER

1 Getting Started

Check Your Understanding

1. Background Read the paragraph below and then answer the question.

Miki is in the **process** of preparing a stew for dinner at her campsite. After it is cooked, she sets the pot aside to cool. When she returns, the pot is empty. Immediately, she **poses** questions: Who ate the stew? What animals are active in the evening? She soon finds **evidence:** the pot cover, greasy spills, and a stinky smell. The thief is a skunk.

A **process** is a series of actions or events.

To **pose** is to put forward a question or a problem.

Facts, figures, or signs that help prove a statement are all pieces of **evidence.**

- How does the process of posing questions and looking for evidence help Miki solve the mystery of the missing stew?

____

____

MY READING WEB If you had trouble completing the question above, visit **My Reading Web** and type in ***What Is Science?***

Vocabulary Skill

Identify Related Word Forms Learn related forms of words to increase your vocabulary. The table below lists forms of words related to vocabulary terms.

Verb	Noun	Adjective
observe, *v.* to gather information using the senses	observation, *n.* facts learned by gathering information using the senses	observable, *adj.* able to be heard, seen, touched, tasted, or smelled
predict, *v.* to state or claim what will happen in the future	prediction, *n.* a statement or claim of what will happen in the future	predictable, *adj.* able to be predicted; behaving in a way that is expected

2. Quick Check **Complete the sentence with the correct form of the word.**

- It is difficult to _______________ how much rain will fall.

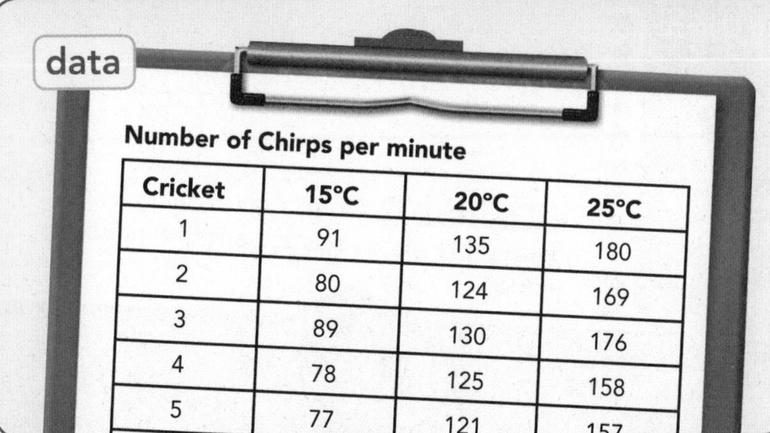

Number of Chirps per minute

Cricket	15°C	20°C	25°C
1	91	135	180
2	80	124	169
3	89	130	176
4	78	125	158
5	77	121	157

Chapter Preview

LESSON 1
- science
- observing
- quantitative observation
- qualitative observation
- inferring
- predicting
- classifying
- evaluating
- making models

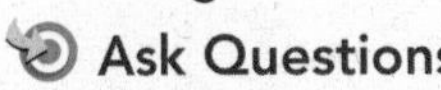

Ask Questions
Predict

LESSON 2
- skepticism
- ethics
- personal bias
- cultural bias
- experimental bias
- objective
- subjective
- deductive reasoning
- inductive reasoning

Relate Cause and Effect
Classify

LESSON 3
- scientific inquiry
- hypothesis
- variable
- manipulated variable
- responding variable
- controlled experiment
- data
- scientific theory
- scientific law

Sequence
Control Variables

VOCAB FLASH CARDS For extra help with vocabulary, visit **Vocab Flash Cards** and type in ***What Is Science?***

LESSON 1

Science and the Natural World

What Skills Do Scientists Use?
LS.1a, LS.1d, LS.1h, LS.1i, LS.1j

my planet Diary

BIOGRAPHY

The Wild Chimpanzees of Gombe

The following words are from the writings of Jane Goodall, a scientist who studied wild chimpanzees in Africa for many years.

"Once, as I walked through thick forest in a downpour, I suddenly saw a chimp hunched in front of me. Quickly I stopped. Then I heard a sound from above. I looked up and there was a big chimp there, too. When he saw me he gave a loud, clear wailing *wraaaaah*—a spine-chilling call that is used to threaten a dangerous animal. To my right I saw a large black hand shaking a branch and bright eyes glaring threateningly through the foliage. Then came another savage *wraaaah* from behind...I was surrounded." Because Jane stood still, the chimps no longer felt threatened, so they went away.

Answer the question.

What is one advantage and one disadvantage of studying wild animals in their natural environment?

____

____

____

____

____

____

PLANET DIARY Go to **Planet Diary** to learn more about science and the natural world.

Lab zone® Do the Inquiry Warm-Up *Is It Really True?*

Vocabulary

- science • observing • quantitative observation
- qualitative observation • inferring • predicting
- classifying • evaluating • making models

Skills

- Reading: Ask Questions
- Inquiry: Predict

What Skills Do Scientists Use?

Jane Goodall trained herself to become a scientist, or a person who does science. **Science** is a way of learning about the natural world. Science also includes all the knowledge gained by exploring the natural world. **Scientists use skills such as observing, inferring, predicting, classifying, evaluating, and making models to study the world.**

Observing

Observing means using one or more of your senses to gather information. It also means using tools, such as a microscope, to help your senses. By observing chimps like the one in **Figure 1,** Jane Goodall learned what they eat. She also learned what sounds chimps make and even what games they play.

Observations can be either quantitative or qualitative. A **quantitative observation** deals with numbers, or amounts. For example, seeing that you have 11 new e-mails is a quantitative observation. A **qualitative observation** deals with descriptions that cannot be expressed in numbers. Noticing that a bike is blue or that a lemon tastes sour is a qualitative observation.

FIGURE 1

Observing

A chimpanzee uses a rock as a tool to crack open a nut.

Observe Write one quantitative observation and one qualitative observation about this chimp.

Science Standards of Learning

LS.1a Organize data into tables showing repeated trials and means.

LS.1d Construct and use models and simulations to illustrate and explain phenomena.

LS.1h Organize, graph, and interpret data, and use data to make predictions.

LS.1i Identify, interpret, and evaluate patterns in data.

LS.1j Use current applications to reinforce life science concepts.

Ask Questions In the graphic organizer ask a *what, how,* or *why* question based on the text under Observing. As you read, write an answer to your question.

Thinking Like a Scientist

Question

Answer

Inferring One day, Jane watched as a chimp peered into a tree hollow. The chimp picked up a handful of leaves and chewed on them. Then, it took the leaves out of its mouth and pushed them into the hollow. When the chimp pulled the leaves out, Jane saw the gleam of water. The chimp then put the wet leaves back into its mouth. Jane reasoned that there was water in the tree. Jane made three observations. She saw the chimp pick up dry leaves, put them in the hollow, and then pull them out wet. But, Jane was not observing when she reasoned that there was water inside the tree. She was inferring. When you explain or interpret the things you observe, you are **inferring,** or making an inference. Inferring is not guessing. Inferences are based on reasoning from what you already know. They could also be based on assumptions you make about your observations. See what inferences you can make about the chimps in **Figure 2**.

FIGURE 2

Inferring

What can you infer about the chimps and the termite mound?

Complete the activities below.

1. **Observe** In the chart below, write two observations about the chimp on the left.
2. **Infer** Use the observations you wrote to make two related inferences.

Observation	Inference

Predicting Jane's understanding of chimp behavior grew over time. Sometimes, she could predict what a chimp would do next. **Predicting** means making a statement or a claim about what will happen in the future based on past experience or evidence.

By observing, Jane learned that when a chimp was frightened or angry its hairs stood on end. This response was sometimes followed by threatening gestures such as charging, throwing rocks, and shaking trees. Therefore, when Jane saw a chimp with its hair on end, she was able to predict that there was danger.

Predictions and inferences are closely related. While inferences are attempts to explain what is happening or *has* happened, predictions are statements or claims about what *will* happen. If you see a broken egg on the floor by a table, you might infer that the egg had rolled off the table. If, however, you see an egg rolling toward the edge of a table, you can predict that it's about to create a mess.

FIGURE 3

Predicting

Predictions are forecasts of what will happen next.

Predict **Write a prediction about what this angry chimp might do next.**

____

____

____

____

do the math!

Like all animals, chimps prefer to eat certain foods when they are available.

Chimp Diet in May	
Fruits	52%
Seeds	30%
Leaves	12%
Other foods	6%

1. **Graph** Use the information in the table to create a bar graph.
2. Label the *x*-axis and the *y*-axis. Then write a title for the graph.
3. **Interpret Data** Did chimps feed more on seeds or leaves during May?

____

____

4. **Infer** What might chimps eat more of if fruits are not available in June?

____

____

____

____

100

80

60

40

20

0

Fruit Seeds Leaves Other

Classifying What did chimps do all day? To find out, Jane's research team followed the chimps through the forest. They took detailed field notes about the chimps' behaviors. **Figure 4** shows some notes about Jomeo, an adult male chimp.

Suppose Jane had wanted to know how much time Jomeo spent feeding or resting that morning. She could have found out by classifying Jomeo's actions. **Classifying** is the grouping together of items that are alike in some way. Jane could have grouped together all the information about Jomeo's feeding habits or his resting behavior.

Evaluating Suppose Jane had found that Jomeo spent most of his time resting. What would this observation have told her about chimp behavior? Before Jane could have reached a conclusion, she would have needed to evaluate her observations. **Evaluating** involves comparing observations and data to reach a conclusion about them. For example, Jane would have needed to compare all of Jomeo's behaviors with those of other chimps to reach a conclusion. She would also need to have evaluated the resulting behavior data of Jomeo and the other chimps.

FIGURE 4

VIRTUAL LAB **Classifying**

By classifying the information related to a chimp's resting, climbing, or feeding, a scientist can better understand chimp behavior.

Classify Use the chart to classify the details from the field notes.

- 6:45 A.M. Jomeo rests in his nest. He lies on his back.
- 6:50 Jomeo leaves his nest, climbs a tree, and feeds on *viazi pori* fruits and leaves.
- 7:16 He wanders along about 175 m from his nest feeding on *budyankende* fruits.
- 8:08 Jomeo stops feeding, rests in a large tree, feeds on *viazi pori* fruits again.
- 8:35 He travels 50 m further, rests by a small lake.

Feeding	Resting	Changing Location
Jomeo eats *viazi pori* fruits, *budyankende* fruits, and leaves.	________	________

Making Models How far do chimps travel? Where do they go? Sometimes, Jane's research team followed a particular chimp for many days at a time. To show the chimp's movements, they might have made a model like the one shown in **Figure 5.** The model shows Jomeo's movements and behaviors during one day. **Making models** involves creating representations of complex objects or processes. Some models can be touched, such as a map. Others are in the form of mathematical equations or computer programs. Models help people study things that can't be observed directly. By using models, Jane and her team shared information that would otherwise be difficult to explain.

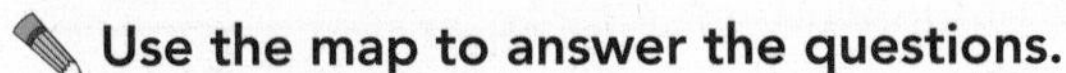

FIGURE 5

INTERACTIVE ART **Making Models**

This model shows Jomeo's movements and behaviors during one day.

Use the map to answer the questions.

1. **Interpret Maps** How far did Jomeo travel during this day?

______

______

2. How many times did Jomeo stop to feed?

______

3. How many times did Jomeo rest?

______

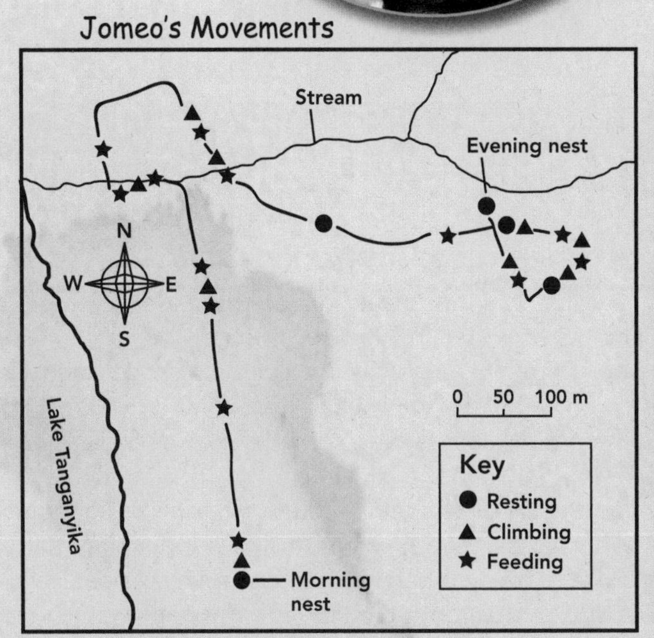

Lab zone Do the Quick Lab *Classifying Objects.*

Assess Your Understanding

1a. Compare and Contrast How do observations differ from inferences?

______

______

______

______

b. Classify Do you think this statement is an observation or an inference? *The cat is ill.* Explain your reasoning.

______

______

______

got it?

○ **I get it!** I know that scientists use skills such as ______

______

○ I need extra help with ______

Go to MY SCIENCE COACH *online for help with this subject.*

Virginia

LESSON 2

Thinking Like a Scientist

What Attitudes Help You Think Scientifically?
LS.1e, LS.1j

What Is Scientific Reasoning?
LS.1a, LS.1d, LS.1e, LS.1j

my planet Diary

DISCOVERY

Incredible Inventions

Most scientific inventions are purposely created and result from curiosity, persistence, and years of hard work. However, some inventions have been accidentally discovered when their inventors were in the process of creating something else. While developing wallpaper cleaner, a type of clay was invented. A coil-shaped toy was originally designed as a spring to be used on ships. Instead of developing a substitute for synthetic rubber, toy putty was created. Self-stick notes, potato chips, and the hook and loop fasteners used on items such as clothing, shoes, and toys are also inventions that were discovered by accident. Like the inventors of these items, your curiosity may help you invent the next "big thing"!

Communicate Discuss the following questions with a partner. Write your answers below.

1. Why do you think it is important for scientists to be curious?

2. What might you want to invent? Why?

PLANET DIARY Go to **Planet Diary** to learn more about thinking like a scientist.

Do the Inquiry Warm-Up *How Keen Are Your Senses?*

Vocabulary
- skepticism
- ethics
- personal bias
- cultural bias
- experimental bias
- objective
- subjective
- deductive reasoning
- inductive reasoning

Skills
- Reading: Relate Cause and Effect
- Inquiry: Classify

What Attitudes Help You Think Scientifically?

Perhaps someone has told you that you have a good attitude. What does that mean? An attitude is a state of mind. Your actions say a lot about your attitude.  **Scientists possess certain important attitudes, including curiosity, honesty, creativity, open-mindedness, skepticism, good ethics, and awareness of bias.**

Curiosity One attitude that drives scientists is curiosity. Scientists want to learn more about the topics they study. **Figure 1** shows some things that may spark the interest of scientists.

Honesty Good scientists always report their observations and results truthfully. Honesty is especially important when a scientist's results go against previous ideas or predictions.

Creativity Whatever they study, scientists may experience problems. Sometimes, it takes creativity to find a solution. Creativity means coming up with inventive ways to solve problems or produce new things.

Science Standards of Learning

LS.1e Identify sources of experimental error.

LS.1j Use current applications to reinforce life science concepts.

FIGURE 1

Curiosity

Curiosity helps scientists learn about the world around them.

Ask Questions For each image, write a question you are curious about in the boxes.

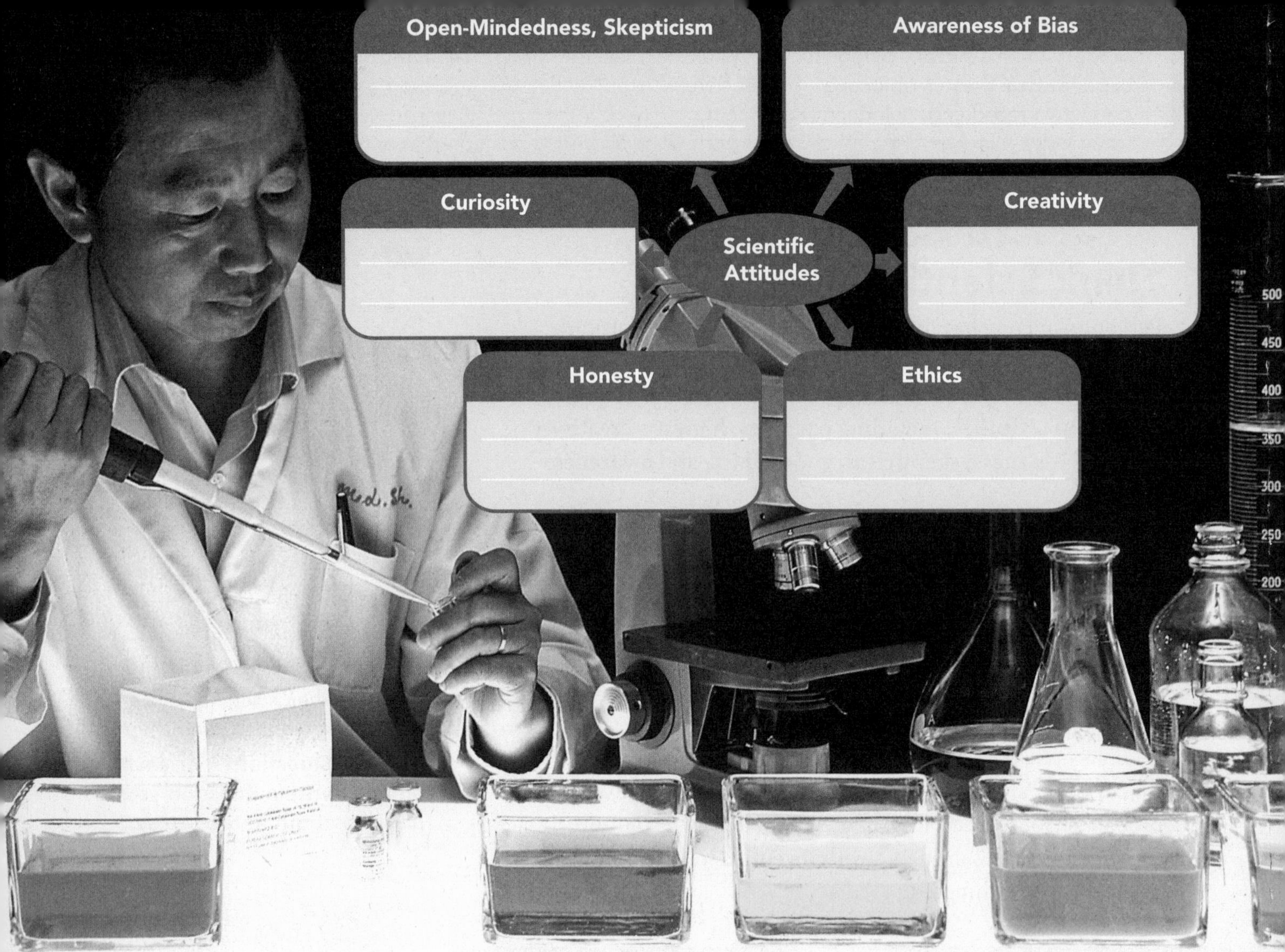

FIGURE 2

Attitudes of Scientists

This scientist is carefully conducting an experiment.

Summarize After you have read the section What Attitudes Help You Think Scientifically?, write a summary of each scientific attitude in the graphic organizer.

Open-Mindedness and Skepticism Scientists need to be open-minded, or capable of accepting new and different ideas. However, open-mindedness should always be balanced by **skepticism,** which is having an attitude of doubt. Skepticism keeps a scientist from accepting ideas that may be untrue.

Ethics Because scientists work with the natural world, they must be careful not to damage it. Scientists need a strong sense of **ethics,** which refers to the rules that enable people to know right from wrong. Scientists must consider all the effects their research may have on people and the environment. They make decisions only after considering the risks and benefits to living things or the environment. For example, scientists test medicine they have developed before the medicine is sold to the public. Scientists inform volunteers of the new medicine's risks before allowing them to take part in the tests. Look at **Figure 2** to review scientific attitudes.

Awareness of Bias What scientists expect to find can influence, or bias, what they observe and how they interpret observations. For example, a scientist might misinterpret the behavior of an animal because of what she already knows about animals.

There are different kinds of bias. **Personal bias** comes from a person's likes and dislikes. For instance, if you like the taste of a cereal, you might think everyone else should, too. **Cultural bias** stems from the culture in which a person grows up. For example, a culture that regards snakes as bad might overlook how well snakes control pests. **Experimental bias** is a mistake in the design of an experiment that makes a particular result more likely. For example, suppose you wanted to determine the boiling point of pure water. If your experiment uses water that has some salt in it, your results would be biased.

Relate Cause and Effect
In the first paragraph, underline an example of bias. Then circle its effect.

$1.00
Salted Peanuts
$1.25
RAISINS
NET WT. 1 ½ OZ. (42.5 g)
$0.75
Cheese CRACKERS

apply it!

Matt likes cheese crackers best and thinks that most other students do too. So he observed what students bought at the vending machine during one lunch. Seven bought crackers, three bought nuts, and none bought raisins.

1. Circle the evidence of personal bias.
2. CHALLENGE Describe the experimental bias.

______

______

______

Lab zone® Do the Quick Lab *Thinking Like a Scientist.*

Assess Your Understanding

1a. Explain What can bias a scientist's observations?

______

______

b. Apply Concepts Debbie discovered a new way to make pizza. What scientific attitude is this an example of?

______

______

got it?

O **I get it!** Now I know that attitudes that help you think scientifically are ______

______

______

O I need extra help with ______

Go to MY SCIENCE COACH *online for help with this subject.*

Science Standards of Learning

LS.1a Organize data into tables showing repeated trials and means.
LS.1d Construct and use models and simulations to illustrate and explain phenomena.
LS.1e Identify sources of experimental error.
LS.1j Use current applications to reinforce life science concepts.

What Is Scientific Reasoning?

You use reasoning, or a logical way of thinking, when you solve word problems. Scientists use reasoning in their work, too. **Scientific reasoning requires a logical way of thinking based on gathering and evaluating evidence.** There are two types of scientific reasoning. Scientific reasoning can be deductive or inductive.

Because scientific reasoning relies on gathering and evaluating evidence, it is objective reasoning. Being **objective** means that you make decisions and draw conclusions based on available evidence. For example, scientists used to think chimps ate only plants. However, Jane Goodall observed chimps eating meat. Based on this evidence, she concluded that chimps ate meat and plants.

In contrast, being **subjective** means that personal feelings have entered into a decision or conclusion. Personal opinions, values, and tastes are subjective because they are based on your feelings about something. For example, if you see a clear stream in the woods, you might take a drink because you think clear water is clean. However, you have not objectively tested the water's quality. The water might contain microorganisms you cannot see and be unsafe to drink.

apply it!

Classify Read the sentences below. Then decide if each example uses objective reasoning or subjective reasoning to reach a conclusion. Place a check mark in the corresponding column.

	Objective	Subjective
Jane Goodall saw a chimp chewing on wet leaves. She reasoned that chimps sometimes used leaves to drink water.		
I like to run. I must be the fastest person in the class.		
Emily is 1.2 m tall. No one else in class is taller than 1 m. So, Emily is the tallest person in class.		
I dislike dogs. Dogs must be the least friendly animals.		

Deductive Reasoning Scientists who study Earth think that the uppermost part of Earth's surface is made up of many sections they call plates. The theory of plate tectonics states that earthquakes should happen mostly where plates meet. There are many earthquakes in California. Therefore, California must be near a place where plates meet. This is an example of deductive reasoning. **Deductive reasoning** is a way to explain things by starting with a general idea and then applying the idea to a specific observation.

You can think about deductive reasoning as being a process. First, you state the general idea. Then you relate the general idea to the specific case you are investigating. Then you reach a conclusion. You can use this process in **Figure 3.** The process for the plate tectonics example is shown here.

- Earthquakes should happen mostly where plates meet.
- California has many earthquakes.
- California must be near a place where plates meet.

did you know?

Did you know that deductive reasoning is used by detectives? Sherlock Holmes, a fictional detective in the novels and short stories of Sir Arthur Conan Doyle, solved many mysteries using deductive reasoning.

FIGURE 3

Deductive Reasoning

Deductive reasoning occurs when a general idea is applied to a specific example and a conclusion is reached.

Apply Concepts Apply each general idea to a specific example and then draw a conclusion.

Dinner is always at 6 P.M.

____

____

____

Classes end when the bell rings.

____

____

____

Triangles have three sides.

____

____

____

Inductive Reasoning Scientists also use inductive reasoning, which can be considered the opposite of deductive reasoning. **Inductive reasoning** uses specific observations to make generalizations. For example, suppose you notice that leaf-cutter ants appear to follow other ants along specific paths, as shown in **Figure 4**. The ants follow the paths to sources of food, water, and nest material. Then they return to their nests. These observations about the leaf-cutter ants are specific. From these specific observations you conclude that these ants must communicate to be able to always follow the same path. This conclusion is a generalization about the behavior of leaf-cutter ants based on your observations. Scientists frequently use inductive reasoning. They collect data and then reach a conclusion based on that data.

FIGURE 4

INTERACTIVE ART **Scientific Reasoning**

Leaf-cutter ants follow a chemical trail to find and harvest leaves.

Identify Look at the statements below. Write *D* next to the statements that use deductive reasoning. Write *I* next to the statements that use inductive reasoning.

1. Turtles have shells. They must use shells for protection. ______
2. A puddle has frozen. It must be below 0°C outside. ______
3. Because of gravity, everything that goes up must come down. ______
4. Many birds fly toward the equator in fall. Birds prefer warm weather. ______

Faulty Reasoning Scientists must be careful not to use faulty reasoning, because it can lead to faulty conclusions. If you draw a conclusion based on too little data, your reasoning might lead you to the wrong general idea. For example, to conclude accurately that all ants communicate with each other, you would have to observe leaf-cutter ants and many other kinds of ants many times. In addition, based on observations of how leaf-cutter ants follow paths, you cannot conclude how they communicated. For example, you cannot say they follow the tiny footprints of the ants ahead of them. Such a conclusion would be a guess not based on observation.

apply it!

Joy drew lines of symmetry on a square. She saw that a rectangle has four straight sides and four right angles, so she drew the same lines of symmetry on a rectangle.

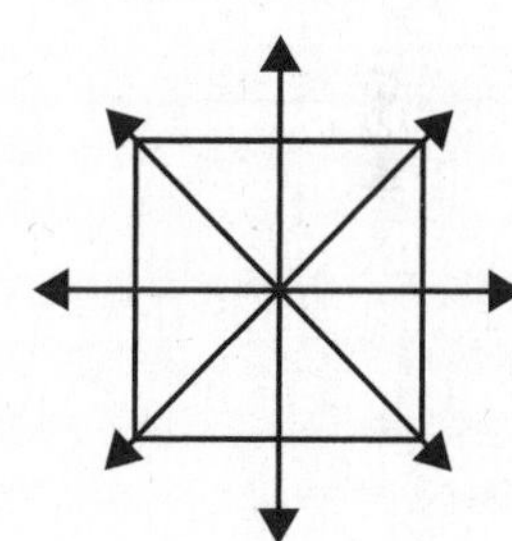

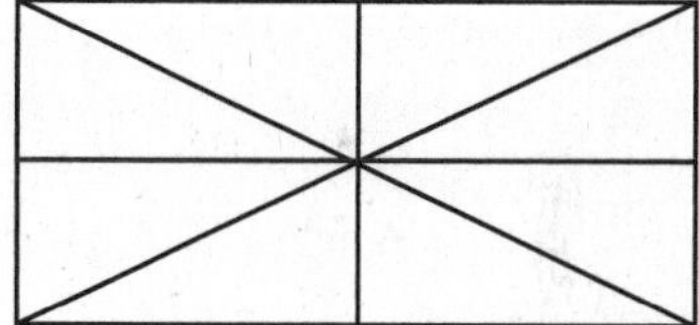

1 Make Models Fold a piece of rectangular notebook paper according to the lines of symmetry Joy drew on the rectangle. Are her lines of symmetry correct? Explain how you know.

____

____

2 Identify Faulty Reasoning Underline Joy's reasoning for drawing the lines of symmetry on the rectangle. What other characteristic should Joy have considered?

____

____

Lab® zone Do the Quick Lab *Using Scientific Thinking.*

Assess Your Understanding

2a. Define ______________ reasoning uses a general idea to make a specific observation.

b. Relate Cause and Effect What is a cause of faulty reasoning?

____

____

got it?

O **I get it!** Now I know that scientific reasoning includes ______________________________

____

O I need extra help with ______________________________

Go to **MY SCIENCE COACH** *online for help with this subject.*

Scientific Inquiry

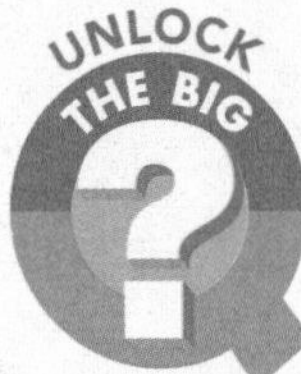

What Is Scientific Inquiry?
LS.1j

How Do You Design and Conduct an Experiment?
LS.1a, LS.1d, LS.1e, LS.1f, LS.1g, LS.1h, LS.1i, LS.1j

What Are Scientific Theories and Laws?
LS.1j

my planet Diary

MISCONCEPTION

The Law of Falling Objects

Misconception: Heavier objects fall faster than lighter ones. This assumption is not true. They actually fall at the same rate, or with the same acceleration. The misconception was introduced by a philosopher named Aristotle and accepted for more than 2,000 years. But in the late 1500s, Galileo Galilei discovered something different—all free-falling objects fall with the same acceleration. To prove this, Galileo performed a number of experiments. Galileo's experiments involved rolling balls with different masses down a ramp called an inclined plane and making careful measurements.

Galileo and one of his acceleration experiments

Communicate **Discuss the following questions with a partner. Write your answers below.**

1. Why did Galileo perform experiments to see if all objects fall with the same acceleration?

2. Do you think a feather and a book that are dropped from the same height at the same time will hit the ground at the same time? Explain your answer in terms of Galileo's discovery.

PLANET DIARY Go to **Planet Diary** to learn more about scientific inquiry.

Do the Inquiry Warm-Up *What's Happening?*

Vocabulary

- scientific inquiry • hypothesis • variable
- manipulated variable • responding variable
- controlled experiment • data
- scientific theory • scientific law

Skills

Reading: Sequence
Inquiry: Control Variables

What Is Scientific Inquiry?

Chirp, chirp, chirp. It is one of the hottest nights of summer and your bedroom windows are wide open. On most nights, the quiet chirping of crickets gently lulls you to sleep, but not tonight. The noise from the crickets is almost deafening. Why do all the crickets in your neighborhood seem determined to keep you awake tonight? Your thinking and questioning is the start of the **scientific inquiry** process.  **Scientific inquiry refers to the diverse ways in which scientists study the natural world and propose explanations based on the evidence they gather.** Some scientists run experiments in labs, but some cannot. For example, geologists use observations of rock layers to draw inferences about how Earth has changed over time.

Science Standards of Learning

LS.1j Use current applications to reinforce life science concepts.

Posing Questions Scientific inquiry often begins with a question about an observation. Your observation about the frequent chirping may lead you to ask a question: Why are the crickets chirping so much tonight? Questions come from your experiences, observations, and inferences. Curiosity plays a role, too. Because others may have asked similar questions, you should do research to find what information is already known about the topic before you go on with your investigation. Look at **Figure 1** to pose a scientific question about an observation.

FIGURE 1

Posing Questions

The photo at the right is of a Roesel's bush cricket from England.

Pose Questions Make an observation about this cricket. Then pose a question about this observation that you can study.

____

____

____

Developing a Hypothesis How could you answer your question about cricket chirping? In trying to answer the question, you are developing a hypothesis. A **hypothesis** (plural: *hypotheses*) is a possible answer to a scientific question. You may suspect that the hot temperatures affected the chirping. Your hypothesis would be that cricket chirping increases as a result of warmer air temperatures. Use **Figure 2** to practice developing a hypothesis.

A hypothesis is *not* a fact. In science, a fact is an observation that has been confirmed repeatedly. For example, that a cricket rubs its forelegs together to make the chirping noise is a fact. A hypothesis, on the other hand, is one possible answer to a question. For example, perhaps the crickets only seemed to be chirping more that night because there were fewer other sounds than usual.

In science, a hypothesis must be testable. Researchers must be able to carry out investigations and gather evidence that will either support or disprove the hypothesis. Disproven hypotheses are still useful, because they can lead to further investigations.

FIGURE 2

Developing a Hypothesis

Develop Hypotheses Write two hypotheses that might answer this student's question.

Hypothesis A	Hypothesis B

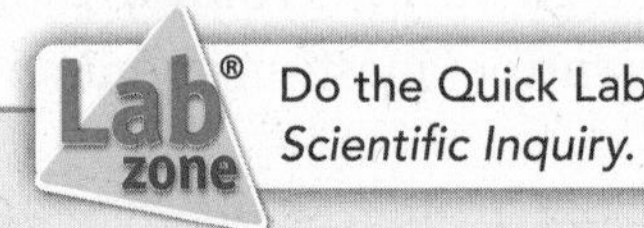

Assess Your Understanding

1a. Explain Can you test a hypothesis that crickets chirp more when they hide under logs? Explain.

b. Develop Hypotheses What other hypothesis might explain why crickets chirp more frequently on some nights?

got it?

○ **I get it!** Now I know that scientific inquiry is ______

○ I need extra help with ______

Go to **MY SCIENCE COACH** *online for help with this subject.*

How Do You Design and Conduct an Experiment?

After developing your hypothesis, you are ready to test it by designing an experiment. **An experiment must follow sound scientific principles for its results to be valid.** You know your experiment will involve counting cricket chirps at warm temperatures. But, how will you know how often a cricket would chirp at a low temperature? You cannot know unless you count other cricket chirps at low temperatures for comparison.

Controlling Variables To test your hypothesis, you will observe crickets at different air temperatures. All other **variables,** or factors that can change in an experiment, must be the same. This includes variables such as food and hours of daylight. By keeping these variables the same, you will know that any difference in cricket chirping is due to temperature alone.

The one variable that is purposely changed to test a hypothesis is the **manipulated variable,** or independent variable. The manipulated variable here is air temperature. The factor that may change in response to the manipulated variable is the **responding variable,** or dependent variable. The responding variable here is the number of cricket chirps.

Science Standards of Learning

LS.1a Organize data into tables showing repeated trials and means.
LS.1d Construct and use models and simulations to illustrate and explain phenomena.
LS.1e Identify sources of experimental error.
LS.1f Identify dependent variables, independent variables, and constants.
LS.1g Control variables to test hypotheses, and repeat trials.
LS.1h Graph, and interpret data, and use data to make predictions.
LS.1i Identify, interpret, and evaluate patterns in data.
LS.1j Use current applications to reinforce life science concepts.

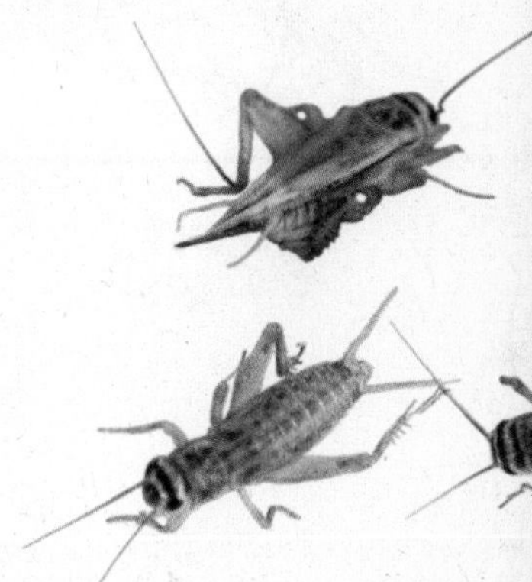

apply it!

A student performs an experiment to determine whether 1 g of sugar or 1 g of salt dissolves more quickly in water.

1 **Control Variables** Identify the manipulated variable and the responding variable.

____

2 **Identify** What are two other variables in this experiment?

____

3 **Draw Conclusions** Write a hypothesis for this experiment.

____

Setting Up a Controlled Experiment An experiment in which only one variable is manipulated at a time is called a **controlled experiment.** You decide to test the crickets at three different temperatures: 15°C, 20°C, and 25°C, as shown in **Figure 3.** All other variables are kept the same. Otherwise, your experiment would have more than one manipulated variable. Then there would be no way to tell which variable influenced your results.

Experimental Bias In any experiment there is a risk of introducing bias. For example, if you expect crickets to chirp more at 25°C, you may run experiments at just that temperature. Or, without meaning to, you might bias your results by selecting only the crickets that chirp the most often to test. Having a good sample size, or the number of crickets tested, is also important. Having too few crickets may bias your results because individual differences exist from cricket to cricket.

FIGURE 3

A Controlled Experiment

The manipulated variable in the experiment below is temperature.

Design Experiments In the boxes, write the number of crickets you would test for this controlled experiment. On the lines below, write three other variables that must be kept the same.

____

____

____

Collecting and Interpreting Data You are almost ready to begin your experiment. You decide to test five crickets, one at a time, at each temperature. You also decide to run multiple trials for each cricket. Before you begin your experiment, decide what observations you will make and what data you will collect. **Data** are the facts, figures, and other evidence gathered through qualitative and quantitative observations. To organize your data, you may want to make a data table. A data table provides you with an organized way to collect and record your observations. Decide what your table will look like. Then you can start to collect your data.

After your data have been collected, they need to be interpreted. Probeware is one tool that will not only help you collect and record data, but it can also help you interpret it by creating graphs. Graphs can reveal patterns or trends in data. Sometimes, there is more than one interpretation for a set of data. For example, scientists all agree that global temperatures have gone up over the past 100 years. What they do not agree on is how much they are likely to go up over the next 100 years.

Sequence Underline and number the steps involved in collecting and interpreting data.

do the math!

A data table helps you organize the information you collect in an experiment. Graphing the data may reveal any patterns in your data.

1 Read Graphs Identify the manipulated variable and the responding variable.

2 Read Graphs As the temperature increases from 15°C to 25°C, what happens to the number of chirps per minute?

3 Predict How many chirps per minute would you expect when the temperature is 10°C?

Number of Chirps per Minute

Cricket	15°C	20°C	25°C
1	91	135	180
2	80	124	169
3	89	130	176
4	78	125	158
5	77	121	157
Average	83	127	168

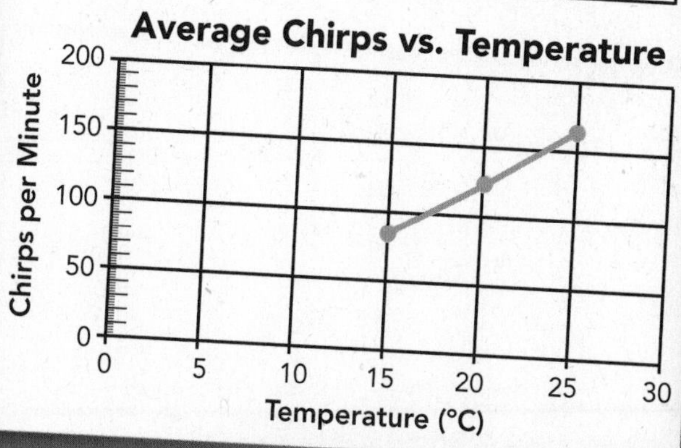

Average Chirps vs. Temperature

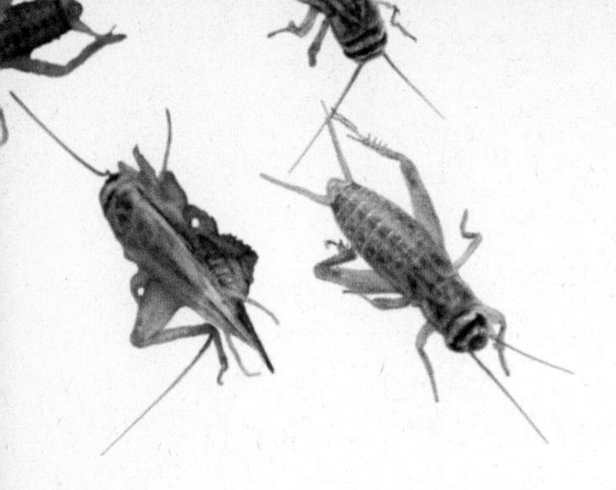

Drawing Conclusions Now you can draw conclusions about your hypothesis. A conclusion is a summary of what you have learned from an experiment. To draw your conclusion, you must examine your data objectively to see if they support or do not support your hypothesis. You also must consider whether you collected enough data.

You may decide that the data support your hypothesis. You conclude that the frequency of cricket chirping increases with temperature. Now, repeat your experiment to see if you get the same results. A conclusion is unreliable if it comes from an experiment with results that cannot be repeated. Many trials are needed before a hypothesis can be accepted as true.

Your data won't always support your hypothesis. When this happens, check your experiment for things that went wrong, or for improvements you can make. Then fix the problem and do the experiment again. If the experiment was done correctly the first time, your hypothesis was probably not correct. Propose a new hypothesis that you can test. Scientific inquiry usually doesn't end once an experiment is done. Often, one experiment leads to another.

Number of Chirps per Minute			
Cricket	15°C	20°C	25°C
1	98	100	120
2	92	95	105
3	101	93	99
4	102	85	97
5	91	89	98
Average	96	92	103

FIGURE 4

VIRTUAL LAB **Drawing Conclusions**

Sometimes the same experiment can have very different data.

Answer the questions below.

1. **Interpret Tables** Look at the data in the table. Do the data support the hypothesis that crickets chirp more in warmer temperatures? Explain.

2. **Analyze Sources of Error** If the data in this table were yours, what might you do next? Explain.

3. CHALLENGE Can you draw a conclusion from these data? Why or why not?

Communicating Communicating is the sharing of ideas and results with others through writing and speaking. Scientists communicate by giving talks at scientific meetings, exchanging information on the Internet, or publishing articles in scientific journals.

When scientists share the results of their research, they describe their procedures so that others can repeat their experiments. It is important for scientists to wait until an experiment has been repeated many times before accepting a result. Therefore, scientists must keep accurate records of their methods and results. This way, scientists know that the result is accurate. Before the results are published, other scientists review the experiment for sources of error, such as bias, data interpretation, and faulty conclusions.

Sometimes, a scientific inquiry can be part of a huge project in which many scientists are working together around the world. For example, the Human Genome Project involved scientists from 18 different countries. The scientists' goal was to create a map of the information in your cells that makes you who you are. On such a large project, scientists must share their ideas and results regularly. Come up with ideas for communicating the results of your cricket experiment in **Figure 5.**

Vocabulary **Identify Related Word Forms** *Communication* is the noun form of the verb *communicate.* Write a sentence using the noun *communication.*

The Human Genome Project logo

FIGURE 5

Communicating Results

Since the Human Genome Project touched upon many areas of science, communication was important.

Communicate **Get together as a group and write three ways to share the results of your cricket experiment with other students.**

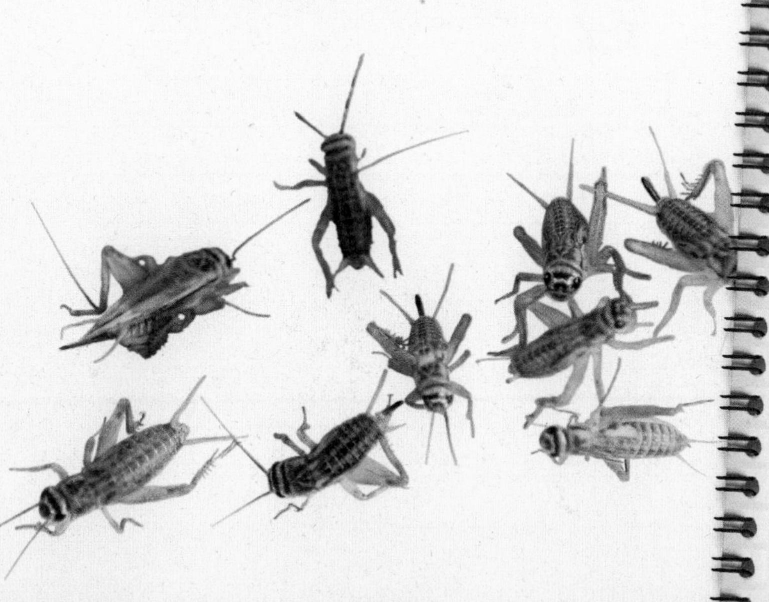

EXPLORE THE BIG ?

In a Scientist's Shoes

How do scientists investigate the natural world?

Design an Experiment

QUESTION ______

SCIENTIFIC ATTITUDES INVOLVED ______

HYPOTHESIS ______

VARIABLES

Manipulated Variables ______

Responding Variables ______

Factors to Consider ______

COLLECT DATA

Number of Trials ______

Units of Measure ______

SCIENTIFIC SKILLS USED ______

NEXT STEPS ______

FIGURE 6

INTERACTIVE ART When you think like a scientist, you develop hypotheses and design experiments to test them.

Design Experiments Think like a scientist to find out which falls fastest: an unfolded sheet of paper, a sheet of paper folded in fourths, or a crumpled sheet of paper.

Lab zone® Do the Lab Investigation *Keeping Flowers Fresh.*

Assess Your Understanding

2a. Name Name two ways scientists communicate their results.

______

b. ANSWER THE BIG ? How do scientists investigate the natural world?

______

got it?

O **I get it!** Now I know that an experimental design must ______

O I need extra help with ______

Go to MY SCIENCE COACH *online for help with this subject.*

What Are Scientific Theories and Laws?

Science Standards of Learning

LS.1j Use current applications to reinforce life science concepts.

Sometimes, a large set of related observations can be connected by a single explanation. This explanation can lead to the development of a scientific theory. In everyday life, a theory can be an unsupported guess. Everyday theories are not scientific theories. A **scientific theory** is a well-tested explanation for a wide range of observations and experimental results. For example, according to the atomic theory, all substances are composed of particles called atoms. Atomic theory helps to explain many observations, such as why iron nails rust. Scientists accept a theory only when it can explain the important observations. If the theory cannot explain new observations, then the theory is changed or thrown out. In this way, theories are constantly being developed, revised, or discarded as more information is collected.

A **scientific law** is a statement that describes what scientists expect to happen every time under a particular set of conditions. **Unlike a theory, a scientific law describes an observed pattern in nature without attempting to explain it.** For example, the law of gravity states that all objects in the universe attract each other. Look at **Figure 7.**

FIGURE 7

A Scientific Law

According to the law of gravity, this parachutist will eventually land on Earth.

Apply Concepts Give another example of a scientific law.

____

____

____

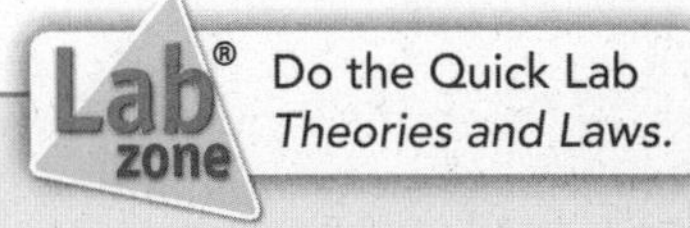

Do the Quick Lab *Theories and Laws.*

Assess Your Understanding

got it?

O **I get it!** Now I know that the difference between a scientific theory and a law is that _______________

____

O I need extra help with _______________

Go to my science COACH *online for help with this subject.*

CHAPTER 1

Study Guide

To think like a scientist, you must use ____________________, ____________________, and ____________________ to observe the world.

LESSON 1 Science and the Natural World

Scientists use skills such as observing, inferring, predicting, classifying, evaluating, and making models to study the world.

Vocabulary

- science
- observing
- quantitative observation
- qualitative observation
- inferring
- predicting
- classifying
- evaluating
- making models

LESSON 2 Thinking Like a Scientist

Scientists possess certain important attitudes, including curiosity, honesty, creativity, open-mindedness, skepticism, good ethics, and awareness of bias.

Scientific reasoning requires a logical way of thinking based on gathering and evaluating evidence.

Vocabulary

- skepticism
- ethics
- personal bias
- cultural bias
- experimental bias
- objective
- subjective
- deductive reasoning
- inductive reasoning

LESSON 3 Scientific Inquiry

Scientific inquiry refers to the diverse ways in which scientists study the natural world and propose explanations based on the evidence they gather.

An experiment must follow sound scientific principles for its results to be valid.

Unlike a theory, a scientific law describes an observed pattern in nature without attempting to explain it.

Vocabulary

- scientific inquiry
- hypothesis
- variable
- manipulated variable
- responding variable
- controlled experiment
- data
- scientific theory
- scientific law

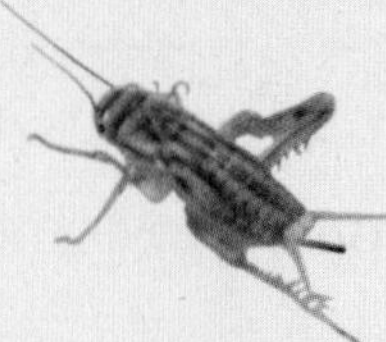

Review and Assessment

LESSON 1 Science and the Natural World

1. When you explain or interpret an observation, you are
   a. making models. b. classifying.
   c. inferring. d. predicting.

2. When scientists group observations that are alike in some way, they are ______________

3. **Predict** How do scientists use observations to make predictions?

4. **Infer** Suppose you come home to the scene below. What can you infer happened?

5. **Observe** What is a quantitative observation you might make in your school cafeteria?

LESSON 2 Thinking Like a Scientist

6. The scientific attitude of having doubt is called
   a. open-mindedness. b. curiosity.
   c. honesty. d. skepticism.

7. When a person allows personal opinions, values, or tastes to influence a conclusion, that person is using ______________ reasoning.

8. **Compare and Contrast** Describe the three types of bias that can influence a science experiment.

9. **Draw Conclusions** Why is it important to report experimental results honestly, even when the results might be the opposite of the results you expect to see?

10. **Write About It** A team of scientists is developing a new medicine to improve memory. Write about how the attitudes of curiosity, honesty, creativity, and open-mindedness help the scientists in their work. When might they need to think about ethics? How could bias influence their results?

CHAPTER 1

Review and Assessment

LESSON 3 Scientific Inquiry

11. The facts, figures, and other evidence gathered through observations are called

a. conclusions.
b. data.
c. predictions.
d. hypotheses.

12. The one variable that is changed to test a hypothesis is

a. the responding variable.
b. the other variable.
c. the manipulated variable.
d. the dependent variable.

13. A ______________________________ is a well-tested explanation for a wide range of observations.

14. Communicate What are some ways that scientists communicate with each other?

____
____
____
____
____
____
____

15. Write About It Suppose you want to find out which dog food your dog likes best. Write about the experiment you would design. What variables would you need to control? What kinds of data would you collect? How could you avoid experimental bias?

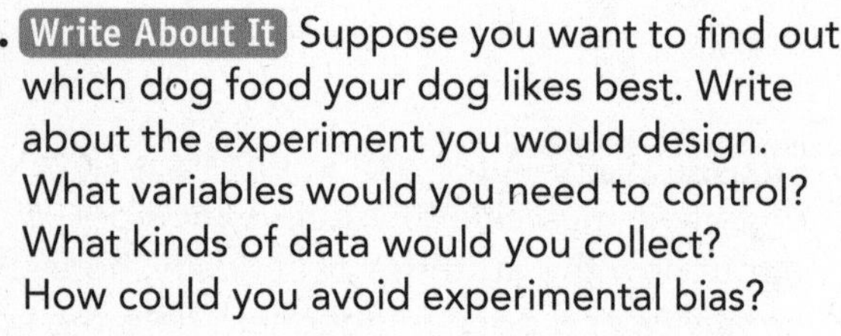

How do scientists investigate the natural world?

16. Central Middle School is having problems with attendance during the winter. Many students get sick and miss school. The principal wants to fix the problem, but she is not sure what to do. One idea is to install hand sanitizer dispensers in the classrooms.

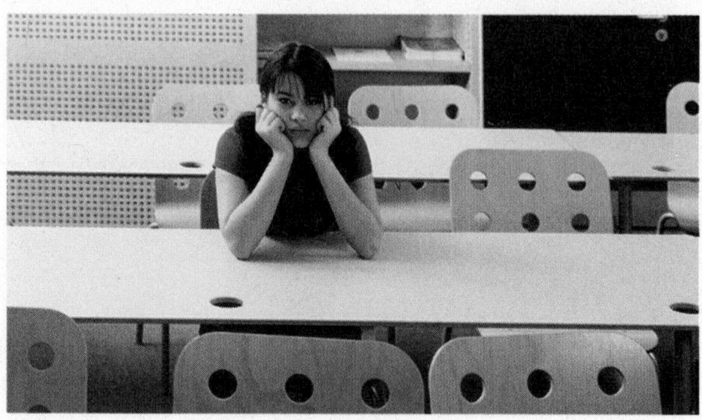

Think about this problem scientifically. What is a possible hypothesis in this situation? What experiment could you design to test it? Mention at least three attitudes or skills that will be important in finding the answer.

____
____
____
____
____
____
____
____
____
____
____
____
____
____

Virginia SOL Test Prep

Read each question and choose the best answer.

1 **Sophia noticed that many birds pick through the seeds in her bird feeder until they get a sunflower seed. What is an inference she could make from this observation?**

A Birds are attracted to white objects.
B Sunflower seeds are crunchy.
C Birds do not like seeds.
D Birds prefer sunflower seeds.

2 **Which of the following attitudes do good scientists possess?**

F curiosity about the world
G certainty that a hypothesis is correct
H ambition to be famous and respected
J a strong sense of cultural bias

3 **Marie observed people at a store. Which is a qualitative observation she may have made?**

A Twenty people walked into the store.
B The store sells clothes.
C It was 1:00 P.M.
D all of the above

4 **Which of the following statements *best* describes a scientific theory?**

F It is a well-tested explanation for a wide range of experimental results.
G It is an educated guess based on experience.
H It is a statement that describes what scientists expect to happen.
J It is a hypothesis that was confirmed by an experiment.

5 **Tara was collecting data about rainfall by measuring water levels in a bucket in her yard. She saw her dog drinking from the bucket. This is an example of—**

A cultural bias
B personal bias
C experimental bias
D data collection

6 **This graph compares how well two different brands of insulated mugs retain heat. Which of the following statements *best* describes the data at the 20-minute mark?**

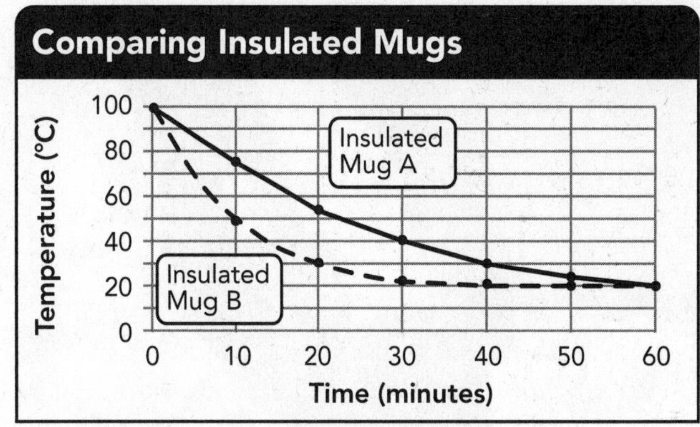

F Mug A retains less heat than Mug B.
G Mug A retains more heat than Mug B.
H Mug A and Mug B retain the same amount of heat.
J Mug A has twice as much heat as Mug B.

Science and History

When We Think We Know but It Isn't So

Science is a way of thinking and learning about the world. It is not rigid or unchanging. In fact, scientists are constantly learning new things. And sometimes, they make mistakes! That's just what René Blondlot and his co-workers at Nancy University in France did in 1903.

X-rays had just been discovered. Scientists everywhere, including Blondlot, were experimenting with them. In a series of photographs taken in an experiment, Blondlot observed strange lights. He was convinced he had discovered another new form of radiation. He named his discovery the N-ray, in honor of Nancy University where he worked. Dozens of other scientists repeated his experiments expecting to see the lights. Some were convinced that they actually had seen them. But there was one very big problem—N-rays do not exist! Scientists who were skeptical did not see these lights and could not repeat the results of the experiment. It was soon discovered that when they looked for N-rays, Blondlot and his colleagues were just seeing what they expected and hoped to see.

This is a clear case of expectations influencing observations. Because some scientists did not do enough to avoid their bias, they made a big mistake.

Research It Research about Robert W. Wood, the scientist who disproved the existence of N-rays. Write a paragraph summarizing how he came to this conclusion. What questions did he ask?

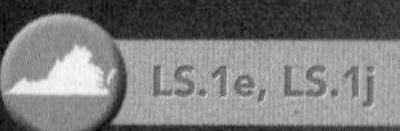

◄ René Blondlot was a famous scientist who allowed his ambition to overrule his powers of observation.

READY FOR A CLOSE-UP

Whether they are filming animal behavior in the wild or documenting new medical technologies, science filmmakers never know what's going to happen next. For one film, a filmmaker spent 16 weeks sitting hidden under an animal skin for 14 hours every day, just so he could film bird behavior. To film a lion attack, another film crew put themselves in danger by parking a few meters away from some very hungry lions in the middle of the night.

Making a good science film is about more than getting the perfect shot. Crews working in fragile ecosystems like the Arctic or in deserts take care not to wreck habitats. This means they travel light—sometimes using just one hand-held camera.

Writers and producers also try to avoid bias. If there is more than one theory about a topic, they try to find experts who can discuss each theory, and they present as many facts as possible. The makers of a film about the Jarkov woolly mammoth relied heavily on their scientific advisors to make sure scientific facts weren't sacrificed for a good story.

Patience, an adventurous spirit, and science knowledge are all part of being a great science filmmaker!

Research It Research one species of animal. Write a proposal for a documentary about that animal. Include a list of four or five questions you hope to answer with your film.

 LS.1d, LS.1j, LS.4d

WHY IS THIS SCIENTIST WEIGHING A POLAR BEAR?

How is mathematics important to the work of scientists?

UNTAMED SCIENCE Watch the **Untamed Science** video to learn more about how tools help scientists.

Scientists weighed this small female polar bear while she was asleep. They also measured the bear's body and skull. Similar measurements were done on bears throughout the Beaufort Sea of Alaska. The bears live on a frozen portion of the ocean called sea ice. Scientists are also measuring the sea ice to determine how much the ice is shrinking. By taking these measurements, scientists can figure out how the bears are affected by their environment.

Develop Hypotheses **Write a hypothesis that could be tested with these scientists' measurements.**

The Tools of Science

Virginia CHAPTER 2

Science Standards of Learning

LS.1a, LS.1c, LS.1d, LS.1e, LS.1f, LS.1g, LS.1h, LS.1i, LS.1j

CHAPTER

2 Getting Started

Check Your Understanding

1. **Background** Read the paragraph below and then answer the question.

> Emi studied hard to prepare for her science lab investigation. Emi was concerned because her investigation was **complex.** She had been earning high marks all year and wanted to maintain this **trend.** Emi also wanted to use her lab report as a **sample** of her science work.

To be **complex** is to have many parts.

A **trend** is the general direction that something tends to move.

A **sample** is a portion of something that is used to represent the whole thing.

- Why would preparing help Emi maintain her high marks?

____

____

MY READING WEB If you had trouble completing the question above, visit **My Reading Web** and type in ***The Tools of Science.***

Vocabulary Skill

Identify Multiple Meanings Some words have more than one meaning. The table below lists multiple meaning words used in science and in daily life.

Word	Everyday Meaning	Scientific Meaning
mean	*v.* to indicate; to intend **Example:** They didn't *mean* to hurt her.	*n.* the numerical average **Example:** The *mean* of 11, 7, 5, and 9 is 8.
volume	*n.* the loudness of a sound **Example:** Turn up the *volume* so we can hear the song.	*n.* the amount of space an object or substance takes up **Example:** Record the *volume* of water in the graduated cylinder.

2. **Quick Check** **In the table above, circle the meaning of the word *volume* that is used in the following sentence.**
   - The *volume* of juice in the container is 1.89 liters.

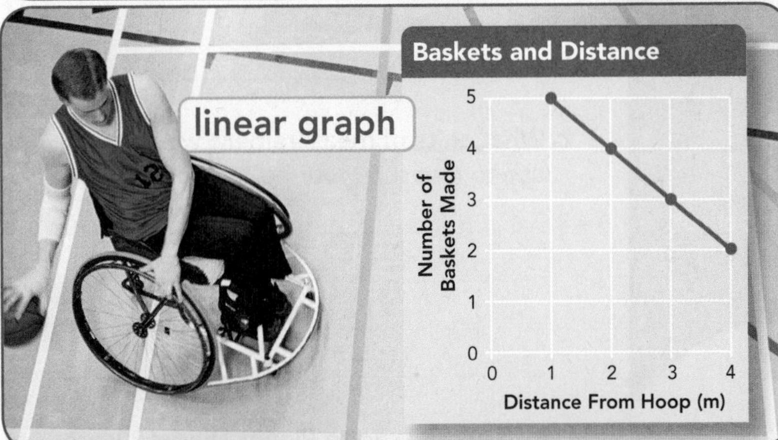

Chapter Preview

LESSON 1

- metric system
- SI
- mass
- weight
- volume
- meniscus
- density

Compare and Contrast

Measure

LESSON 2

- estimate
- accuracy
- precision
- significant figures
- percent error
- mean
- median
- mode
- range
- anomalous data

Relate Cause and Effect

Calculate

LESSON 3

- graph
- linear graph
- nonlinear graph

Relate Text and Visuals

Predict

LESSON 4

- model
- system
- input
- process
- output
- feedback

Identify the Main Idea

Make Models

LESSON 5

- safety symbol
- field

Summarize

Observe

VOCAB FLASH CARDS For extra help with vocabulary, visit **Vocab Flash Cards** and type in ***The Tools of Science.***

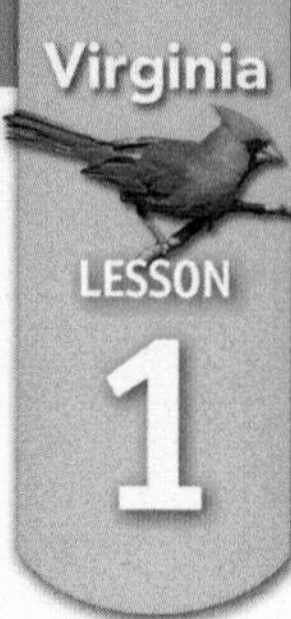

Measurement— A Common Language

Why Do Scientists Use a Standard Measurement System?
LS.1i

What Are Some SI Units of Measure?
LS.1a, LS.1c, LS.1d, LS.1e, LS.1f, LS.1g, LS.1i, LS.1j

my planet Diary

FUN FACTS

Extreme Measurements

Here are some fascinating animal measurements.

- The Queen Alexandra's Birdwing butterfly has a wingspan of 30 centimeters.
- A newborn giraffe stands 1.8 meters tall.
- When a blue whale exhales, the spray from its blowhole can reach up to 9 meters into the air.
- A colossal squid's eye measures about 28 centimeters across.
- With a mass of only 20 grams, the rhinoceros beetle can lift 850 times its own mass.
- A hummingbird's egg has a mass of about half a gram while an ostrich egg has a mass of about 1,500 grams.

Read the following questions. Write your answers below.

1. What problems could arise if some scientists measured length in inches and others measured length in centimeters?

____

____

____

2. What units of measurement would you use to measure your height and mass?

____

____

____

____

> PLANET DIARY Go to **Planet Diary** to learn more about measurement.

Ostrich egg

Lab zone® Do the Inquiry Warm-Up *History of Measurement.*

Hummingbird eggs

Vocabulary
- metric system • SI • mass • weight
- volume • meniscus • density

Skills
- Reading: Compare and Contrast
- Inquiry: Measure

Why Do Scientists Use a Standard Measurement System?

Science Standards of Learning

LS.1i Identify, interpret, and evaluate patterns in data.

Standard measurement is important. Without it, cooks would use handfuls and pinches instead of cups and tablespoons.

Scientists also use standard measurements. This allows scientists everywhere to repeat experiments. In the 1790s, scientists in France developed the metric system of measurement. The **metric system** is a measurement system based on the number 10. Modern scientists use a version of the metric system called the International System of Units, or **SI** (from the French, *Système International d'Unités*). **Using SI as the standard system of measurement allows scientists to compare data and communicate with each other about their results.** The prefixes used in the SI system are shown in **Figure 1.**

FIGURE 1

SI Prefixes

SI units are similar to our money units, in which a dime is ten times more than a penny.

Complete the tasks below.

1. **Name** In the table at the right, finish filling in the Example column.
2. **Calculate** How many times larger is a *kilo-* than a *deka-*?

____

____

Common SI Prefixes

Prefix	Meaning	Example
kilo- (k)	1,000	______
hecto- (h)	100	______
deka- (da)	10	dekameter
no prefix	1	meter
deci- (d)	0.1 (one tenth)	______
centi- (c)	0.01 (one hundredth)	______
milli- (m)	0.001 (one thousandth)	______

Lab zone® Do the Quick Lab *How Many Shoes?*

Assess Your Understanding

got it?

○ **I get it!** Now I know that scientists use a standard measurement system to _______________

○ **I need extra help with** _______________

Go to **my science COACH** *online for help with this subject.*

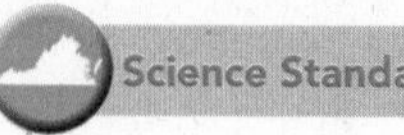

Science Standards of Learning

LS.1a Organize data into tables showing repeated trials and means.
LS.1c Use triple beam and electronic balances, thermometers, metric rulers, graduated cylinders, and probeware to gather data.
LS.1d Construct and use models and simulations to illustrate and explain phenomena.
LS.1e Identify sources of experimental error.
LS.1f Identify dependent variables, independent variables, and constants.
LS.1g Control variables to test hypotheses, and repeat trials.
LS.1i Identify, interpret, and evaluate patterns in data.
LS.1j Use current applications to reinforce life science concepts.

Conversions for Length		
1 km	=	1,000 m
1 m	=	100 cm
1 m	=	1,000 mm
1 cm	=	10 mm

What Are Some SI Units of Measure?

Scientists regularly measure attributes such as length, mass, volume, density, temperature, and time. Each attribute is measured in an SI unit.

Length Length is the distance from one point to another. **In SI, the basic unit for measuring length is the meter (m).** Many distances can be measured in meters. For example, you can measure a softball throw or your height in meters. One meter is about the distance from the floor to a doorknob. A tool used to measure length is a metric ruler.

For measuring lengths smaller than a meter, you use the centimeter (cm) and millimeter (mm). For example, the length of this page is about 28 centimeters. For measuring a long distance, such as the distance between cities, you use the unit called a kilometer (km). The table at the left shows you how to convert between different metric length units. Try measuring the turtle's shell in **Figure 2**.

FIGURE 2

Measuring Length

To use a metric ruler, line up one end of an object with the zero mark. Then read the number at the object's other end.

Use the ruler to measure the length of the turtle's shell and record it above the arrow. Then working in small groups, complete the activity below.

The centimeter markings are the longer lines. Each centimeter is divided into 10 millimeters, which are marked by the shorter lines.

1. **Measure** Measure the width of a penny and a dime in millimeters.

____

____

2. **Calculate** Convert the width of each coin in millimeters into centimeters.

____

____

____

Mass A balance, such as the one shown in **Figure 3,** is used to measure mass. **Mass** is a measure of the amount of matter in an object. A balance compares the mass of an object to a known mass. **In SI, the basic unit for measuring mass is the kilogram (kg).** The mass of cars, bicycles, and people is measured in kilograms. If you want to measure much smaller masses, you would use grams (g) or milligrams (mg). The table at the right shows how to convert between kilograms, grams, and milligrams.

Unlike mass, **weight** is a measure of the force of gravity acting on an object. A scale is used to measure weight. When you stand on a scale on Earth, gravity pulls you downward. This compresses springs inside the scale. The more you weigh, the more the springs compress. On the moon, the force of gravity is weaker than it is on Earth. So the scale's springs would not compress as much on the moon as on Earth. Unlike weight, your mass on the moon is the same as your mass on Earth.

Conversions for Mass		
1 kg	=	1,000 g
1 g	=	1,000 mg

Compare and Contrast Use the chart to compare and contrast mass and weight.

Alike	Different

FIGURE 3

Measuring Mass

A triple-beam balance can be used to measure mass.

Measure Read the balance to find the mass of the turtle. Record your answer in grams and then in milligrams.

____

____

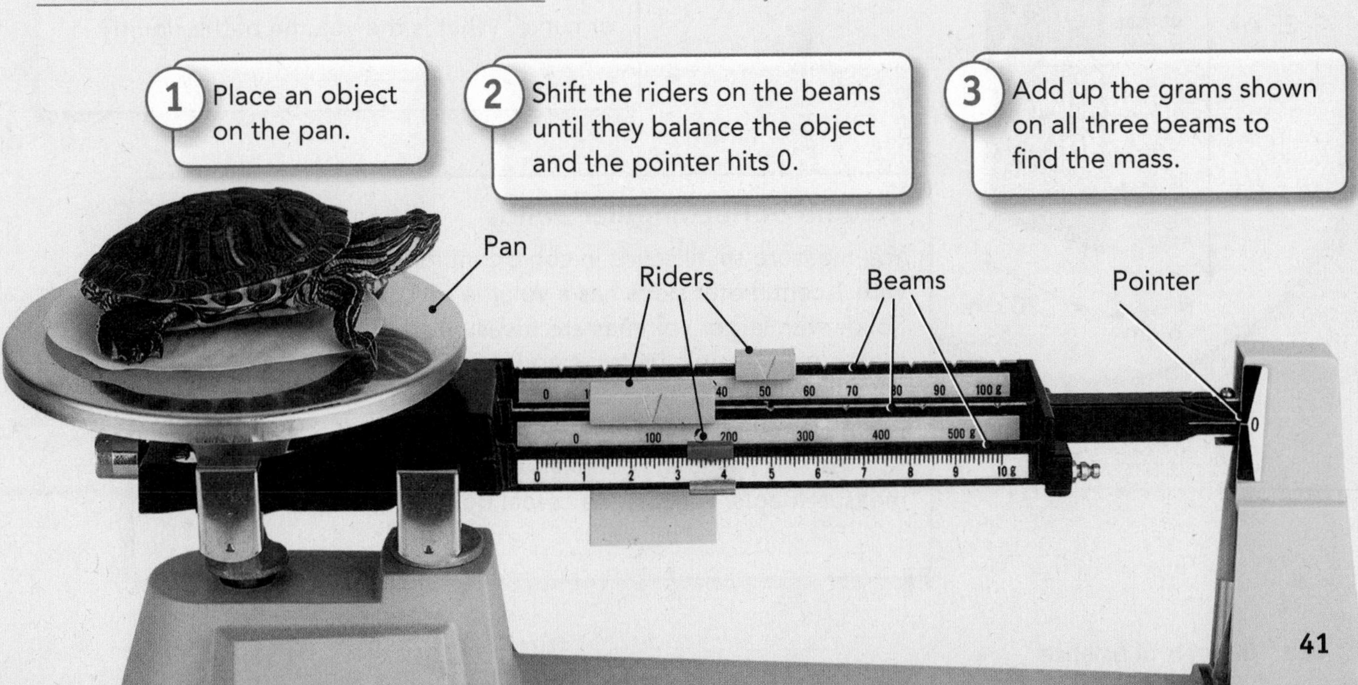

Conversions for Volume		
1 m^3	=	1,000,000 cm^3
1 cm^3	=	1 mL
1 L	=	1,000 mL
1 L	=	1,000 cm^3

Volume Instead of measuring your juice, you just look to see how much of the glass you have filled up. **Volume** is the amount of space an object or substance takes up. **In SI, the basic unit for measuring volume is the cubic meter (m^3).** Other units include the liter (L) and the cubic centimeter (cm^3). Cubic meters or centimeters are used to measure the volume of solids. The liter is commonly used for measuring the volume of liquids. The green table shows how to convert between these units.

FIGURE 4

Volume of Liquids, Rectangular Solids, and Irregular Solids

Measuring the volume of liquids and rectangular solids requires different methods.

Complete the activity on this page. Then follow the steps to measure the volume of an irregular solid on the next page.

Explain In the boxes, find the volume of the liquid and the cereal box. Below, explain which has a greater volume.

___

___

___

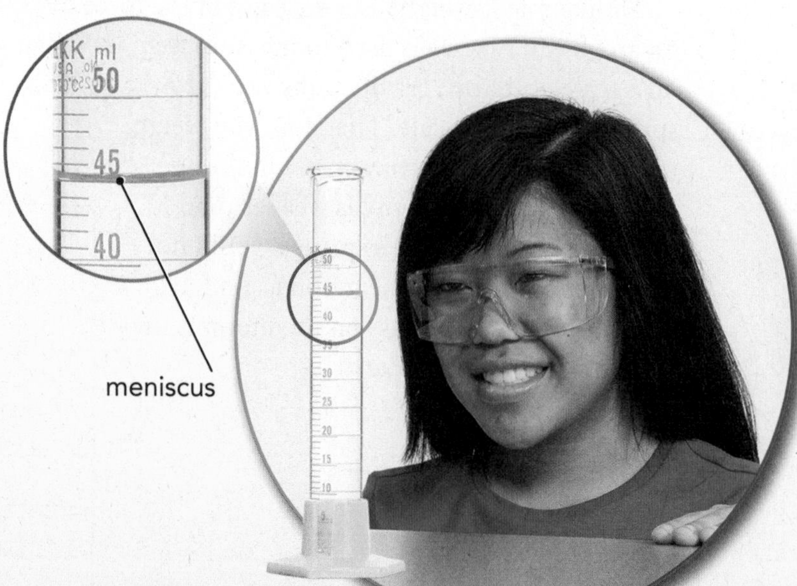

25 cm

6 cm

20 cm

Volume of Liquids

You are probably familiar with the liter from seeing 1-liter and 2-liter bottles. You can measure smaller liquid volumes by using milliliters (mL). There are 1,000 milliliters in one liter. To measure the volume of a liquid, read the level at the bottom of the **meniscus,** or curve. What is the volume of this liquid?

___

Volume of Rectangular Solids

You measure small solids in cubic centimeters (cm^3). A cube with 1-centimeter sides has a volume of 1 cubic centimeter. Solids with larger volumes are measured with the cubic meter (m^3). A cubic meter is equal to the volume of a cube with 1-meter sides. To calculate a rectangular solid's volume, multiply length times width times height. When you use this formula, you must use the same units for all measurements. What is the cereal box's volume?

___

Volume of Irregular Solids

Suppose you wanted to measure the volume of a rock. Because of its irregular shape, you cannot measure a rock's length, width, or height. However, you can use the displacement method shown on this page. To use this method, you immerse the object in water and measure how much the water level rises.

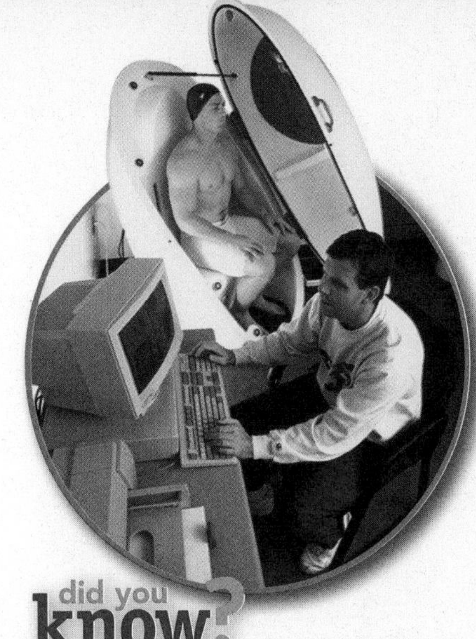

did you know?

Athletes may have their body volume measured to calculate their density, which can be used to determine their body fat percentage. One method for measuring an athlete's volume involves displacement of air by the athlete in an airtight device.

1 **Fill a graduated cylinder about two thirds full of water.**

What is the volume of water in the graduated cylinder?

____

2 **Place the object into the water.**

What is the volume of the water plus the object?

____

3 **Find the volume of the object by subtracting the volume of the water alone from the volume of the water plus the object.**

What is the volume of the object?

____

Density Look at **Figure 5.** Two objects of the same size can have different masses. This is because different materials have different densities. **Density** is a measure of how much mass is contained in a given volume.

Units of Density Because density is made up of two measurements, mass and volume, an object's density is expressed as a relationship between two units. **In SI, the basic unit for measuring density is kilograms per cubic meter (kg/m^3).** Other units of density are grams per cubic centimeter (g/cm^3) and grams per milliliter (g/mL).

FIGURE 5

Comparing Densities

The bowling ball and the beach ball have the same volume but not the same mass.

Form Operational Definitions Use this information to decide which object has a greater density. Explain your answer in terms of volume and mass.

____

____

____

do the math!

Calculating Density

The density of an object is the object's mass divided by its volume. To find the density of an object, use the formula below.

$$\text{Density} = \frac{\text{mass}}{\text{volume}}$$

1. **Calculate** Find the density of a piece of metal that has a mass of 68 g and a volume of 6 cm^3.

____

2. **Predict** Suppose a piece of metal has the same mass as the metal in Question 1 but a greater volume. How would its density compare to the metal in Question 1?

____

____

____

Density of Substances The table in **Figure 6** lists the densities of some common substances. The density of a pure substance is the same for all samples of that substance. For example, all samples of pure gold, no matter how large or small, have a density of 19.3 g/cm^3.

Once you know an object's density, you can determine whether the object will float in a given liquid. An object will float if it is less dense than the surrounding liquid. For example, the density of water is 1 g/cm^3. A piece of wood with a density of 0.8 g/cm^3 will float in water. A ring made of pure silver, which has a density of 10.5 g/cm^3, will sink.

FIGURE 6

A Density Experiment

Knowing the density of an object helps you predict how it will float and identify what it is made of.

Complete the tasks below.

1. **Infer** An object has a density of 0.7 g/cm^3. Do you think it floats or sinks in water? Explain.

____

____

2. **Design Experiments** Use what you know about density and measuring tools to describe the steps you might use to determine if a bar of metal is gold. Write your procedure in the notebook.

Densities of Some Common Substances	
Substance	**Density (g/cm^3)**
Air	0.001
Ice	0.9
Water	1.0
Aluminum	2.7
Gold	19.3

Density Experiment

Procedure:

____

____

____

____

____

____

____

____

____

____

____

____

____

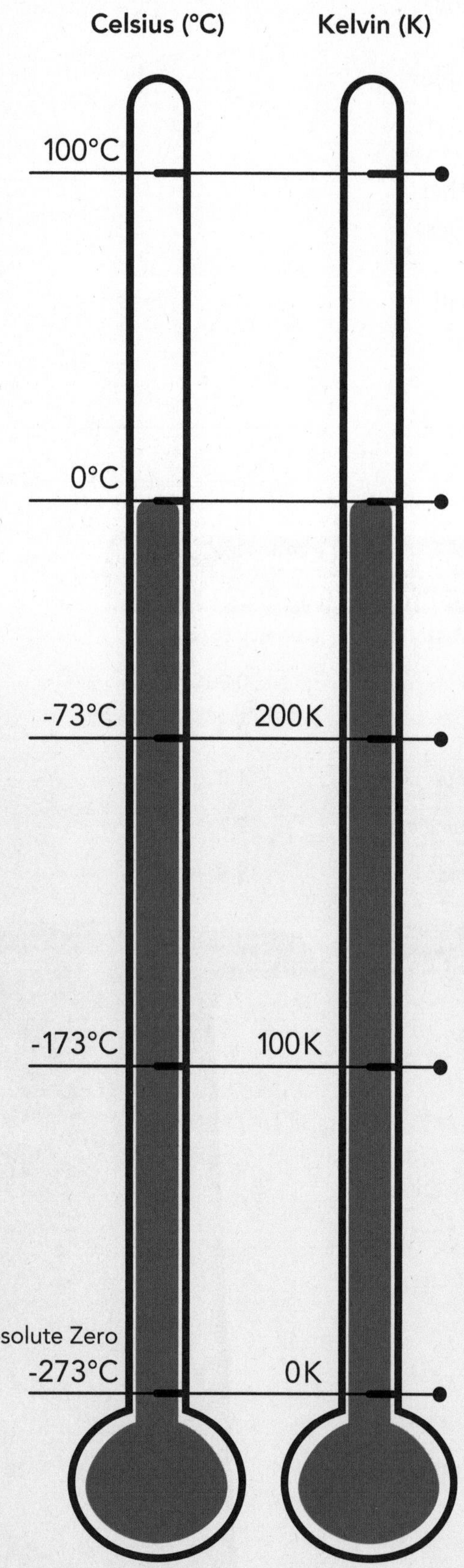

Temperature Is it cold out this morning? How high will the temperature rise? You probably use temperature measurements often in your everyday life. So do scientists.

Scientists commonly use the Celsius temperature scale to measure temperature. On the Celsius scale, water freezes at 0°C and boils at 100°C. **In addition to the Celsius scale, scientists sometimes use another temperature scale, called the Kelvin scale. In fact, the kelvin (K) is the official SI unit for temperature.** Kelvin is useful in science because there are no negative numbers. Units on the Kelvin scale are the same size as those on the Celsius scale, as shown in **Figure 7.** The table below shows how to convert between Celsius and Kelvin.

A thermometer or temperature probe is used to measure temperature. When you place a liquid thermometer in a substance, the liquid inside the thermometer will increase or decrease in volume. This makes the level rise or fall. Wait until the level stops changing. Then read the number next to the top of the liquid in the thermometer. A temperature probe is like a digital thermometer. It records temperature as electrical signals, which are converted into electronic data..

FIGURE 7

Temperature Scales

Zero on the Kelvin scale (0 K) is the coldest possible temperature. It is called absolute zero.

Complete the activities.

1. **Identify** On the Celsius thermometer, label the boiling point and freezing point of water.
2. **Interpret Diagrams** Determine the boiling point and freezing point of water in Kelvins. Label these temperatures on the Kelvin thermometer.
3. CHALLENGE In Fahrenheit, water boils at 212° and freezes at 32°. Are Fahrenheit units the same size as Kelvin units? Explain.

____

____

____

Conversions for Temperature

0°C	=	273 K
100°C	=	373 K

Time You push to run even faster with the finish line in sight. But an opponent is catching up. Just one second can mean the difference between winning and losing. What is a second?

The second (s) is the SI unit used to measure time. Just like all the SI units, the second is divided into smaller units based on the number 10. For example, a millisecond (ms) is one thousandth of a second. You use minutes or hours for longer periods of time. There are 60 seconds in a minute, and 60 minutes in an hour.

Clocks and watches are used to measure time. Some clocks are more accurate than others. Most digital stopwatches measure time accurately to one hundredth of a second, as shown in **Figure 8.** Devices used for timing Olympic events measure time to a thousandth of a second or even closer.

FIGURE 8

It's About Time

This stopwatch measured Jessie's best time in a school race.

Write Jessie's time in the chart and then complete the activity.

Interpret Tables In the last column, write the order that the runners finished.

Runner	Time	Place
George	00:15.74	
Sarah	00:26.78	
Saul	00:20.22	
Jessie		

Lab zone® Do the Quick Lab *Measuring Length in Metric.*

Assess Your Understanding

1a. Identify What tool would you use to measure the mass of a baseball?

______

______

b. Sequence What steps would you take to determine the density of a baseball?

______

______

______

______

______

got it?

O **I get it!** Now I know that basic SI units of measurement are ______

______

______

______

______

O I need extra help with ______

Go to **MY SCIENCE COACH** *online for help with this subject.*

Mathematics and Science

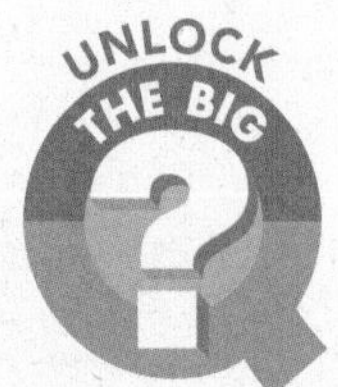

What Math Skills Do Scientists Use?
LS.1d, LS.1e, LS.1i

What Math Tools Do Scientists Use?
LS.1a, LS.1e, LS.1f, LS.1g, LS.1i, LS.1j

my planet Diary

BLOG

Posted by: Anh

Location: King George, Virginia

People all over the world can use math in their everyday lives. Here are some examples:

Let's say you went to a furniture store. You see a couch you like, and it's priced at $1,150 on sale for 40% off. What do you do? You take 0.40 x $1,150 and subtract that answer from the original price. In the kitchen, recipes tell you certain amounts of ingredients, so you use a measuring cup. People also use math while they're playing board games, such as rolling dice or playing with cards.

Math might not be appealing to some people, but they do need to acknowledge that it can be very important in their daily lives.

Write your answers to the questions below.

1. What examples does Anh give of how we use math in our every day lives?

____

____

2. Describe a time you used math to help you solve a problem in your daily life.

____

____

____

PLANET DIARY Go to **Planet Diary** to learn more about math in science.

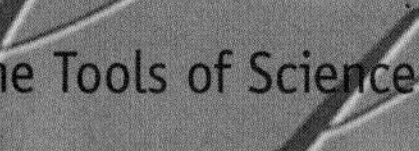

Lab zone® Do the Inquiry Warm-Up *How Many Marbles Are There?*

Vocabulary
- estimate
- accuracy
- precision
- significant figures
- percent error
- mean
- median
- mode
- range
- anomalous data

Skills
- Reading: Relate Cause and Effect
- Inquiry: Calculate

What Math Skills Do Scientists Use?

Science Standards of Learning

LS.1d Construct and use models and simulations to illustrate and explain phenomena.

LS.1e Identify sources of experimental error.

LS.1i Identify, interpret, and evaluate patterns in data.

From measuring to collecting data, scientists use math every day. **Math skills that scientists use to collect data include estimation, accuracy and precision, and significant figures.**

Estimation An **estimate** is an approximation of a number based on reasonable assumptions. An estimate is not a guess. It is always based on known information. Scientists often rely on estimates when they cannot obtain exact numbers. Their estimates might be based on indirect measurements, calculations, and models. For example, they may estimate the distance between stars based on indirect measurements because they can't measure the distance directly. Other estimates might be based on a sample.

do the math!

Estimation

Estimating from a sample is a quick way to determine the large number of birds in this photo.

1. **Interpret Photos** How many birds are in the yellow square? This number is your sample.

____

2. **Explain** By what number should you multiply the sample to find an estimate for the total number of birds in the total area? Explain your answer.

____

3. **Estimate** Calculate your estimate for the total number of birds. Show your work.

____

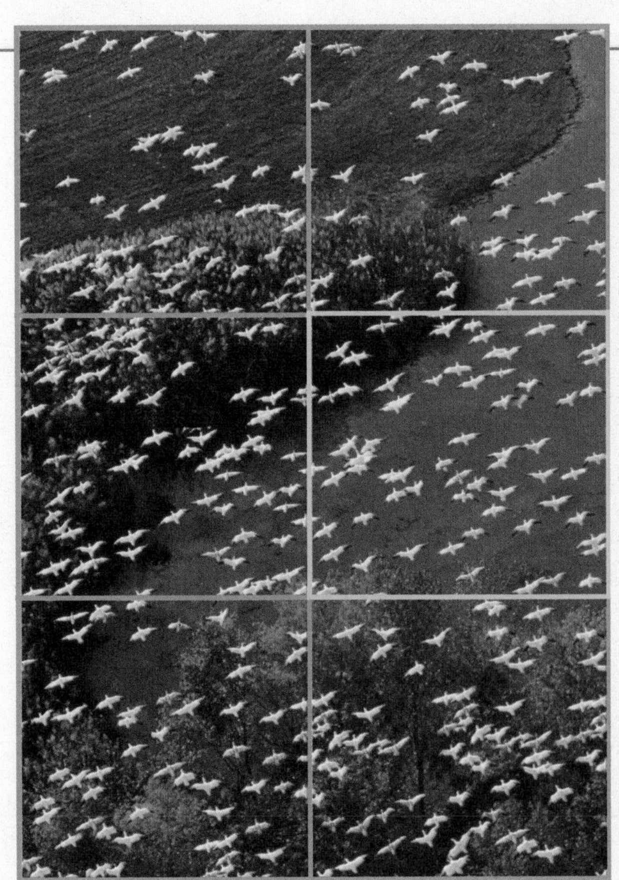

Accuracy and Precision

People often use the words *accuracy* and *precision* to describe the same idea. In science, these words have different meanings. **Accuracy** refers to how close a measurement is to the true or accepted value. **Precision** refers to how close a group of measurements are to each other.

How can you be sure that a measurement is both accurate and precise? First, use a high-quality measurement tool. Second, measure carefully. Finally, repeat the measurement a few times. If your measurement is the same each time, you can assume that it is reliable. A reliable measurement is both accurate and precise. Look at **Figure 1**.

FIGURE 1

Accuracy and Precision

In a game of darts, accurate throws land close to the bull's eye. Precise throws land close to one another.

Apply Concepts Draw dots on boards C and D to show the situations described.

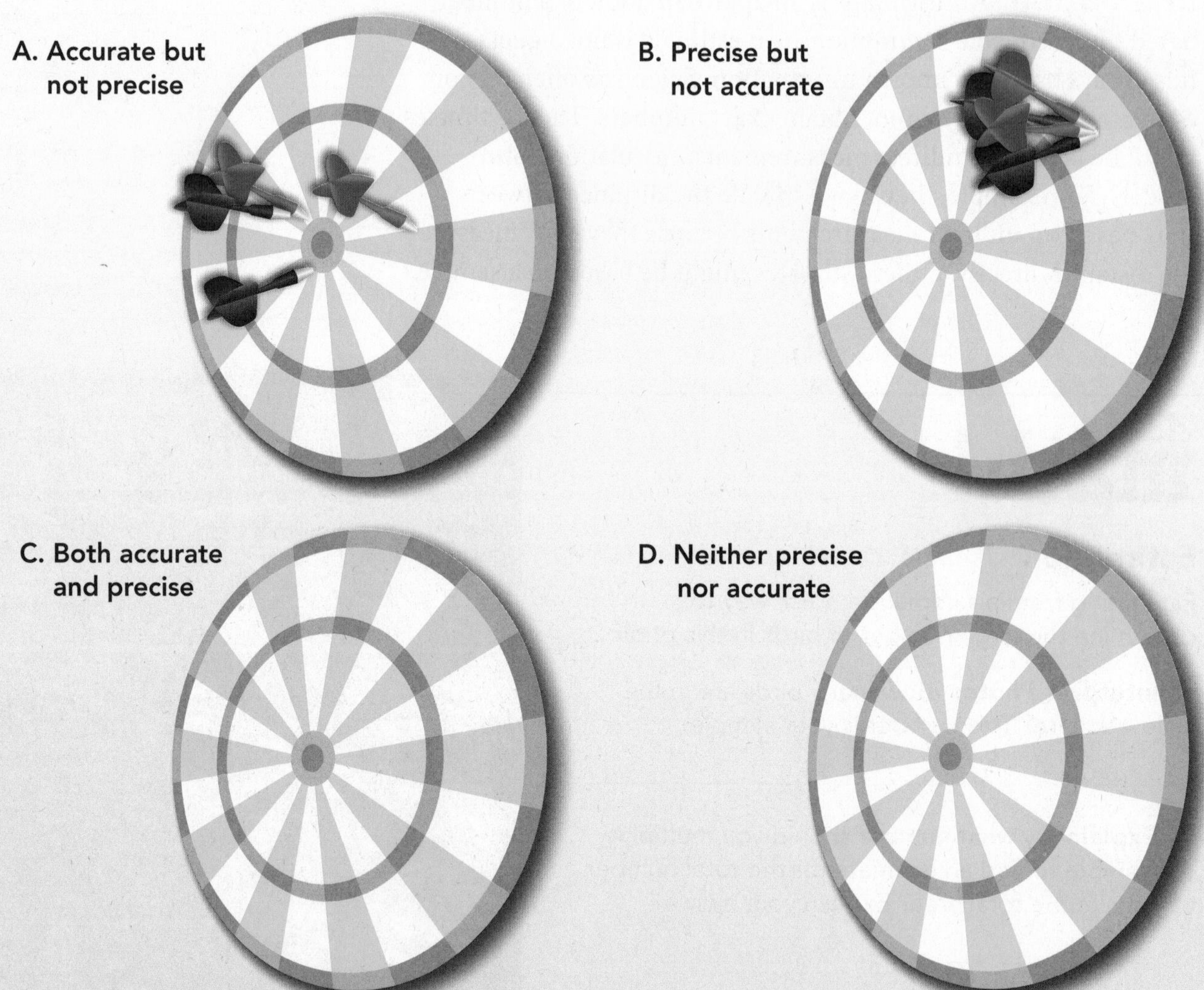

Significant Figures

Significant figures communicate how precise measurements are. The **significant figures** in a measurement include all digits measured exactly, plus one estimated digit. If the measurement has only one digit, you must assume it is estimated. Use **Figure 2** to learn more about significant figures.

FIGURE 2

Significant Figures

Suppose you are tiling a bathroom. You might estimate that the tile is 5.3 cm long. The measurement 5.3 cm has two significant figures, or sig figs. You are certain of the 5, but you have estimated the 3.

Calculate **Read about adding, subtracting, and multiplying measurements. Then complete the activities in the boxes.**

Adding or Subtracting Measurements

When you add or subtract measurements, your answer can only have as many places after the decimal point as the measurement with the fewest places after the decimal point. For example, suppose you add a tile that is 5.3 centimeters long to a row of tiles that is 21.94 centimeters long. Find the new length of the row.

21.94 cm (2 places after the decimal)
+ 5.3 cm (1 place after the decimal)
27.24 cm → 27.2 cm (1 place after the decimal)

If you remove a tile that is 5.3 centimeters long from a row of tiles that is 21.94 centimeters long, what is the new length of the row? How many significant figures are in this measurement?

____

____

Multiplying Measurements

When you multiply measurements, the answer should only have the same number of significant figures as the measurement with the fewest significant figures. For example, suppose you need to find the area of a space that measures 2.25 meters by 3 meters.

2.25 m (3 sig figs)
× 3 m (1 sig fig)
6.75 m² → 7 m² (1 sig fig)

Find the area of a space that measures 4.4 meters by 2 meters. How many significant figures are in this measurement?

____

____

Lab zone® Do the Quick Lab *For Good Measure.*

Assess Your Understanding

1a. Review What math skill do scientists rely on when they cannot obtain exact numbers?

____

b. Interpret Data Lia measures a wall of her room to be 3.7 meters by 2.45 meters. How many significant figures are in the measurement of its area? Explain.

____

____

got it?

○ **I get it!** Now I know that the math skills scientists use to collect data include _______________

____

____

○ I need extra help with _______________

Go to MY SCIENCE COACH *online for help with this subject.*

Science Standards of Learning

LS.1a Organize data into tables showing repeated trials and means.

LS.1e Identify sources of experimental error.

LS.1f Identify dependent variables, independent variables, and constants.

LS.1g Control variables to test hypotheses, and repeat trials.

LS.1i Identify, interpret, and evaluate patterns in data.

LS.1j Use current applications to reinforce life science concepts.

What Math Tools Do Scientists Use?

Mathematics is just as powerful a tool for analyzing data as it is for collecting it. **Scientists use certain math tools to analyze data. These tools include calculating percent error; finding the mean, median, mode, and range; and checking the reasonableness of data.**

Percent Error Often, scientists must make measurements that already have accepted values. For example, an accepted, or true, value for the density of the metal copper is 8.92 g/cm^3. Suppose you measure the mass and volume of a sample of the metal copper, and calculate a density of 9.37 g/cm^3. You know your calculation is not accurate, but by how much? **Percent error** calculations are a way to determine how accurate an experimental value is. A low percent error means that the result you obtained was accurate. A high percent error means that your result was not accurate. It may not be accurate because you did not measure carefully or something was wrong with your measurement tool.

Relate Cause and Effect
Underline the causes of a high percent error.

do the math! Sample Problem

Percent Error

The experimental density of copper is 9.37 g/cm^3. The true value is 8.92 g/cm^3. To calculate the percent error, use the following formula and substitute.

$$\text{Percent error} = \frac{\text{Difference between experimental value and true value}}{\text{true value}} \times 100\%$$

$$\%E = \frac{9.37\ \text{g/cm}^3 - 8.92\ \text{g/cm}^3}{8.92\ \text{g/cm}^3} \times 100\%$$

The percent error in the calculation of the density of copper was 5.04%.

1 **Calculate** Suppose you measured the density of a silver ring to be 11.2 g/cm^3, but you know that the true value for the density of silver is 10.5 g/cm^3. Find the percent error for the density you measured.

2 **CHALLENGE** What are two possible sources of error when measuring a sample's mass and volume?

Mean, Median, Mode, and Range Walking along a beach one night, you see a sea turtle laying her eggs in the sand. You start to wonder about sea turtle nests. What is the average number of eggs in a nest? What is the range of eggs in a group of nests? Scientists ask questions like these, too. Their answers come from analyzing data. Use **Figure 3** to analyze sea turtle egg data yourself.

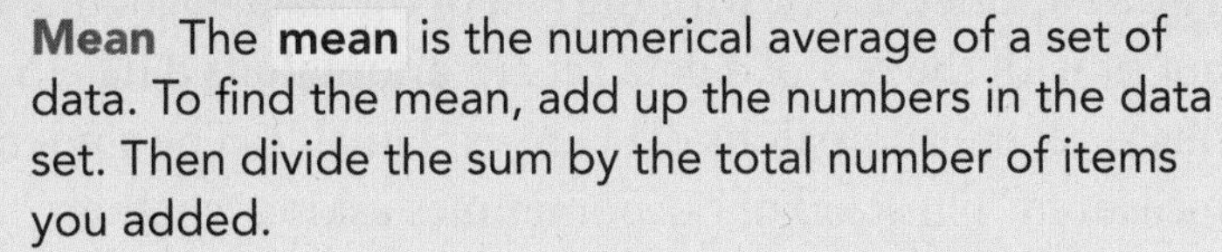

Mean The **mean** is the numerical average of a set of data. To find the mean, add up the numbers in the data set. Then divide the sum by the total number of items you added.

Find the mean for the egg data.

____

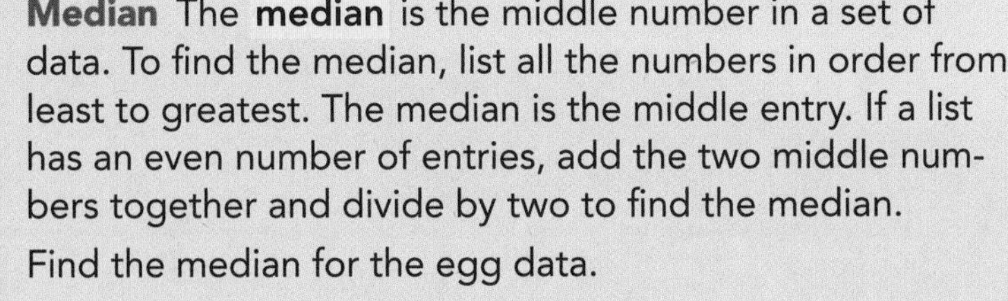

Median The **median** is the middle number in a set of data. To find the median, list all the numbers in order from least to greatest. The median is the middle entry. If a list has an even number of entries, add the two middle numbers together and divide by two to find the median.

Find the median for the egg data.

____

____

Mode The **mode** is the number that appears most often in a list of numbers.

Find the mode for the egg data.

____

Range The **range** of a set of data is the difference between the greatest value and the least value in the set.

Find the range for the egg data.

____

FIGURE 3

Sea Turtle Egg Data

You can use math to analyze the data in the table below about the number of sea turtle eggs in seven nests.

Calculate **Fill in the boxes with the mean, median, mode, and range of the sea turtle data.**

Nest	Number of Eggs
A	110
B	102
C	94
D	110
E	107
F	110
G	109

Sea Turtles at Nesting Beach	
Day	Turtles
Day 1	7
Day 2	7
Day 3	8
Day 4	7
Day 5	2

FIGURE 4

Collected Data

On Day 5, only two turtles are at the beach.

Analyze Experimental Results Describe an unknown variable that could have affected the data.

____

____

____

____

Reasonable and Anomalous Data An important part of analyzing any set of data is to ask, "Are these data reasonable? Do they make sense?" For example, suppose a scientist who studies sea turtles measures the ocean water temperature each night for five nights. His data for the first four nights are 26°C, 23°C, 25°C, and 24°C. On the last night, he asks a student to make the measurement. The student records 81 in the data book.

Are the data reasonable? The reading on Day 5 is very different. Some variation in ocean temperature makes sense within a small range. But it doesn't make sense for ocean temperature to rise 57°C in one day, from 24°C to 81°C. The 81°C does not fit with the rest of the data. Data that do not fit with the rest of a data set are **anomalous data.** In this case, the anomalous data are explainable. The student measured °F instead of °C. Sometimes asking whether data are reasonable can uncover sources of error or unknown variables. Investigating the reason for anomalous data can lead to new discoveries.

How is mathematics important to the work of scientists?

THINK LIKE A SCIENTIST

The pale green coloring on the map shows areas where green sea turtles have nested in Florida.

FIGURE 5

INTERACTIVE ART Scientists use mathematics to help answer the question, "How and why are the number of sea turtle nests in Florida changing?"

Design Experiments Answer the questions below.

1 How would you collect accurate and precise turtle nest data?

2 What properties of the nests could you measure?

3 How might a hurricane in Florida cause anamolous nest data?

4 How could you estimate the total number of nests in Florida?

Do the Quick Lab *How Close Is It?*

Assess Your Understanding

2a. Describe Why is it important for scientists to calculate percent error?

b. ANSWER THE BIG ? How is mathematics important to the work of scientists?

got it? ....

O **I get it!** Now I know that math tools scientists use to analyze data include ______

O I need extra help with ______

Go to MY SCIENCE COACH *online for help with this subject.*

Graphs in Science

What Kinds of Data Do Line Graphs Display?
LS.1a, LS.1f, LS.1g, LS.1h

Why Are Line Graphs Powerful Tools?
LS.1d, LS.1e, LS.1f, LS.1h, LS.1i, LS.1j

my planet Diary

SCIENCE STATS

Waste and Recycling Data

The information below shows the amount of waste generated and recovered for recycling per person per day for each year listed.

- 1980: Generated waste was about 1.68 kg and recovered waste was about 0.16 kg.
- 1990: Generated waste was about 2.04 kg and recovered waste was about 0.33 kg.
- 2000: Generated waste was 2.09 kg and recovered waste was about 0.51 kg.
- 2002: Generated waste was about 2.09 kg and recovered waste was about 0.61 kg.
- 2007: Generated waste was about 2.09 kg and recovered waste was about 0.70 kg.

Communicate Discuss the following questions with a partner. Write your answers below.

How do you think society's view on recycling has changed over the years?

____

____

____

____

____

PLANET DIARY Go to **Planet Diary** to learn more about graphs in science.

Do the Inquiry Warm-Up *What's in a Picture?*

Science Standards of Learning

LS.1a Organize data into tables showing repeated trials and means.
LS.1f Identify dependent variables, independent variables, and constants.
LS.1g Control variables to test hypotheses, and repeat trials.
LS.1h Organize, graph, and interpret data, and use data to make predictions.

What Kinds of Data Do Line Graphs Display?

Could the saying "A watched pot never boils" really be true? Or does it take longer to boil water when there is more water in the pot? You could do an experiment to find out. The table in **Figure 1** shows data from such an experiment. But what do the data mean? Does it take longer to boil a larger volume of water?

Vocabulary

- graph
- linear graph
- nonlinear graph

Skills

- Reading: Relate Text and Visuals
- Inquiry: Predict

Line Graphs To help see what the data mean, you can use a graph. A **graph** is a "picture" of your data. One kind of graph is a line graph. **Line graphs display data that show how one variable (the responding variable) changes in response to another variable (the manipulated variable).**

Using Line Graphs Scientists control changes in the manipulated variable. Then they collect data about how the responding variable changes. A line graph is used when a manipulated variable is continuous, which means there are other points between the tested ones. For example, in the water-boiling experiment, many volumes are possible between 500 mL and 2,000 mL.

FIGURE 1

INTERACTIVE ART **A Line Graph**

This line graph plots the data from the table below.

Identify **Identify the manipulated variable and the responding variable in the experiment.**

____

____

____

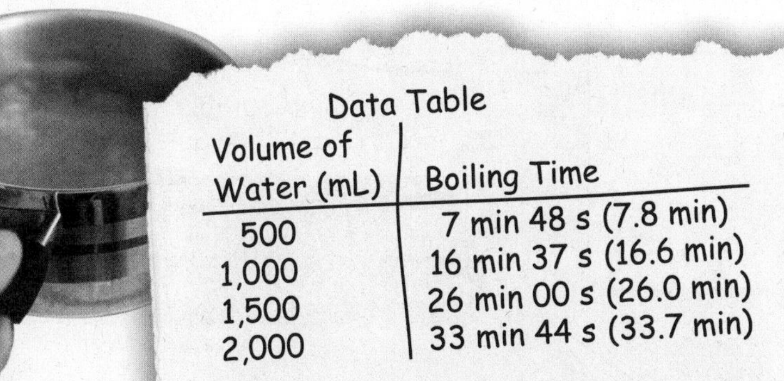

Data Table

Volume of Water (mL)	Boiling Time
500	7 min 48 s (7.8 min)
1,000	16 min 37 s (16.6 min)
1,500	26 min 00 s (26.0 min)
2,000	33 min 44 s (33.7 min)

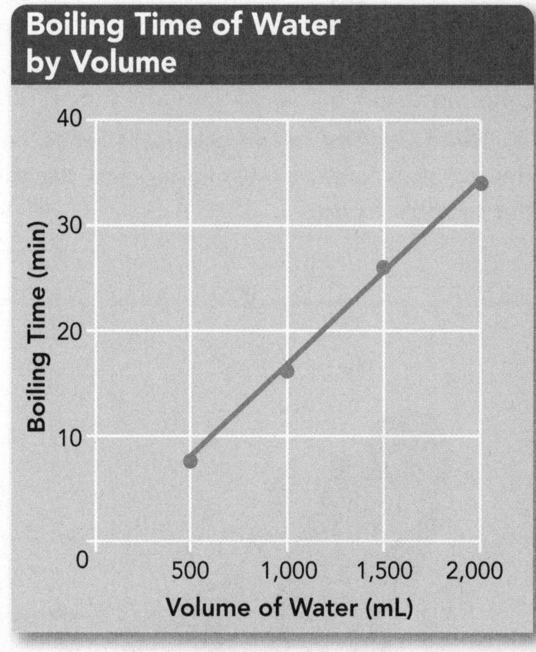

Lab zone® Do the Quick Lab *What's a Line Graph?*

Assess Your Understanding

got it?

○ **I get it!** Now I know that line graphs display data that ____

____

○ I need extra help with ____

Go to MY SCIENCE COACH *online for help with this subject.*

Science Standards of Learning

LS.1d Construct and use models and simulations to illustrate and explain phenomena.
LS.1e Identify sources of experimental error.
LS.1f Identify dependent variables, independent variables, and constants.
LS.1h Organize, graph, and interpret data, and use data to make predictions.
LS.1i Identify, interpret, and evaluate patterns in data.
LS.1j Use current applications to reinforce life science concepts.

Relate Text and Visuals Underline statements in the text that describe the graphs in **Figure 2.**

Why Are Line Graphs Powerful Tools?

A line graph in which the data points yield a straight line is a **linear graph.** The kind of graph in which the data points do not fall along a straight line is called a **nonlinear graph.** As shown in **Figure 2,** both kinds of line graphs are useful. **Line graphs are powerful tools in science because they allow you to identify trends, make predictions, and recognize anomalous data.**

For example, the graph of experimental data in **Figure 3** on the next page shows that the trend is linear, even though most points do not fall exactly on the line. One point is clearly not part of the trend. It is an anomalous data point. Graphs make it easy to see anomalous data points like this one. When a graph does not have any clear trends, it probably means that the variables are not related.

FIGURE 2

Linear Trends

Data plotted in a line graph may show a trend.

Read Graphs In the boxes, tell whether the graph is linear or nonlinear, and describe the graph's trend.

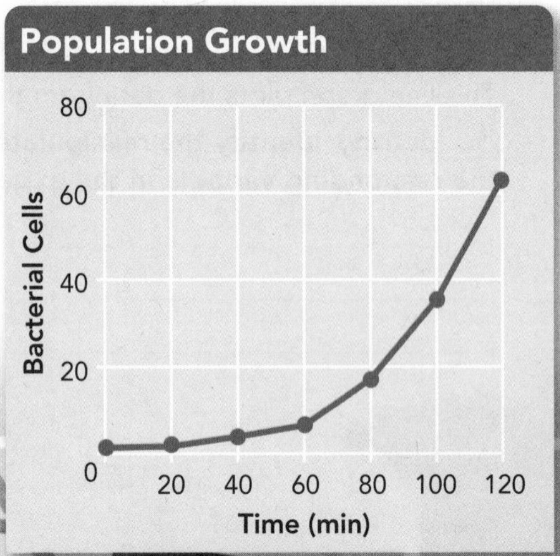

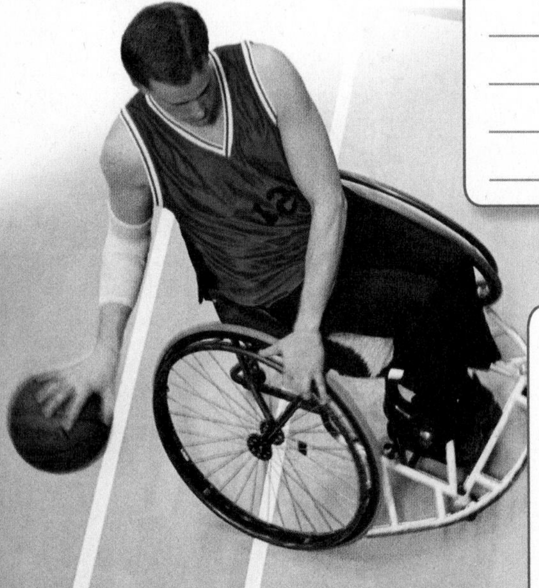

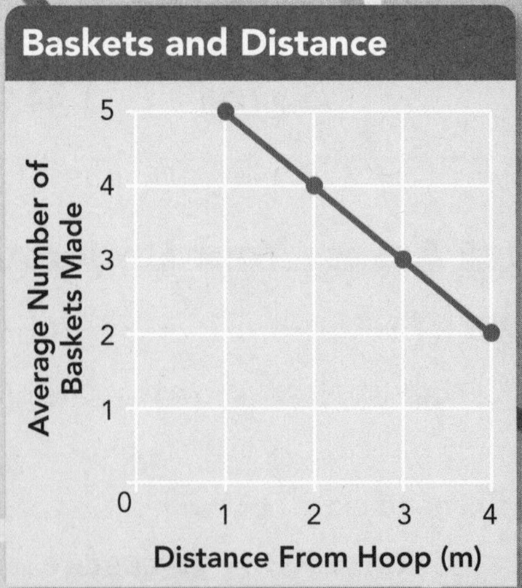

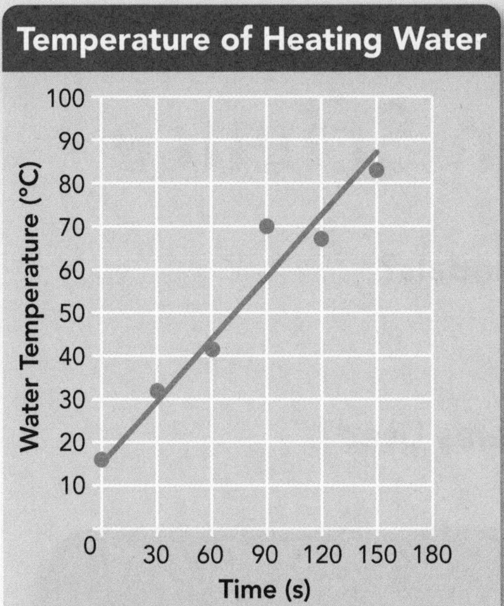

FIGURE 3

Data Variation

Even though some points do not fall on the line, this graph shows a trend.

Complete the following tasks.

1. **Identify** Label the anomalous data point.
2. **Predict** Use the graph to predict the temperature of the water after 180 seconds.

____

apply it!

This graph shows the distance two friends biked in one hour.

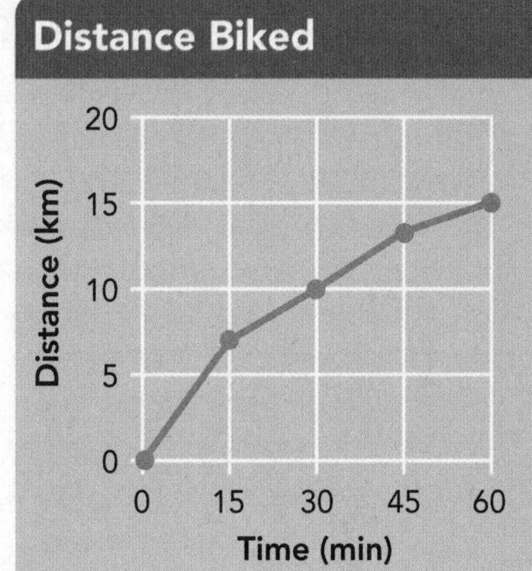

1 Interpret Data What is the relationship between the variables distance and time?

____

2 CHALLENGE During which time interval were the friends biking fastest? Explain.

____

____

Do the Lab Investigation *Density Graphs.*

Assess Your Understanding

1a. Review What does a graph with no trend show about the variables?

____

____

b. Compare and Contrast How does a graph with no trend differ from a graph with anomalous data points?

____

____

____

got it?

○ **I get it!** Now I know that line graphs are powerful tools because _______________

____

____

____

○ I need extra help with _______________

Go to **MY SCIENCE COACH** *online for help with this subject.*

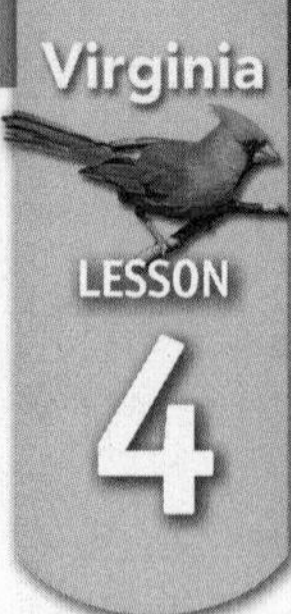

Models as Tools in Science

- Why Do Scientists Use Models? LS.1d, LS.1j
- What Is a System? LS.1d, LS.1j
- How Are Models of Systems Used? LS.1d, LS.1j

my planet Diary

FUN FACTS

Flying Through Space

You don't have to be an astronaut to experience what it's like to fly in space. Thanks to technological advances, space flight simulation software programs have been created. These programs range from simple and straightforward to detailed and complicated. Depending on which one you use, you can experience what it might feel like to fly to the moon, command a mission to Mars, and even explore other solar systems. If you've ever wondered what it's like to be an astronaut, now you have the chance to find out!

Read the following questions. Write your answers below.

1. Why would a flight simulation software program created today be more realistic than one that was created ten years ago?

2. Would you be able to really fly in space if you knew how to use a space flight simulation software program? Explain.

PLANET DIARY Go to **Planet Diary** to learn more about models as tools in science.

Lab zone Do the Inquiry Warm-Up *Scale Models.*

Inside a flight simulator

Vocabulary
- model • system • input
- process • output • feedback

Skills
- Reading: Identify the Main Idea
- Inquiry: Make Models

Why Do Scientists Use Models?

Science Standards of Learning

LS.1d Construct and use models and simulations to illustrate and explain phenomena.

LS.1j Use current applications to reinforce life science concepts.

"Who is that model on the cover?" "I still have that model car I built." The word *model* has many meanings. But, as with many words, *model* has a specific meaning in science. In science, a **model** is any representation of an object or process. Pictures, diagrams, computer programs, and mathematical equations are all examples of scientific models.

Scientists use models to understand things they cannot observe directly. For example, scientists use models as reasonable representations of things that are either very large, such as Earth's core, or very small, such as an atom. These kinds of models are physical models—drawings or three-dimensional objects. Other models, such as mathematical equations or word descriptions, are models of processes. Look at the models in **Figure 1.**

FIGURE 1

Two Science Models

Models may be three-dimensional objects or equations.

Explain Tell whether each of these models represents an object or a process and why each is useful.

Photosynthesis

____

Carbon dioxide + Water —sunlight→ Food + Oxygen

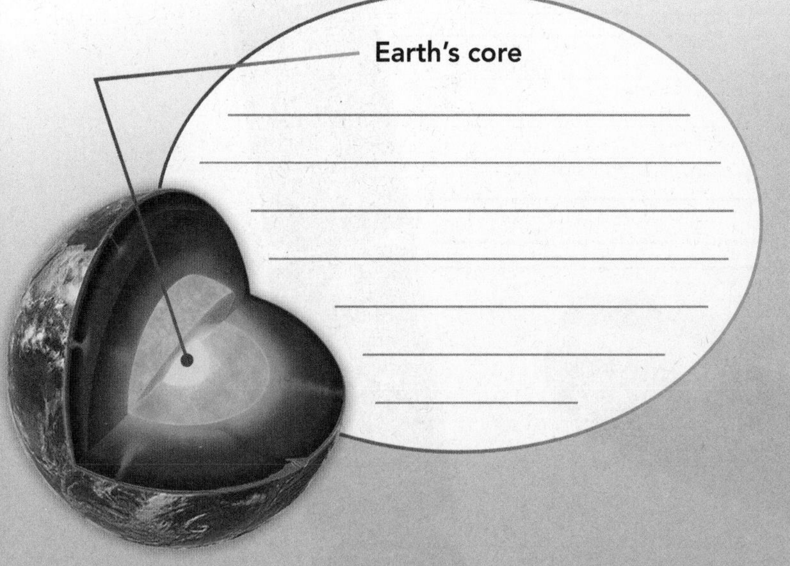

____

Assess Your Understanding

got it?

O **I get it!** Now I know that scientists use models to _______________

O I need extra help with _______________

Go to **MY SCIENCE COACH** *online for help with this subject.*

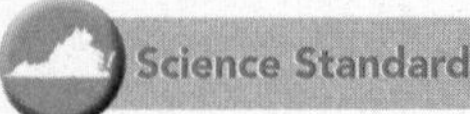

Science Standards of Learning

LS.1d Construct and use models and simulations to illustrate and explain phenomena.

LS.1j Use current applications to reinforce life science concepts.

What Is a System?

Many things you see and use are systems. For example, a toaster oven, your town's water pipes, and your bicycle are all systems. **A system is a group of parts that work together to perform a function or produce a result.**

Systems have common properties. All systems have input, process, and output. **Input** is the material or energy that goes into a system. **Process** is what happens in a system. **Output** is the material or energy that comes out of a system. In addition, some systems have feedback. **Feedback** is output that changes the system in some way. For example, the heating and cooling system in most homes has feedback. A sensor in the thermostat recognizes when the desired temperature has been reached. The sensor provides feedback that turns the system off temporarily. Look at **Figure 2** to see another example of a system.

Identify the Main Idea
Circle the main idea in the second paragraph. Underline the details.

FIGURE 2

An Everyday System

In a flashlight, many parts work together as a system.

Apply Concepts Look at the flashlight and use what you know to fill in the chart.

	Flashlight
Parts of System	
Input	
Process	
Output	

apply it!

Sun, air, land, and water are the parts of a system that produce a sea breeze. During the day, the sun's energy heats both the land and the water. The land and water, in turn, heat the air above them. Air over the land becomes much warmer than the air over water. As the warmer air rises, the cooler air from over the water rushes in to replace it. A sea breeze is the result.

1 **Identify** Identify the input, output, and process of the sea breeze system.

____

____

____

____

2 **CHALLENGE** Which parts of this system will change after the sun sets? How will it change?

____

____

Lab zone® Do the Quick Lab *Systems.*

Assess Your Understanding

1a. List What are the properties of a system?

____

____

____

____

____

b. Apply Concepts A student uses a calculator to solve a math problem. Is this an example of a system? Explain your answer.

____

____

____

____

got it?

O **I get it!** Now I know that a system is ____

____

____

O I need extra help with ____

Go to **my science coach** *online for help with this subject.*

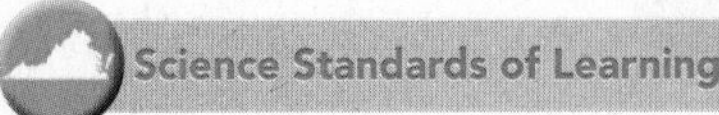

LS.1d Construct and use models and simulations to illustrate and explain phenomena.

LS.1j Use current applications to reinforce life science concepts.

How Are Models of Systems Used?

It's easy to identify the materials and energy that make up the inputs and outputs of a system. It's not easy to observe a system's process. **Scientists use models to understand how systems work. They also use models to predict changes in a system as a result of feedback or input changes.** However, they keep in mind that predictions based on models are uncertain.

When scientists construct a model of a system, they begin with certain assumptions. These assumptions allow them to make a basic model that accurately reflects the parts of the system and their relationships. A scientist who wants to study how energy moves through living things in an environment might use a model called a food chain. A food chain is a series that shows who eats whom to obtain energy in an environment. The food chain shown in **Figure 3** assumes that largemouth bass only eat flagfish. Largemouth bass actually eat many kinds of animals. However, the model still accurately reflects the relationship between the parts of a system.

Largemouth bass

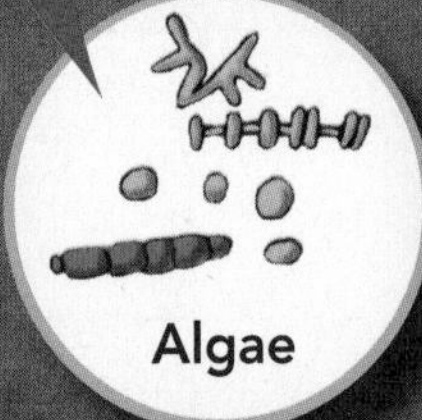

FIGURE 3

A Basic Model

In this model of a food chain in the Florida Everglades, the algae make food using the sun's energy. Algae are tiny living things that make their own food.

Complete the tasks below.

1. **Make Models** On the line next to each part of the system, write who eats it.
2. **CHALLENGE** What is the energy source for this system?

____

The arrows show the direction in which energy moves. You can "read" an arrow as saying "are eaten by."

Flagfish: ______________

Bass: ______________

Algae: ______________

Modeling a Simple System A food chain is a good model to begin to understand how energy moves through living things in an environment. However, it shows how only a few of those living things are related. So a scientist may build a food web to model a more complete picture of the system. In **Figure 4** you can see a food web with many overlapping food chains. The food web is more detailed than one food chain. But it does not provide information about other factors, such as weather, that affect energy flow in the system.

FIGURE 4

INTERACTIVE ART **A Model of a Simple System**

This model of an Everglades food web contains overlapping food chains.

Interpret Diagrams Study the food web model. On the notebook page write two things you learned from this complex model.

Modeling a Complex System Some systems that scientists study are complex. Many parts and many variables interact in these systems. So scientists may use a computer to keep track of all the variables. Because such systems are difficult to model, scientists may model only the specific parts of the system they want to study. Their model may be used to show the processes in the system or to make predictions. For example, the system that involves the melting of sea ice in the Arctic is a complex system. **Figure 5** shows how some parts of that system affect each other.

FIGURE 5

How Arctic Sea Ice Melts

The Arctic sea-ice system can be modeled by a diagram.

Identify List some of the variables in the Arctic sea-ice system. Then identify the input, process, and output in this model and fill in the boxes.

____

____

Arctic Sea-Ice System

In the spring and summer, the sun shines longer and the angle of the sun's rays are more direct than in the winter and fall. Sunlight transfers energy.

Sun

North Pole

Sea ice reflects most of the energy from sunlight, so it doesn't get very warm.

Ocean water absorbs most of the energy from sunlight, so it gets warm.

Sea Ice

When the ocean water gets warm, it melts nearby sea ice.

Input

____

____

Process

____

____

____

____

Output

____

____

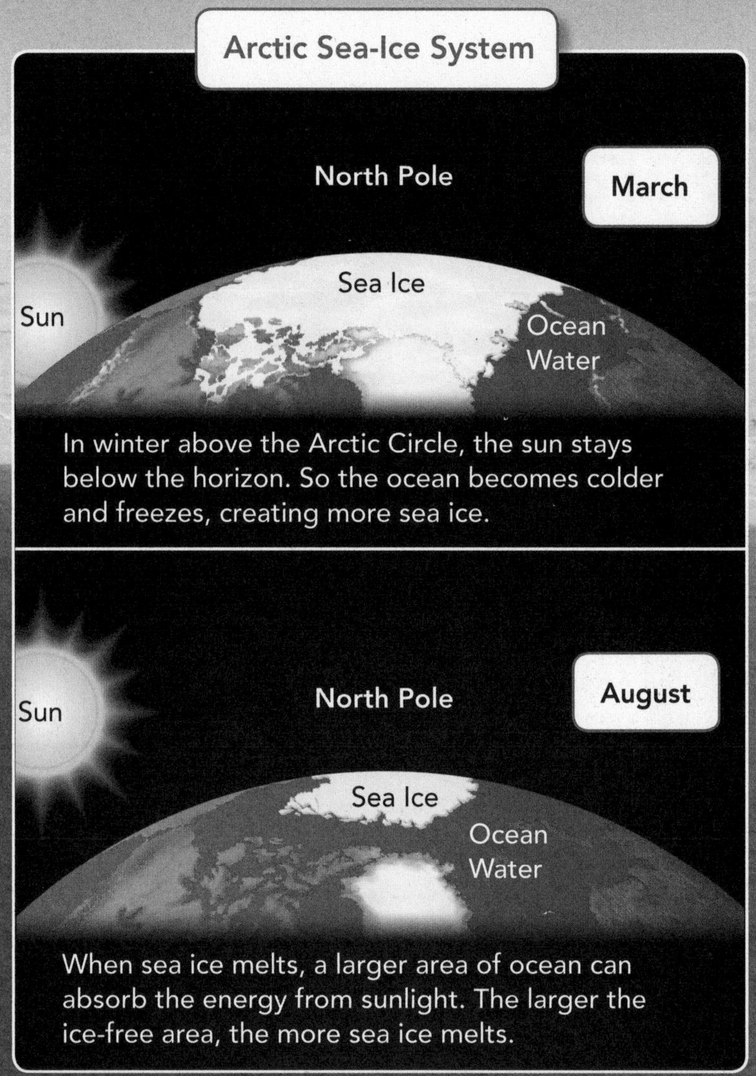

FIGURE 6

Arctic Sea-Ice System

These two diagrams show the amount of Arctic sea ice in March and August.

Answer the questions.

1. **Describe** In August, what is the feedback in this system?

2. **Explain** What causes changes in the system of melting Arctic sea ice to break the feedback in the system?

Lab zone® Do the Quick Lab *Models in Nature.*

Assess Your Understanding

2a. Explain Why do scientists use models?

b. Summarize Why aren't models of complex systems completely accurate?

got it?

O **I get it!** Now I know that scientists use models of systems to

O I need extra help with

Go to my science COACH *online for help with this subject.*

Safety in the Science Laboratory

- Why Prepare for a Laboratory Investigation? LS.1d, LS.1j
- What Should You Do if an Accident Occurs? LS.1d, LS.1j

my planet Diary

DISASTER

Oil Refinery Explosion

On March 23, 2005, an explosion at an oil refinery in Texas took the lives of 15 people and wounded at least 170 others. Sadly, experts agree that this accident could have been prevented had safety codes not been ignored. Investigators found old, worn equipment and noticed that several repairs had not been made. One positive thing that has come out of this accident is a safety video made by the U.S. Chemical Safety Board. The video is based on the refinery accident and includes safety information about how to prevent such an accident from ever occurring again.

Read the following questions. Write your answers below.

1. How do investigators believe this accident might have been prevented?

2. What kind of information would you include in a safety video based on the accident?

PLANET DIARY Go to **Planet Diary** to learn more about safety in the science laboratory.

Lab zone® Do the Inquiry Warm-Up *Where Is the Safety Equipment in Your School?*

Vocabulary
- safety symbol
- field

Skills

 Reading: Summarize

 Inquiry: Observe

Why Prepare for a Laboratory Investigation?

After hiking for many hours, you reach the campsite. You rush to set up your tent. The tent is lopsided, but it's up, so you run off with your friends. Later that night, heavy rain falls. Water pours into the tent and soaks you. You look for a flashlight. Then you realize that you forgot to pack one. If you had only prepared better, you would be dry and able to see.

Science Standards of Learning

LS.1d Construct and use models and simulations to illustrate and explain phenomena.

LS.1j Use current applications to reinforce life science concepts.

Preparing for a Lab

Just like for camping, you must prepare before you begin a laboratory investigation, or lab. **Good preparation helps you stay safe when doing laboratory investigations.** You should prepare for a lab before you do it. Read through any procedures carefully, and make sure you understand all the directions. If anything is unclear, ask your teacher about it before you begin the lab. Investigations may include safety symbols like the ones you see in **Figure 1.** **Safety symbols** alert you to possible sources of accidents in a laboratory.

FIGURE 1

Safety Symbols

Safety symbols identify how to work carefully and what safety equipment to use.

Apply Concepts In the notebook, list symbols that would appear for a lab investigation in which you measure the temperature of water as it heats to boiling.

Safety Symbols

Measuring the Temperature of Water

Lab Safety

___

___

___

___

___

___

___

___

___

___

FIGURE 2

Safety in the Lab

Recognizing and preventing safety hazards are important skills to practice in the lab.

Complete the tasks.

1. **Make Models** In the empty boxes on each page, draw a safety symbol for wearing closed-toe shoes and one for tying back long hair.
2. CHALLENGE How might the student on this page protect himself from breathing in fumes from the flask or beakers?

____

____

____

____

Performing a Lab Whenever you do a science lab, your chief concern must be your safety and that of your classmates and your teacher. The most important safety rule is simple: *Always follow your teacher's instructions and the directions exactly.* Never try anything on your own without asking your teacher first.

Figure 2 shows a number of things that you can do to make your lab experience safe and successful. When performing a lab, keep your work area clean and organized. Label all containers so you do not use the wrong chemical accidentally. Also, do not rush through any of the steps. When you need to move around the room, move slowly and carefully so you do not trip or bump into another group's equipment. Finally, always show respect and courtesy to your teacher and classmates.

Wear safety goggles to protect your eyes from chemical splashes, glass breakage, and sharp objects.

Wear an apron to protect yourself and your clothes from chemicals.

Wear heat-resistant gloves when handling hot objects.

Keep your work area clean and uncluttered.

Wear closed-toe shoes when working in the laboratory.

Make sure electric cords are untangled and out of the way.

End-of-Lab Procedures There are important things you need to do at the end of every lab. When you have completed a lab, be sure to clean up your work area. Turn off and unplug any equipment and return it to its proper place. It is very important that you dispose of any waste materials properly. Some wastes should not be thrown in the trash or poured down the drain. Follow your teacher's instructions about proper disposal. Finally, be sure to wash your hands thoroughly after working in the laboratory.

Summarize In the boxes provided, summarize the procedures you perform before, during, and after a lab-investigation.

Before

During

After

Wear plastic gloves to protect your skin when handling animals, plants, or chemicals.

Tie back long hair to keep it away from flames, chemicals, or equipment.

Handle live animals and plants with care.

Vocabulary Identify Multiple Meanings The noun *field* has several meanings. You have learned one meaning. Give two other meanings for *field*.

Safety in the Field Some of your science investigations will be done in the **field,** or any area outside a science laboratory. Just as in the laboratory, good preparation helps you stay safe. For example, there can be many safety hazards outdoors. You could encounter severe weather, traffic, wild animals, or poisonous plants. Whenever you set out to work in the field, you should always tell an adult where you will be. Never carry out a field investigation alone. Use common sense to avoid any potentially dangerous situations.

apply it!

These two students have not taken proper precautions to work in the field.

1 **Observe** Identify the clothing that is not appropriate for working in this field environment.

2 **Draw Conclusions** Explain how one piece of clothing a student is wearing might expose the student to hazards in the field.

Lab zone® Do the Quick Lab *Be Prepared.*

Assess Your Understanding

1a. List List two things you should do before you begin a lab.

b. Make Generalizations Why would field investigation take more preparation than a lab investigation?

got it?

O **I get it!** Now I know that the key to working safely in the lab and in the field is

O I need extra help with

Go to MY SCIENCE COACH *online for help with this subject.*

What Should You Do if an Accident Occurs?

Science Standards of Learning

LS.1d Construct and use models and simulations to illustrate and explain phenomena.

LS.1j Use current applications to reinforce life science concepts.

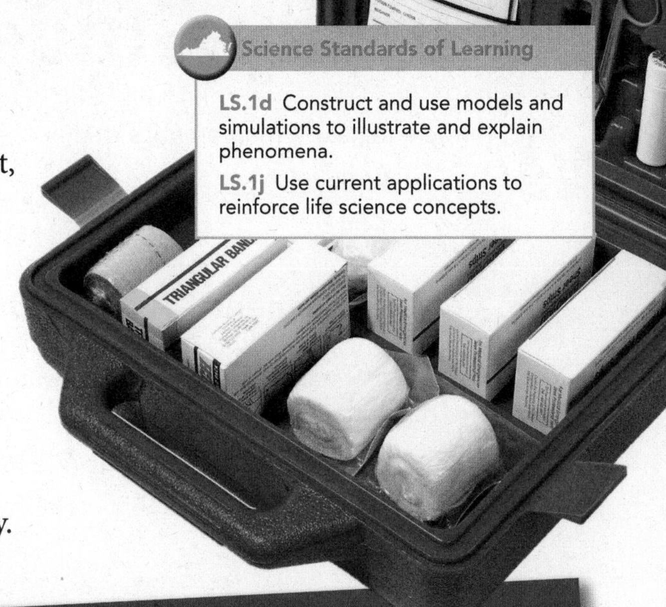

Although you may have prepared carefully, at some point, an accident may occur. Would you know what to do? You should always start by telling an adult.

When any accident occurs, no matter how minor, tell your teacher immediately. Then listen to your teacher's directions and carry them out quickly. Make sure you know the location and the proper use of all the emergency equipment in your laboratory. Knowing safety and first-aid procedures beforehand will prepare you to handle accidents properly. **Figure 3** lists some emergency procedures.

FIGURE 3

In Case of Emergency

These first-aid tips can help you in emergency situations in the lab.

Read and answer the questions.

1. **Review** Complete the sentence in the chart to identify the first step in responding to a lab emergency.
2. **Make Judgments** Suppose your teacher is involved in a lab accident. What should you do?

____

____

____

____

In Case of an Emergency

The first thing to do in an emergency is

____

Injury	What to Do
Burns	Immerse burns in cold water.
Cuts	Cover cuts with a dressing. Apply direct pressure to stop bleeding.
Spills on Skin	Flush the skin with large amounts of water.
Object in Eye	Flush the eye with water. Seek medical help.

Do the Quick Lab *Just in Case.*

Assess Your Understanding

got it?

○ **I get it!** Now I know that the first thing I should do in case of an accident is _______________

○ I need extra help with _______________

Go to **MY SCIENCE COACH** *online for help with this subject.*

CHAPTER 2

Study Guide

Scientists use mathematics to make ______________________________, and to collect, analyze, and display ____________.

LESSON 1 Measurement—A Common Language

Using SI as the standard system of measurement allows scientists to compare data and communicate with each other about their results.

In SI, some units of measurement include meter (m), kilogram (kg), cubic meter (m^3), kilograms per cubic meter (kg/m^3), kelvin (K), and second (s).

Vocabulary

- metric system
- SI
- mass
- weight
- volume
- meniscus
- density

LESSON 2 Mathematics and Science

Math skills that scientists use to collect data include estimation, accuracy and precision, and significant figures.

Scientists calculate percent error; find the mean, median, mode, and range; and check reasonableness to analyze data.

Vocabulary

- estimate
- accuracy
- precision
- significant figures
- percent error
- mean
- median
- mode
- range
- anomalous data

LESSON 3 Graphs in Science

Line graphs display data that show how the responding variable changes in response to the manipulated variable.

Line graphs are powerful tools in science because they allow you to identify trends, make predictions, and recognize anomalous data.

Vocabulary

- graph
- linear graph
- nonlinear graph

LESSON 4 Models as Tools in Science

Models help scientists understand things they cannot observe directly.

A system is a group of parts that work together to produce a specific function or result.

Scientists use models to understand how systems work and to predict how systems might change from feedback or input changes.

Vocabulary

- model
- system
- input
- process
- output
- feedback

LESSON 5 Safety in the Science Laboratory

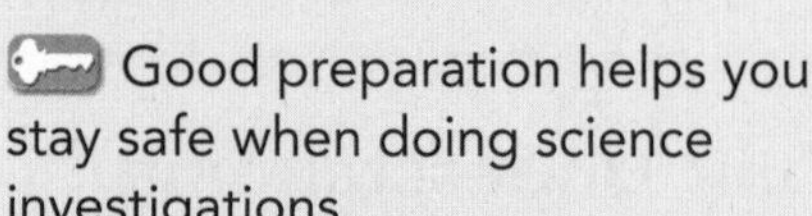

Good preparation helps you stay safe when doing science investigations.

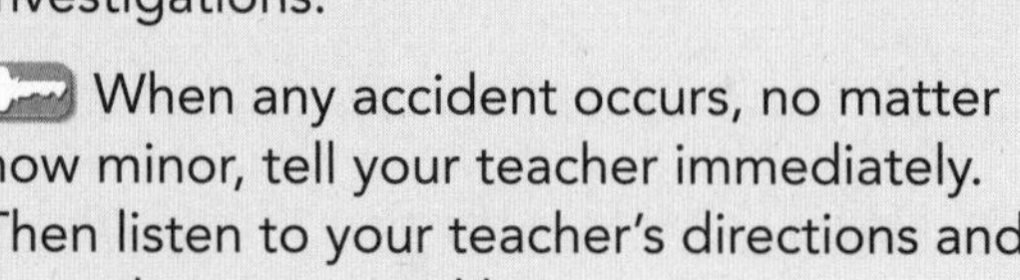

When any accident occurs, no matter how minor, tell your teacher immediately. Then listen to your teacher's directions and carry them out quickly.

Vocabulary

- safety symbol
- field

Review and Assessment

LESSON 1 Measurement—A Common Language

1. The amount of matter an object contains is its
   - a. length.
   - b. mass.
   - c. weight.
   - d. volume.

2. The basic SI unit of length is the

   ____

3. **Measure** 0 K is equal to what temperature in Celsius?

   ____

4. **Compare and Contrast** Which of the objects below has a greater volume? Explain.

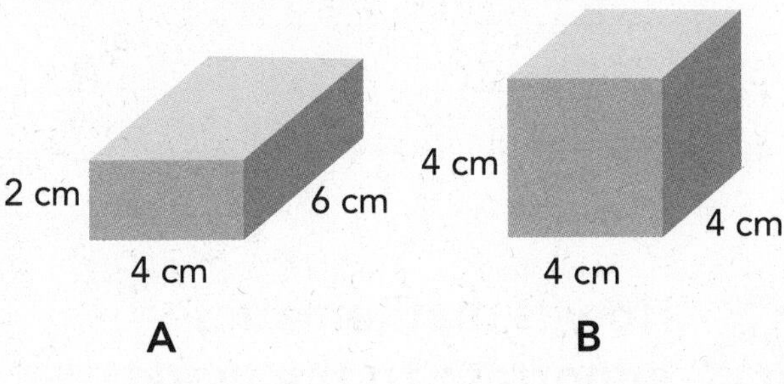

   ____

5. **Calculate** A 12.5 g marble displaces 5.0 mL of water. What is its density?

   ____

6. **Write About It** You are a sports reporter interviewing an Olympic swimmer who lost the silver medal by a few hundredths of a second. Write a one-page interview in which you discuss the meaning of time and the advanced instruments used to measure time.

LESSON 2 Mathematics and Science

7. The significant figures in a measurement
   - a. include only the first two digits.
   - b. include only the estimated digits.
   - c. include only the digits that have been measured exactly.
   - d. include all of the digits that have been measured exactly, plus one estimated digit.

8. ____________ refers to how close a measurement is to the true or accepted value.

9. **Apply Concepts** What is the median of 7, 31, 86, 6, 20, 85, and 12?

   ____

10. **Analyze Sources of Error** You rush through your lab activity and obtain a percent error of 50 percent. Why might your percent error be so high?

    ____

11. **math!** You measure the mass of a mystery object to be 658 g. The actual mass of the object is 755 g. What is your percent error?

CHAPTER 2

Review and Assessment

LESSON 3 Graphs in Science

12. A line graph is used when a manipulated variable is
    a. responsive. b. linear.
    c. continuous. d. anomalous.

13. A ______________________ is a graph in which the data points do not fall along a straight line.

14. **Make Generalizations** What do line graphs help you see about your data?

LESSON 4 Models as Tools in Science

15. Material or energy that goes into a system is
    a. output. b. input.
    c. feedback. d. process.

16. A ________________ system has many parts and variables.

17. **Write About It** The output of the system below is text displayed on the screen. Describe the input and process that produces this output.

LESSON 5 Safety in the Science Laboratory

18. The outdoor area in which some of your scientific investigations will be done is called the
    a. yard. b. lawn.
    c. park. d. field.

19. Good ________________ will help you stay safe when performing scientific investigations.

20. **Make Judgments** Why do you think that you should never bring food into a laboratory?

APPLY THE BIG Q How is mathematics important to the work of scientists?

21. Civil engineers help plan the construction of buildings. Name three ways the engineers use math during the planning process.

Virginia SOL Test Prep

Read each question and choose the best answer.

1 Study the graph below. What is the general trend in the data?

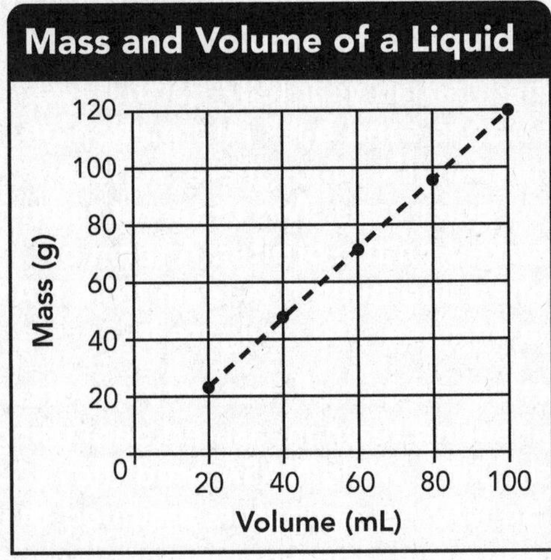

A linear
B no trend
C nonlinear
D linear at first and then nonlinear

2 A student grows tomatoes for an experiment. Which piece of equipment will be needed to determine the mass of the tomato?

F graduated cylinder
G meter stick
H stopwatch
J triple-beam balance

3 Ranida measured a string and got these measurements: 21.5 cm, 21.3 cm, 21.7 cm, and 21.6 cm. The string actually measures 25.5 cm. Which best describes Ranida's measurements?

A They were accurate.
B They were not accurate but they were precise.
C They were both accurate and precise.
D They were neither accurate nor precise.

4 Ellis measured the mass of five samples of quartz. His results were 39.75 g, 38.91 g, 37.66 g, 39.75 g, and 39.55 g. What was the mean mass of the samples?

F 39.55 g
G 39.75 g
H 39.12 g
J 38.91 g

5 Tanya measured an object's mass and volume and calculated its density to be 18 g/cm^3. The object's actual density was 15 g/cm^3. What is Tanya's percent error?

A 17%
B 20%
C 30%
D 83%

6 Clark decides to measure the volume of a rock he found outside. What is the volume of the rock?

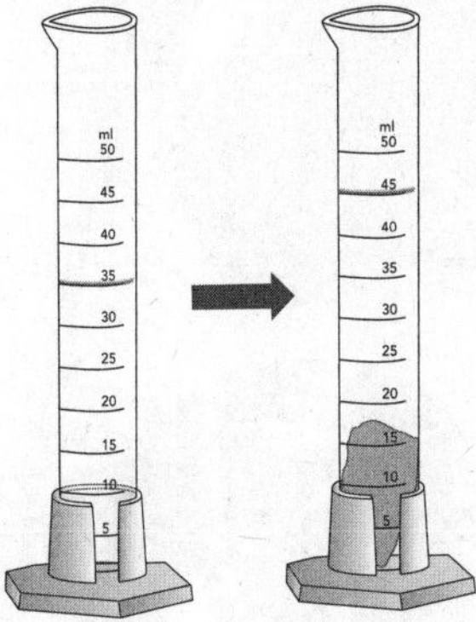

F 10 mL
G 17.5 mL
H 35 mL
J 45 mL

YOU LOST WHAT?!

In 1999, the National Aeronautics and Space Administration (NASA) made a 125-million-dollar mistake.

That year, the Mars Climate Orbiter was supposed to orbit Mars for one Martian year (687 Earth days). It was to send back information on the planet's atmosphere, surface, and polar caps. Two different teams worked on the orbiter. A team of engineers designed and built it. A team from NASA worked with the engineers to navigate it.

Both teams overlooked a small, but very important detail. The engineering team measured data using Imperial (English) units, while NASA used the metric system. So NASA's navigators assumed that the unit of measurements used to measure how hard the spacecraft's thrusters fired was Newtons per second. Unfortunately, the engineers had programmed the thrusters in pounds per second!

These tiny calculations added up to a big mistake. The spacecraft traveled too close to the surface of Mars and the signal was lost. The 125-million-dollar spacecraft may have been damaged beyond repair when it entered the Martian atmosphere. If not, it bounced off the atmosphere and was lost in space.

Differing measurement systems caused the Mars Climate Orbiter to fly off course and vanish. ▼

Explain It Think of some other examples where a mistake in units could have disastrous results. Write a note to a friend in which you explain why it is always important to include the units with the measurements you are reporting. Include your examples in the note.

Smallpox on the loose

These days, most people don't worry about contracting smallpox. The last known victim of smallpox died in 1978 and, even then, smallpox was a rare disease. People thought that smallpox was safely contained in labs and that nobody could get sick with it. Then someone did.

Janet Parker was a medical photographer at the University of Birmingham Medical School in England. Scientists working in a lab below her darkroom were researching the smallpox virus. Unfortunately, the laboratory did not have good safety and containment procedures for the deadly virus. Even now, nobody knows exactly how Janet was exposed to the virus, but one theory is that the virus traveled through the air ducts to the darkroom. She became ill and died in September 1978.

Research It The World Health Organization (WHO) declared smallpox completely gone in 1980. What steps did the WHO take to ensure that no one else would contract the disease? In 2002, the WHO decided not to ask the remaining labs to destroy the smallpox stocks. What value do they think the stocks might have? Write a report that answers these questions and include suggestions on what else could or should be done.

HOW ARE THIS MANATEE AND HYRAX ALIKE?

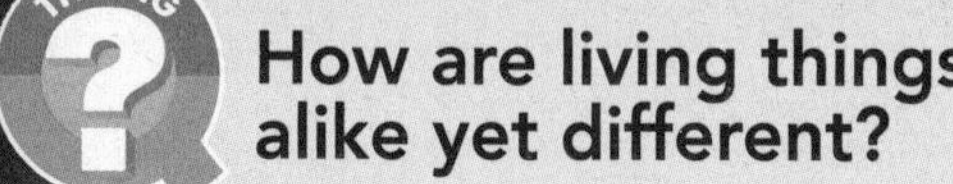

How are living things alike yet different?

Living in Florida waters, a manatee can grow to be longer than 3 meters and weigh over 350 kilograms. A rock hyrax is a small, tailless, rodentlike animal that lives in rocky areas of Africa. While these animals appear to be very different, they are actually related.

Develop Hypotheses **What could these two animals have in common?**

UNTAMED SCIENCE Watch the **Untamed Science** video to learn more about living things.

Virginia

CHAPTER 3

Introduction to Living Things

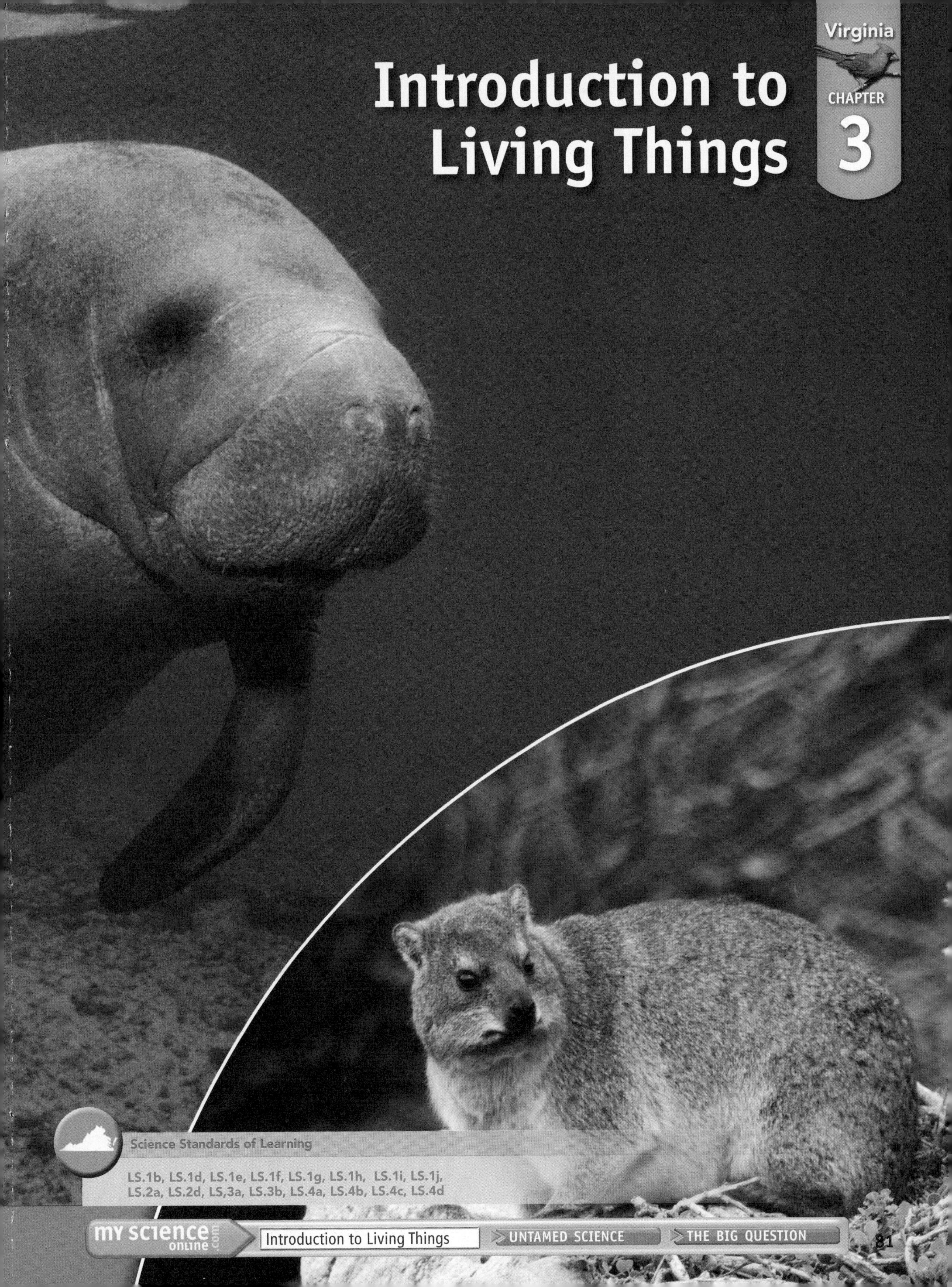

Science Standards of Learning

LS.1b, LS.1d, LS.1e, LS.1f, LS.1g, LS.1h, LS.1i, LS.1j, LS.2a, LS.2d, LS,3a, LS.3b, LS.4a, LS.4b, LS.4c, LS.4d

CHAPTER 3

Getting Started

Check Your Understanding

1. **Background** Read the paragraph below and then answer the question.

> You eat **microscopic** organisms all the time without realizing it! Some microscopic organisms are necessary to prepare common foods. **Yeast,** for example, is a tiny organism that is used to make bread. **Bacteria** are used to make yogurt, sauerkraut, and many other foods.

Something **microscopic** is so small that it cannot be seen without a magnifying lens or a microscope.

Yeast is a single-celled organism that has a nucleus.

Bacteria are single-celled organisms that do not have nuclei.

• What is one kind of food that bacteria are used to make?

____

MY READING WEB If you had trouble completing the question above, visit **My Reading Web** and type in ***Introduction to Living Things.***

Vocabulary Skill

Greek Word Origins Many science words come from ancient Greek words. Learning the word parts that have Greek origins can help you understand some of the vocabulary in this chapter.

Greek Word Part	Meaning	Example
autos	self	autotroph, *n.* an organism that makes its own food
taxis	order, arrangement	taxonomy, *n.* the scientific study of how living things are classified
homos	similar, same	homeostasis, *n.* the maintenance of stable internal conditions

2. **Quick Check Circle the part of the word *taxonomy* that lets you know that the word's meaning has something to do with ordering or classifying things.**

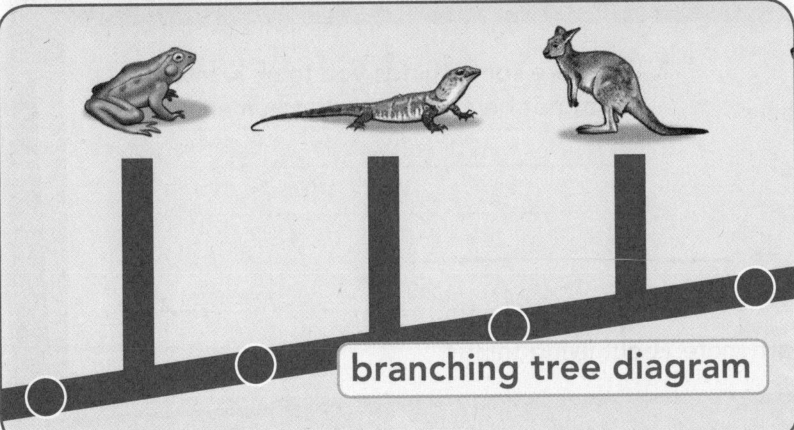

Chapter Preview

LESSON 1

- organism
- cell
- unicellular
- multicellular
- metabolism
- stimulus
- response
- development
- asexual reproduction
- sexual reproduction
- spontaneous generation
- controlled experiment
- autotroph
- heterotroph
- homeostasis

Compare and Contrast
Control Variables

LESSON 2

- classification
- taxonomy
- binomial nomenclature
- genus
- species

Ask Questions
Observe

LESSON 3

- prokaryote
- nucleus
- eukaryote

Identify the Main Idea
Classify

LESSON 4

- evolution
- branching tree diagram
- shared derived characteristic
- convergent evolution

Summarize
Infer

VOCAB FLASH CARDS For extra help with vocabulary, visit **Vocab Flash Cards** and type in ***Introduction to Living Things.***

What Is Life?

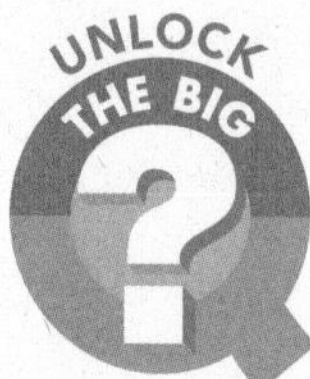

- **What Are the Characteristics of All Living Things?** LS.2a, LS.2d, LS.3a, LS.3b
- **Where Do Living Things Come From?** LS.1e, LS.1f, LS.1g, LS.1i, LS.1j
- **What Do Living Things Need to Survive?** LS.3b

my planet Diary

TECHNOLOGY

It's Kismet!

If you hear a loud noise, do you turn toward the sound to see what caused it? When someone smiles at you, do you smile back? If somebody shook something in front of your face, would you back away? Most people react in these ways, and so does Kismet, a humanlike robot! Scientists developed Kismet to interact with, cooperate with, and learn from humans. Kismet can understand information that it sees and hears as if it were a young child. When responding to information, Kismet's face changes so that it seems interested, happy, or frightened. Kismet's expressions are so convincing that it is sometimes hard to remember that Kismet isn't really alive!

Answer the questions below.

1. What does Kismet do that makes it seem human?

____

2. What are some things you think Kismet might not be able to do that humans can?

____

PLANET DIARY Go to **Planet Diary** to learn more about living things.

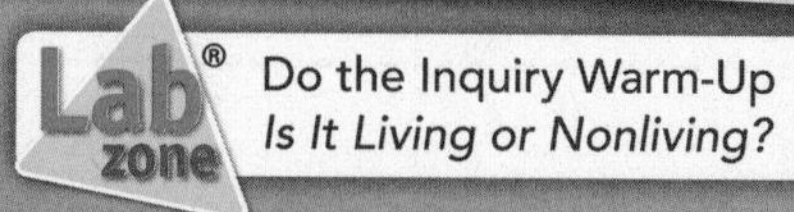

Vocabulary

- organism • cell • unicellular • multicellular • metabolism
- stimulus • response • development • asexual reproduction
- sexual reproduction • spontaneous generation
- controlled experiment • autotroph • heterotroph • homeostasis

Skills

- Reading: Compare and Contrast
- Inquiry: Control Variables

Science Standards of Learning

LS.2a Investigate and understand cell structure and organelles.

LS.2d Investigate and understand cell division.

LS.3a Investigate and understand cells, tissues, organs, and systems.

LS.3b Investigate and understand patterns of cellular organization and their relationship to life processes in living things.

What Are the Characteristics of All Living Things?

If you were asked to name some living things, or **organisms,** you might name yourself, a pet, and some insects or plants. You would probably not mention a moss growing in a shady spot, the mildew on bathroom tiles, or the slime molds that ooze across lawns. But all of these things are organisms that share several important characteristics with all other living things. **All living things have a cellular organization, contain similar chemicals, use energy, respond to their surroundings, grow and develop, and reproduce.**

FIGURE 1

It's Alive . . . or Is It?

Look at the photos. Then answer the questions.

1. **Identify** List the letter of the photo(s) that you think show living thing(s). ______
2. **Describe** What characteristics helped you decide whether or not the things shown were living or nonliving?

______

______

______

Characteristics of Living Things

Cellular Organization

All organisms are made of small building blocks called cells. A **cell,** like the one shown here, is the basic unit of structure and function in an organism. Organisms may be composed of only one cell or of many cells.

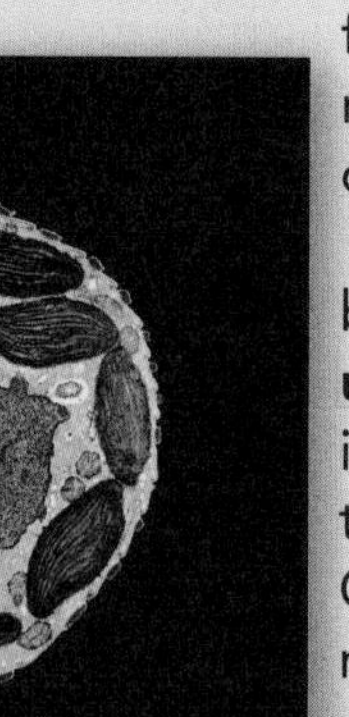

Single-celled organisms, like bacteria (bak TIHR ee uh), are **unicellular** organisms. The single cell is responsible for carrying out all of the functions necessary to stay alive. Organisms that are composed of many cells are **multicellular.** For example, you are made of trillions of cells. In many multicellular organisms, the cells are specialized to do certain tasks. Specialized cells in your body, such as muscle and nerve cells, work together to keep you alive. Nerve cells carry messages to your muscle cells, making your body move.

The Chemicals of Life

The cells of living things are made of chemicals. The most abundant chemical in cells is water. Other chemicals, called carbohydrates (kahr boh HY drayts) are a cell's main energy source. Two other chemicals, proteins and lipids, are the building materials of cells, much as wood and bricks are the building materials of houses. Finally, nucleic (noo KLEE ik) acids are the genetic material of cells—the chemical instructions that cells need to carry out the functions of life.

Energy Use

Organisms get energy from taking in and breaking down materials. The combination of chemical reactions through which an organism builds up or breaks down materials is called **metabolism.** The cells of organisms use energy to do what living things must do, such as grow and repair injured parts. An organism's cells are always hard at work. For example, as you read these words, not only are your eye and brain cells busy, but most of your other cells are working, too. Young sooty terns, like the one shown above, need lots of energy to fly. These birds can fly four to five years without ever setting foot on land!

FIGURE 2

Living Things

All living things share the same characteristics.

Make Judgments Which characteristic on these two pages do you think best identifies an object as a living thing? Explain your choice.

Response to Surroundings

If you've ever seen a plant in a sunny window, you may have observed that the plant's stems have bent so that the leaves face the sun. Like a plant bending toward the light, all organisms react to changes in their environment. A change in an organism's surroundings that causes the organism to react is called a **stimulus** (plural *stimuli*). Stimuli include changes in light, sound, and other factors.

An organism reacts to a stimulus with a **response**—an action or a change in behavior. For example, has someone ever knocked over a glass of water by accident during dinner, causing you to jump? The sudden spilling of water was the stimulus that caused your startled response.

Lab zone® Do the Quick Lab *React!*

Growth and Development

All living things grow and develop. Growth is the process of becoming larger. **Development** is the process of change that occurs during an organism's life, producing a more complex organism. As they develop and grow, organisms use energy and make new cells.

Reproduction

Another characteristic of organisms is the ability to reproduce, or produce offspring that are similar to the parents. Organisms reproduce in different ways. **Asexual reproduction** involves only one parent and produces offspring that are identical to the parent. **Sexual reproduction** involves two parents and combines their genetic material to produce a new organism that differs from both parents. Mammals, birds, and most plants sexually reproduce. Penguins lay eggs that develop into young penguins that closely resemble their parents.

Assess Your Understanding

1a. Review A change in an organism's surroundings is a (stimulus/response).

b. Infer A bird sitting in a tree flies away as you walk by. Which of the life characteristics explains the bird's behavior?

___

c. CHALLENGE Trees do not move like birds do, but they are living things. Why?

___

___

___

___

___

got it?

O I get it! Now I know that all living things ___

___

___

___

___

O I need extra help with ___

___

Go to MY SCIENCE COACH *online for help with this subject.*

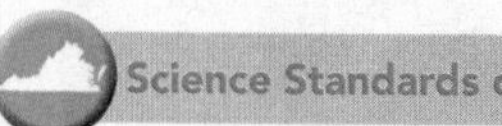

Science Standards of Learning

LS.1e Identify sources of experimental error.

LS.1f Identify dependent variables, independent variables, and constants.

LS.1g Control variables to test hypotheses, and repeat trials.

LS.1i Identify, interpret, and evaluate patterns in data.

LS.1j Use current applications to reinforce life science concepts.

Where Do Living Things Come From?

Today, when people see weeds poking out of cracks in sidewalks or find mice in their cabinet, as shown in **Figure 3,** they know that these organisms are the result of reproduction. **Living things arise from other living things through reproduction.**

Four hundred years ago, however, people believed that life could appear from nonliving material. For example, when people saw flies swarming around decaying meat, they concluded that flies were produced by rotting meat. The mistaken idea that living things can arise from nonliving sources is called **spontaneous generation.** It took hundreds of years of experiments to convince people that spontaneous generation does not occur.

FIGURE 3

Spontaneous Generation

Sometimes unexpected visitors, like this mouse, can be found in kitchen cabinets.

Answer the questions.

1. **Develop Hypotheses** If you lived 400 years ago, where might you think the mouse in the cabinet came from?

2. CHALLENGE Describe a way in which you could test your hypothesis.

Redi's Experiment In the 1600s, an Italian doctor named Francesco Redi helped to disprove spontaneous generation. Redi designed a controlled experiment to show that maggots, which develop into new flies, do not arise from decaying meat. In a **controlled experiment,** a scientist carries out a series of tests that are identical in every respect except for one factor. The one factor that a scientist changes in an experiment is called the manipulated variable. The factor that changes as a result of changes to the manipulated variable is called the responding variable. Redi's experiment is shown in **Figure 4.**

FIGURE 4

Redi's Experiment

Francesco Redi designed one of the first controlled experiments. Redi showed that flies do not spontaneously arise from decaying meat. Here's how he did it:

Uncovered jar | Covered jar

STEP 1 Redi placed meat in two identical jars. He left one jar uncovered. He covered the other jar with a cloth that let in air.

STEP 2 After a few days, Redi saw maggots (young flies) on the decaying meat in the open jar. There were no maggots on the meat in the covered jar.

STEP 3 Redi reasoned that flies had laid eggs on the meat in the open jar. The eggs hatched into maggots. Because flies could not lay eggs on the meat in the covered jar, there were no maggots there. Redi concluded that decaying meat did not produce maggots.

apply it!

Use **Figure 4** to answer the following questions about Redi's experiment.

1 **Control Variables** What is the manipulated variable in this experiment?

2 **Control Variables** What is the responding variable?

3 **Analyze Sources of Error** Name two factors that would need to be kept constant in this experiment to avoid causing error. Why?

Pasteur's Experiment Even after Redi's experiment, many people continued to believe in spontaneous generation. In the mid-1800s, Louis Pasteur, a French chemist, designed another experiment to test spontaneous generation. That experiment, shown in **Figure 5,** along with Redi's work, finally disproved spontaneous generation.

FIGURE 5

INTERACTIVE ART **Pasteur's Experiment**

Louis Pasteur's carefully controlled experiment demonstrated that bacteria arise only from existing bacteria. **Design Experiments Read each step of the experiment below. Why do you think flasks with curved necks were important?**

______

______

______

Step 1 Experiment Begins

Pasteur put clear broth into flasks with curved necks. The necks let in air but kept out bacteria. He boiled the broth in the flasks to kill all bacteria present.

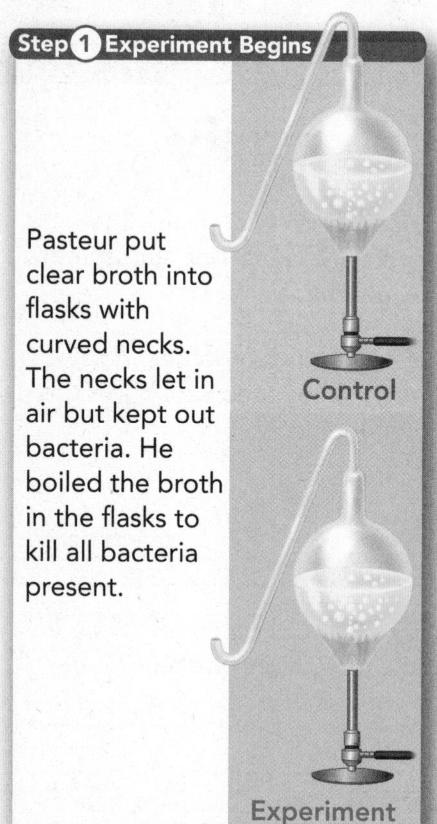

Step 2 A Year Passes

The boiled broth remained clear. Pasteur then left some of the flasks as is.

Pasteur broke the curved necks off the other flasks. Bacteria from the outside air now entered these flasks.

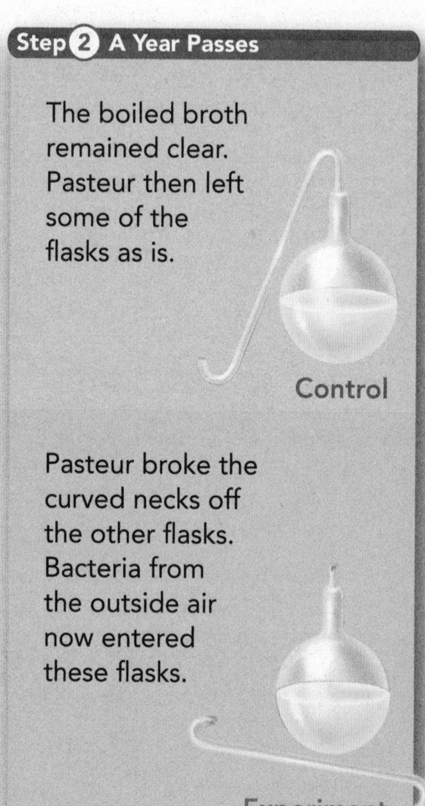

Step 3 A Few Days Later

The broth in the unbroken flasks remained clear. Pasteur concluded that bacteria could not arise from the broth.

The broth in the broken flasks became cloudy, showing bacterial growth. This evidence confirmed that new bacteria arise only from existing bacteria.

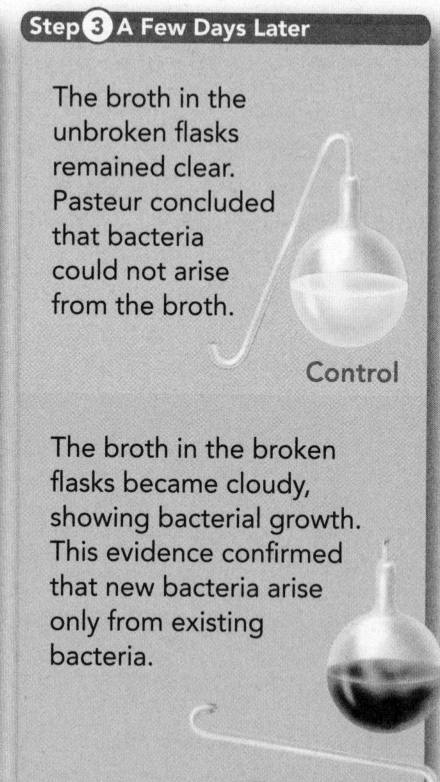

Lab zone® Do the Quick Lab *Compare Broth Samples.*

Assess Your Understanding

2a. Identify A ______ is the one factor that changes in a controlled experiment.

b. Explain Why is the idea of spontaneous generation incorrect?

______

______

got it?

O **I get it!** Now I know that living things come from ______

______

O I need extra help with ______

______

Go to MY SCIENCE COACH *online for help with this subject.*

What Do Living Things Need to Survive?

Though it may seem surprising, flies, bacteria, and all other organisms have the same basic needs as you.  **All living things must satisfy their basic needs for food, water, living space, and stable internal conditions.**

Food Recall that organisms need a source of energy to live. They use food as their energy source. Organisms differ in the ways they obtain energy. Some organisms, such as plants, capture the sun's energy and use it to make food. Organisms that make their own food are called **autotrophs** (AW toh trohfs). *Auto-* means "self" and *-troph* means "feeder." Autotrophs use the food they make to carry out their own life functions.

Organisms that cannot make their own food are called **heterotrophs** (HET uh roh trohfs). Heterotrophs obtain energy by feeding on other organisms. Some heterotrophs eat autotrophs for food. Other heterotrophs consume heterotrophs that eat autotrophs. They use the energy in the autotrophs' bodies. Therefore, a heterotroph's energy source is also the sun—but in an indirect way. Animals, mushrooms, and slime molds are examples of heterotrophs.

Science Standards of Learning

LS.3b Investigate and understand patterns of cellular organization and their relationship to life processes in living things.

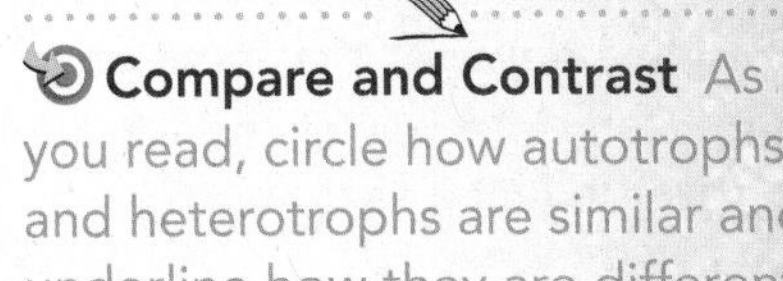

Compare and Contrast As you read, circle how autotrophs and heterotrophs are similar and underline how they are different.

Vocabulary Greek Word Origins The Greek word part *hetero-* means "other." How does this word help you to understand how heterotrophs get their food?

FIGURE 6

Food

This giraffe, a heterotroph, obtains its energy by feeding on trees and shrubs.

Identify From your own habitat, name two examples of autotrophs and two examples of heterotrophs.

did you know?

During the summer, when desert temperatures can exceed 47°C, a camel only needs to drink water every five days. At that time, a camel can drink up to 189 liters of water in just a few hours!

Water All living things need water to survive. In fact, most organisms can live for only a few days without water. Organisms need water to obtain chemicals from their surroundings, break down food, grow, move substances within their bodies, and reproduce.

One property of water that is vital to living things is its ability to dissolve more chemicals than any other substance on Earth. In fact, water makes up about 90 percent of the liquid part of your blood. The food that your cells need dissolves in blood and is transported to all parts of your body. Waste from cells dissolves in blood and is carried away. Your body's cells also provide a watery environment for chemicals to dissolve.

Living Space All organisms need a place to live—a place to get food and water and find shelter. Whether an organism lives in the freezing Arctic or the scorching desert, its surroundings must provide what it needs to survive.

Because there is a limited amount of space on Earth, some organisms must compete for space. Trees in a forest, for example, compete with other trees for sunlight above ground. Below ground, their roots compete for water and minerals.

FIGURE 7

Desert Oasis

You might be surprised to see so much green in the middle of a desert. In a desert oasis, there is water beneath the surface. The groundwater can bubble to the surface and create springs.

Draw Conclusions How can a small area in the middle of a desert provide an organism what it needs to survive?

FIGURE 8

Homeostasis

During the winter months, birds rely on their feathers to maintain homeostasis. By fluffing its feathers, this bluebird is able to trap body heat to keep warm. **Make Generalizations How do people maintain homeostasis when exposed to cold temperatures?**

Stable Internal Conditions

Organisms must be able to keep the conditions inside their bodies stable, even when conditions in their surroundings change significantly. For example, your body temperature stays steady despite changes in the air temperature. The maintenance of stable internal conditions is called **homeostasis** (hoh mee oh STAY sis).

Homeostasis keeps internal conditions just right for cells to function. Think about your need for water after a hard workout. When water levels in your body decrease, chemicals in your body send signals to your brain, which cause you to feel thirsty.

Other organisms have different mechanisms for maintaining homeostasis. Consider barnacles, which as adults are attached to rocks at the edge of the ocean. At high tide, they are covered by water. But at low tide, the watery surroundings disappear, and barnacles are exposed to hours of sun and wind. Without a way to keep water in their cells, they would die. Fortunately, a barnacle can close up its hard outer plates, trapping some water inside. In this way, a barnacle can keep its body moist until the next high tide. Refer to **Figure 8** to see another example of how an organism maintains homeostasis.

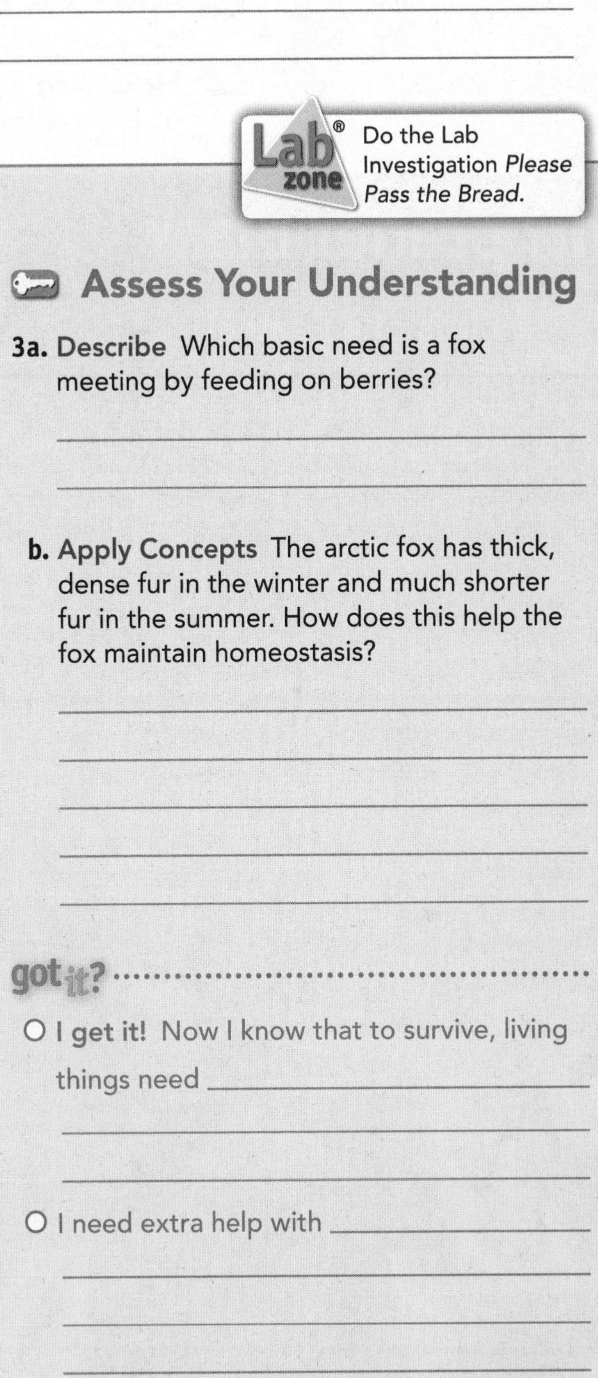

Lab zone® Do the Lab Investigation *Please Pass the Bread.*

Assess Your Understanding

3a. Describe Which basic need is a fox meeting by feeding on berries?

b. Apply Concepts The arctic fox has thick, dense fur in the winter and much shorter fur in the summer. How does this help the fox maintain homeostasis?

got it?

O **I get it!** Now I know that to survive, living things need ______

O I need extra help with ______

Go to MY SCIENCE COACH *online for help with this subject.*

Virginia

LESSON

2 Classifying Life

Why Do Biologists Classify Organisms?
LS.1b, LS.1h, LS.1i, LS.1j, LS.4d

What Are the Levels of Classification?
LS.4a, LS.4b, LS.4c, LS.4d

How Are Taxonomic Keys Useful?
LS.1d, LS.1i, LS.1j

my planet Diary

CAREER

Birds of a Feather

When people first began to travel in airplanes, birds often caused crashes. In 1960, 62 people were killed when birds flew into an airplane's engine. Something had to be done, but no one knew what kinds of birds were causing the crashes. Usually only a tiny, burnt piece of feather remained. Engineers didn't know how big or heavy the birds were, so they couldn't design planes to keep birds out of the engines. Then a scientist named Roxie Laybourne invented a way to classify birds using a tiny piece of feather. She identified the birds from many crashes. Her work helped engineers design engines to reduce bird collisions. She also helped develop bird management programs for major airports. Roxie's work has saved passengers' lives!

Answer the questions below.

1. What did Roxie Laybourne invent?

____

2. Why was her invention so important?

____

PLANET DIARY Go to **Planet Diary** to learn more about classification.

Lab zone® Do the Inquiry Warm-Up *Can You Organize a Junk Drawer?*

Vocabulary
- classification
- taxonomy
- binomial nomenclature
- genus
- species

Skills
- Reading: Ask Questions
- Inquiry: Observe

Why Do Biologists Classify Organisms?

So far, scientists have identified more than one million kinds of organisms on Earth. That's a large number, and it keeps growing as scientists discover new organisms. Imagine how difficult it would be to find information about one particular organism if you had no idea even where to begin. It would be a lot easier if similar organisms were placed into groups.

Organizing living things into groups is exactly what biologists have done. Biologists group organisms based on similarities, just as grocers group milk with dairy products and tomatoes with other produce. **Classification** is the process of grouping things based on their similarities, as shown in **Figure 1**.

Biologists use classification to organize living things into groups so that the organisms are easier to study. The scientific study of how organisms are classified is called **taxonomy** (tak SAHN uh mee). Taxonomy is useful because once an organism is classified, a scientist knows a lot of information about that organism. For example, if you know that a crow is classified as a bird, then you know that a crow has wings, feathers, and a beak.

Science Standards of Learning

LS.1b Develop a classification system based on multiple attributes.
LS.1h Organize, graph, and interpret data, and use data to make predictions.
LS.1i Identify, interpret, and evaluate patterns in data.
LS.1j Use current applications to reinforce life science concepts.
LS.4d Investigate and understand characteristics that define a species.

Ask Questions Before you read, preview the headings. Ask a *what, why,* or *how* question that you would like answered. As you read, write the answer to your question.

FIGURE 1

Classifying Insects

These bees and wasps belong to a large insect collection in a natural history museum. They have been classified according to the characteristics they share.

Observe What characteristics do you think may have been used to group these insects?

***Felis concolor* (puma)**
Concolor means "the same color" in Latin. Notice that this animal's coat is mostly the same color.

The Naming System of Linnaeus

Taxonomy also involves naming organisms. In the 1730s, the Swedish botanist Carolus Linnaeus devised a system of naming organisms that is still used today. Linnaeus placed organisms in groups based on their observable features. Each organism was given a unique, two-part scientific name. This system is called **binomial nomenclature** (by NOH mee ul NOH men klay chur). *Binomial* means "two names."

FIGURE 2

Binomial Nomenclature

These three different species of cats belong to the same genus. The cats' scientific names share the same first word, *Felis*. The second word of their names describes a feature of the animals.

Infer Suppose someone told you that a jaguarundi is classified in the same genus as house cats. What characteristics and behaviors do you think a jaguarundi might have?

____
____
____
____
____
____

Genus and Species The first word in an organism's scientific name is its genus. A **genus** (JEE nus; plural *genera*) is a classification grouping that contains similar, closely related organisms. As shown in **Figure 2,** pumas, house cats, and marbled cats are all classified in the genus *Felis.* Organisms that are classified in the genus *Felis* share characteristics such as sharp, retractable claws and behaviors such as hunting other animals.

The second word in a scientific name often describes a distinctive feature of an organism, such as where it lives or its appearance. Together, the two words form the scientific name of a unique kind of organism. A **species** (SPEE sheez) is a group of similar organisms that can mate with each other and produce offspring that can also mate and reproduce.

***Felis domesticus* (house cat)**
Domesticus means "of the house" in Latin.

***Felis marmorata* (marbled cat)**
Marmorata means "marble" in Latin. Notice the marbled pattern of this animal's coat.

Using Binomial Nomenclature A complete scientific name is written in italics. Only the first letter of the first word in a scientific name is capitalized. Notice that scientific names contain Latin words. Linnaeus used Latin words in his naming system because Latin was the language that scientists used during that time.

Binomial nomenclature makes it easy for scientists to communicate about an organism because everyone uses the same scientific name for the same organism. Using different names or common names for the same organism can get very confusing, as **Figure 3** describes.

FIGURE 3

What Are You Talking About?

Is this animal a groundhog, a woodchuck, a marmot, or a whistlepig? Depending on where you live, all of these names are correct. Luckily, this animal has only one scientific name, *Marmota monax*.

Describe How is a scientific name written?

______

______

______

do the math!

Aristotle and Classification

Aristotle, an ancient Greek scholar, also developed a classification system for animals.

Animals With Blood

Group	Percentage
Animals that swim (sharks, bass, dolphins)	32%
Animals that fly (eagles, gulls, pigeons)	46%
Animals that walk, run, or hop (tortoises, frogs, lions)	22%

1. **Read Graphs** Which group made up the largest percentage of animals?

   ______

2. **Calculate** ______ percent of these animals either fly or swim.

3. **Classify** What new categories would you use to make a graph that classifies animals that move in more than one way?

   ______

   ______

   ______

Lab zone® Do the Quick Lab *Classifying Seeds.*

Assess Your Understanding

1a. Define The scientific study of how living things are classified is called

______

b. Make Generalizations What is the advantage of using scientific names instead of using common names, like cat or dog?

______

______

______

______

______

______

got it?

O **I get it!** Now I know that organisms are classified ______

______

______

O I need extra help with ______

______

Go to MY SCIENCE COACH *online for help with this subject.*

Science Standards of Learning

LS.4a Investigate and understand distinguishing characteristics of domains of organisms.

LS.4b Investigate and understand distinguishing characteristics of kingdoms of organisms.

LS.4c Investigate and understand distinguishing characteristics of major animal phyla and plant divisions.

LS.4d Investigate and understand characteristics that define a species.

What Are the Levels of Classification?

The classification system that scientists use today is based on the contributions of Linnaeus. But today's classification system uses a series of many levels to classify organisms.

To help you understand the levels of classification, imagine a room filled with everybody who lives in your state. First, all of the people who live in your town raise their hands. Then those who live in your neighborhood raise their hands. Then those who live on your street raise their hands. Finally, those who live in your house raise their hands. Each time, fewer people raise their hands. The more levels you share with others, the more you have in common with them.

The Major Levels of Classification Of course, organisms are not grouped by where they live, but by their shared characteristics. Most biologists today classify organisms into the levels shown in **Figure 4.** First, an organism is placed in a broad group, which in turn is divided into more specific groups.

A domain is the broadest level of organization. Within a domain, there are kingdoms. Within kingdoms, there are phyla (FY luh; singular *phylum*). Within phyla are classes. Within classes are orders. Within orders are families. Each family contains one or more genera. Finally, each genus contains one or more species. The more classification levels two organisms share, the more characteristics they have in common and the more closely related they are.

FIGURE 4

VIRTUAL LAB **Levels of Classification**

The figure on the facing page shows how the levels of organization apply to a great horned owl.

Answer the questions.

1. **Observe** List the characteristics that the organisms share at the kingdom level.

____

2. **Observe** List the characteristics that the organisms share at the class level.

____

____

____

3. **Observe** List the characteristics that the organisms share at the genus level.

____

____

____

4. **Draw Conclusions** How does the number of shared characteristics on your list change at each level? _______________

____

____

5. **Interpret Diagrams** Robins have more in common with (lions/owls).

Levels of Classification

Domain Eukarya

Kingdom Animalia

Phylum Chordata

Class Aves

Order Strigiformes

Family Strigidae

Genus *Bubo*

Species *Bubo virginianus*

As you move down these levels of classification, the number of organisms decreases. The organisms that remain share more characteristics with one another and are more related.

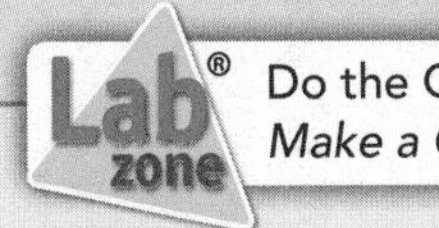

Do the Quick Lab *Make a Classification Chart.*

Assess Your Understanding

got it? ....

○ **I get it!** Now I know that the levels of classification are ____________________

____

____

○ I need extra help with ____________________

____

Go to my science COACH *online for help with this subject.*

Science Standards of Learning

LS.1d Construct and use models and simulations to illustrate and explain phenomena.

LS.1i Identify, interpret, and evaluate patterns in data.

LS.1j Use current applications to reinforce life science concepts.

How Are Taxonomic Keys Useful?

Why should you care about taxonomy? Suppose that you are watching television and feel something tickling your foot. Startled, you look down and see a tiny creature crawling across your toes. Although it's only the size of a small melon seed, you don't like the looks of its two claws waving at you. Then, in a flash, it's gone.

How could you find out what the creature was? You could use a field guide. Field guides are books with illustrations that highlight differences between similar-looking organisms. You could also use a taxonomic key. **Taxonomic keys are useful tools that help determine the identity of organisms.** A taxonomic key consists of a series of paired statements that describe the various physical characteristics of different organisms. The taxonomic key shown in **Figure 5** can help you identify the mysterious organism.

FIGURE 5

INTERACTIVE ART **Identifying Organisms**

The six paired statements in this taxonomic key describe physical characteristics of different organisms.

Identify ___________ different organisms can be identified using this key. The mysterious organism is a ___________

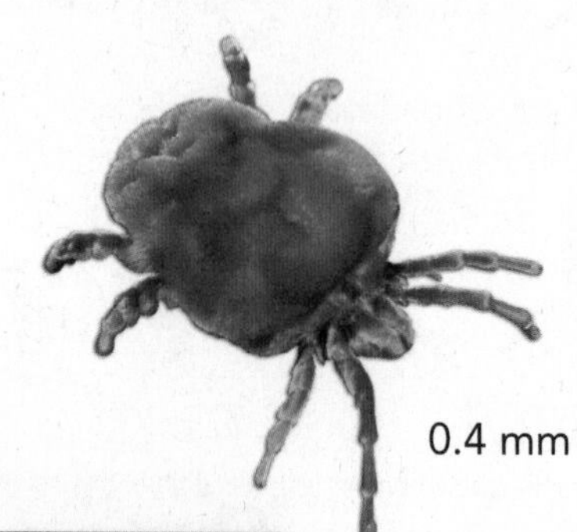

Taxonomic Key

Step		Characteristics	Organism
1	1a.	Has 8 legs	Go to Step 2.
	1b.	Has more than 8 legs	Go to Step 3.
2	2a.	Has one oval-shaped body region	Go to Step 4.
	2b.	Has two body regions	Go to Step 5.
3	3a.	Has one pair of legs on each body segment	Centipede
	3b.	Has two pairs of legs on each body segment	Millipede
4	4a.	Is less than 1 millimeter long	Mite
	4b.	Is more than 1 millimeter long	Tick
5	5a.	Has clawlike pincers	Go to Step 6.
	5b.	Has no clawlike pincers	Spider
6	6a.	Has a long tail with a stinger	Scorpion
	6b.	Has no tail or stinger	Pseudoscorpion

Start Here

First: For each set of statements, choose the one that best describes the organism; for example, 1a.

Second: Follow the direction to the next step.

Third: Continue process until organism is identified.

Use the taxonomic key in **Figure 5** to answer the following questions.

1 Interpret Tables Identify each pictured organism.

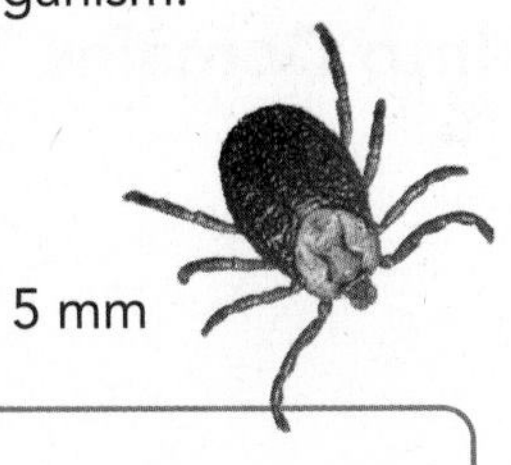

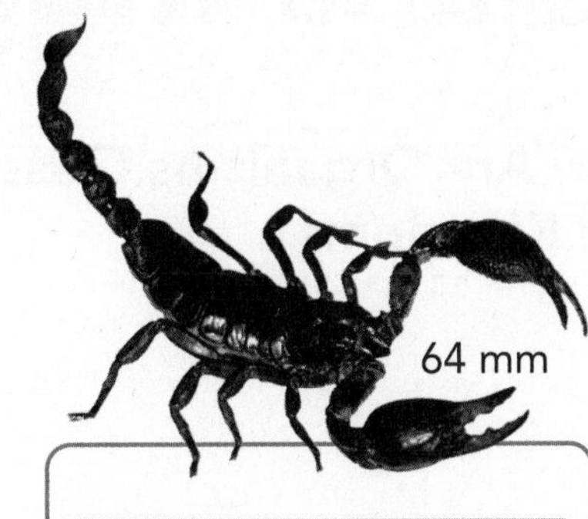

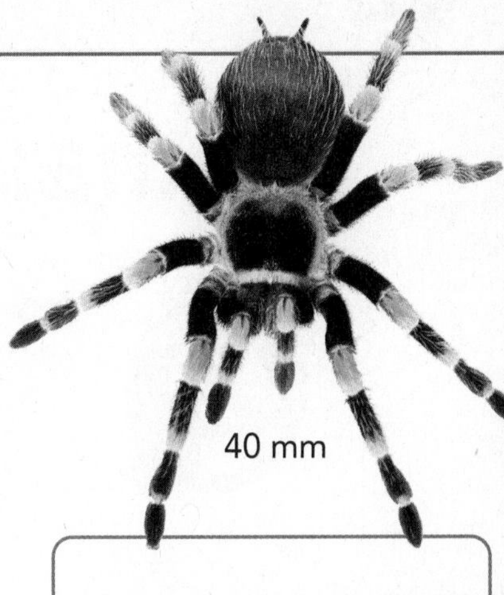

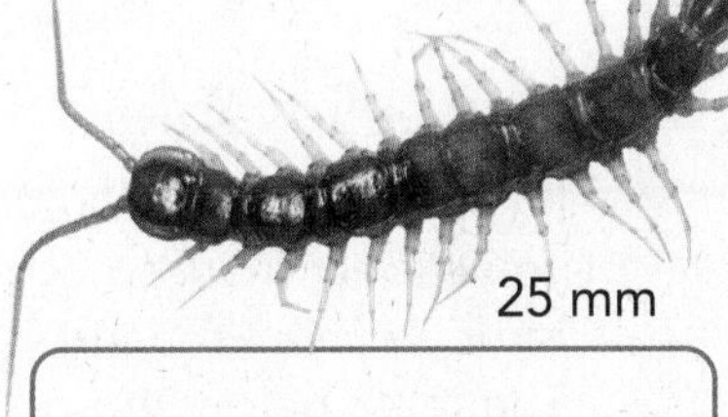

2 Draw Conclusions What other information could have been helpful in identifying these organisms?

3 CHALLENGE Is this information necessary for the key in **Figure 5?** Explain your answer.

Do the Quick Lab *Living Mysteries.*

Assess Your Understanding

got it? ....

O **I get it!** Now I know that taxonomic keys are used to ____________

O I need extra help with ____________

Go to my science coach *online for help with this subject.*

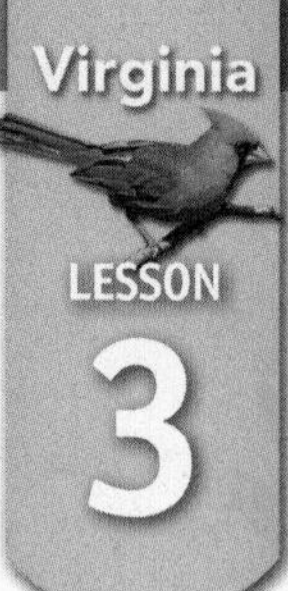

3 Domains and Kingdoms

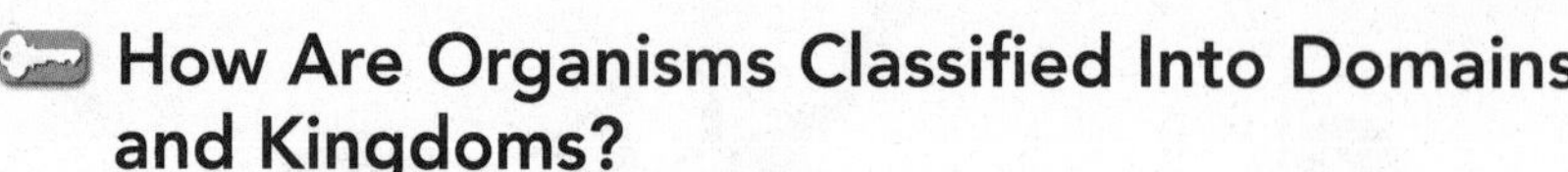

How Are Organisms Classified Into Domains and Kingdoms?

LS.1b, LS.1d, LS.1i, LS.1j, LS.3b, LS.4a, LS.4b

my planet Diary

Unbeelievable!

If you were classifying organisms, would you expect there to be more bees, more birds, or more mammals in the world? The table below shows the number of species of bees, mammals, and birds that scientists have found so far!

Number of Species

Bees	Mammals	Birds
19,200	5,400	10,000

SCIENCE STATS

Answer the question below.

Why do you think that bee species outnumber mammal and bird species combined?

____

____

____

____

PLANET DIARY Go to **Planet Diary** to learn more about domains and kingdoms.

Do the Inquiry Warm-Up *Which Organism Goes Where?*

Science Standards of Learning

LS.1b Develop a classification system based on multiple attributes.

LS.1d Construct and use models and simulations to illustrate and explain phenomena.

LS.1i Identify, interpret, and evaluate patterns in data.

LS.1j Use current applications to reinforce life science concepts.

LS.3b Investigate and understand patterns of cellular organization and their relationship to life processes in living things.

LS.4a Investigate and understand distinguishing characteristics of domains of organisms.

LS.4b Investigate and understand distinguishing characteristics of kingdoms of organisms.

How Are Organisms Classified Into Domains and Kingdoms?

Suppose you helped Linnaeus classify organisms. You probably would have identified organisms as either plants or animals. That's because in Linnaeus' time there were no microscopes to see the tiny organisms that are known to exist today. Microscopes helped to discover new organisms and identify differences among cells.

Today, a three-domain system of classification is commonly used. As shown in the table on the top of the next page, the three domains are Bacteria, Archaea, and Eukarya. Within the domains are kingdoms. **Organisms are placed into domains and kingdoms based on their cell type, their ability to make food, and the number of cells in their bodies.**

Vocabulary
- prokaryote
- nucleus
- eukaryote

Skills
- Reading: Identify the Main Idea
- Inquiry: Classify

Three Domains of Life

Bacteria	Archaea	Eukarya			
		Protists	Fungi	Plants	Animals

Domain Bacteria Although you may not know it, members of the domain Bacteria are all around you. You can find them on the surfaces you touch and inside your body. Some bacteria are autotrophs, while others are heterotrophs.

Members of the domain Bacteria are called prokaryotes (proh KA ree ohtz). **Prokaryotes** are unicellular organisms whose cells lack a nucleus. A **nucleus** (NOO klee us; plural *nuclei*) is a dense area in a cell that contains nucleic acids—the chemical instructions that direct the cell's activities. In prokaryotes, nucleic acids are not contained within a nucleus.

FIGURE 1
Bacteria
Most bacteria, such as *Lactobacillus acidophilus*, are helpful. These bacteria help to produce yogurt and milk for people who are lactose intolerant.

Domain Archaea Deep in the Pacific Ocean, hot gases and molten rock spew out from a vent in the ocean floor. It is hard to imagine that any living thing could exist in such harsh conditions. Surprisingly, a group of tiny organisms thrives in such a place. They are members of the domain Archaea (ahr KEE uh), whose name comes from the Greek word for "ancient."

Like bacteria, archaea are unicellular prokaryotes. And like bacteria, some archaea are autotrophs and others are heterotrophs. Archaea are classified in their own domain because their chemical makeup differs from that of bacteria. Bacteria and archaea also differ in the structure of their cells. The bacteria in **Figure 1** and the archaea in **Figure 2** have been stained and magnified to make them easier to see.

FIGURE 2
Archaea
Archaea can be found in extreme environments such as hot springs, very salty water, and the intestines of cows! Scientists think that the harsh conditions in which archaea live are similar to those of ancient Earth.

Compare and Contrast How are archaea and bacteria similar? How are they different?

____

____

____

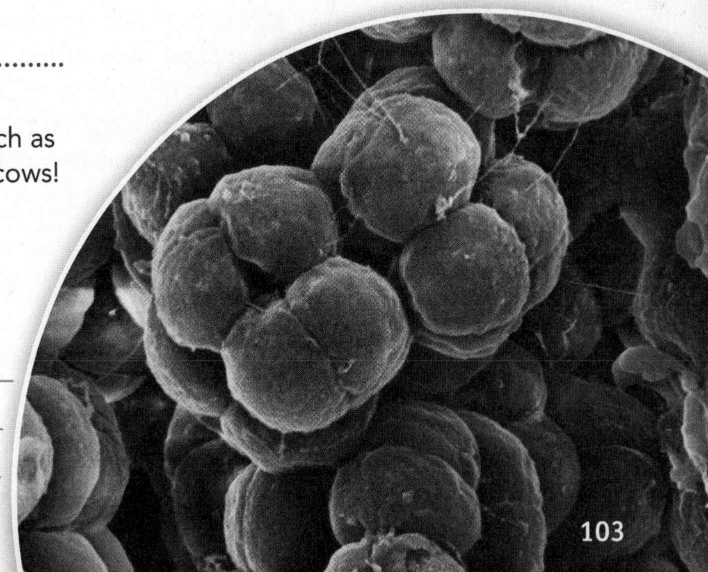

FIGURE 3

Eukarya

You can encounter organisms from all four kingdoms of Eukarya on a trip to a salt marsh.

Three Domains of Life

Bacteria	Archaea	Eukarya			
		Protists	Fungi	Plants	Animals

Domain Eukarya

What do seaweeds, mushrooms, tomatoes, and dogs have in common? They are all members of the domain Eukarya. Organisms in this domain are **eukaryotes** (yoo KA ree ohtz)—organisms with cells that contain nuclei. Scientists classify organisms in the domain Eukarya into one of four kingdoms: protists, fungi, plants, or animals.

Protists

A protist (PROH tist) is any eukaryotic organism that cannot be classified as a fungus, plant, or animal. Because its members are so different from one another, the protist kingdom is sometimes called the "odds and ends" kingdom. For example, some protists are autotrophs, while others are heterotrophs. Most protists are unicellular, but some, such as seaweeds, are multicellular.

Fungi

If you have eaten mushrooms, then you have eaten fungi (FUN jy). Mushrooms, molds, and mildew are all fungi. The majority of fungi are multicellular eukaryotes. A few, such as the yeast used in baking, are unicellular eukaryotes. Fungi are found almost everywhere on land, but only a few live in fresh water. All fungi are heterotrophs. Most fungi feed by absorbing nutrients from dead or decaying organisms.

Aspergillus fumigatus

Classify While on a walk, you find an organism that you've never seen before. You are determined to figure out what kingdom it belongs to. Starting with the first observation below, circle the kingdom(s) the organism could fit into. Using the process of elimination, determine what kingdom the organism belongs to.

1. There are nuclei present. (Protists/Fungi/Plants/Animals)
2. You can count more than one cell. (Protists/Fungi/Plants/Animals)
3. The organism cannot make its own food. (Protists/Fungi/Plants/Animals)
4. The organism gets nutrients from dead organisms. (Protists/Fungi/Plants/Animals)
5. Other members of this kingdom can be unicellular. (Protists/Fungi/Plants/Animals)

Plants

Dandelions on a lawn, peas in a garden, and the marsh grass shown here are familiar members of the plant kingdom. Plants are all multicellular eukaryotes, and most live on land. Also, plants are autotrophs that make their own food. Plants provide food for most of the heterotrophs on land.

The plant kingdom includes a great variety of organisms. Some plants produce flowers, while others do not. Some plants, such as giant redwood trees, can grow very tall. Others, like mosses, never grow taller than a few centimeters.

Identify the Main Idea In the text under Domain Eukarya, underline the main idea.

Snowy egret

Animals

A dog, a flea on the dog's ear, and a cat that the dog chases have much in common because all are animals. All animals are multicellular eukaryotes. In addition, all animals are heterotrophs. Animals have different adaptations that allow them to locate food, capture it, eat it, and digest it. Members of the animal kingdom live in diverse environments throughout Earth. Animals can be found from ocean depths to mountaintops, from hot, scalding deserts to cold, icy landscapes.

Lab zone® Do the Quick Lab *Staining Leaves.*

Assess Your Understanding

1a. Define A cell that lacks a nucleus is called a (eukaryote/prokaryote).

b. List Two ways that the members of the two domains of prokaryotes differ are in the

____

____

c. CHALLENGE You learn that a dandelion is in the same kingdom as pine trees. Name three characteristics that these organisms share.

____

____

got it?

O **I get it!** Now I know that organisms are classified into domains and kingdoms based on their ______________________________

____

____

____

O I need extra help with ______________________________

____

Go to MY SCIENCE COACH *online for help with this subject.*

Evolution and Classification

 **How Are Evolution and Classification Related?**
LS.1b, LS.1d, LS.1j, LS.4a, LS.4b

my planet Diary

DISCOVERY

If It Looks Like a Duck...

The first scientist to see the pelt of the platypus thought it was a joke. Could a four-legged, duck-billed, egg-laying mammal exist? How had it evolved? Native people from Australia believed that the first platypus was born when a water rat mated with a duck. But scientists put the platypus into a new group of egg-laying mammals. Then many years later, scientists began to argue. Had the platypus really evolved later with younger marsupials such as kangaroos? Would the platypus have to be reclassified? Scientists studied its DNA and discovered that the platypus was in the right place!

Answer the question below.

How did DNA help classify the platypus?

____

____

____

____

____

____

PLANET DIARY Go to **Planet Diary** to learn more about evolution and classification.

Do the Inquiry Warm-Up *Observing Similarities.*

LS.1b Develop a classification system based on multiple attributes.
LS.1d Construct and use models and simulations to illustrate and explain phenomena.
LS.1j Use current applications to reinforce life science concepts.
LS.4a Investigate and understand distinguishing characteristics of domains of organisms.
LS.4b Investigate and understand distinguishing characteristics of kingdoms of organisms.

How Are Evolution and Classification Related?

When Linnaeus developed his classification system, people thought that species never changed. In 1859, a British naturalist named Charles Darwin published an explanation for how species could change over time. Recall that the process of change over time is called **evolution.** Darwin thought that evolution occurs by means of natural selection. Natural selection is the process by which individuals that are better adapted to their environment are more likely to survive and reproduce than other members of the same species.

Vocabulary
- evolution
- branching tree diagram
- shared derived characteristic
- convergent evolution

Skills
- Reading: Summarize
- Inquiry: Infer

As understanding of evolution increased, biologists changed how they classify species. Scientists now understand that certain organisms may be similar because they share a common ancestor and an evolutionary history. The more similar the two groups are, the more recent the common ancestor probably is. Today's system of classification considers the history of a species. **Species with similar evolutionary histories are classified more closely together.**

Summarize Name two things that similar organisms share.

____

____

____

____

Branching Tree Diagrams Two groups of organisms with similar characteristics may be descended from a common ancestor. A **branching tree diagram,** like the one in **Figure 1,** shows probable evolutionary relationships among organisms and the order in which specific characteristics may have evolved. Branching tree diagrams begin at the base with the common ancestor of all the organisms in the diagram. Organisms are grouped according to their shared derived characteristics.

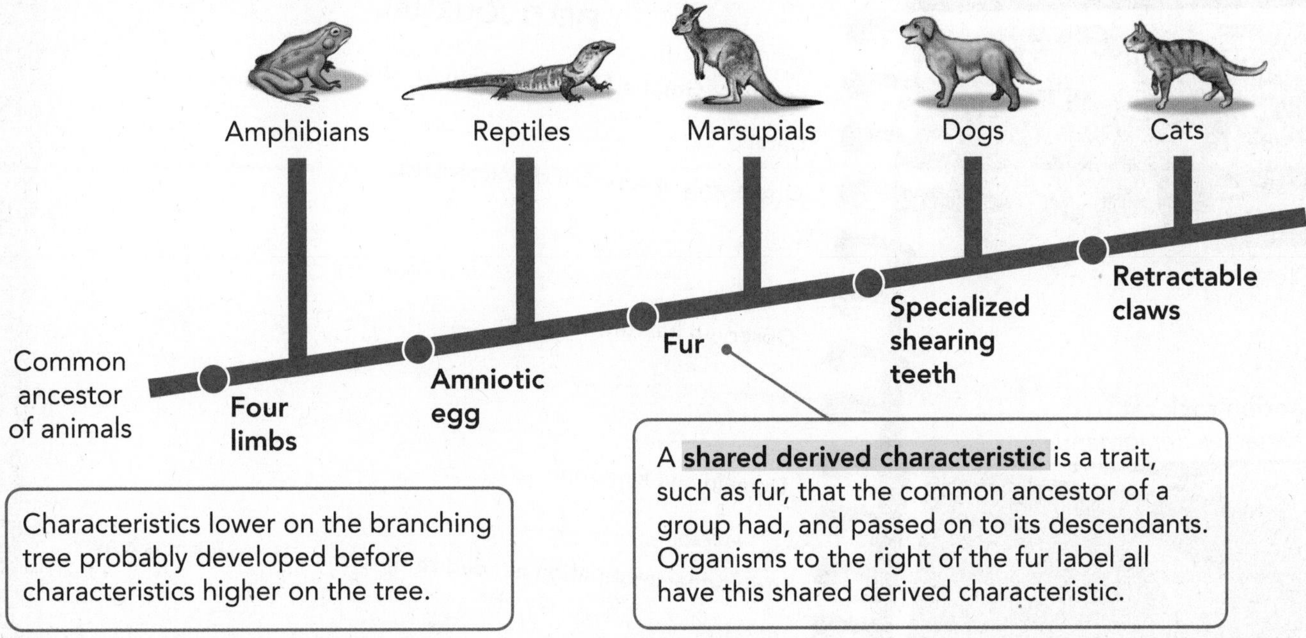

FIGURE 1

ART IN MOTION **A Branching Tree**

This branching tree diagram shows how cats have evolved.

Complete the tasks.

1. **Interpret Diagrams** Put squares around the shared derived characteristics.
2. **Interpret Diagrams** Circle the animal(s) that belong to the smallest group.
3. **Apply Concepts** Cats are more closely related to (reptiles/marsupials).

Note the characteristics of Figures A, B, C, and D.

A B

C D

1 Infer Which figure is the most similar to Figure B?

2 CHALLENGE Suppose these shapes are fossils of extinct organisms. Which organism do you think might be the ancestor of all the others? Why?

Finding a New Species

How are living things alike yet different?

FIGURE 2

While on an expedition, you photograph what you think is a new species.

Draw Conclusions Use the camera image of the new species and the photos of organisms previously identified from the same area to record your observations in your field journal.

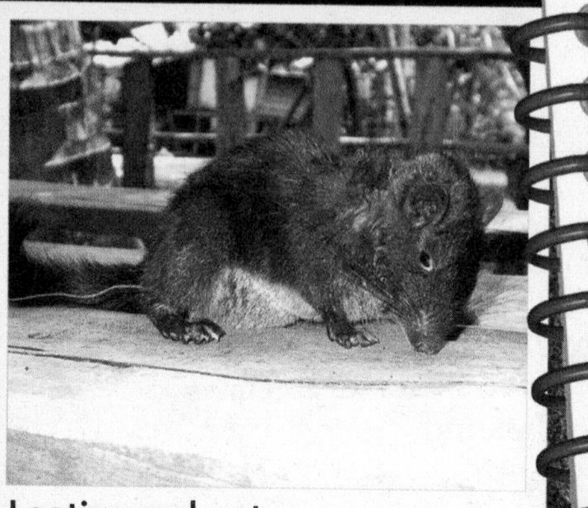

Laotian rock rat
Laonastes aenigmanus

Golden-crowned flying fox
Acerodon jubatus

FIELD JOURNAL

Location: Greater Mekong region of Asia

Date:

Organism's observable characteristics:

Observed habitat(s):

Domain and kingdom:

Additional information needed to determine if organism is a new species:

Name (assuming it's a new species):

Significance/meaning of name:

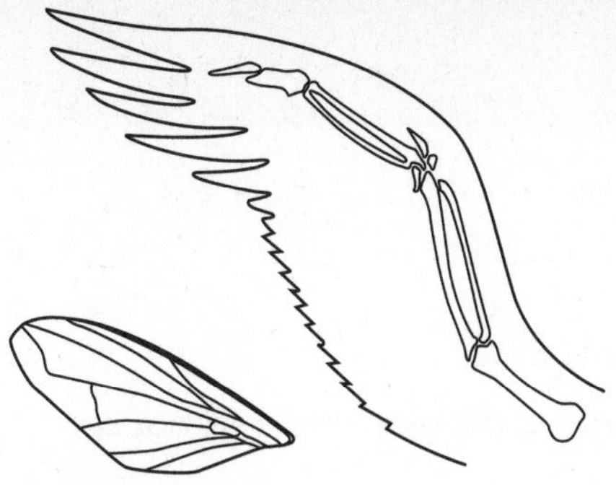

FIGURE 3

Convergent Evolution

Birds and insects both use wings to help them fly. However, these two organisms are not closely related.

Determining Evolutionary Relationships

How do scientists determine the evolutionary history of a species? One way is to compare the structure of organisms. Scientists can also use information about the chemical makeup of the organisms' cells.

Sometimes unrelated organisms evolve similar characteristics because they evolved in similar environments, like organisms that move through the water or eat similar foods. Because the organisms perform similar functions, their body structures may look similar. Look at **Figure 3.** The process by which unrelated organisms evolve characteristics that are similar is called **convergent evolution.**

When studying the chemical makeup of organisms, sometimes new information is discovered that results in reclassification. For example, skunks and weasels were classified in the same family for 150 years. When scientists compared nucleic acids from the cells of skunks and weasels, they found many differences. These differences suggest that the two groups are not that closely related. As a result, scientists reclassified skunks into a separate family.

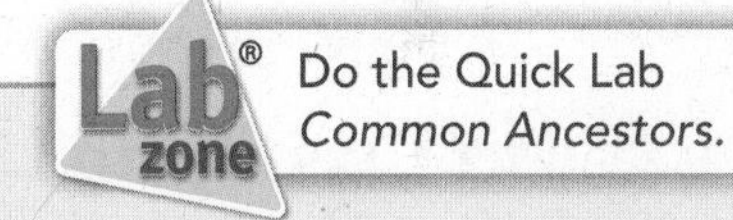

Do the Quick Lab *Common Ancestors.*

Assess Your Understanding

1a. Identify Look back at **Figure 1.** What characteristics do all reptiles share?

____

b. ANSWER THE BIG ? How are living things alike yet different? ______________________________

____

____

____

got it?

O **I get it!** Now I know that evolution and classification are related because ______________________________

____

____

____

O I need extra help with ______________________________

____

Go to **MY SCIENCE COACH** *online for help with this subject.*

CHAPTER 3

Study Guide

Living things can vary. For example, organisms may be prokaryotes or ________________. Yet all living things are made of ________________, which grow, develop, and reproduce.

LESSON 1 What Is Life?

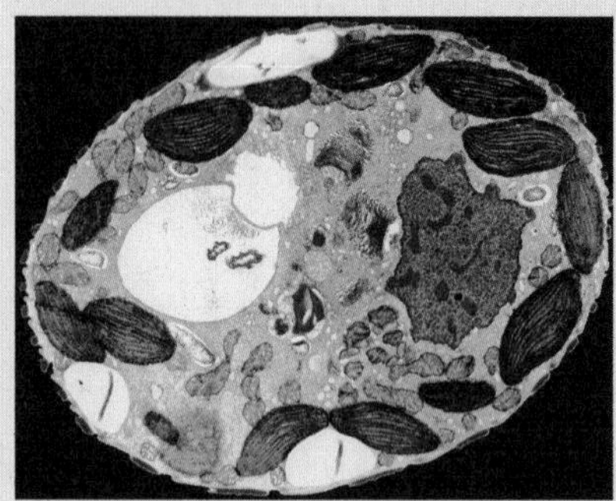

All living things have a cellular organization, contain similar chemicals, use energy, respond to their surroundings, grow and develop, and reproduce.

Living things arise from other living things through reproduction.

All living things must satisfy their basic needs for food, water, living space, and stable internal conditions.

Vocabulary

• organism • cell • unicellular • multicellular • metabolism • stimulus • response • development
• asexual reproduction • sexual reproduction • spontaneous generation • controlled experiment
• autotroph • heterotroph • homeostasis

LESSON 2 Classifying Life

Biologists use classification to organize living things into groups so that the organisms are easier to study.

The levels of classification are domain, kingdom, phylum, class, order, family, genus, and species.

Taxonomic keys are useful tools that help determine the identity of organisms.

Vocabulary

• classification • taxonomy • binomial nomenclature
• genus • species

LESSON 3 Domains and Kingdoms

Organisms are placed into domains and kingdoms based on their cell type, ability to make food, and the number of cells in their bodies.

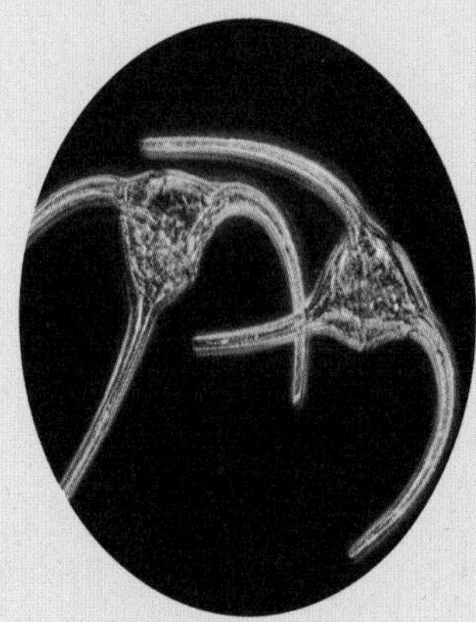

Vocabulary

• prokaryote
• nucleus • eukaryote

LESSON 4 Evolution and Classification

Species with similar evolutionary histories are classified more closely together.

Vocabulary

• evolution
• branching tree diagram
• shared derived characteristic
• convergent evolution

Review and Assessment

LESSON 1 What Is Life?

1. The maintenance of stable internal conditions is called
   - a. stimulus.
   - b. autotrophy.
   - c. homeostasis.
   - d. response.

2. ______________________________ involves only one parent and produces offspring that are identical to the parent.

3. **Apply Concepts** Pick an organism in your home and describe how this organism meets the four basic conditions for survival.

____

____

____

____

____

____

4. **Control Variables** A student is designing a controlled experiment to test whether the amount of water that a plant receives affects its growth. Which variables should the student hold constant and which variable should the student manipulate?

____

____

____

____

____

5. **Write About It** Suppose you are searching for new life forms as part of an expedition in a remote region of Alaska. At one site you find 24 greenish-brown objects, each measuring around 1 cm^3. The objects do not appear to have heads, tails, or legs, but you suspect they may be alive. Describe what you would do to determine if the objects are alive.

LESSON 2 Classifying Life

6. Which of the following is the broadest level of classification?
   - a. genus
   - b. species
   - c. domain
   - d. kingdom

7. The two-part naming system called ______________________________ was devised by Linnaeus in the 1700s.

8. **Predict** The scientific name for the red maple tree is *Acer rubrum.* Another organism is called *Acer negundo.* Based on its name, what can you predict about this organism? Explain.

____

____

____

____

____

9. **Make Models** Develop a taxonomic key that a person could use to identify each of the plants shown below.

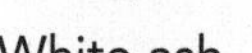
White ash

Red oak

White oak

Pasture rose

CHAPTER 3

Review and Assessment

LESSON 3 Domains and Kingdoms

10. Which four kingdoms belong to the domain Eukarya?
    - **a.** prokarya, archaea, eukarya, bacteria
    - **b.** protists, fungi, plants, animals
    - **c.** mite, tick, scorpion, spider
    - **d.** class, order, family, genus

11. All eukaryotes belong to domain Eukarya, while ______________________ belong to domain Bacteria or domain Archaea.

12. **Compare and Contrast** Both plants and fungi belong to the domain Eukarya. What is one main difference between these organisms?

____

____

____

____

LESSON 4 Evolution and Classification

13. Which of the following factors is most important when classifying an organism?
    - **a.** size
    - **b.** shape
    - **c.** habitat
    - **d.** evolutionary history

14. A diagram that shows probable evolutionary relationships among organisms is called a

____

15. **Apply Concepts** If you discovered two unrelated organisms that looked very similar, how could you explain it?

____

____

____

____

How are living things alike yet different?

16. With the advances in commercial space travel, some day you may have the opportunity to visit another planet and see things you've never seen before! How would you go about identifying things on the other planet as being living or nonliving? If an object turns out to be living, what characteristics would you look for in order to classify it? Use four vocabulary terms from the chapter in your answer.

____

____

____

____

____

____

____

____

____

____

____

____

____

____

____

____

____

____

Virginia SOL Test Prep

Read each question and choose the best answer.

1 **How many kingdoms are represented by the organisms shown below?**

A 1
B 2
C 3
D 4

2 **According to the system of binomial nomenclature, which of the following is a properly written scientific name?**

F Acer rubrum
G Acer Rubrum
H *Acer rubrum*
J *acer rubrum*

3 **Which of the following is an example of an autotroph?**

A a lion
B a tree
C an eagle
D a mushroom

4 **Which domain does *not* contain prokaryotes?**

F Archaea
G Bacteria
H Eukarya
J None of the above. All three domains contain prokaryotes.

5 **A branching tree diagram shows evolutionary relationships by—**

A grouping organisms according to their differences
B determining the identity of organisms.
C grouping organisms according to their shared derived characteristics
D giving an organism a unique, two-part scientific name

6 **Based on the information in the table below, which two of the four trees are most closely related?**

Some Types of Trees

Common Name of Tree	Kingdom	Family	Species
Bird cherry	Plants	Rosaceae	*Prunus avium*
Flowering cherry	Plants	Rosaceae	*Prunus serrula*
Smooth-leaved elm	Plants	Ulmaceae	*Ultimus minor*
Whitebeam	Plants	Rosaceae	*Sorbus aria*

F *Prunus avium* and *Sorbus aria*
G *Ultimus minor* and *Sorbus aria*
H *Prunus avium* and *Prunus serrula*
J *Prunus serrula* and *Sorbus aria*

A Recipe for Success

Before the 1800s, people thought that living things could appear from nonliving material. But Louis Pasteur did not think that this accepted theory was correct. He suspected that bacteria traveled on particles in the air and reproduced when they landed on biological material—like broth. Pasteur experimented to test his theory. His experiments were successful because they followed a good experimental design. Pasteur tested only one variable, included a control, and repeated his experiments.

Pasteur put broth into two flasks with curved necks. The necks would let in oxygen but keep out bacteria in air. Pasteur boiled the broth in one flask to kill any bacteria in the broth. He did not boil the broth in the other flask.

In a few days, the unboiled broth turned cloudy, showing that new bacteria were growing. The boiled broth remained clear. Pasteur then took the flask with clear broth and broke its curved neck. Bacteria from the air could enter the flask. In a few days, the broth became cloudy. Pasteur's results showed that bacteria were introduced into the broth through the air, and did not grow from the broth itself. He repeated the experiment, and showed that the results were not an accident.

Recipe for a Successful Experiment

1. Make a hypothesis.
2. Write a procedure.
3. Identify the control.
4. Identify the variable.
5. Observe and record data.
6. Repeat.
7. Make a conclusion.

Design It The Dutch scientist Jean-Baptiste van Helmont proposed a recipe for generating mice. He set up an experiment using dirty rags and a few grains of wheat in an open barrel. After about 21 days, mice appeared. The results, he concluded, supported his hypothesis that living things come from nonliving sources. What is wrong with van Helmont's experimental design? Using his hypothesis, design your own experimental procedure. What is your control? What is your variable?

 LS.1e, LS.1f, LS.1g

Are you going to Eat That?

Bacteria are everywhere. Most bacteria have no effect on you. Some even help you. But bacteria in your food can be dangerous and can make you sick.

Milk and many juices are treated by a process called pasteurization. The process is named after Louis Pasteur, who invented it. Before the milk or juice reaches the grocery store, it is heated to a temperature that is high enough to kill the most harmful bacteria. Fewer bacteria means slower bacterial growth, giving you enough time to finish your milk before it spoils.

Tips for Keeping Food Safe in Homes and Restaurants

- Keep foods refrigerated until cooking them to prevent any bacteria in the foods from reproducing.
- Cook meat thoroughly, so that the meat reaches a temperature high enough to kill any bacteria that has been growing on it.
- Wash fresh foods, such as fruits and vegetables, to remove bacteria on the surface.
- Do not use the same utensils or cutting board for cutting raw meat and fresh foods, so that any bacteria in raw meat are not transferred to other foods.

Write About It Some champions of raw-food diets suggest that traditional methods of pasteurization reduce the nutritional value of milk and cause milk to spoil rather than to sour. Research the debate about raw dairy products and write a persuasive article that explains whether you support pasteurization of dairy products.

HOW ARE YOU LIKE THIS CREATURE?

What are cells made of?

You sure don't see this sight when you look in the mirror! This deep-sea animal does not have skin, a mouth, or hair like yours. It's a young animal that lives in the Atlantic Ocean and may grow up to become a crab or shrimp. Yet you and this creature have more in common than you think.

Infer **What might you have in common with this young sea animal?**

UNTAMED SCIENCE Watch the **Untamed Science** video to learn more about cells.

Introduction to Cells

Science Standards of Learning

LS.1b, LS.1d, LS.1h, LS.1i, LS.1j, LS.2a, LS.2b, LS.2c, LS.3a, LS.3b, LS.12f

CHAPTER

4 Getting Started

Check Your Understanding

1. **Background** Read the paragraph below and then answer the question.

> You heard that a pinch of soil can contain millions of **organisms,** and you decide to check it out. Many organisms are too small to see with just your eyes, so you bring a hand **lens.** You see a few organisms, but you think you would see more with greater **magnification.**

An **organism** is a living thing.

A **lens** is a curved piece of glass or other transparent material that is used to bend light.

Magnification is the condition of things appearing larger than they are.

- How does a hand lens help you see more objects in the soil than you can see with just your eyes?

____

____

MY READING WEB If you had trouble answering the question above, visit **My Reading Web** and type in ***Introduction to Cells.***

Vocabulary Skill

Prefixes Some words can be divided into parts. A root is the part of the word that carries the basic meaning. A prefix is a word part that is placed in front of the root to change the word's meaning. The prefixes below will help you understand some of the vocabulary in this chapter.

Prefix	Meaning	Example
chroma-	color	chromatin, *n.* the genetic material in the nucleus of a cell, that can be colored with dyes
multi-	many	multicellular, *adj.* having many cells

2. **Quick Check Circle the prefix in the boldface word below. What does the word tell you about the organisms?**
   - Fishes, insects, grasses, and trees are examples of **multicellular** organisms.

____

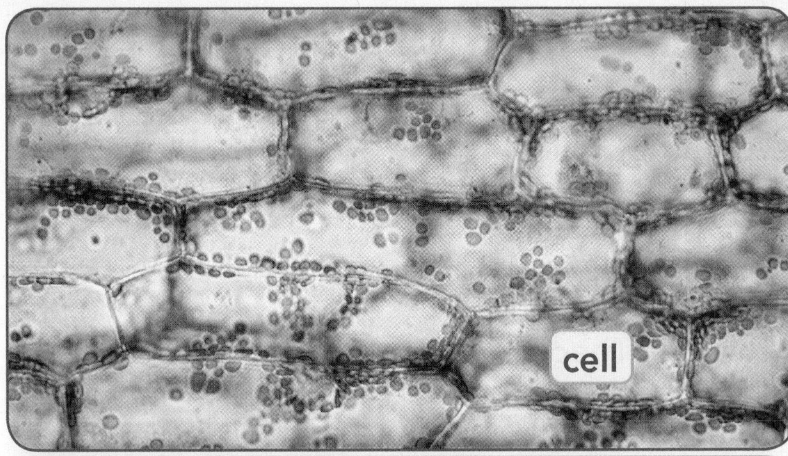

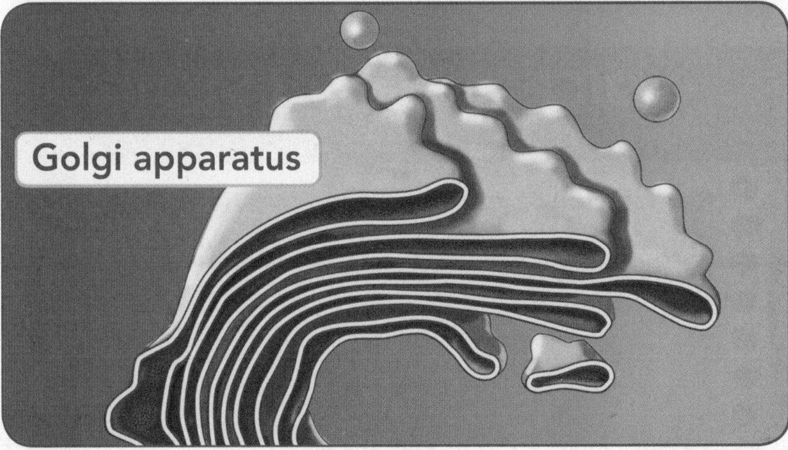

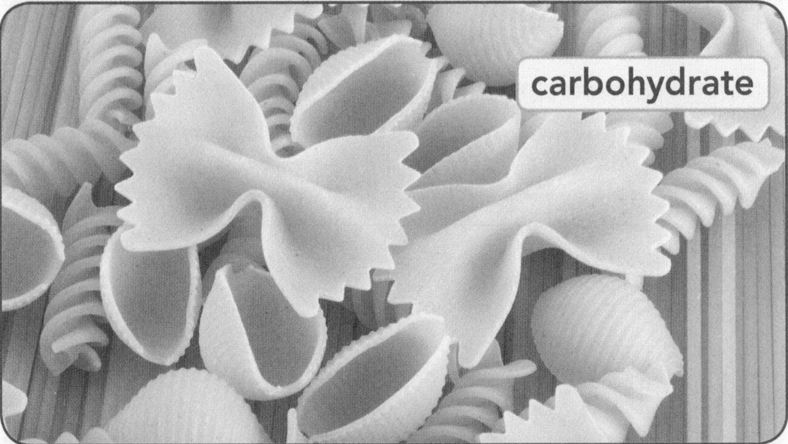

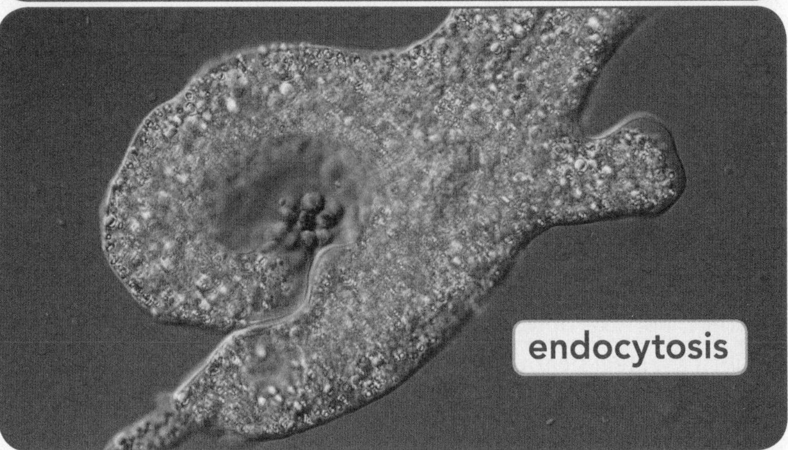

Chapter Preview

LESSON 1

- cell
- microscope
- cell theory

Sequence
Measure

LESSON 2

- cell wall • cell membrane
- nucleus • organelle • ribosome
- cytoplasm • mitochondria
- endoplasmic reticulum
- Golgi apparatus • vacuole
- chloroplast • lysosome
- multicellular • unicellular
- tissue • organ • organ system

Identify the Main Idea
Make Models

LESSON 3

- element • compound
- carbohydrate • lipid • protein
- enzyme • nucleic acid • DNA
- double helix

Compare and Contrast
Draw Conclusions

LESSON 4

- selectively permeable
- passive transport • diffusion
- osmosis • active transport
- endocytosis • exocytosis

Relate Cause and Effect
Predict

> VOCAB FLASH CARDS For extra help with vocabulary, visit **Vocab Flash Cards** and type in ***Introduction to Cells.***

Discovering Cells

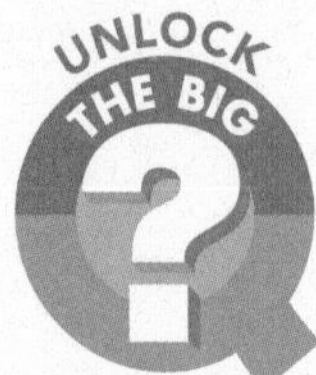

What Are Cells?
LS.2a

What Is the Cell Theory?
LS.2b, LS.2c

How Do Microscopes Work?
LS.1d, LS.1i, LS.1j

my planet Diary

VOICES FROM HISTORY

Life at First Sight

Anton van Leeuwenhoek was the first researcher to see bacteria under a microscope. In his journal, he described how he felt after discovering this new and unfamiliar form of life.

"For me . . . no more pleasant sight has met my eye than this of so many thousand of living creatures in one small drop of water."

Read the quote, and answer the question below.
Why do you think Leeuwenhoek was so excited about what he saw?

____

____

PLANET DIARY Go to **Planet Diary** to learn more about studying cells.

A modern view of bacteria similar to those seen by Leeuwenhoek

Do the Inquiry Warm-Up *What Can You See?*

LS.2a Investigate and understand cell structure and organelles.

What Are Cells?

What do you think a mushroom, a tree, a spider, a bird, and you have in common? All are living things, or organisms. Like all organisms, they are made of cells. **Cells** form the parts of an organism and carry out all of its functions. **Cells are the basic units of structure and function in living things.**

Cells and Structure When you describe the structure of an object, you describe what it is made of and how its parts are put together. For example, the structure of a building depends on the way bricks, steel beams, or other materials are arranged. The structure of a living thing is determined by the amazing variety of ways its cells are put together.

Vocabulary
- cell
- microscope
- cell theory

Skills
- Reading: Sequence
- Inquiry: Measure

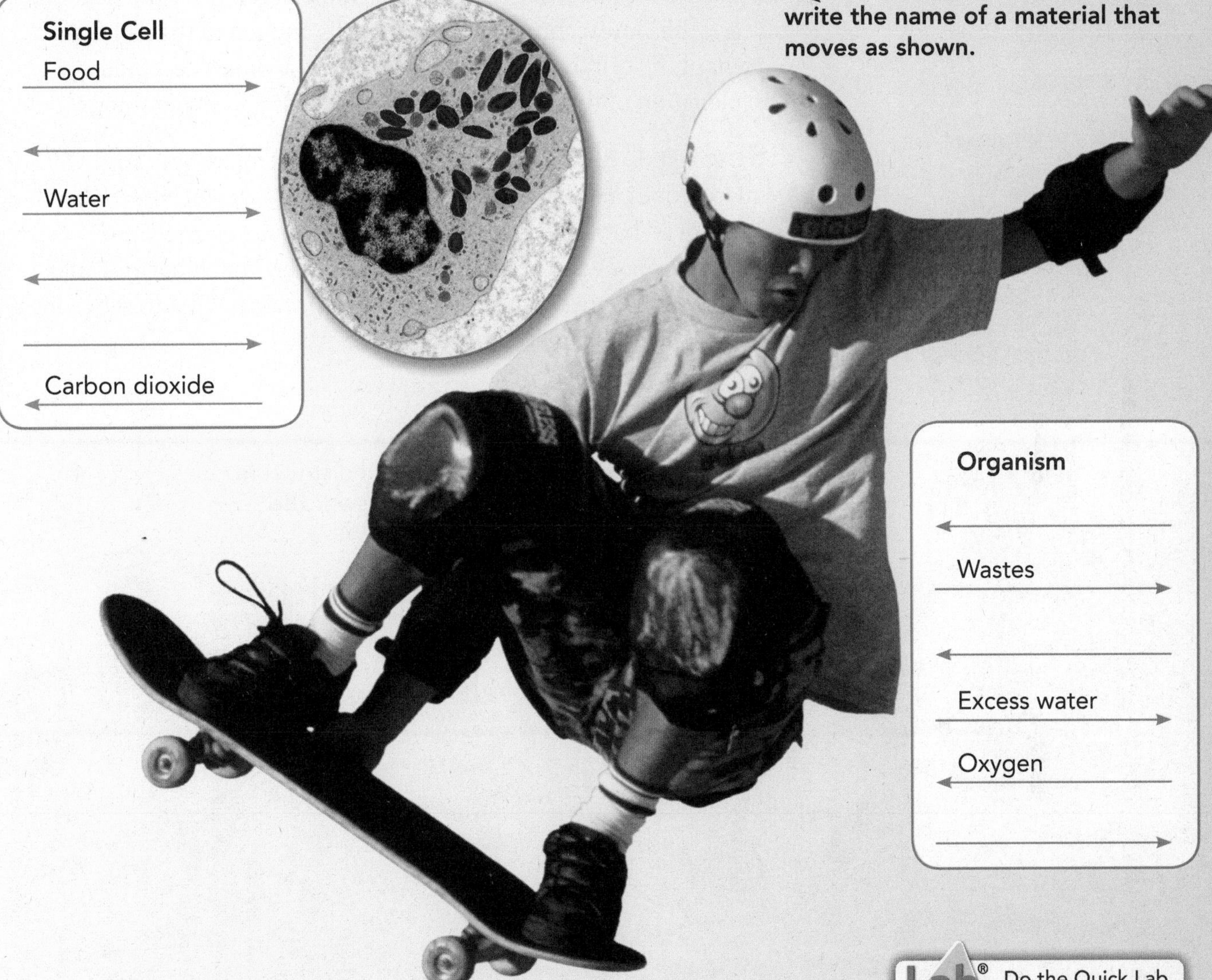

FIGURE 1

Needs of Cells

A single cell has the same needs as an entire organism.

Classify **On each blank arrow, write the name of a material that moves as shown.**

Cells and Function

An organism's functions are the processes that enable it to live, grow, and reproduce. Those functions include obtaining oxygen, food, and water and getting rid of wastes. Cells are involved in all these functions. For example, cells in your digestive system absorb food. The food provides your body with energy and materials needed for growth. Cells in your lungs help you get oxygen. Your body's cells work together, keeping you alive. And for each cell to stay alive, it must carry out many of the same functions as the entire organism.

Lab zone® Do the Quick Lab *Comparing Cells.*

Assess Your Understanding

got it?

○ **I get it!** Now I know that a cell is the basic unit of ______________________

○ I need extra help with ______________

Go to MY SCIENCE COACH *online for help with this subject.*

Science Standards of Learning

LS.2b Investigate and understand similarities and differences between plant and animal cells.

LS.2c Investigate and understand development of cell theory.

What Is the Cell Theory?

Until the 1600s, no one knew cells existed because there was no way to see them. Around 1590, the invention of the first microscope allowed people to look at very small objects. A **microscope** is an instrument that makes small objects look larger. Over the next 200 years, this new technology revealed cells and led to the development of the cell theory. The **cell theory** is a widely accepted explanation of the relationship between cells and living things.

Seeing Cells English scientist Robert Hooke built his own microscopes and made drawings of what he saw when he looked at the dead bark of certain oak trees. Hooke never knew the importance of what he saw. A few years later, Dutch businessman Anton van Leeuwenhoek (LAY von hook) was the first to see living cells through his microscopes.

FIGURE 2

Growth of the Cell Theory

The cell theory describes how cells relate to the structure and function of living things. 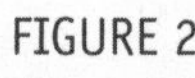 **Review Answer the questions in the spaces provided.**

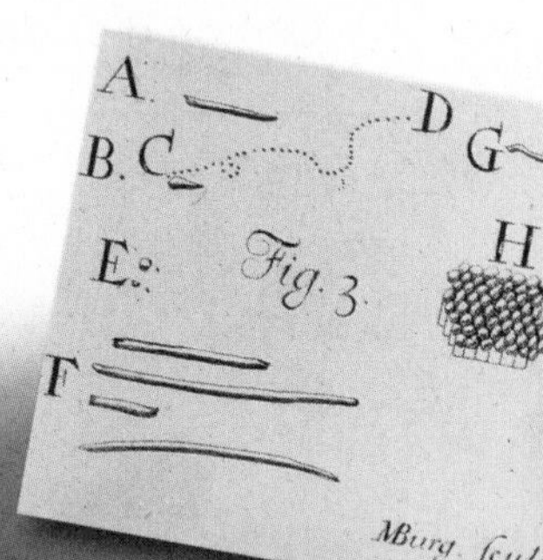

Drawing by Leeuwenhoek

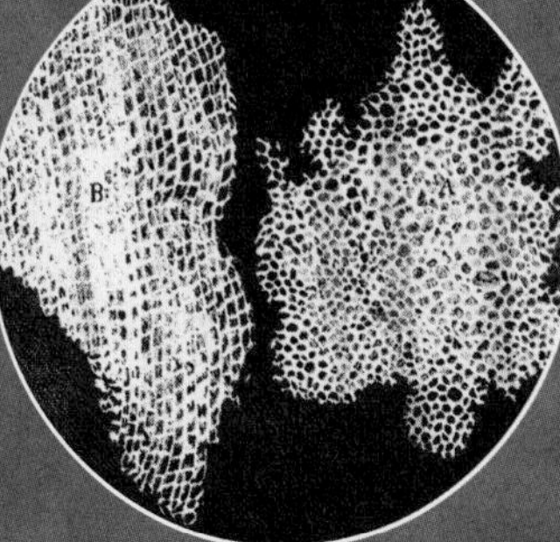

Hooke's drawing of cork

Hooke's Microscope

In 1663, Robert Hooke used his microscope to observe a thin slice of cork. Cork, the bark of the cork oak tree, is made up of cells that are no longer alive. To Hooke, the empty spaces in the cork looked like tiny rectangular rooms. Therefore, Hooke called the empty spaces cells, which means "small rooms."

What was important about Hooke's work?

____

____

Leeuwenhoek's Microscope

Leeuwenhoek built microscopes in his spare time. Around 1674, he looked at drops of lake water, scrapings from teeth and gums, and water from rain gutters. Leeuwenhoek was surprised to find a variety of one-celled organisms. He noted that many of them whirled, hopped, or shot through water like fast fish. He called these moving organisms animalcules, meaning "little animals."

What did Leeuwenhoek's observations reveal?

____

____

What the Cell Theory Says

Figure 2 highlights people who made key discoveries in the early study of cells. Their work and the work of many others led to the development of the cell theory. **The cell theory states the following:**

- **All living things are composed of cells.**
- **Cells are the basic units of structure and function in living things.**
- **All cells are produced from other cells.**

Living things differ greatly from one another, but all are made of cells. The cell theory holds true for all living things, no matter how big or how small. Because cells are common to all living things, cells can provide clues about the functions that living things perform. And because all cells come from other cells, scientists can study cells to learn about growth and reproduction.

Sequence Fill in the circle next to the name of the person who was the first to see living cells through a microscope.

- ○ Matthias Schleiden
- ○ Robert Hooke
- ○ Anton van Leeuwenhoek
- ○ Rudolf Virchow
- ○ Theodor Schwann

Schleiden, Schwann, and Virchow

In 1838, using his own research and the research of others, Matthias Schleiden concluded that all plants are made of cells. A year later, Theodor Schwann reached the same conclusion about animals. In 1855, Rudolf Virchow proposed that new cells are formed only from cells that already exist. "All cells come from cells," wrote Virchow.

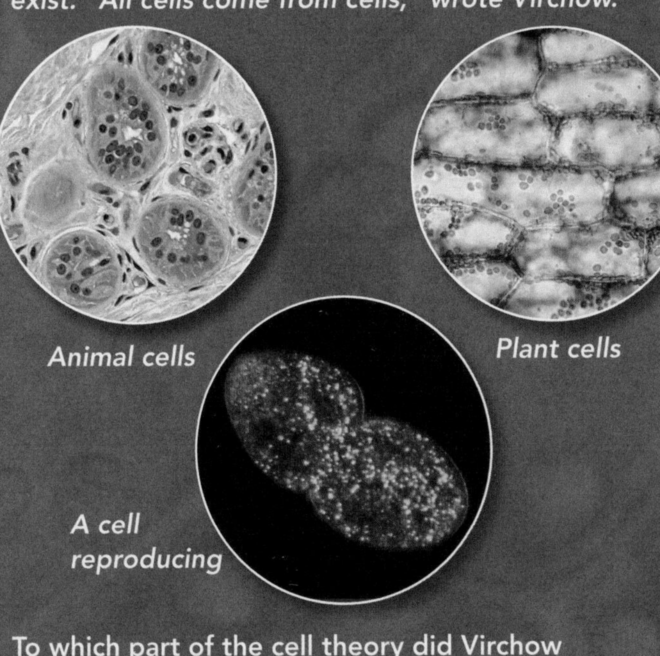

Animal cells

Plant cells

A cell reproducing

To which part of the cell theory did Virchow contribute?

___

Do the Quick Lab *Observing Cells.*

Assess Your Understanding

1a. Relate Cause and Effect Why would Hooke's discovery have been impossible without a microscope?

___

b. Apply Concepts Use Virchow's ideas to explain why plastic plants and stuffed animals are not alive.

___

got it?

○ **I get it!** Now I know that the cell theory describes ___

○ I need extra help with ___

Go to MY SCIENCE COACH *online for help with this subject.*

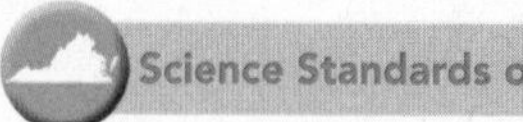

Science Standards of Learning

LS.1d Construct and use models and simulations to illustrate and explain phenomena.

LS.1i Identify, interpret, and evaluate patterns in data.

LS.1j Use current applications to reinforce life science concepts.

Vocabulary Prefixes The prefix *magni-* means "great" or "large." Underline all the words in the paragraph at the right that you can find with this prefix.

How Do Microscopes Work?

The cell theory could not have been developed without microscopes. **Some microscopes focus light through lenses to produce a magnified image, and other microscopes use beams of electrons.** Both light microscopes and electron microscopes do the same job in different ways. For a microscope to be useful, it must combine two important properties—magnification and resolution.

Magnification and Lenses Have you ever looked at something through spilled drops of water? If so, did the object appear larger? Magnification is the condition of things appearing larger than they are. Looking through a magnifying glass has the same result. A magnifying glass consists of a convex lens, which has a center that is thicker than its edge. When light passes through a convex lens and into your eye, the image you see is magnified. Magnification changes how you can see objects and reveals details you may not have known were there, as shown in **Figure 3.**

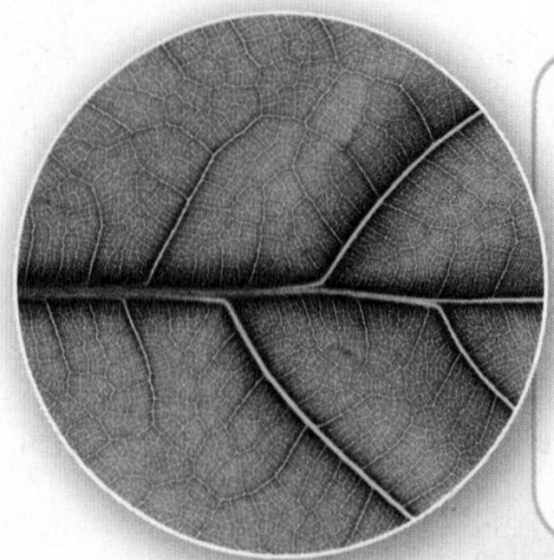

1 Leaf; green color and veins

2

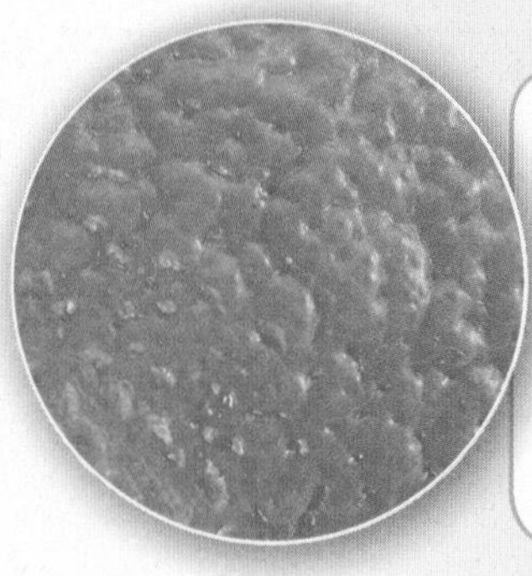

3

4

FIGURE 3

Magnification

The images above have all been magnified, which makes them look unfamiliar. **Infer On the lines, write what you think each photograph shows, and explain your reasoning. (One answer is completed for you.)**

Magnification With a Compound Microscope

Figure 4 shows a microscope that is similar to one you may use in your classroom. This type of instrument, called a compound microscope, magnifies the image using two lenses at once. One lens is fixed in the eyepiece. A second lens is chosen from a group of two or three lenses on the revolving nosepiece. Each of these lenses has a different magnifying power. By turning the nosepiece, you can select the lens you want. A glass slide on the stage holds the object to be viewed.

A compound microscope can magnify an object more than a single lens can. Light from a lamp (or reflecting off a mirror) passes through the object on the slide, the lower lens, and then the lens in the eyepiece. The total magnification of the object equals the magnifications of the two lenses multiplied together. For example, suppose the lower lens magnifies the object 10 times, and the eyepiece lens also magnifies the object 10 times. The total magnification of the microscope is 10 × 10, or 100 times, which is written as "100×."

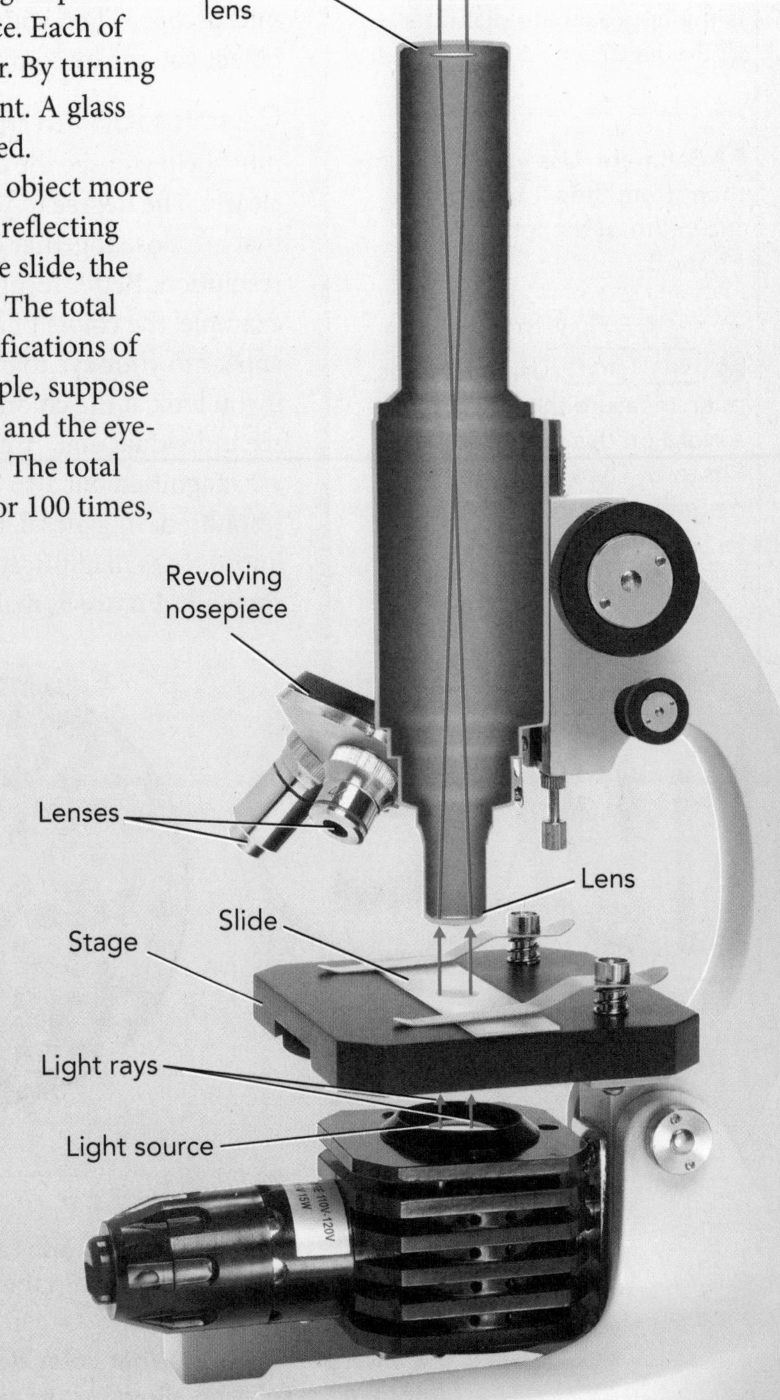

FIGURE 4

> VIRTUAL LAB **A Compound Microscope**

This microscope has a 10× lens in the eyepiece. The revolving nosepiece holds three different lenses: 4×, 10×, and 40×.

Complete these tasks.

1. **Calculate** Calculate the three total magnifications possible for this microscope.

____

____

____

2. **Predict** What would happen if the object on the slide were too thick for light to pass through it?

____

____

____

apply it!

1 **Measure** In Photo A, you can see the millimeter markings of a metric ruler in the field of the microscope. What is the approximate diameter of the field?

2 **Estimate** Use your measurement from Step 1 to estimate the width of the letter in Photo B.

3 CHALLENGE Using a metric ruler, measure the letter **e** in a word on this page and in Photo B. Then calculate the magnification in the photo.

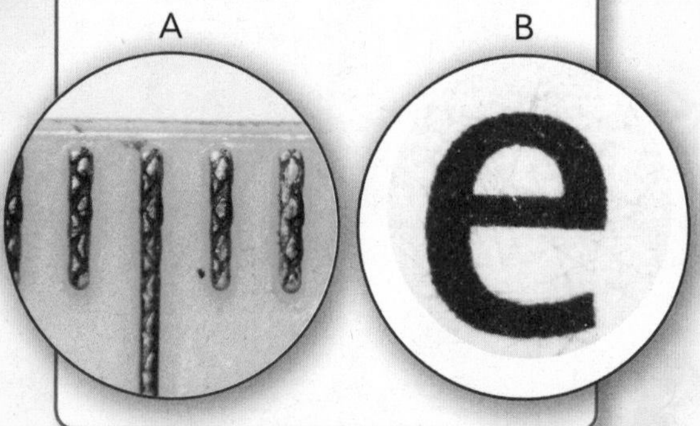

Measuring Microscopic Objects

When you see objects through a microscope, they look larger than they really are. How do you know their true size? One way is to use a metric ruler to measure the size of the circular field in millimeters as you see it through the microscope. Then you can estimate the size of the object you see by comparing it to the width of the field.

Resolution To create a useful image, a microscope must help you see the details of the object's structure clearly. The degree to which two separate structures that are close together can be distinguished is called resolution. Better resolution shows more details. For example, the colors of a newspaper photograph may appear to your eye to be solid patches of color. However, if you look at the colors through a microscope, you will see individual dots. You see the dots not only because they are magnified but also because the microscope improves resolution. In general, for light microscopes, resolution improves as magnification increases. Good resolution, as shown in **Figure 5**, makes it easier to study cells.

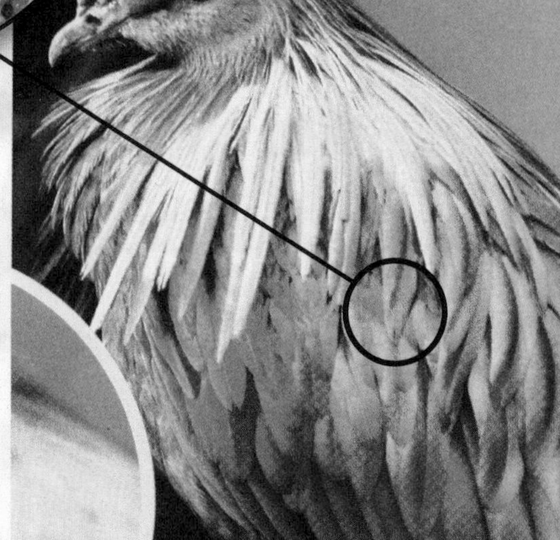

FIGURE 5

Resolution

The images in colorful photographs actually consist of only a few ink colors in the form of dots.

Interpret Photos What color dots does improved resolution allow you to see?

Electron Microscopes The microscopes used by Hooke, Leeuwenhoek, and other early researchers were all light microscopes. Since the 1930s, scientists have developed several types of electron microscopes. Electron microscopes use a beam of electrons instead of light to produce a magnified image. (Electrons are tiny particles that are smaller than atoms.) By using electron microscopes, scientists can obtain pictures of objects that are too small to be seen with light microscopes. Electron microscopes allow higher magnification and better resolution than light microscopes.

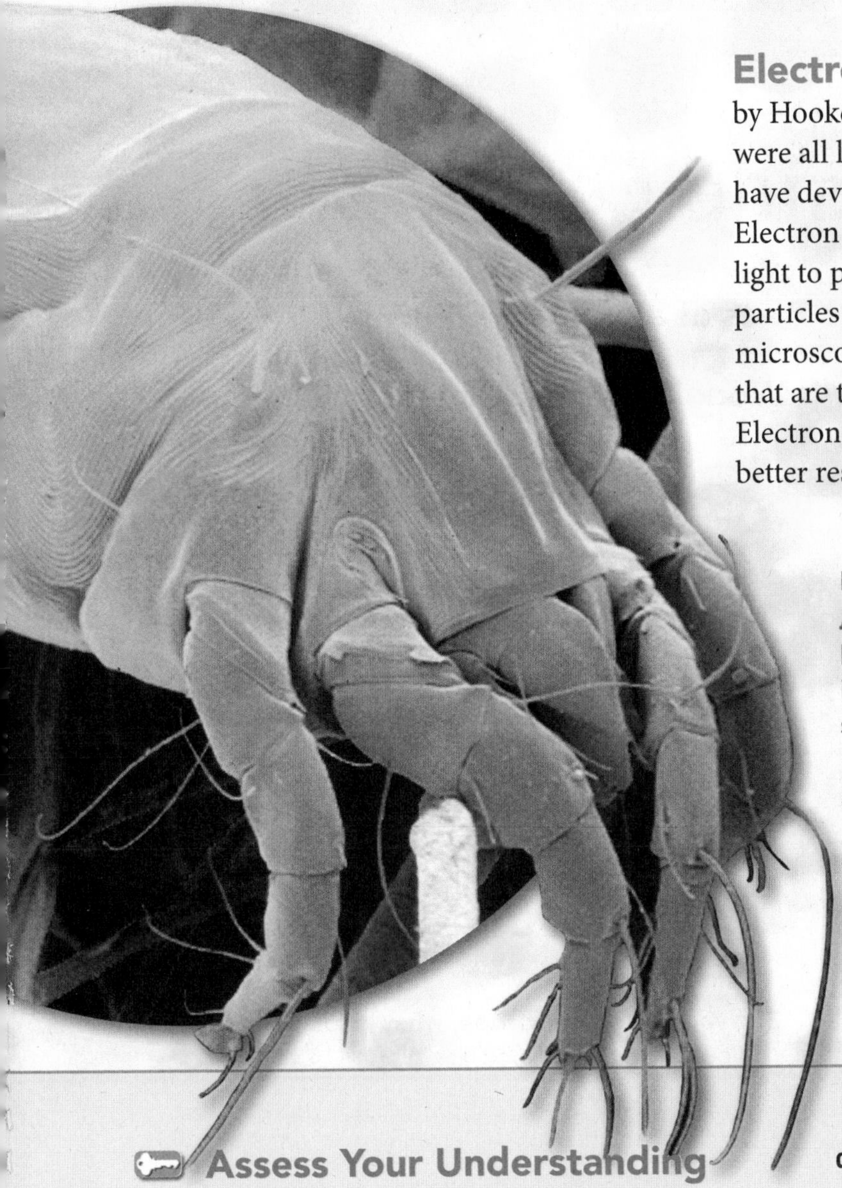

FIGURE 6

A Dust Mite

Dust mites live in everyone's homes. A colorized image made with an electron microscope reveals startling details of a mite's body.

Observe List at least three details that you can see in the photo.

____

____

____

Do the Lab Investigation *Design and Build a Microscope.*

Assess Your Understanding

2a. Define Magnification makes objects look (smaller/larger) than they really are.

b. Estimate The diameter of a microscope's field of view is estimated to be 0.9 mm. About how wide is an object that fills two thirds of the field? Circle your answer.

1.8 mm 0.6 mm 0.3 mm

c. Compare and Contrast How are magnification and resolution different?

____

____

____

____

d. Explain How do the characteristics of electron microscopes make them useful for studying cells?

____

____

____

____

____

got it?

O **I get it!** Now I know that light microscopes work by______________________________

____

O I need extra help with ______________________________

Go to **MY SCIENCE COACH** *online for help with this subject*

Virginia

LESSON 2

Looking Inside Cells

- How Do the Parts of a Cell Work?
  LS.1d, LS.1i, LS.1j, LS.2a, LS.2b
- How Do Cells Work Together in an Organism?
  LS.1d, LS.3a, LS.3b

my planet Diary

TECHNOLOGY

Glowing Globs

Do these cells look as if they're glowing? This photograph shows cells that have been stained with dyes that make cell structures easier to see. Scientists view such treated cells through a fluorescent microscope, which uses strong light to activate the dyes and make them glow. Here, each green area is a cell's nucleus, or control center. The yellow "fibers" form a kind of support structure for the cell.

Communicate **Discuss these questions with a partner. Then write your answers below.**

1. Why is staining useful when studying cells through a microscope?

____

____

2. If you had a microscope, what kinds of things would you like to look at? Why?

____

____

____

PLANET DIARY Go to **Planet Diary** to learn more about cell parts.

Lab zone® Do the Inquiry Warm-Up *How Large Are Cells?*

Vocabulary

- cell wall • cell membrane • nucleus • organelle
- ribosome • cytoplasm • mitochondria
- endoplasmic reticulum • Golgi apparatus • vacuole
- chloroplast • lysosome • multicellular • unicellular
- tissue • organ • organ system

Skills

- Reading: Identify the Main Idea
- Inquiry: Make Models

How Do the Parts of a Cell Work?

When you look at a cell through a microscope, you can usually see the outer edge of the cell. Sometimes you can also see smaller structures within the cell.  **Each kind of cell structure has a different function within a cell.** In this lesson, you will read about the structures that plant and animal cells have in common. You will also read about some differences between the cells.

Science Standards of Learning

LS.1d Construct and use models and simulations to illustrate and explain phenomena.
LS.1i Identify, interpret, and evaluate patterns in data.
LS.1j Use current applications to reinforce life science concepts.
LS.2a Investigate and understand cell structure and organelles.
LS.2b Investigate and understand similarities and differences between plant and animal cells.

Cell Wall The **cell wall** is a rigid layer that surrounds the cells of plants and some other organisms. The cells of animals, in contrast, do not have cell walls. A plant's cell wall helps protect and support the cell. The cell wall is made mostly of a strong material called cellulose. Still, many materials, including water and oxygen, can pass through the cell wall easily.

Cell Membrane Think about how a window screen allows air to enter and leave a room but keeps insects out. One of the functions of the cell membrane is something like that of a screen. The **cell membrane** controls which substances pass into and out of a cell. Everything a cell needs, such as food particles, water, and oxygen, enters through the cell membrane. Waste products leave the same way. In addition, the cell membrane prevents harmful materials from entering the cell.

All cells have cell membranes. In plant cells, the cell membrane is just inside the cell wall. In cells without cell walls, the cell membrane forms the border between the cell and its environment.

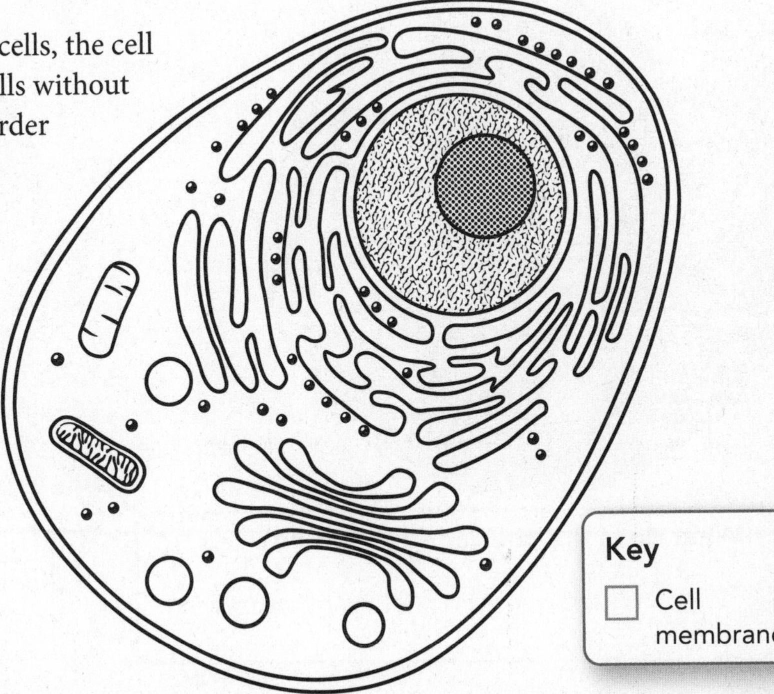

FIGURE 1
A Typical Animal Cell
You will see this diagram of a cell again in this lesson.
Identify Use a colored pencil to shade the cell membrane and fill in the box in the key.

Key
☐ Cell membrane

FIGURE 2

Organelles of a Cell

The structures of a cell look as different as their functions.

Complete each task.

1. **Review** Answer the questions in the boxes.
2. **Relate Text and Visuals** In the diagram on the facing page, use different-colored pencils to color each structure and its matching box in the color key.

Nucleus A cell doesn't have a brain, but it has something that functions in a similar way. A large oval structure called the **nucleus** (NOO klee us) acts as a cell's control center, directing all of the cell's activities. The nucleus is the largest of many tiny cell structures, called **organelles,** that carry out specific functions within a cell. Notice in **Figure 2** that the nucleus is surrounded by a membrane called the nuclear envelope. Materials pass in and out of the nucleus through pores in the nuclear envelope.

Chromatin You may wonder how the nucleus "knows" how to direct the cell. Chromatin, thin strands of material that fill the nucleus, contains information for directing a cell's functions. For example, the instructions in the chromatin ensure that leaf cells grow and divide to form more leaf cells.

Nucleolus Notice the small, round structure in the nucleus. This structure, the nucleolus, is where ribosomes are made. **Ribosomes** are small grain-shaped organelles that produce proteins. Proteins are important substances in cells.

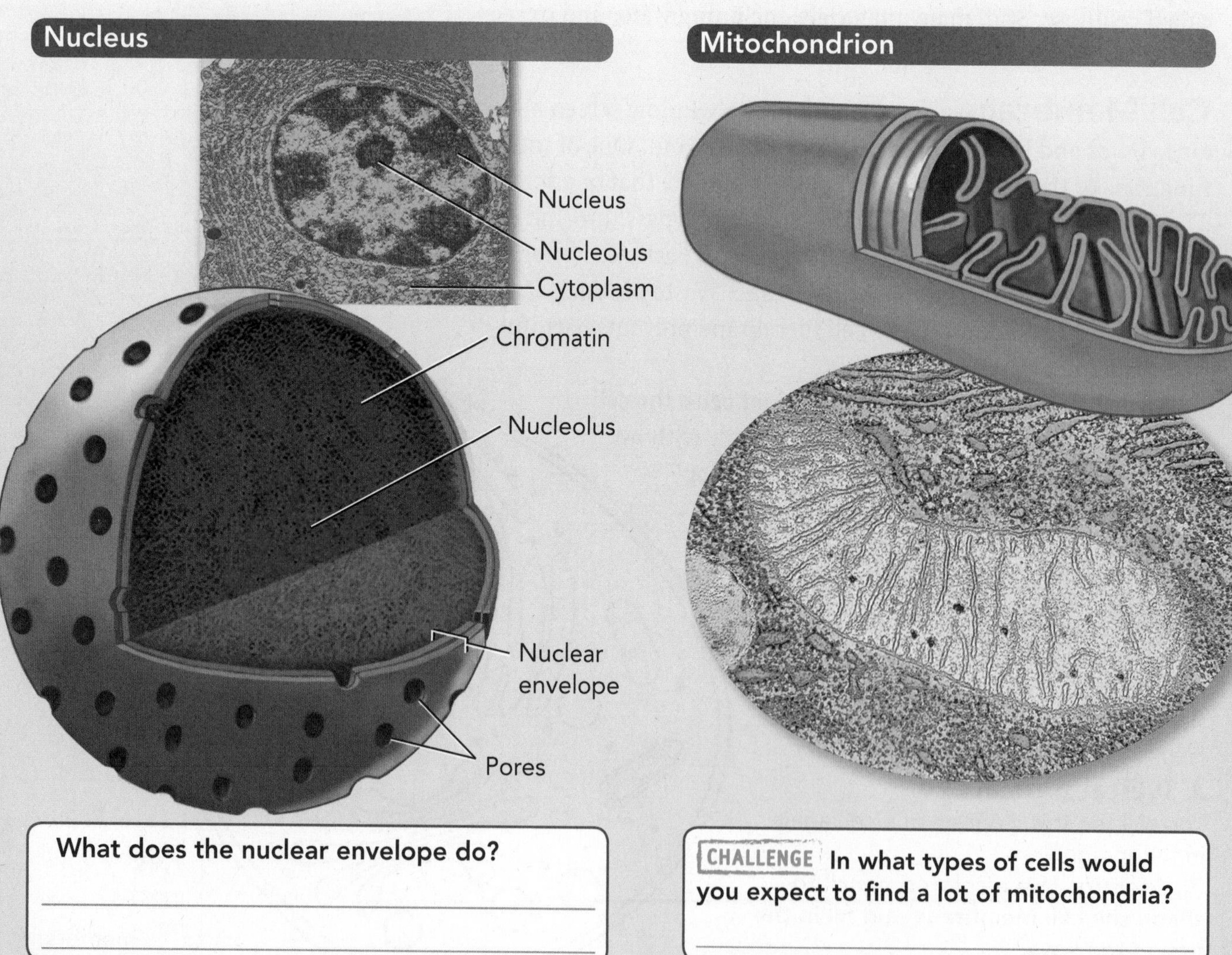

What does the nuclear envelope do?

CHALLENGE In what types of cells would you expect to find a lot of mitochondria?

Organelles in the Cytoplasm

Most of a cell consists of a thick, clear, gel-like fluid. The **cytoplasm** fills the region between the cell membrane and the nucleus. The fluid of the cytoplasm moves constantly within a cell, carrying along the nucleus and other organelles that have specific jobs.

Mitochondria Floating in the cytoplasm are rod-shaped structures that are nicknamed the "powerhouses" of a cell. Look again at **Figure 2. Mitochondria** (myt oh KAHN dree uh; singular *mitochondrion*) convert energy stored in food to energy the cell can use to live and function.

Endoplasmic Reticulum and Ribosomes In **Figure 2,** you can see what looks something like a maze of passageways. The **endoplasmic reticulum** (en doh PLAZ mik rih TIK yuh lum), often called the ER, is an organelle with a network of membranes that produces many substances. Ribosomes dot some parts of the ER, while other ribosomes float in the cytoplasm. The ER helps the attached ribosomes make proteins. These newly made proteins and other substances leave the ER and move to another organelle.

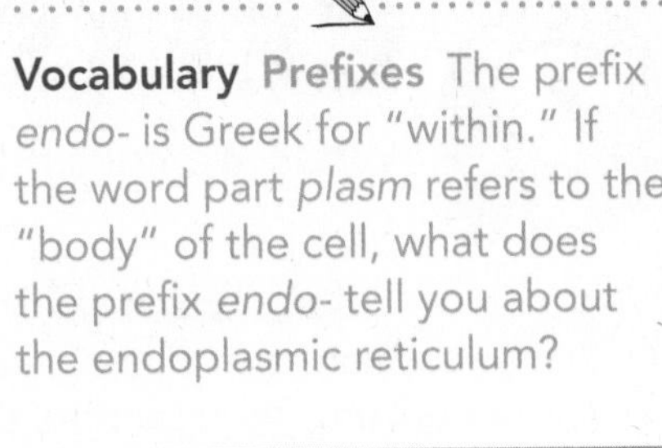

Vocabulary Prefixes The prefix *endo-* is Greek for "within." If the word part *plasm* refers to the "body" of the cell, what does the prefix *endo-* tell you about the endoplasmic reticulum?

____

____

Endoplasmic Reticulum and Ribosomes

Ribosomes

What do ribosomes do?

____

Key

- ☐ Nucleus
- ☐ Nucleolus
- ☐ Cytoplasm
- ☐ Mitochondria
- ☐ ER
- ☐ Ribosomes

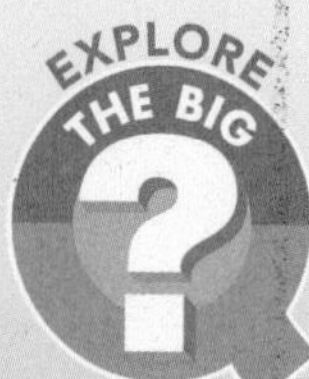

CELLS IN LIVING THINGS

What are cells made of?

FIGURE 3

INTERACTIVE ART These illustrations show typical structures found in plant and animal cells. Other living things share many of these structures, too. Describe **Describe the function of each structure in the boxes provided.**

Endoplasmic Reticulum

___

___

___

___

Nucleus

___

___

___

Cytoplasm

Ribosomes

Cell Wall

___

___

___

___

Golgi Apparatus

Cell membrane

Chloroplast

___

___

___

___

Vacuole

___

___

___

___

Mitochondrion

Plant Cell

Check the box for each structure present in plant cells or animal cells.											
Structure	Cell wall	Cell membrane	Cytoplasm	Nucleus	Mitochondria	Chloroplasts	Ribosomes	Endoplasmic reticulum	Vacuoles	Golgi apparatus	Lysosomes
Plant cells											
Animal cells											

Ribosomes

____

____

Cytoplasm

____

____

____

Mitochondria

____

____

____

____

Endoplasmic Reticulum

Golgi Apparatus

____

____

____

____

Lysosomes

____

____

____

____

Cell Membrane

____

____

____

____

Vacuole

Animal Cell

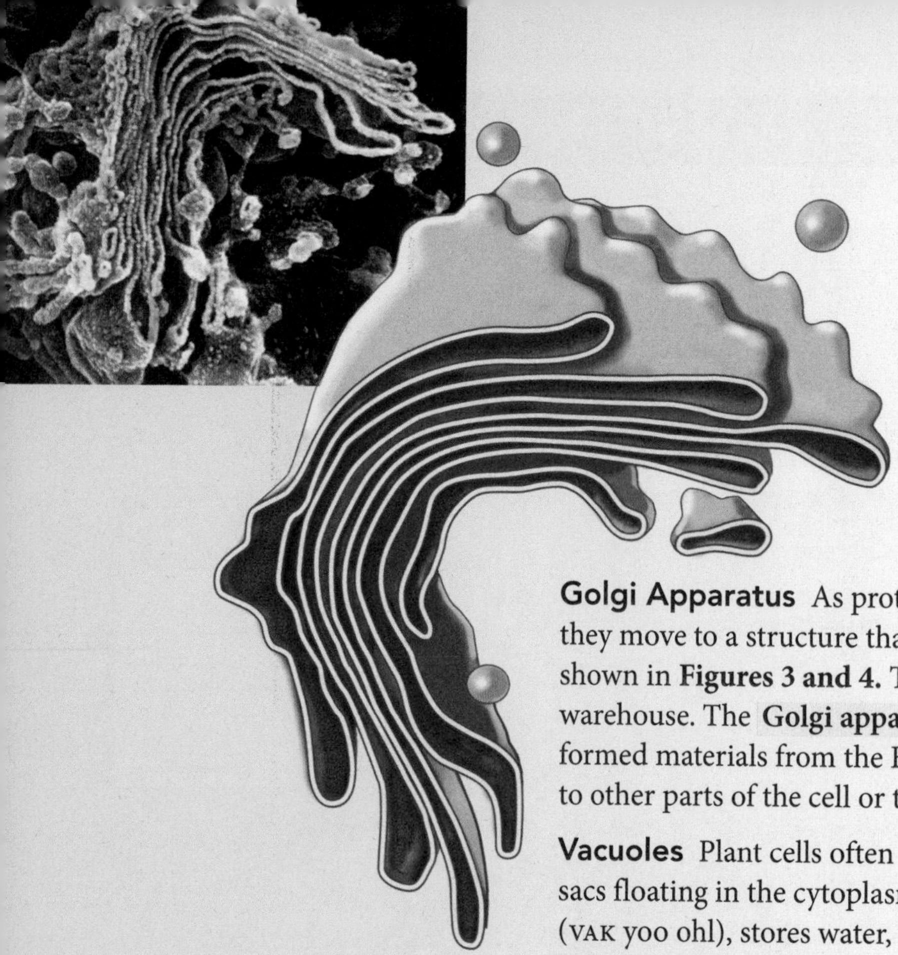

FIGURE 4

Golgi Apparatus

Define The Golgi apparatus is an organelle that ____________ and ____________ materials made in the ____________

Golgi Apparatus As proteins leave the endoplasmic reticulum, they move to a structure that looks like the flattened sacs and tubes shown in **Figures 3 and 4.** This structure can be thought of as a cell's warehouse. The **Golgi apparatus** receives proteins and other newly formed materials from the ER, packages them, and distributes them to other parts of the cell or to the outside of the cell.

Vacuoles Plant cells often have one or more large, water-filled sacs floating in the cytoplasm. This type of sac, called a **vacuole** (VAK yoo ohl), stores water, food, or other materials needed by the cell. Vacuoles can also store waste products until the wastes are removed. Some animal cells do not have vacuoles, while others do.

apply it!

Can a store's building be a model for a cell? If so, how do the parts of a cell function in ways that are similar to the parts of a building? See if you can figure it out. In each blank space on the picture, write the name of a cell structure that functions most like that part of the store.

Make Models How do you think making real-world comparisons with cells helps you understand cell structure and function?

____

____

____

____

____

Chloroplasts A typical plant cell contains green structures, called chloroplasts, in the cytoplasm. A **chloroplast,** shown in **Figure 5,** captures energy from sunlight and changes it to a form of energy cells can use in making food. Animal cells don't have chloroplasts, but the cells of plants and some other organisms do. Chloroplasts make leaves green because leaf cells contain many chloroplasts.

Lysosomes Look again at the animal cell in **Figure 3**. Notice the saclike organelles, called **lysosomes** (LY suh sohmz), which contain substances that break down large food particles into smaller ones. Lysosomes also break down old cell parts and release the substances so they can be used again. You can think of lysosomes as a cell's recycling centers.

FIGURE 5

A Chloroplast

Infer In which part of a plant would you NOT expect to find cells with chloroplasts?

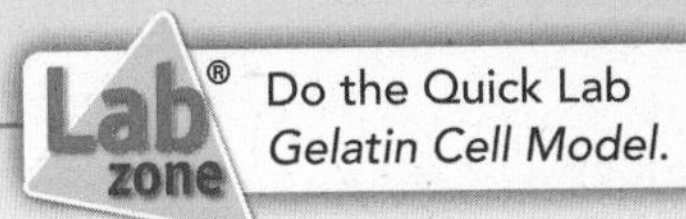

Assess Your Understanding

1a. Interpret Tables Use the table you completed in **Figure 3** to summarize the differences between a plant cell and an animal cell.

b. Make Generalizations How are the functions of the endoplasmic reticulum and the Golgi apparatus related?

c. CHALLENGE A solar panel collects sunlight and converts it to heat or electrical energy. How is a solar panel similar to chloroplasts?

d. ANSWER THE BIG Q What are cells made of?

got it?

○ **I get it!** Now I know that different kinds of organelles in a cell

○ I need extra help with

Go to **MY SCIENCE COACH** *online for help with this subject.*

Science Standards of Learning

LS.1d Construct and use models and simulations to illustrate and explain phenomena.

LS.3a Investigate and understand cells, tissues, organs, and systems.

LS.3b Investigate and understand patterns of cellular organization and their relationship to life processes in living things.

How Do Cells Work Together in an Organism?

Plants and animals (including you) are **multicellular,** which means "made of many cells." Single-celled organisms are called **unicellular.** In a multicellular organism, the cells often look quite different from one another. They also perform different functions.

Specialized Cells All cells in a multicellular organism must carry out key functions, such as getting oxygen, to remain alive. However, cells also may be specialized. That is, they perform specific functions that benefit the entire organism. These specialized cells share what can be called a "division of labor." One type of cell does one kind of job, while other types of cells do other jobs. For example, red blood cells carry oxygen to other cells that may be busy digesting your food. Just as specialized cells differ in function, they also differ in structure. **Figure 6** shows specialized cells from plants and animals. Each type of cell has a distinct shape. For example, a nerve cell has thin, fingerlike extensions that reach toward other cells. These structures help nerve cells transmit information from one part of your body to another. The nerve cell's shape wouldn't be helpful to a red blood cell.

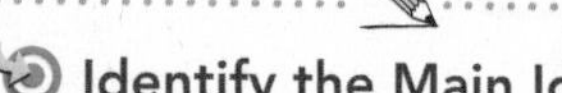

Identify the Main Idea Reread the paragraph about specialized cells. Then underline the phrases or sentences that describe the main ideas about specialized cells.

FIGURE 6

INTERACTIVE ART **The Right Cell for the Job**

Many cells in plants and animals carry out specialized functions.

Draw Conclusions Write the number of each kind of cell in the circle of the matching function.

Specialized Cells	Function
1, 2	◯ Animal cells that can bend and squeeze easily through narrow spaces
	◯ Animal cells that can relay information to other cells
3, 4	◯ Plant root cells that can absorb water and minerals from the soil
	◯ Plant cells that can make food

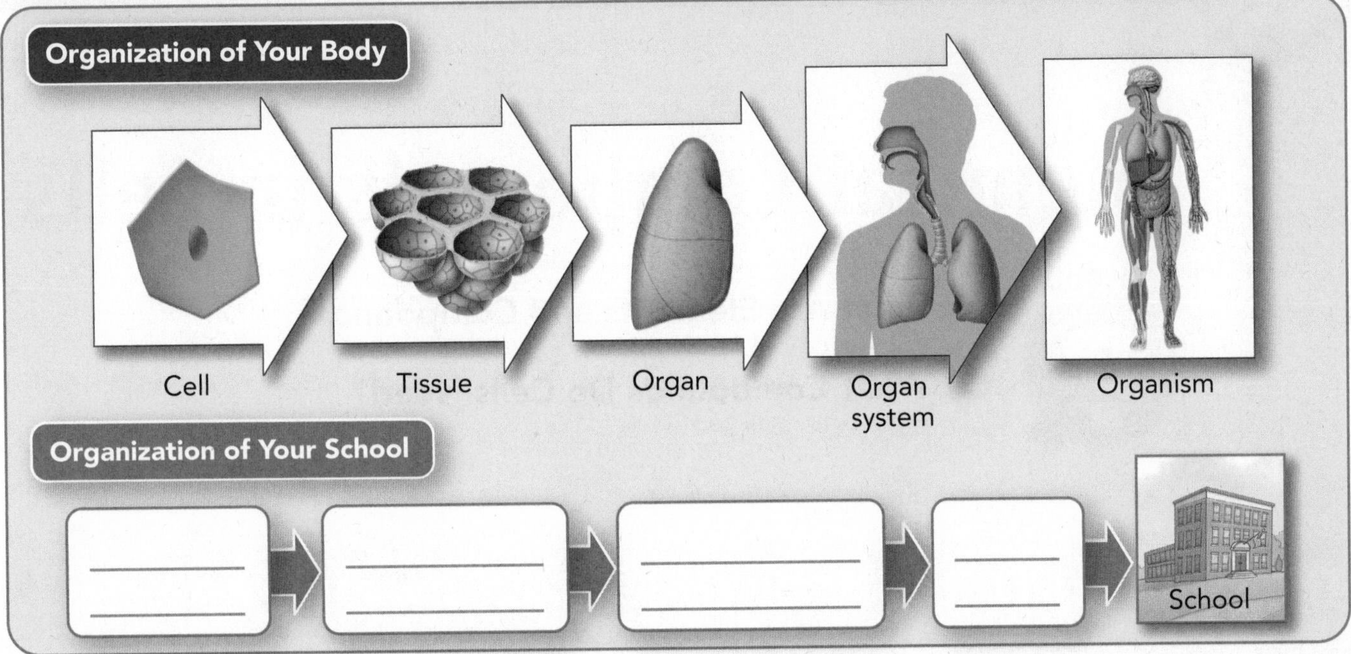

Cells Working Together

A division of labor occurs among specialized cells in an organism. It also occurs at other levels of organization. **In multicellular organisms, cells are organized into tissues, organs, and organ systems.** A **tissue** is a group of similar cells that work together to perform a specific function. For example, your brain is made mostly of nerve tissue, which consists of nerve cells that relay information to other parts of your body. An **organ,** such as your brain, is made of different kinds of tissues that function together. For example, the brain also has blood vessels that carry the blood that supplies oxygen to your brain cells. Your brain is part of your nervous system, which directs body activities and processes. An **organ system** is a group of organs that work together to perform a major function. As **Figure 7** shows, the level of organization in an organism becomes more complex from cell, to tissue, to organ, to organ systems.

FIGURE 7

Levels of Organization

Living things are organized in levels of increasing complexity. Many nonliving things, like a school, have levels of organization, too.

Apply Concepts On the lines above, write the levels of organization of your school building, from the simplest level, such as your desk, to the most complex.

Do the Quick Lab *Tissues, Organs, Systems.*

Assess Your Understanding

2a. Describe What does the term *division of labor* mean as it is used in this lesson?

____

b. Infer Would a tissue or an organ have more kinds of specialized cells? Explain your answer.

____

got it?

○ **I get it!** Now I know that the levels of organization in a multicellular organism include ______________________________

○ I need extra help with ______________________________

Go to **MY SCIENCE COACH** *online for help with this subject.*

Chemical Compounds in Cells

What Are Elements and Compounds?
LS.1d, LS.1j, LS.2a

What Compounds Do Cells Need?
LS.1b, LS.1d, LS.1h, LS.1i, LS.2a

my planet Diary

Energy Backpacks

Some people think a camel's humps carry water. Not true! They actually store fat. A hump's fatty tissue supplies energy when the camel doesn't eat. When a camel has enough food, the hump remains hard and round. But when food is scarce, the hump gets smaller and may sag to the side. If the camel then gets more food, the hump can regain its full size and shape in about three or four months.

MISCONCEPTION

Communicate **Discuss this question with a group of classmates. Then write your answer below.**

How do you think the camel might be affected if it didn't have humps?

___

___

___

PLANET DIARY Go to **Planet Diary** to learn more about chemical compounds in cells.

Do the Inquiry Warm-Up *Detecting Starch.*

Science Standards of Learning

LS.1d Construct and use models and simulations to illustrate and explain phenomena.

LS.1j Use current applications to reinforce life science concepts.

LS.2a Investigate and understand cell structure and organelles.

What Are Elements and Compounds?

You are made of many substances. These substances supply the raw materials that make up your blood, bones, muscles, and more. They also take part in the processes carried out by your cells.

Elements You have probably heard of carbon, hydrogen, oxygen, and nitrogen—maybe phosphorus and sulfur, too. All of these are examples of **elements** found in your body. **An element is any substance that cannot be broken down into simpler substances.** The smallest unit of an element is a particle called an atom. Any single element is made up of only one kind of atom.

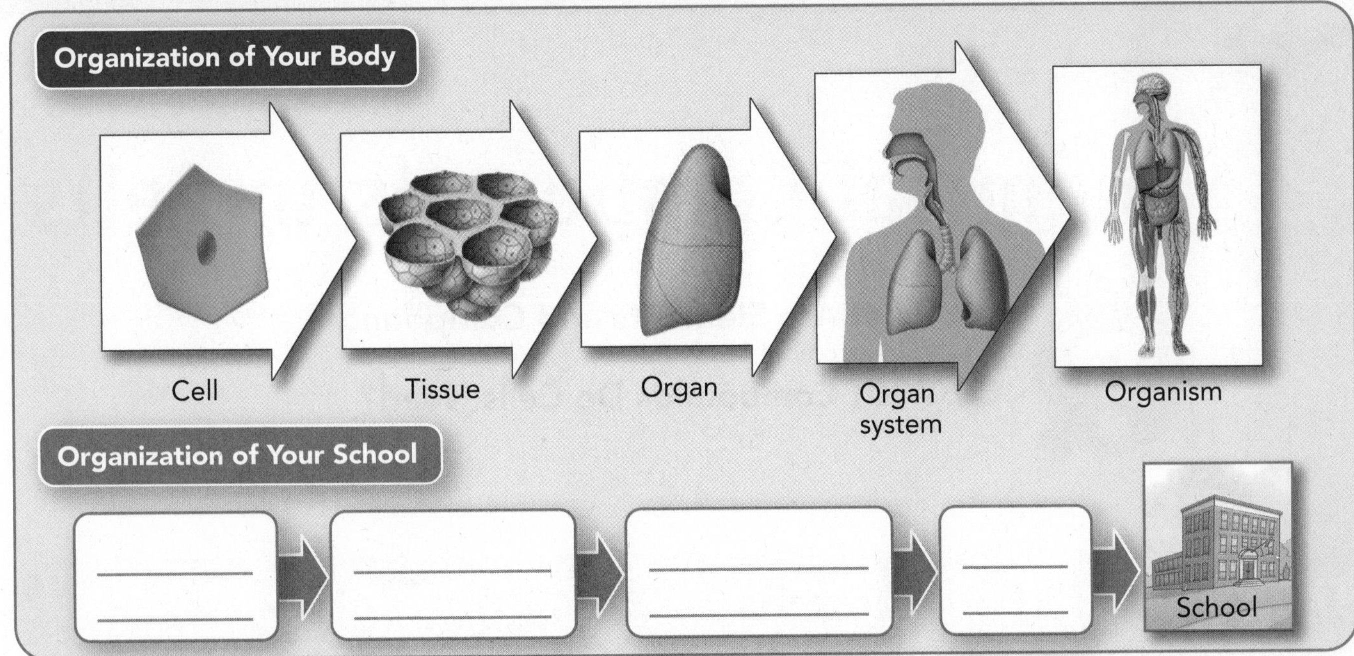

Cells Working Together

A division of labor occurs among specialized cells in an organism. It also occurs at other levels of organization. **In multicellular organisms, cells are organized into tissues, organs, and organ systems.** A **tissue** is a group of similar cells that work together to perform a specific function. For example, your brain is made mostly of nerve tissue, which consists of nerve cells that relay information to other parts of your body. An **organ,** such as your brain, is made of different kinds of tissues that function together. For example, the brain also has blood vessels that carry the blood that supplies oxygen to your brain cells. Your brain is part of your nervous system, which directs body activities and processes. An **organ system** is a group of organs that work together to perform a major function. As **Figure 7** shows, the level of organization in an organism becomes more complex from cell, to tissue, to organ, to organ systems.

FIGURE 7

Levels of Organization

Living things are organized in levels of increasing complexity. Many nonliving things, like a school, have levels of organization, too.

Apply Concepts On the lines above, write the levels of organization of your school building, from the simplest level, such as your desk, to the most complex.

Do the Quick Lab *Tissues, Organs, Systems.*

Assess Your Understanding

2a. Describe What does the term *division of labor* mean as it is used in this lesson?

____

b. Infer Would a tissue or an organ have more kinds of specialized cells? Explain your answer.

____

got it?

O **I get it!** Now I know that the levels of organization in a multicellular organism include ______________________

O I need extra help with ______________________

Go to my science COACH *online for help with this subject.*

Chemical Compounds in Cells

What Are Elements and Compounds?
LS.1d, LS.1j, LS.2a

What Compounds Do Cells Need?
LS.1b, LS.1d, LS.1h, LS.1i, LS.2a

my planet Diary

Energy Backpacks

Some people think a camel's humps carry water. Not true! They actually store fat. A hump's fatty tissue supplies energy when the camel doesn't eat. When a camel has enough food, the hump remains hard and round. But when food is scarce, the hump gets smaller and may sag to the side. If the camel then gets more food, the hump can regain its full size and shape in about three or four months.

MISCONCEPTION

Communicate **Discuss this question with a group of classmates. Then write your answer below.**

How do you think the camel might be affected if it didn't have humps?

____

____

____

PLANET DIARY Go to **Planet Diary** to learn more about chemical compounds in cells.

Do the Inquiry Warm-Up *Detecting Starch.*

Science Standards of Learning

LS.1d Construct and use models and simulations to illustrate and explain phenomena.

LS.1j Use current applications to reinforce life science concepts.

LS.2a Investigate and understand cell structure and organelles.

What Are Elements and Compounds?

You are made of many substances. These substances supply the raw materials that make up your blood, bones, muscles, and more. They also take part in the processes carried out by your cells.

Elements You have probably heard of carbon, hydrogen, oxygen, and nitrogen—maybe phosphorus and sulfur, too. All of these are examples of **elements** found in your body. **An element is any substance that cannot be broken down into simpler substances.** The smallest unit of an element is a particle called an atom. Any single element is made up of only one kind of atom.

Lipids Have you ever seen a cook trim fat from a piece of meat before cooking it? The cook is trimming away one kind of lipid. **Lipids** are compounds that are made mostly of carbon and hydrogen and some oxygen. Cell membranes consist mainly of lipids.

Fats, oils, and waxes are all lipids. Gram for gram, fats and oils contain more energy than carbohydrates. Cells store energy from fats and oils for later use. For example, during winter, an inactive bear lives on the energy stored in its fat cells. Foods high in fats include whole milk, ice cream, and fried foods.

Proteins What do a bird's feathers, a spider's web, and a hamburger have in common? They consist mainly of proteins. **Proteins** are large organic molecules made of carbon, hydrogen, oxygen, nitrogen, and, in some cases, sulfur. Foods that are high in protein include meat, dairy products, fish, nuts, and beans.

Much of a cell's structure and function depends on proteins. Proteins form part of a cell's membrane. Proteins also make up parts of the organelles within a cell. A group of proteins known as **enzymes** speed up chemical reactions in living things. Without enzymes, the many chemical reactions that are necessary for life would take too long. For example, an enzyme in your saliva speeds up the digestion of starch. The starch breaks down into sugars while still in your mouth.

FIGURE 3
Proteins
A parrot's beak, feathers, and claws are made of proteins.
Apply Concepts **What part of your body most likely consists of proteins similar to those of a parrot's claws?**

Compare and Contrast
As you read, complete the table below to compare carbohydrates, lipids, and proteins.

Type of Compound	Elements	Functions
Carbohydrate		
Lipid		
Protein		

FIGURE 4

DNA

Smaller molecules connect in specific patterns and sequences, forming DNA.

Interpret Diagrams In the diagram below, identify the pattern of colors. Then color in the ones that are missing.

Nucleic Acids

Nucleic acids are very long organic molecules. These molecules consist of carbon, oxygen, hydrogen, nitrogen, and phosphorus. Nucleic acids contain the instructions that cells need to carry out all the functions of life. Foods high in nucleic acids include red meat, shellfish, mushrooms, and peas.

One kind of nucleic acid is deoxyribonucleic acid (dee AHK see RY boh noo KLEE ik), or DNA. **DNA** is the genetic material that carries information about an organism and is passed from parent to offspring. This information directs a cell's functions. Most DNA is found in a cell's nucleus. The shape of a DNA molecule is described as a **double helix.** Imagine a rope ladder that's been twisted around a pole, and you'll have a mental picture of the double helix of DNA. The double helix forms from many small molecules connected together. The pattern and sequence in which these molecules connect make a kind of chemical code the cell can "read."

do the math!

Most cells contain the same compounds. The graph compares the percentages of some compounds found in a bacterial cell and in an animal cell. Write a title for the graph and answer the questions below.

1. **Read Graphs** Put a check above the bar that shows the percentage of water in an animal cell. How does this number compare to the percentage of water in a bacterial cell?

____

2. **Read Graphs** (Proteins/Nucleic acids) make up a larger percentage of an animal cell.

3. **Draw Conclusions** In general, how do you think a bacterial cell and an animal cell compare in their chemical composition?

____

____

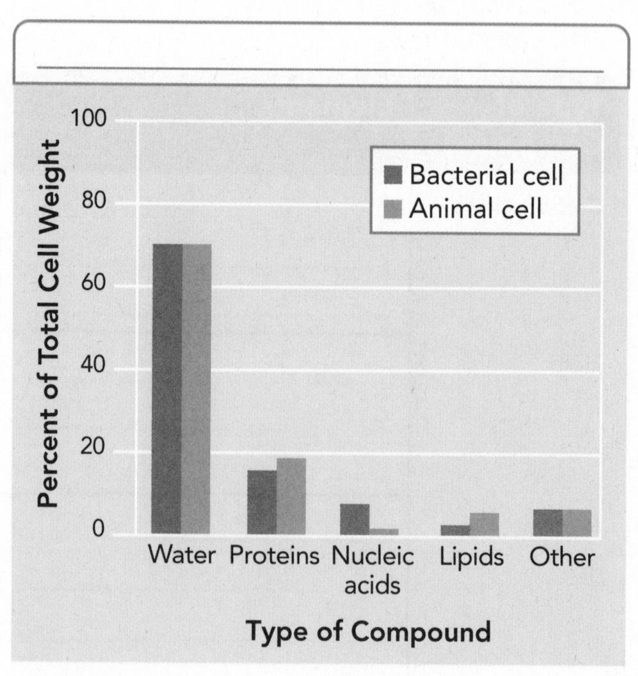

FIGURE 5

Mostly Water

About two thirds of the human body is water. But you know you don't really look like a tank of water with a fish! **Graph Complete and label the circle graph to show the percentage of water in your body.**

Water and Living Things

Water plays many important roles in cells. For example, most chemical reactions in cells depend on substances that must be dissolved in water to react. And water itself takes part in many chemical reactions in cells.

Water also helps cells keep their shape. A cell without water would be like a balloon without air! Think about how the leaves of a plant wilt when the plant needs water. After you add water to the soil, the cells absorb the water, and the leaves perk up.

Water changes temperature slowly, so it helps keep the temperature of cells from changing rapidly—a change that can be harmful. Water also plays a key role in carrying substances into and out of cells. Without water, life as we know it would not exist on Earth.

Lab zone® Do the Quick Lab *What's That Taste?*

Assess Your Understanding

1a. Describe An organic compound that contains only the elements carbon, hydrogen, and oxygen is most likely (a carbohydrate/ a protein/DNA). Explain your answer.

______

b. Classify Which groups of organic compounds found in living things are NOT energy rich?

______

c. Review What is the function of DNA?

______

d. CHALLENGE Describe ways a lack of water could affect cell functions.

______

got it?

○ **I get it!** Now I know that the important compounds in living things include ______

○ I need extra help with ______

Go to **MY SCIENCE COACH** *online for help with this subject.*

Virginia

LESSON 4

The Cell in Its Environment

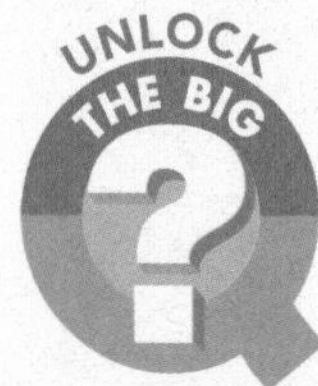

How Do Materials Move Into and Out of Cells?
LS.1d, LS.1j, LS.2a

my planet Diary

FUN FACTS

Something Good in the Air

You're in your bedroom studying, and you smell something good. Someone is cooking lunch! How did the smell travel from the kitchen to your nose? During cooking, molecules from soup and many other foods diffuse, or spread farther and farther apart. The molecules are also carried by air currents. Your nose sniffs in the molecules and sends a message to your brain. Even if only one molecule in ten million carries the odor, your nose will send a "smell" message! Amazingly, your brain can identify about ten thousand different smells.

Communicate Discuss this question with a classmate and write your answers below.
If the kitchen door is closed, how will that affect your ability to smell cooking odors in your room?

______

______

______

______

______

______

PLANET DIARY Go to **Planet Diary** to learn more about cells in their environments.

Do the Inquiry Warm-Up *Diffusion in Action.*

Science Standards of Learning

LS.1d Construct and use models and simulations to illustrate and explain phenomena.
LS.1j Use current applications to reinforce life science concepts.
LS.2a Investigate and understand cell structure and organelles.

How Do Materials Move Into and Out of Cells?

Cells have structures that protect their contents from the world outside the cell. To live and function, however, cells must let certain materials enter and leave. Oxygen and water and particles of food must be able to move into a cell, while carbon dioxide and other waste materials must move out. Much as a gatekeeper controls the flow of traffic into and out of a parking lot, the cell membrane controls how materials move into or out of a cell.

Vocabulary

- selectively permeable
- passive transport
- diffusion
- osmosis
- active transport
- endocytosis
- exocytosis

Skills

- Reading: Relate Cause and Effect
- Inquiry: Predict

Importance of the Cell Membrane Every cell is surrounded by a cell membrane. In **Figure 1** you can see that the cell membrane consists of a double layer of lipid molecules lined up side by side. Remember that lipids are a group of organic compounds found in living things. Here and there in the double layer of lipid molecules, you can see proteins, some with chains of carbohydrates attached. Other carbohydrate chains sit on the surface of the membrane. All these molecules play important roles in helping materials move through the cell membrane.

Some materials move freely across the cell membrane. Others move less freely or not at all. The cell membrane is **selectively permeable,** which means that some substances can cross the membrane while others cannot. **Substances that can move into and out of a cell do so by means of one of two processes: passive transport or active transport.**

FIGURE 1

A Selective Barrier

Make Models In what way is the cell membrane like a gatekeeper?

____

____

Diffusion and Osmosis: Forms of Passive Transport If you have ever ridden a bicycle down a hill, you know that it takes hardly any of your energy to go fast. But you do have to use energy to pedal back up the hill. Moving materials across the cell membrane sometimes requires the cell to use its own energy. At other times, the cell uses no energy. The movement of dissolved materials across a cell membrane without using the cell's energy is called **passive transport.**

FIGURE 2

Diffusion

A drop of food coloring in a plate of gelatin gradually spreads as molecules of the dye diffuse. **Predict In the third plate, draw how you think the plate would look if diffusion continues.**

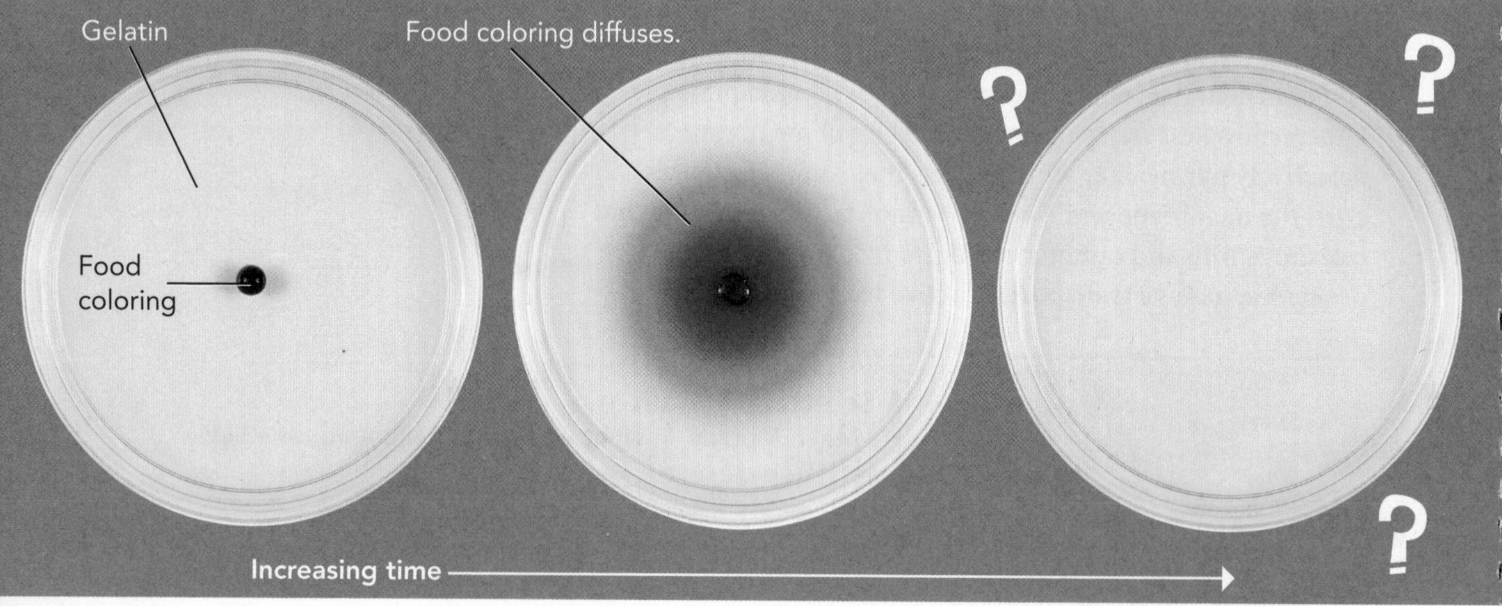

Relate Cause and Effect

Diffusion causes molecules to move from areas of ________ concentration to areas of ________ concentration.

Diffusion Molecules are always moving. As they move, they bump into one another. The more molecules there are in a space, the more they are said to be concentrated in that space. So they collide more often. Collisions cause molecules to push away from one another. Over time, as molecules continue colliding and moving apart, they become less concentrated. Eventually, they spread evenly throughout the space. **Diffusion** (dih FYOO zhun) is the process by which molecules move from an area of higher concentration to an area of lower concentration. See **Figure 2.**

Consider a unicellular organism that lives in pond water. It gets oxygen from that water. Many more molecules of oxygen are dissolved in the water outside the cell than inside the cell. In other words, the concentration of oxygen is higher outside the cell. What happens? Oxygen moves easily into the cell. The diffusion of oxygen into the cell does not require the cell to use any of its energy. Diffusion is one form of passive transport.

Osmosis Like oxygen, water passes easily into and out of a cell across the cell membrane. **Osmosis** is the diffusion of water molecules across a selectively permeable membrane. Because cells cannot function properly without adequate water, many cellular processes depend on osmosis. Osmosis is a form of passive transport.

Osmosis can have important effects on cells and entire organisms. The plant cells in the top photo of **Figure 3** have a healthy flow of water both into and out of each cell. Under certain conditions, osmosis can cause water to move out of the cells more quickly than it moves in. When that happens, the cytoplasm shrinks and the cell membrane pulls away from the cell wall, as shown in the bottom photo. If conditions do not change, the cells can die.

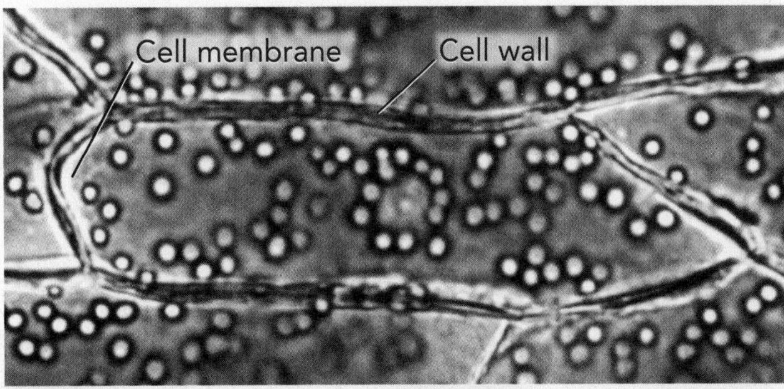

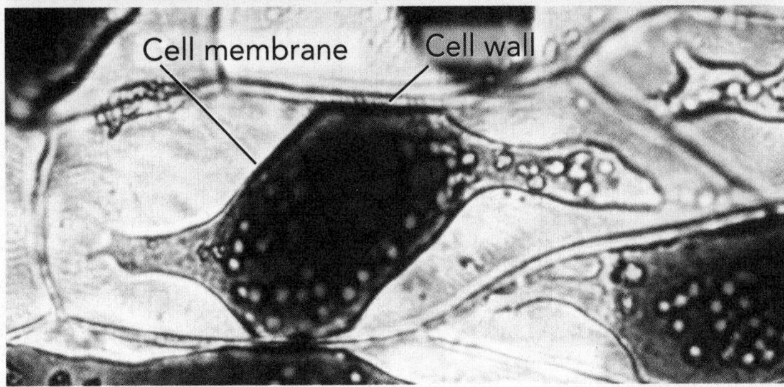

FIGURE 3

Effects of Osmosis

Cells shrink and die when they lose too much water.

Infer Using a colored pencil, shade the cells in the bottom photo to show how they would change if the flow of water was reversed.

apply it!

Most cells are too small to be seen without a microscope. What does cell size have to do with moving materials into and out of a cell? Suppose the diagrams at the right represent two cells. One cell is three times the width of the other cell. Think about how this difference could affect processes in the cells.

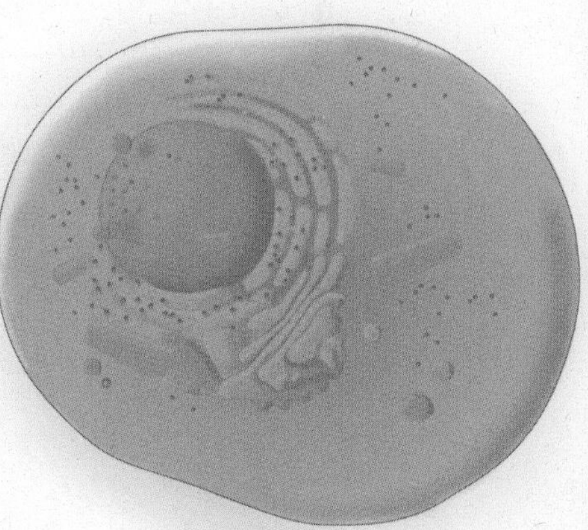

Large cell

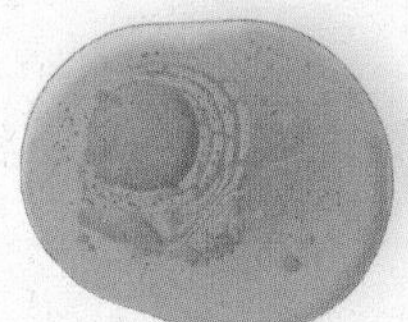

Small cell

1 **Infer** Cytoplasm streams within a cell, moving materials somewhat as ocean currents move a raft. In which cell will materials move faster from the cell membrane to the center of the cell? Why?

____

____

2 **Predict** Wastes are poisonous to a cell and must be removed from the cytoplasm. Predict how cell size could affect the removal process and the survival of a cell.

____

____

____

Facilitated Diffusion Oxygen and carbon dioxide diffuse freely across a cell membrane. Other molecules, such as sugar, do not. Sugars cannot cross easily through the membrane's lipid molecules. In a process called facilitated diffusion, proteins in the cell membrane form channels through which the sugars can pass. The word *facilitate* means "to make easier." As shown in **Figure 4,** these proteins provide a pathway for the sugars to diffuse. The proteins function much the way downspouts guide water that flows from the roof of a house to the ground. Facilitated diffusion uses no cell energy and is another form of passive transport.

Active Transport

Molecules in cells must often move in the opposite direction from the way they would naturally move due to diffusion. That is, the molecules move from a place of *lower* concentration to a place of *higher* concentration. Cells have to supply the energy to do this work—just as you would supply the energy to pedal a bike uphill. **Active transport** is the movement of materials across a cell membrane using cellular energy.

As in facilitated diffusion, proteins within the cell membrane play a key role in active transport. Using the cell's energy, transport proteins "pick up" specific molecules and carry them across the membrane. Substances that are carried into and out of cells by this process include calcium, potassium, and sodium.

FIGURE 4

ART IN MOTION Crossing the Cell Membrane

Molecules move into and out of a cell by means of passive or active transport.

1. **Name** Fill in the words missing in the boxes.
2. CHALLENGE On the diagram, write an "H" where the concentration of each substance is high and an "L" where the concentration is low.

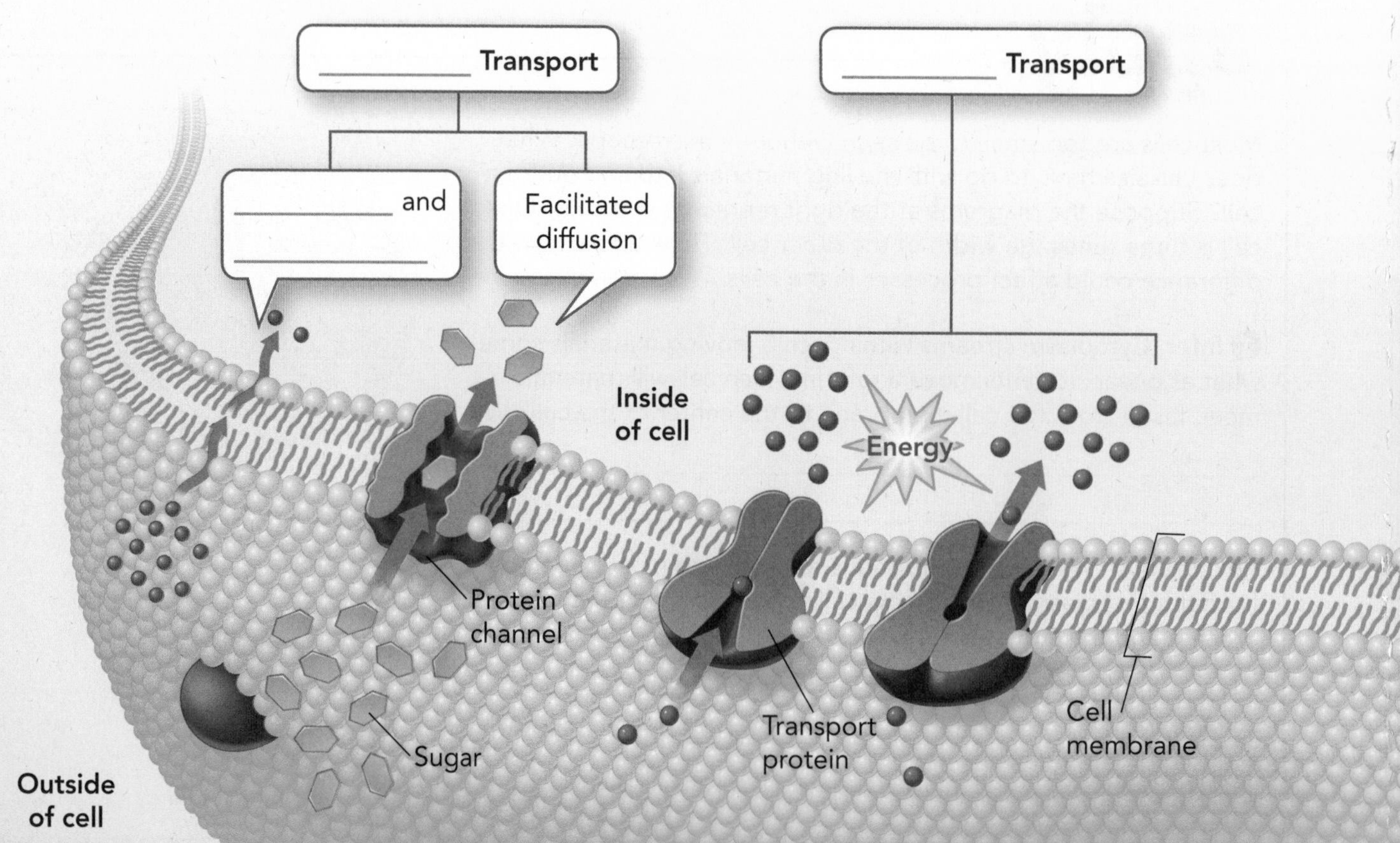

Moving Large Particles Some materials, such as food particles, are too large to cross the cell membrane. In a process called **endocytosis** (ehn doh sigh TOH sihs), the cell membrane changes shape and engulfs the particle. You can see this process happening in **Figure 5.** Once the food particle is engulfed, the cell membrane fuses, pinching off a vacuole within the cell. The reverse process, called **exocytosis** (ehk soh sigh TOH sihs), allows large particles to leave a cell. During exocytosis, a vacuole first fuses with the cell membrane. Then the cell membrane forms an opening to the outside and spills out the contents of the vacuole. Both endocytosis and exocytosis require energy from the cell.

FIGURE 5

Amoeba Engulfing Food

A single-celled amoeba slowly surrounds bits of food.

Observe Look at these photographs. They show (endocytosis/exocytosis).

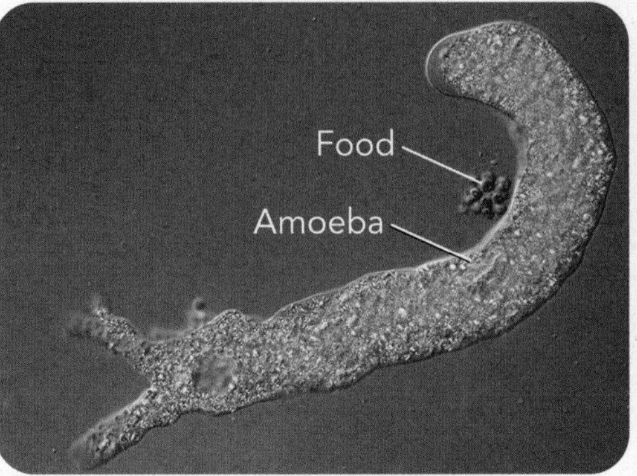

1 Amoeba's cytoplasm streams toward food particles.

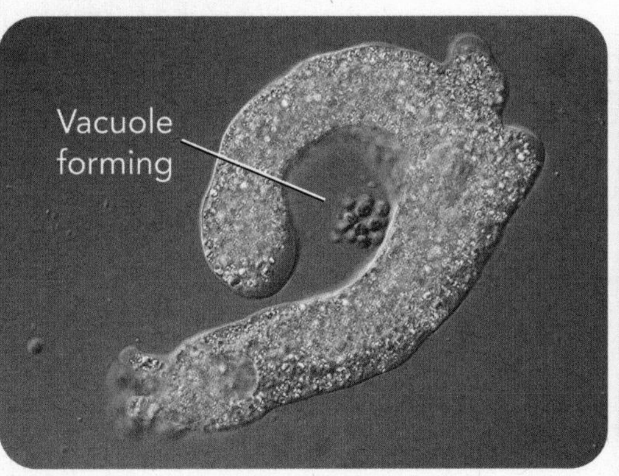

2 Cytoplasm surrounds food particles as vacuole begins to form.

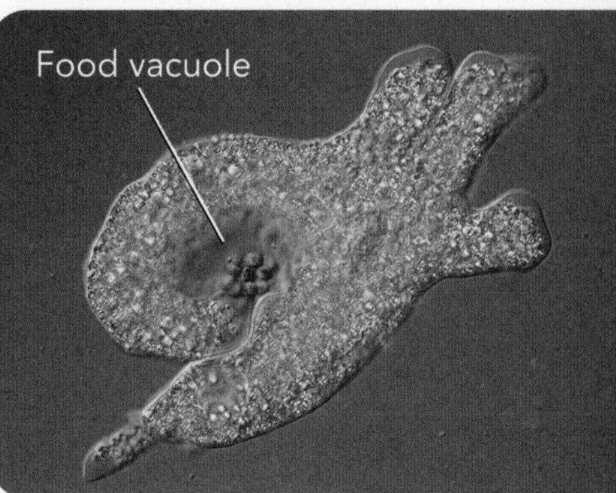

3 Cell membrane fuses, trapping food particles in new vacuole.

Do the Quick Lab *Effect of Concentration on Diffusion.*

Assess Your Understanding

1a. Review Use diffusion to tell what happens when you drop a sugar cube into water.

______

______

______

b. Predict Draw an arrow to show the overall direction water will travel as a result of osmosis. (The yellow line is the cell membrane.)

Water molecule

c. Identify Active transport depends on (sugars/proteins) to move molecules across the cell membrane.

d. Compare and Contrast How does active transport differ from passive transport?

______

______

______

______

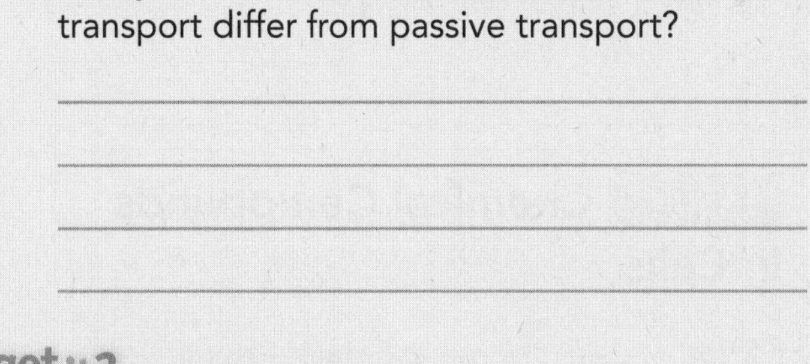

got it?

O **I get it!** Now I know that a key function of the cell membrane is to ______

______

______

O I need extra help with ______

Go to **MY SCIENCE COACH** *online for help with this subject.*

CHAPTER 4

Study Guide

All living things are made of ___________, which are the smallest units of _______________

and _______________________

LESSON 1 Discovering Cells

Cells are the basic units of structure and function in living things.

All living things are composed of cells, and all cells come from other cells.

Some microscopes focus light through lenses to produce a magnified image, and other microscopes use beams of electrons.

Vocabulary

• cell • microscope • cell theory

LESSON 2 Looking Inside Cells

Each kind of cell structure has a different function within a cell.

In multicellular organisms, cells are organized into tissues, organs, and organ systems.

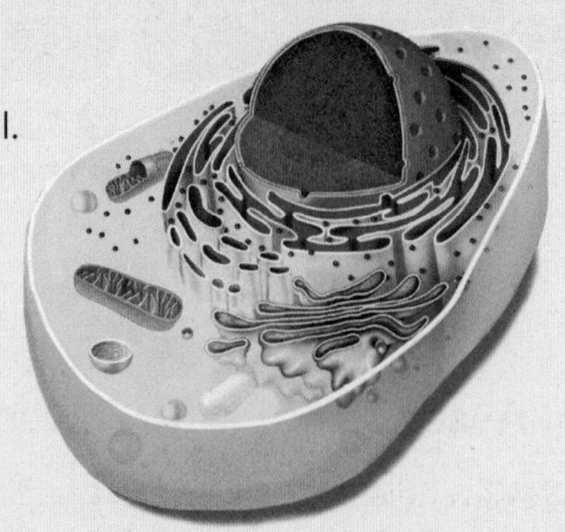

Vocabulary

• cell wall • cell membrane • nucleus • organelle
• ribosome • cytoplasm • mitochondria
• endoplasmic reticulum • Golgi apparatus • vacuole
• chloroplast • lysosome • multicellular • unicellular
• tissue • organ • organ system

LESSON 3 Chemical Compounds in Cells

Elements are the simplest substances. Compounds form when elements combine.

Important compounds in living things include carbohydrates, lipids, proteins, nucleic acids, and water.

Vocabulary

• element • compound • carbohydrate
• lipid • protein • enzyme
• nucleic acid • DNA • double helix

LESSON 4 The Cell in Its Environment

Substances move into and out of a cell by one of two processes: passive transport or active transport.

Vocabulary

• selectively permeable • passive transport
• diffusion • osmosis • active transport
• endocytosis • exocytosis

Review and Assessment

LESSON 1 Discovering Cells

1. Which tool could help you see a plant cell?
   a. a filter
   b. a microscope
   c. a microwave
   d. an electromagnet

2. The ________________ states that all living things are made of cells.

3. **Classify** Your cells take in oxygen, water, and food. What is one waste product that leaves your cells?

4. **Compare and Contrast** How is a light microscope similar to an electron microscope? How do the two types of microscopes differ?

5. **Estimate** Using a microscope, you see the one-celled organism shown below. The diameter of the microscope's field of view is 0.8 mm. Estimate the cell's length and width, and write your answer in the space provided.

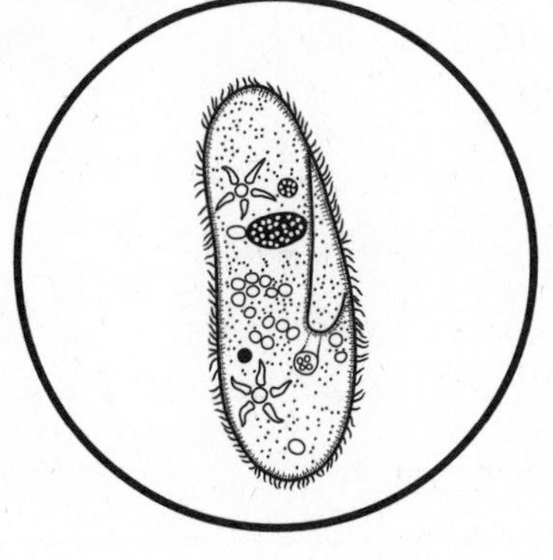

LESSON 2 Looking Inside Cells

6. Which cellular structures are found in plant cells but NOT in animal cells?
   a. chloroplast and cell wall
   b. Golgi apparatus and vacuole
   c. mitochondrion and ribosome
   d. endoplasmic reticulum and nucleus

7. Mitochondria and chloroplasts are two types of ________________

8. **Interpret Diagrams** What is the function of the cell structure shown in purple in the cell at the right?

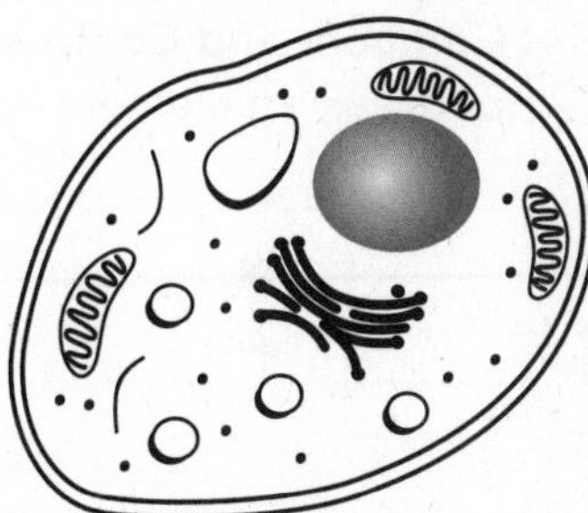

9. **Sequence** Arrange the following, from smallest to largest level of organization: organ system, tissue, cell, organ.

10. **Infer** A certain cell can no longer package and release materials out of the cell. Which of the cell's organelles is not working?

11. **Write About It** Imagine you are a tour guide. You and the tour group have shrunk to the size of water molecules. You are now ready to start a tour of the cell! Write a narrative of your tour that you could give a new tour guide to use.

CHAPTER 4
Review and Assessment

LESSON 3 Chemical Compounds in Cells

12. Starch is an example of a

a. lipid. **b.** protein.
c. nucleic acid. **d.** carbohydrate.

13. Which type of organic molecule is found primarily in a cell's nucleus?

____

14. **Compare and Contrast** What is the difference between an element and a compound?

____
____
____
____

15. **Infer** How may a lack of proteins in a person's diet affect the body?

____
____
____

16. **math!** The graph below shows the amounts of different compounds that make up an animal cell. What percentage of the total cell weight is made up of lipids?

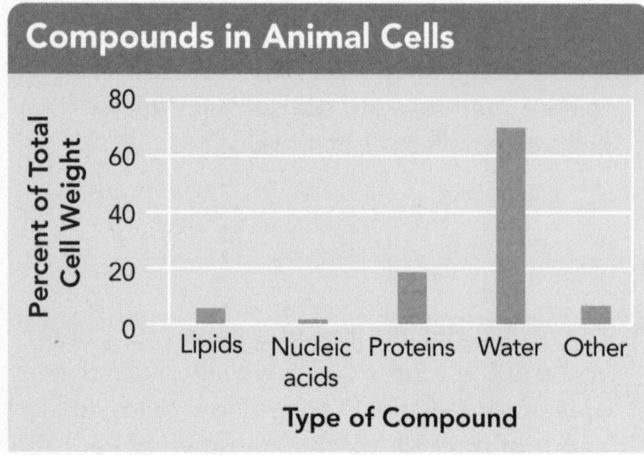

____

LESSON 4 The Cell in Its Environment

17. The process by which water moves across a cell's membrane is called

a. osmosis. **b.** exocytosis.
c. resolution. **d.** active transport.

18. Some substances but not others can cross the ______________ membrane of a cell.

19. **Compare and Contrast** How are facilitated diffusion and active transport similar? How are they different?

____
____
____
____
____

What are cells made of?

20. At right is a photograph of a multicellular plant called a primrose. List three conclusions you can make about the primrose as a living thing.

____
____
____
____
____
____
____
____
____

Virginia SOL Test Prep

Read each question and choose the best answer.

1 Which transport process is shown in the illustration below?

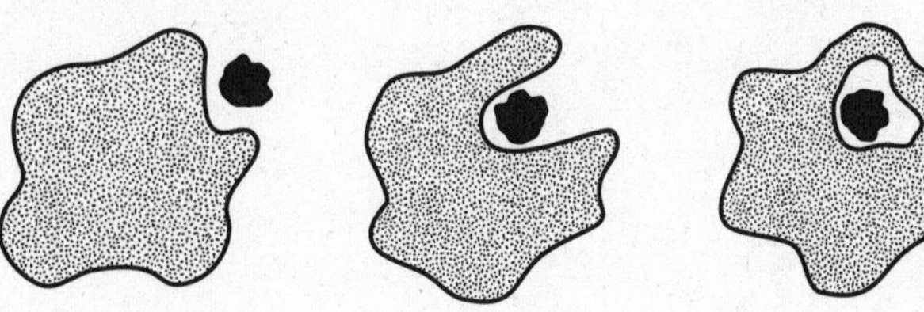

A osmosis B diffusion
C endocytosis D exocytosis

2 Which of the following types of cells have cell walls?

F plant cells G muscle cells
H blood cells J animal cells

3 A compound microscope has two lenses. One lens has a magnification of 15× and the other has a magnification of 40×. What is the total magnification?

A 25× B 55×
C 150× D 600×

4 Which of the following is an example of an element?

F cell G water
H hydrogen J starch

5 The cell membrane is made mostly of a double layer of molecules called—

A lipids B proteins
C nucleic acids D carbohydrates

6 The structure surrounding the plant cell shown below is called the—

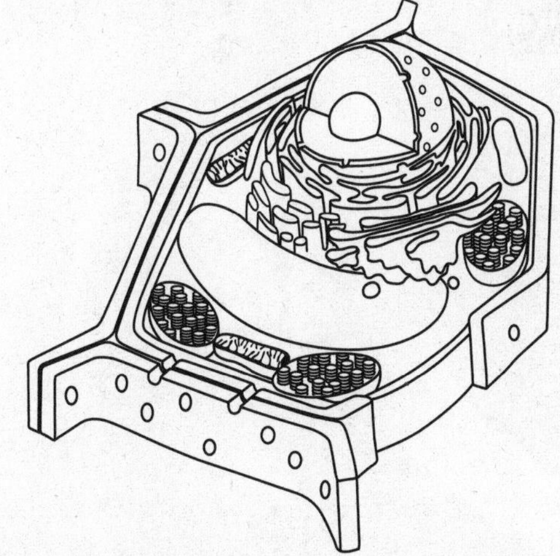

F cell wall
G nucleus
H Golgi apparatus
J ribosome

SCIENCE MATTERS

Technology and History

Electron EYES

The invention of the optical microscope around the year 1600 caused a revolution in science. For the first time, scientists were able to see the cells that make up living things. However, even the most modern optical microscopes that focus light through lenses to produce an enlarged image can magnify an object only about 1,000 times.

Beginning in the early 1930s, new kinds of microscopes have caused new revolutions in science. The electron microscope uses electrons, instead of light, to make very detailed images of specimens. Today, powerful microscopes can magnify images up to 1,000,000 times—enough to enable scientists to see individual atoms!

Scientists use three main types of very powerful microscopes:

▼ Looking through a TEM gives a close-up view of the cells of an onion.

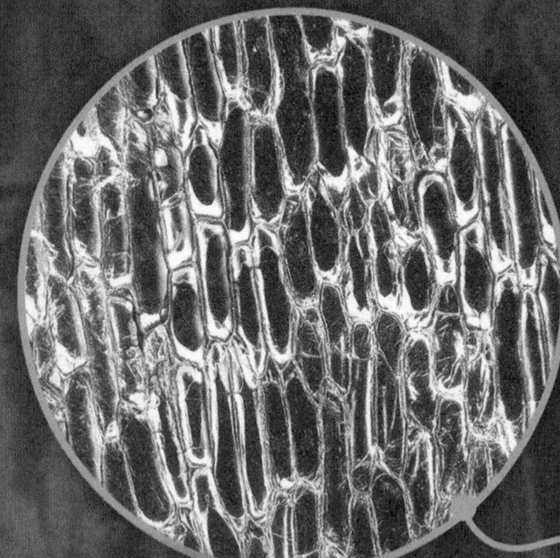

Transmission Electron Microscope (TEM) A TEM focuses a beam of electrons so that they pass through a very thinly sliced specimen. They are very useful for studying the interior structures of cells.

▼ Samples of bread mold as captured by an SEM

Scanning Electron Microscope (SEM) An SEM uses an electron beam to scan the surface of the specimen. The electron beam excites the electrons on the object's surface. The excited electrons are used to make a three-dimensional image of the specimen.

Scanning Tunneling Microscope (STM) An STM works by passing an electrically charged probe very close to the surface of a specimen. As the probe passes over the specimen, the probe moves up and down to keep the current in the probe constant. The path of the probe is recorded and is used to create an image of the specimen's surface.

Design It Research to find images taken by electron or scanning tunneling microscopes. Create a gallery or slide presentation of amazing microscope images to share with your class. See if your classmates can guess what object is shown in each image!

 LS.1b, LS.1j

THE GENOGRAPHIC PROJECT

Have you ever wondered where your earliest ancestors came from? Archaeologists have worked for years to uncover evidence of ancient human migrations. They study the things people left behind, such as arrowheads, beads, and tools. Yet some of the most promising evidence is not found in archaeological sites. It is found in the cells that make up our bodies! The Genographic Project is a research project that uses DNA samples to help uncover the history of the human species.

Participants in the Genographic Project receive a kit that allows them to provide a DNA sample. To give a sample, participants use a cotton swab to gather cells from the inside of their cheek. This sample is mailed to a lab that analyzes the DNA contained in the cells. The DNA in the cells is compared with other DNA samples from around the world.

Then participants receive a report that describes the history of their earliest ancestors. The report includes a map that shows the migration route that these ancestors may have followed. Participants may choose to have their genetic information anonymously added to a genetic database. This database will help researchers build a very detailed map of ancient and modern human migration.

Explore It What has the Genographic Project discovered so far? Research the project, and create a map that shows what it has revealed about ancient human migration.

LS.1d, LS.1j, LS.12f

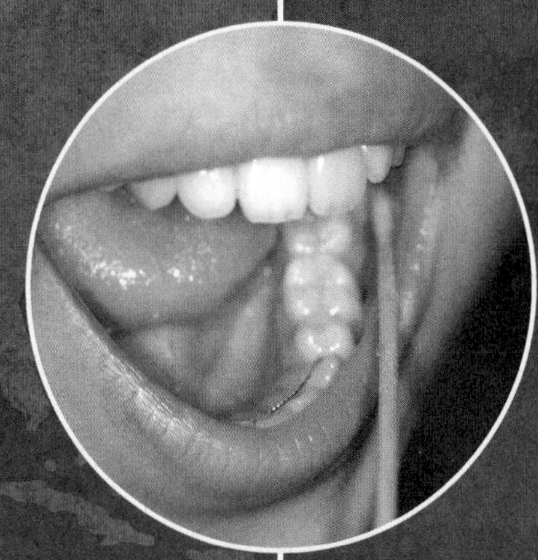

▲ People who want to help the Genographic Project collect cells from their cheeks.

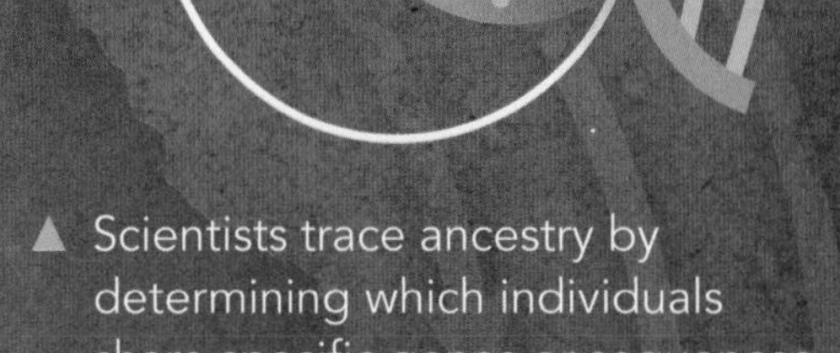

▲ Scientists trace ancestry by determining which individuals share specific genes or sequences of genes called genetic markers.

How do living things get energy?

Looking straight up into the sky from the ground, you can see the tallest trees on Earth. These giant California redwoods can grow up to 110 meters tall, about the size of a 35-story skyscraper! To grow this big takes energy and raw materials from food. These trees don't eat food as you do. But they do get water through their roots, gases from the air, and lots of sunlight. Develop Hypotheses **How do these trees get the energy they need to grow?**

UNTAMED SCIENCE Watch the **Untamed Science** video to learn more about living things and energy.

Virginia

CHAPTER 5

Cell Processes and Energy

Science Standards of Learning

LS.1d, LS.1f, LS.1h, LS.1j, LS.2a, LS.2b, LS.2d, LS.5a, LS.5b, LS.5c

CHAPTER

5 Getting Started

Check Your Understanding

1. **Background** Read the paragraph below and then answer the question.

In science class, we looked at both plant and animal cells under the microscope. I could see the **nucleus** in many cells. In plant cells, we could see green-colored **chloroplasts.** Both plant and animal cells have **mitochondria,** but they were too small for us to see with the microscopes we had.

The **nucleus** is the organelle that acts as the cell's control center and directs the cell's activities.

Chloroplasts are organelles that capture energy from sunlight and use it to produce food for the cell.

Mitochondria are organelles that convert energy in food to energy the cell can use to carry out its functions.

- Circle the names of the organelles found only in plant cells. Underline the organelles found in both plant and animal cells.
nucleus mitochondria chloroplasts

MY READING WEB If you had trouble completing the question above, visit **My Reading Web** and type in ***Cell Processes and Energy.***

Vocabulary Skill

Greek Word Origins The table below shows English word parts that have Greek origins. Learning the word parts can help you understand some of the vocabulary in this chapter.

Greek Word Part	Meaning	Example
auto-	self	**autotroph,** *n.* an organism that makes its own food; a producer
hetero-	other, different	**heterotroph,** *n.* an organism that cannot make its own food; a consumer

2. **Quick Check The word part *-troph* comes from the Greek word *trophe,* which means "food." Circle the word part in two places in the chart above. How does the Greek word relate to the meaning of the terms?**

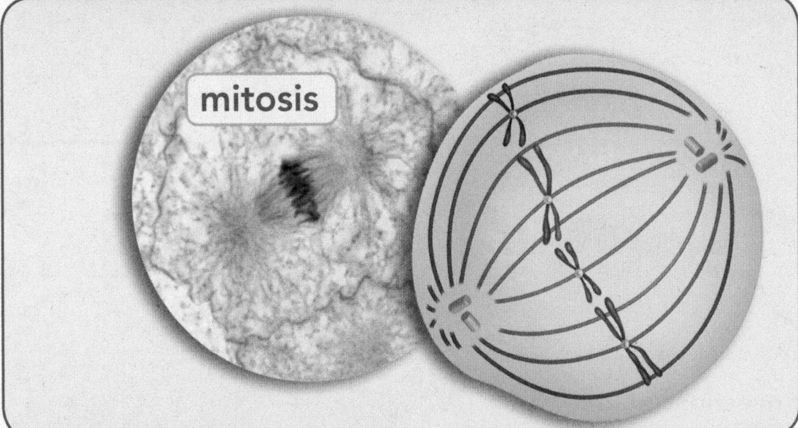

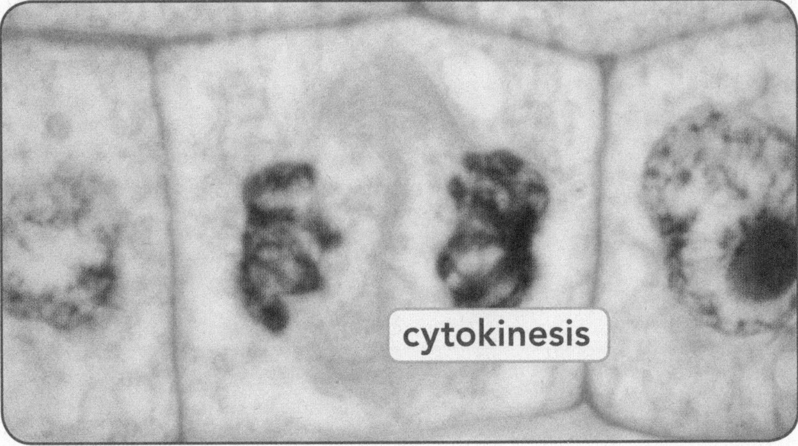

Chapter Preview

LESSON 1

- photosynthesis
- autotroph
- heterotroph
- chlorophyll

Sequence

Classify

LESSON 2

- cellular respiration
- fermentation

Summarize

Control Variables

LESSON 3

- cell cycle
- interphase
- replication
- chromosome
- mitosis
- cytokinesis

Ask Questions

Interpret Data

VOCAB FLASH CARDS For extra help with vocabulary, visit **Vocab Flash Cards** and type in ***Cell Processes and Energy.***

1 Photosynthesis

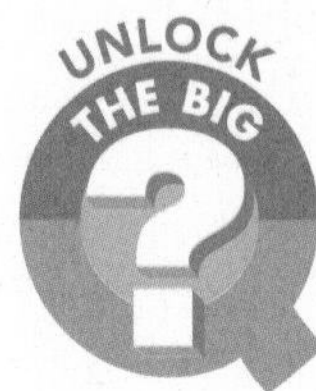

How Do Living Things Get Energy From the Sun?
LS.1d, LS.5c

What Happens During Photosynthesis?
LS.1d, LS.2a, LS.5a, LS.5b, LS.5c

my planet Diary

MISCONCEPTION

When Is Food Not Food?

Misconception: Some people think that the plant food they give to house and garden plants is food for the plants. It isn't.

Plants make their own food—in the form of sugars—using water, carbon dioxide, and sunlight. So what is the "food" that people add to plants? It's fertilizer. Fertilizer is a mixture of minerals, such as potassium, calcium, and phosphorus. It helps plants grow but doesn't supply them with energy as food does. Farmers add fertilizer to soil to grow better quality crops. People do the same to grow bigger and healthier plants at home.

Communicate **Write your answers to the questions below. Then discuss Question 2 with a partner.**

1. What is "plant food"?

____

____

2. What do you think would happen if you put a small seedling in complete darkness for a month but kept all other environmental conditions the same?

____

PLANET DIARY Go to **Planet Diary** to learn more about photosynthesis.

Lab zone® Do the Inquiry Warm-Up *Where Does the Energy Come From?*

Vocabulary
- photosynthesis
- autotroph
- heterotroph
- chlorophyll

Skills
- Reading: Sequence
- Inquiry: Classify

How Do Living Things Get Energy From the Sun?

Science Standards of Learning

LS.1d Construct and use models and simulations to illustrate and explain phenomena.

LS.5c Investigate and understand photosynthesis as the foundation of virtually all food webs.

On a plain in Africa, a herd of zebras peacefully eats grass. But watch out! A group of lions is about to attack the herd. The lions will kill one of the zebras and eat it.

Both the zebras and the lion you see in **Figure 1** use the food they eat to obtain energy. Every living thing needs energy. All cells need energy to carry out their functions, such as making proteins and transporting substances into and out of the cell. Like the raw materials used within a cell, energy used by living things comes from their environment. Zebra meat supplies the lion's cells with energy. Similarly, grass provides the zebra's cells with energy. But where does the energy in the grass come from? Plants and certain other organisms, such as algae and some bacteria, obtain their energy in a different way. These organisms use the energy in sunlight to make their own food.

FIGURE 1

An Energy Chain

All living things need energy.

Interpret Photos In the boxes, write the direct source of energy for each organism. Which organism shown does not depend on another organism for food?

The Sun as an Energy Source The process by which a cell captures energy in sunlight and uses it to make food is called **photosynthesis** (foh toh SIN thuh sis). The term *photosynthesis* comes from the Greek words *photos*, which means "light," and *syntithenai*, which means "putting together."

Nearly all living things obtain energy either directly or indirectly from the energy of sunlight that is captured during photosynthesis. Grass obtains energy directly from sunlight because grass makes its own food during photosynthesis. When the zebra eats grass, it gets energy from the sun that has been stored in the grass. Similarly, the lion obtains energy stored in the zebra. The zebra and lion both obtain the sun's energy indirectly from the energy that the grass obtained through photosynthesis.

Producers and Consumers Plants make their own food through the process of photosynthesis. An organism that makes its own food is called a producer, or an **autotroph** (AWT oh trohf). An organism that cannot make its own food, including animals such as the zebra and the lion, is called a consumer, or a **heterotroph** (HET ur oh trohf). Many heterotrophs obtain food by eating other organisms. Some heterotrophs, such as fungi, absorb their food from other organisms.

apply it!

A spider catches and eats a caterpillar that depends on plant leaves for food.

1 **Sequence** Draw a diagram of your own that tracks how the sun's energy gets to the spider.

2 **Classify** In your diagram, label each organism as a heterotroph or an autotroph.

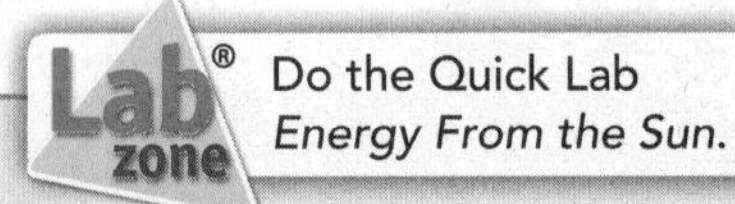

Assess Your Understanding

1a. Identify An organism that makes its own food is a(n) (autotroph/heterotroph).

b. Explain Why do living things need energy?

____

c. Apply Concepts Give an example of how energy from the sun gets into your cells.

____

____

____

got it?

○ **I get it!** Now I know that living things get energy directly from the sun by ______________________________ or indirectly by ______________________________

○ I need extra help with ______________________________

Go to **MY SCIENCE COACH** *online for help with this subject.*

What Happens During Photosynthesis?

You've just read that plants make their own food. So how do they do that? **During photosynthesis, plants and some other organisms absorb energy from the sun and use the energy to convert carbon dioxide and water into sugars and oxygen.** You can think of photosynthesis as taking place in two stages. First, plants capture the sun's energy. Second, plants produce sugars.

Stage 1: Capturing the Sun's Energy In the first stage of photosynthesis, energy from sunlight is captured. In plants, this process occurs mostly in the leaves. Recall that chloroplasts are green organelles inside plant cells. The green color comes from pigments, colored chemical compounds that absorb light. The main pigment for photosynthesis in chloroplasts is **chlorophyll**.

Chlorophyll functions something like the solar cells in a solar-powered calculator. Solar cells capture the energy in light and convert it to a form that powers the calculator. Similarly, chlorophyll captures light energy and converts it to a form that is used in the second stage of photosynthesis.

During Stage 1, water in the chloroplasts is split into hydrogen and oxygen, as shown in **Figure 2.** The oxygen is given off as a waste product. The hydrogen is used in Stage 2.

Science Standards of Learning

LS.1d Construct and use models and simulations to illustrate and explain phenomena.

LS.2a Investigate and understand cell structure and organelles.

LS.5a Investigate and understand energy transfer between sunlight and chlorophyll.

LS.5b Investigate and understand transformation of water and carbon dioxide into sugar and oxygen in photosynthesis.

LS.5c Investigate and understand photosynthesis as the foundation of virtually all food webs.

Vocabulary Greek Word Origins The Greek word part *chloros-* means "pale green." Circle two words in the text that begin with this word part. Which word means "a green compound that absorbs light"?

○ Chloroplast

○ Chlorophyll

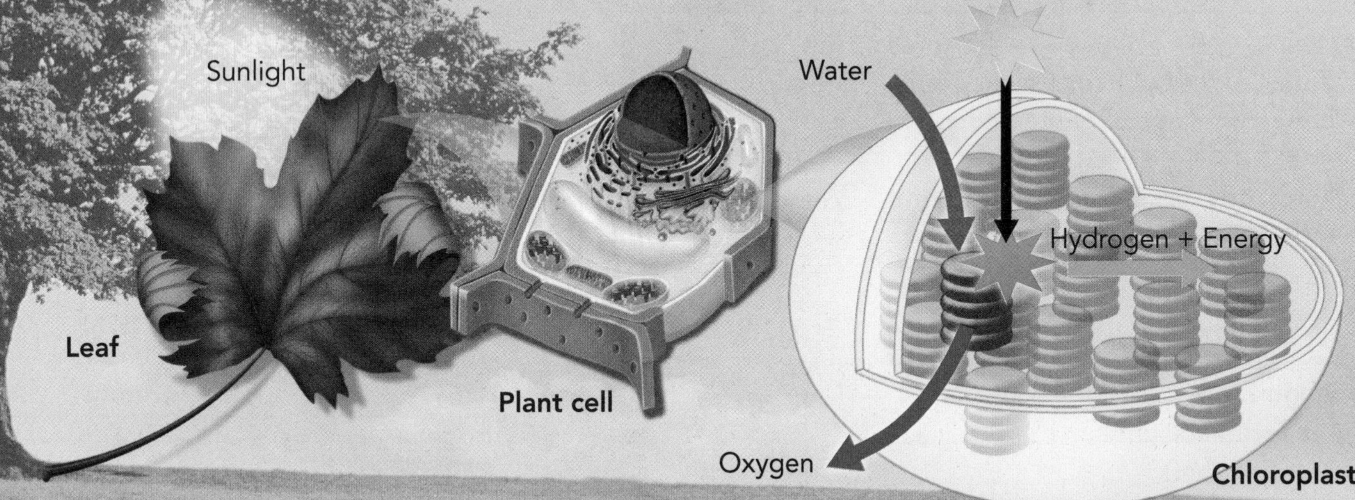

FIGURE 2

VIRTUAL LAB **First Stage of Photosynthesis**

You might say the first stage of photosynthesis powers the "energy engine" of the living world.

Make Generalizations What do you think this sentence means?

____

____

Sequence Complete the flowchart to show the process of photosynthesis.

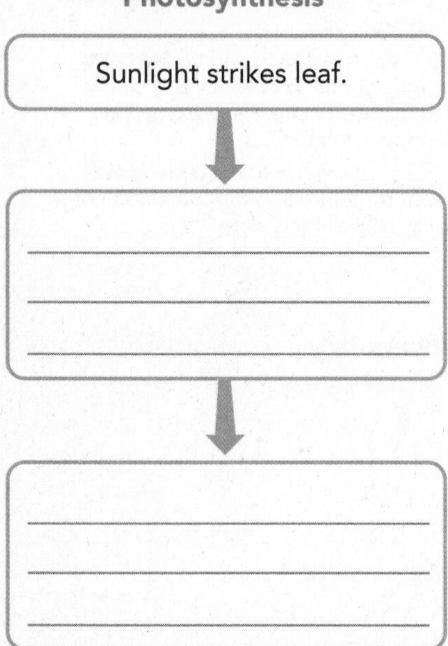

Stage 2: Using Energy to Make Food

In the second stage of photosynthesis, cells produce sugars. As shown in **Figure 3,** cells use hydrogen (H) that came from the splitting of water in Stage 1. Cells also use carbon dioxide (CO_2) from the air. Carbon dioxide enters the plant through small openings on the undersides of the leaves and moves into the chloroplasts.

Powered by the energy captured in Stage 1, hydrogen and carbon dioxide undergo a series of reactions that result in sugars. One important sugar produced is glucose. It has the chemical formula $C_6H_{12}O_6$. You may know that sugars are a type of carbohydrate. Cells can use the energy in glucose to carry out vital cell functions.

The other product of photosynthesis is oxygen gas (O_2). Recall that oxygen forms during the first stage when water molecules are split apart. Oxygen gas exits a leaf through the openings on its underside. Almost all the oxygen in Earth's atmosphere is produced by living things through the process of photosynthesis.

Stage 1

______________________ in plant cells captures energy from ______________________

FIGURE 3

INTERACTIVE ART **Producing Food**

The second stage of photosynthesis makes food for a plant.

Identify Fill in the missing terms in the spaces provided.

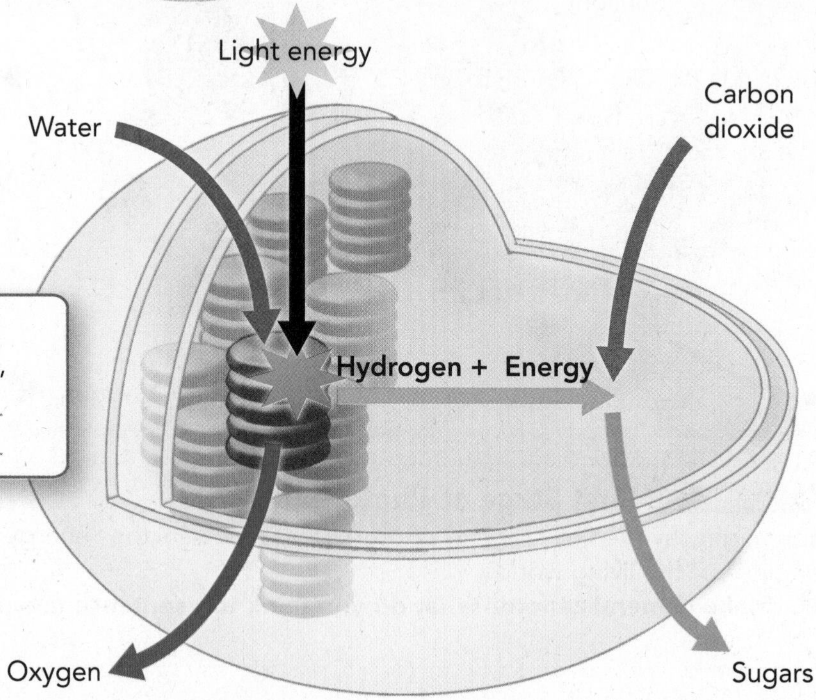

Stage 2

The captured light ______________, hydrogen, and ______________ are used to produce ______________

Light energy

Water

Carbon dioxide

Hydrogen + Energy

Oxygen

Sugars

The Photosynthesis Equation

The events of photosynthesis that lead to the production of glucose can be summed up by the following chemical equation:

$$\underset{\text{light energy}}{} + \underset{\text{carbon dioxide}}{6\,CO_2} + \underset{\text{water}}{6\,H_2O} \longrightarrow \underset{\text{glucose}}{C_6H_{12}O_6} + \underset{\text{oxygen}}{6\,O_2}$$

Notice that six molecules of carbon dioxide and six molecules of water are on the left side of the equation. These compounds are raw materials. One molecule of glucose and six molecules of oxygen are on the right side. These compounds are products. An arrow, meaning "yields," points from the raw materials to the products. Energy is not a raw material, but it is written on the left side of the equation to show that it is used in the reaction.

What happens to the sugars produced in photosynthesis? Plant cells use some of the sugars for food. The cells break down these molecules in a process that releases energy. This energy can then be used to carry out the plant's functions, such as growing and making seeds. Some sugar molecules are made into other compounds, such as cellulose for cell walls. Other sugar molecules may be stored in the plant's cells for later use. When you eat food from plants, such as potatoes or carrots, you are eating the plant's stored energy.

FIGURE 4

From the Sun to You

Carrots store food that is made in the carrot leaf cells.

Explain **How are carrots an energy link between you and the sun?**

____

____

____

____

Lab zone® Do the Quick Lab *Looking at Pigments.*

Assess Your Understanding

2a. Name Circle two products of photosynthesis. glucose/carbon dioxide/oxygen/chlorophyll

b. Interpret Diagrams Refer to **Figure 3** on the facing page. Where does the hydrogen that is used in Stage 2 of photosynthesis come from?

____

____

c. CHALLENGE Would you expect a plant to produce more oxygen on a sunny day or a cloudy day? Explain your answer.

____

____

____

____

got it?

O **I get it!** Now I know that during photosynthesis _______________

____

O I need extra help with _______________

Go to MY SCIENCE COACH *online for help with this subject.*

Virginia

LESSON 2

Cellular Respiration

What Happens During Cellular Respiration?
LS.2a, LS.5a, LS.5b, LS.5c

What Happens During Fermentation?
LS.1f, LS.5c

my planet Diary

FUN FACTS

Going to Extremes

You may not know it, but there are organisms living in rocks deep below Earth's surface. Other organisms hang out in steaming hot lakes, like Grand Prismatic Spring in Yellowstone National Park, shown here. The water in this lake can be as hot as 86°C! Still other organisms nestle inside nuclear waste. All of these organisms are extremophiles, organisms that thrive in extreme habitats. These life forms can get energy in strange ways. Some make food from ocean minerals. Others break down compounds in radioactive rocks!

Pose Questions Write a question about something else you would like to learn about extremophiles.

____

____

____

____

PLANET DIARY Go to **Planet Diary** to learn more about extremophiles.

Lab zone® Do the Inquiry Warm-Up *Cellular Respiration.*

Science Standards of Learning

LS.2a Investigate and understand cell structure and organelles.

LS.5a Investigate and understand energy transfer between sunlight and chlorophyll.

LS.5b Investigate and understand transformation of water and carbon dioxide into sugar and oxygen in photosynthesis.

LS.5c Investigate and understand photosynthesis as the foundation of virtually all food webs.

What Happens During Cellular Respiration?

You and your friend have been hiking all morning. You look for a flat rock to sit on, so you can eat the lunch you packed. The steepest part of the trail is ahead. You'll need a lot of energy to get to the top of the mountain! That energy will come from food.

Vocabulary
- cellular respiration
- fermentation

Skills
- Reading: Summarize
- Inquiry: Control Variables

What Is Cellular Respiration?

After you eat a meal, your body breaks down the food and releases the sugars in the food. The most common sugar in foods is glucose ($C_6H_{12}O_6$). **Cellular respiration** is the process by which cells obtain energy from glucose. **During cellular respiration, cells break down glucose and other molecules from food in the presence of oxygen, releasing energy.** Living things need a constant supply of energy. The cells of living things carry out cellular respiration continuously.

Storing and Releasing Energy Imagine you have money in a savings account. If you want to buy something, you withdraw some money. Your body stores and uses energy in a similar way, as shown in **Figure 1.** When you eat a meal, you add to your body's energy savings account by storing glucose. When cells need energy, they "withdraw" it by breaking down glucose through cellular respiration.

Breathing and Respiration You may have already heard of the word *respiration*. It can mean "breathing"—or moving air in and out of your lungs. Breathing brings oxygen into your lungs, which is then carried to cells for cellular respiration. Breathing also removes the waste products of cellular respiration from your body.

FIGURE 1

Getting Energy

Your body runs on the energy it gets from food.

Complete each task.

1. **Infer** Color in the last three energy scales to show how the hiker's energy changes.
2. CHALLENGE How do you think the hiker's breathing rate changes as she climbs?

____

____

____

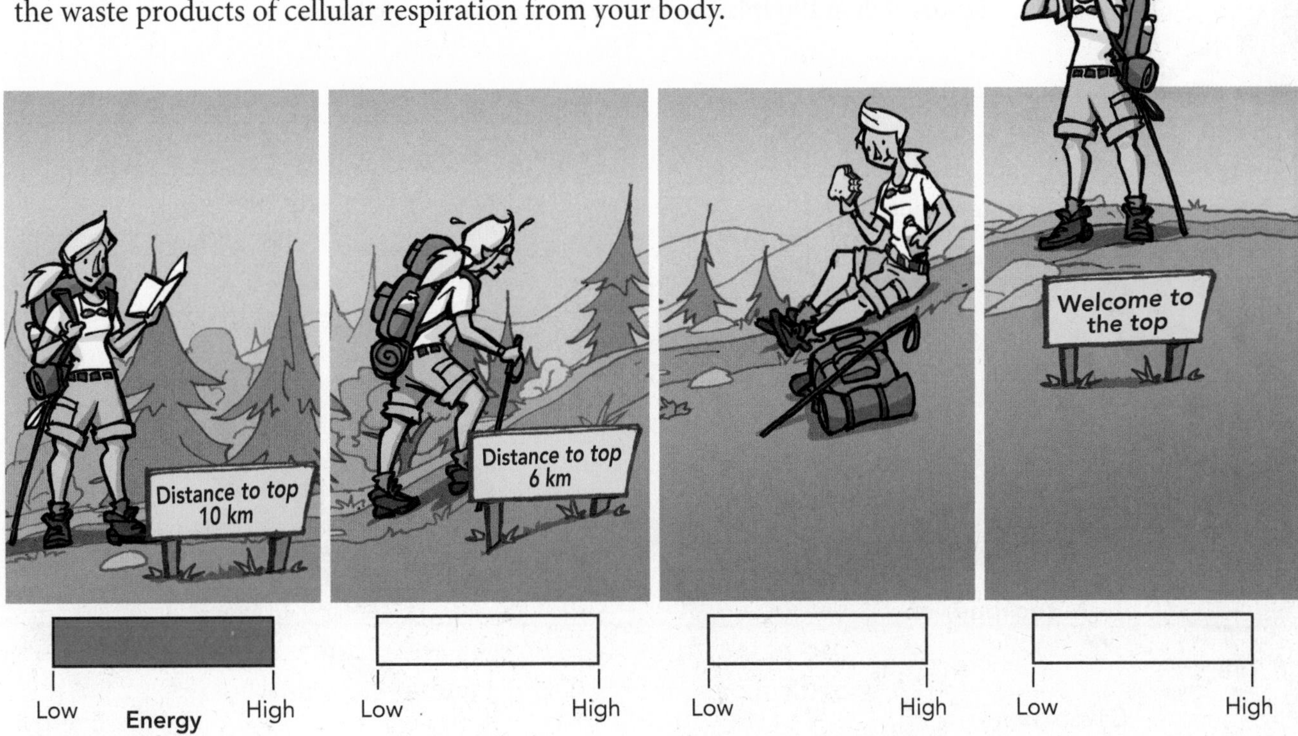

Summarize Complete the concept map below about cellular respiration.

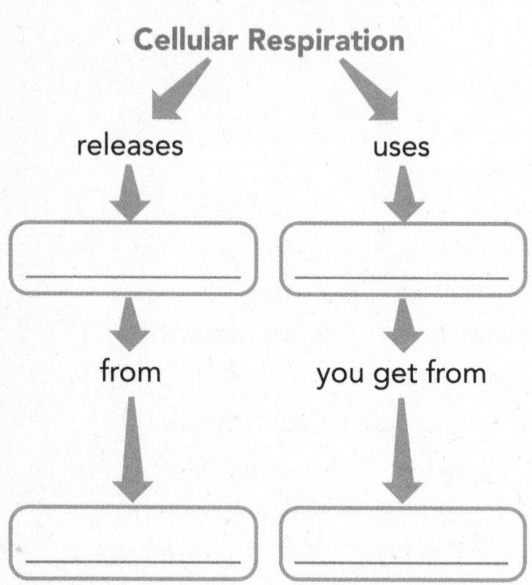

The Two Stages of Cellular Respiration

The Two Stages of Cellular Respiration Like photosynthesis, cellular respiration is a two-stage process. See **Figure 2.** The first stage occurs in the cytoplasm of a cell. There, molecules of glucose are broken down into smaller molecules. Oxygen is not involved in this stage, and only a small amount of energy is released.

The second stage takes place in the mitochondria. There, the small molecules are broken down even more. This change requires oxygen and releases a great deal of energy that the cell can use for all its activities. No wonder mitochondria are sometimes called the "powerhouses" of the cell!

The Cellular Respiration Equation Although respiration occurs in a series of complex steps, the overall process can be summarized in the following equation:

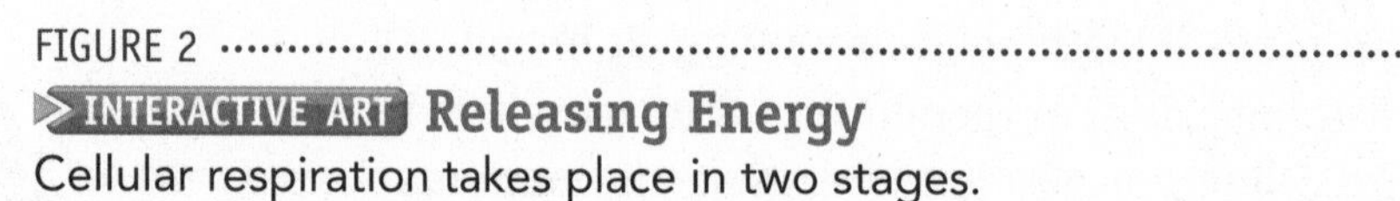

$$\underset{\text{glucose}}{C_6H_{12}O_6} + \underset{\text{oxygen}}{6\ O_2} \longrightarrow \underset{\text{carbon dioxide}}{6\ CO_2} + \underset{\text{water}}{6\ H_2O} + \text{energy}$$

Notice that the raw materials for cellular respiration are glucose and oxygen. Animals get glucose from the foods they consume. Plants and other organisms that carry out photosynthesis are able to produce their own glucose. The oxygen needed for cellular respiration is in the air or water surrounding the organism.

FIGURE 2

INTERACTIVE ART **Releasing Energy**

Cellular respiration takes place in two stages.

Identify Fill in the missing terms in the spaces provided.

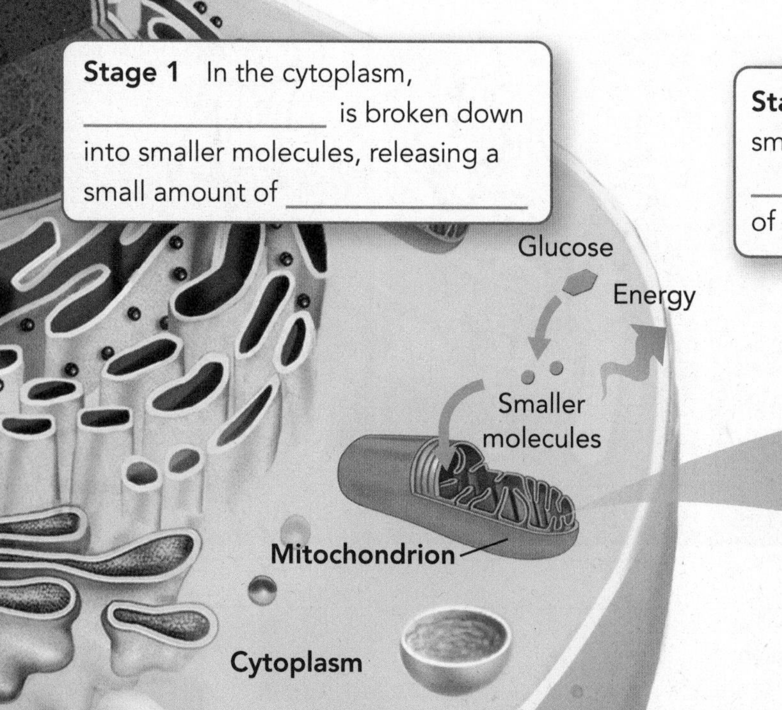

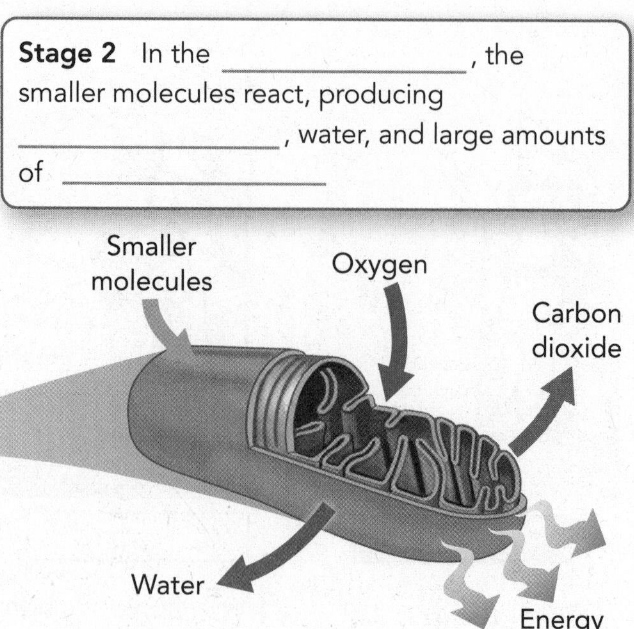

Comparing Two Energy Processes

If you think the equation for cellular respiration is the opposite of the one for photosynthesis, you're right! Photosynthesis and cellular respiration can be thought of as opposite processes. Together, these two processes form a cycle that keeps the levels of oxygen and carbon dioxide fairly constant in Earth's atmosphere. As you can see from **Figure 3,** living things cycle both gases over and over again. The energy released through cellular respiration is used or lost as heat.

FIGURE 3

Opposite Processes

Producers carry out photosynthesis, but producers and consumers both carry out cellular respiration.

Name Use the word bank to fill in the missing terms. Words can be used more than once.

Word Bank	
Oxygen	Energy
Carbon dioxide	Glucose
Water	

Lab zone® Do the Lab Investigation *Exhaling Carbon Dioxide.*

Assess Your Understanding

1a. Interpret Diagrams Look at **Figure 2** on the facing page. How does Stage 2 of cellular respiration benefit a cell?

____

____

____

b. Relate Cause and Effect Why does cellular respiration add carbon dioxide to the atmosphere, but photosynthesis does not?

____

____

____

got it?

O **I get it!** Now I know that during cellular respiration, cells ______________________________

____

O I need extra help with ______________________________

Go to MY SCIENCE COACH *online for help with this subject.*

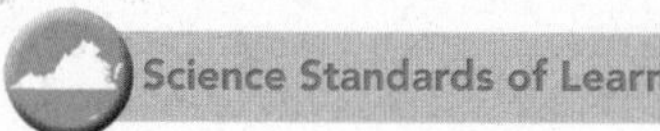

Science Standards of Learning

LS.1f Identify dependent variables, independent variables, and constants.

LS.5c Investigate and understand photosynthesis as the foundation of virtually all food webs.

What Happens During Fermentation?

Some organisms can live in the presence or absence of oxygen. If not enough oxygen is present to carry out cellular respiration, these organisms switch to another process. **Fermentation** is an energy-releasing process that does not require oxygen. **During fermentation, cells release energy from food without using oxygen.** One drawback to fermentation is that it releases far less energy than cellular respiration does.

Alcoholic Fermentation

Did you know that when you eat a slice of bread, you are eating a product of fermentation? Alcoholic fermentation occurs in yeast and other single-celled organisms. This type of fermentation produces alcohol, carbon dioxide, and a small amount of energy. These products are important to bakers and brewers. Carbon dioxide produced by yeast creates gas pockets in bread dough, causing it to rise. Carbon dioxide is also the source of bubbles in alcoholic drinks such as beer and sparkling wine.

Lactic Acid Fermentation

Think of a time when you ran as fast and as long as you could. Your leg muscles were pushing hard against the ground, and you were breathing quickly. But, no matter how quickly you breathed, your muscle cells used up the oxygen faster than it could be replaced. Because your cells lacked oxygen, fermentation occurred. Your muscle cells got energy, but they did so by breaking down glucose without using oxygen. One product of this type of fermentation is a compound known as lactic acid. When lactic acid builds up, you may feel a painful burning sensation in your muscles.

Lactic acid was once thought to be the cause of muscle soreness. Scientists have learned that lactic acid is gone from muscles shortly after exercising and is not responsible for the soreness you feel in the days after you exercise. Instead, the soreness is likely caused by microscopic damage to muscles that occurred during the exercise.

apply it!

A ball of bread dough mixed with yeast is left in a bowl at room temperature. As time passes, the dough increases in size.

1 **Compare and Contrast** How does fermentation that causes dough to rise differ from fermentation in muscles?

____

2 **Control Variables** How would you show that yeast was responsible for making the dough rise?

____

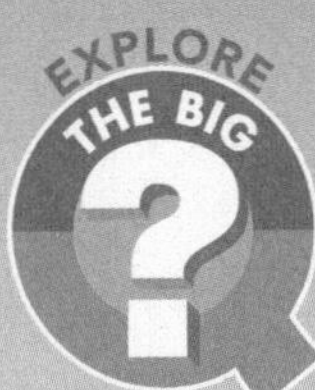

Energy for Life

How do living things get energy?

FIGURE 4

ART IN MOTION Energy processes in living things include photosynthesis, cellular respiration, and fermentation.

Review **Circle the correct answers and complete the sentences in the spaces provided.**

Producers

Plant cells capture energy by way of (photosynthesis/fermentation/cellular respiration).

Plants are autotrophs because

____

____

Plant cells release energy for cell function by way of (photosynthesis/fermentation/cellular respiration).

Plants get this energy when oxygen reacts with

____

____

Consumers

A runner on an easy jog through the woods gets energy by way of (photosynthesis/fermentation/cellular respiration).

The runner is a heterotroph because she gets energy from

____

If the runner makes a long, fast push to the finish, her muscle cells may get energy by way of (photosynthesis/fermentation/cellular respiration).

This process releases less energy and ______________________

____

Do the Quick Lab *Observing Fermentation.*

Assess Your Understanding

2a. Develop Hypotheses When a race ends, why do you think runners continue to breathe quickly and deeply for a few minutes?

____

____

b. ANSWER THE BIG ? How do living things get energy?

____

____

____

____

____

____

got it?

O **I get it!** Now I know fermentation is a way for cells to ______________________

____

____

____

O I need extra help with ______________________

____

____

Go to my science COACH *online for help with this subject.*

Virginia

LESSON 3

Cell Division

What Are the Functions of Cell Division?
LS.2d

What Happens During the Cell Cycle?
LS.1d, LS.1h, LS.1j, LS.2a, LS.2b, LS.2d

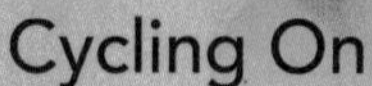

my planet Diary

SCIENCE STATS

Cycling On

How long do you think it takes a cell to grow and reproduce, that is, to complete one cell cycle? The answer depends on the type of cell and the organism. Some cells, such as the frog egg cells shown here, divide every 30 minutes, and others take as long as a year! The table below compares the length of different cell cycles.

Comparing Cell Cycles

Frog Egg Cells	Yeast Cells	Fruit Fly Wing Cells	Human Liver Cells
30 minutes	90 minutes	9–10 hours	Over 1 year

Interpret Data **Use the table to help you answer the following questions.**

1. Which type of cell completes a cell cycle fastest?

2. With each cell cycle, two cells form from one cell. In three hours, how many cells could form from one frog egg cell?

PLANET DIARY Go to **Planet Diary** to learn more about cell division.

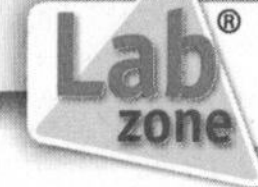

Do the Inquiry Warm-Up *What Are the Yeast Cells Doing?*

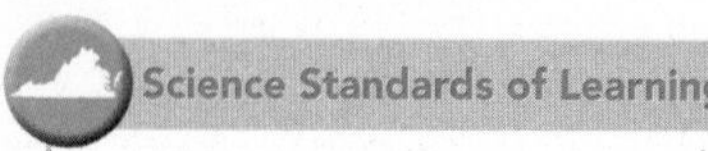

Science Standards of Learning

LS.2d Investigate and understand cell division.

What Are the Functions of Cell Division?

How do tiny frog eggs become big frogs? Cell division allows organisms to grow larger. One cell splits into two, two into four, and so on, until a single cell becomes a multicellular organism.

How does a broken bone heal? Cell division produces new healthy bone cells that replace the damaged cells. Similarly, cell division can replace aging cells and those that die from disease.

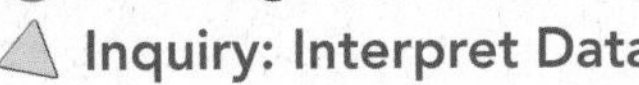

Vocabulary
- cell cycle
- interphase
- replication
- chromosome
- mitosis
- cytokinesis

Skills
- Reading: Ask Questions
- Inquiry: Interpret Data

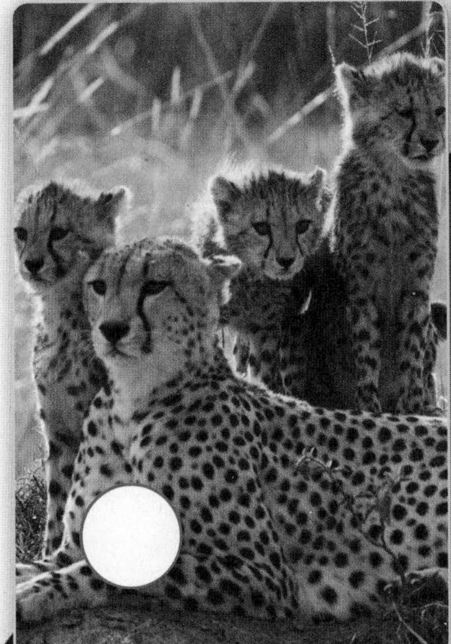

Growth and repair are two functions of cell division. A third function is reproduction. Some organisms reproduce simply through cell division. Many single-celled organisms, such as amoebas, reproduce this way. Other organisms can reproduce when cell division leads to the growth of new structures. For example, a cactus can grow new stems and roots. These structures can then break away from the parent plant and become a separate plant.

Most organisms reproduce when specialized cells from two different parents combine, forming a new cell. This cell then undergoes many divisions and grows into a new organism.

Cell division has more than one function in living things, as shown in **Figure 1.** **Cell division allows organisms to grow, repair damaged structures, and reproduce.**

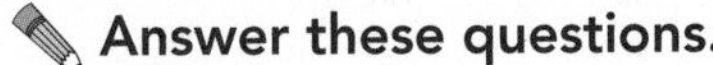

FIGURE 1

Cell Division

Each photo represents at least one function of cell division.

Answer these questions.

1. **Identify** Label each photo as (A) growth, (B) repair, or (C) reproduction.
2. **CHALLENGE** Which photo(s) represents more than one function and what are they?

____

____

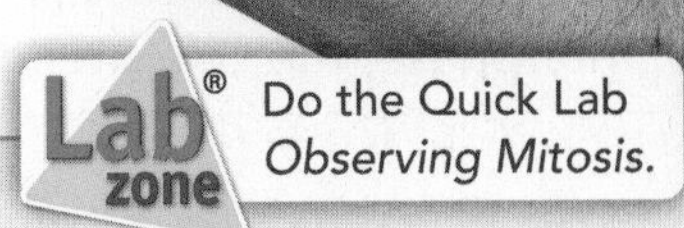

Lab zone® Do the Quick Lab *Observing Mitosis.*

Assess Your Understanding

got it?

○ **I get it!** Now I know the functions of cell division are _______________

○ I need extra help with _______________

Go to **MY SCIENCE COACH** *online for help with this subject.*

Science Standards of Learning

LS.1d Construct and use models and simulations to illustrate and explain phenomena.

LS.1h Interpret data and use data to make predictions.

LS.1j Use current applications to reinforce life science concepts.

LS.2a Investigate and understand cell structure and organelles.

LS.2b Investigate and understand similarities and differences between plant and animal cells.

LS.2d Investigate and understand cell division.

What Happens During the Cell Cycle?

The regular sequence of growth and division that cells undergo is known as the **cell cycle.** **During the cell cycle, a cell grows, prepares for division, and divides into two new cells, which are called "daughter cells."** Each of the daughter cells then begins the cell cycle again. The cell cycle consists of three main stages: interphase, mitosis, and cytokinesis.

Stage 1: Interphase

The first stage of the cell cycle is **interphase.** This stage is the period before cell division. During interphase, the cell grows, makes a copy of its DNA, and prepares to divide into two cells.

Growing Early during interphase, a cell grows to its full size and produces the organelles it needs. For example, plant cells make more chloroplasts. And all cells make more ribosomes and mitochondria. Cells also make more enzymes, substances that speed up chemical reactions in living things.

Copying DNA Next, the cell makes an exact copy of the DNA in its nucleus in a process called **replication.** You may know that DNA holds all the information that a cell needs to carry out its functions. Within the nucleus, DNA and proteins form threadlike structures called **chromosomes.** At the end of replication, the cell contains two identical sets of chromosomes.

Preparing for Division Once the DNA has replicated, preparation for cell division begins. The cell produces structures that will help it to divide into two new cells. In animal cells, but not plant cells, a pair of centrioles is duplicated. You can see the centrioles in the cell in **Figure 2.** At the end of interphase, the cell is ready to divide.

FIGURE 2

Interphase: Preparing to Divide

The changes in a cell during interphase prepare the cell for mitosis.

List **Make a list of the events that occur during interphase.**

Interphase To-Do List

apply it!

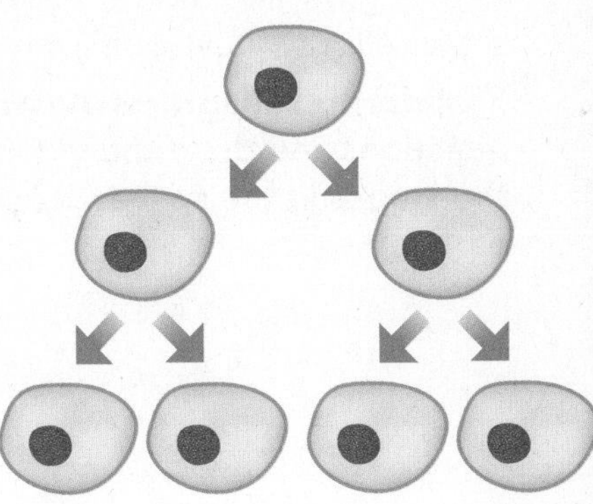

When one cell splits in half during cell division, the result is two new cells. Each of those two cells can divide into two more, and so on.

1 Calculate How many cell divisions would it take to produce at least 1,000 cells from one cell?

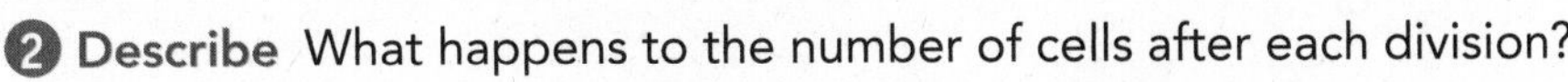

2 Describe What happens to the number of cells after each division?

______

3 CHALLENGE Do you think all human cells divide at the same rate throughout life? Justify your answer.

______

______

______

Stage 2: Mitosis

Once interphase ends, the second stage of the cell cycle begins. During **mitosis** (my TOH sis), the cell's nucleus divides into two new nuclei and one set of DNA is distributed into each daughter cell.

Scientists divide mitosis into four parts, or phases: prophase, metaphase, anaphase, and telophase. During prophase, the chromosomes condense into shapes that can be seen under a microscope. In **Figure 3** you can see that a chromosome consists of two rod-like parts, called chromatids. Each chromatid is an exact copy of the other, containing identical DNA. A structure known as a centromere holds the chromatids together until they move apart later in mitosis. One copy of each chromatid will move into each daughter cell during the final phases of mitosis. When the chromatids separate they are called chromosomes again. Each cell then has a complete copy of DNA. **Figure 4** on the next page summarizes the events of mitosis.

FIGURE 3

Mitosis: Prophase

Mitosis begins with prophase, which involves further changes to the cell.

Compare and Contrast How does prophase look different from interphase?

______

______

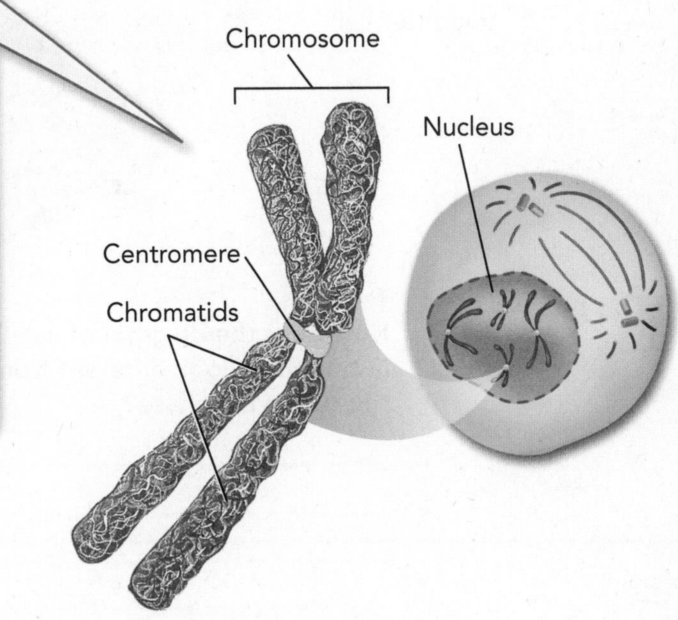

FIGURE 4

INTERACTIVE ART **The Cell Cycle**

Cells undergo an orderly sequence of events as they grow and divide. The photographs show cells of a developing whitefish.

Interpret Diagrams Answer the questions and draw the missing parts of the stages in the spaces provided.

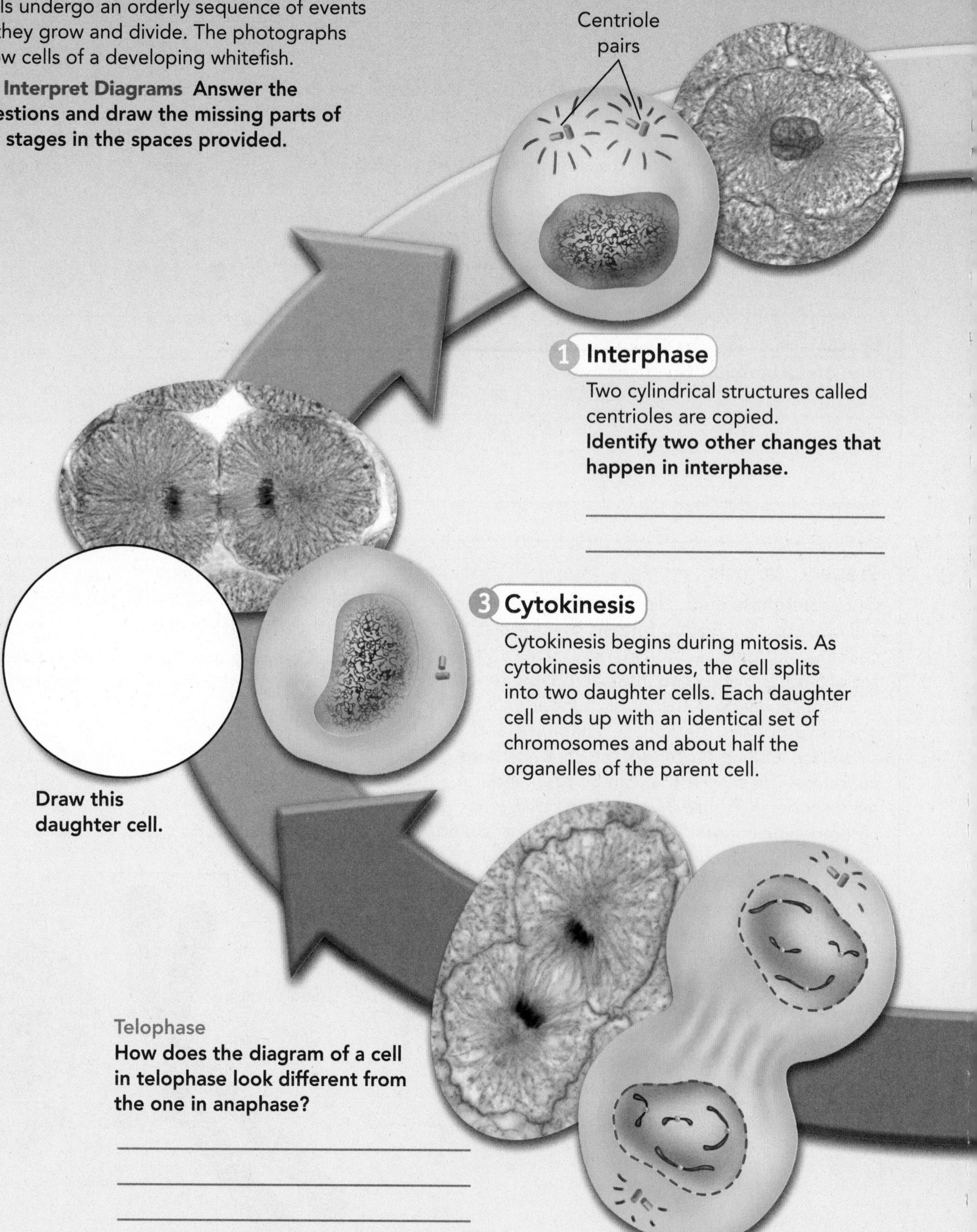

Centriole pairs

1 Interphase

Two cylindrical structures called centrioles are copied.
Identify two other changes that happen in interphase.

____

____

3 Cytokinesis

Cytokinesis begins during mitosis. As cytokinesis continues, the cell splits into two daughter cells. Each daughter cell ends up with an identical set of chromosomes and about half the organelles of the parent cell.

Draw this daughter cell.

Telophase

How does the diagram of a cell in telophase look different from the one in anaphase?

____

____

____

____

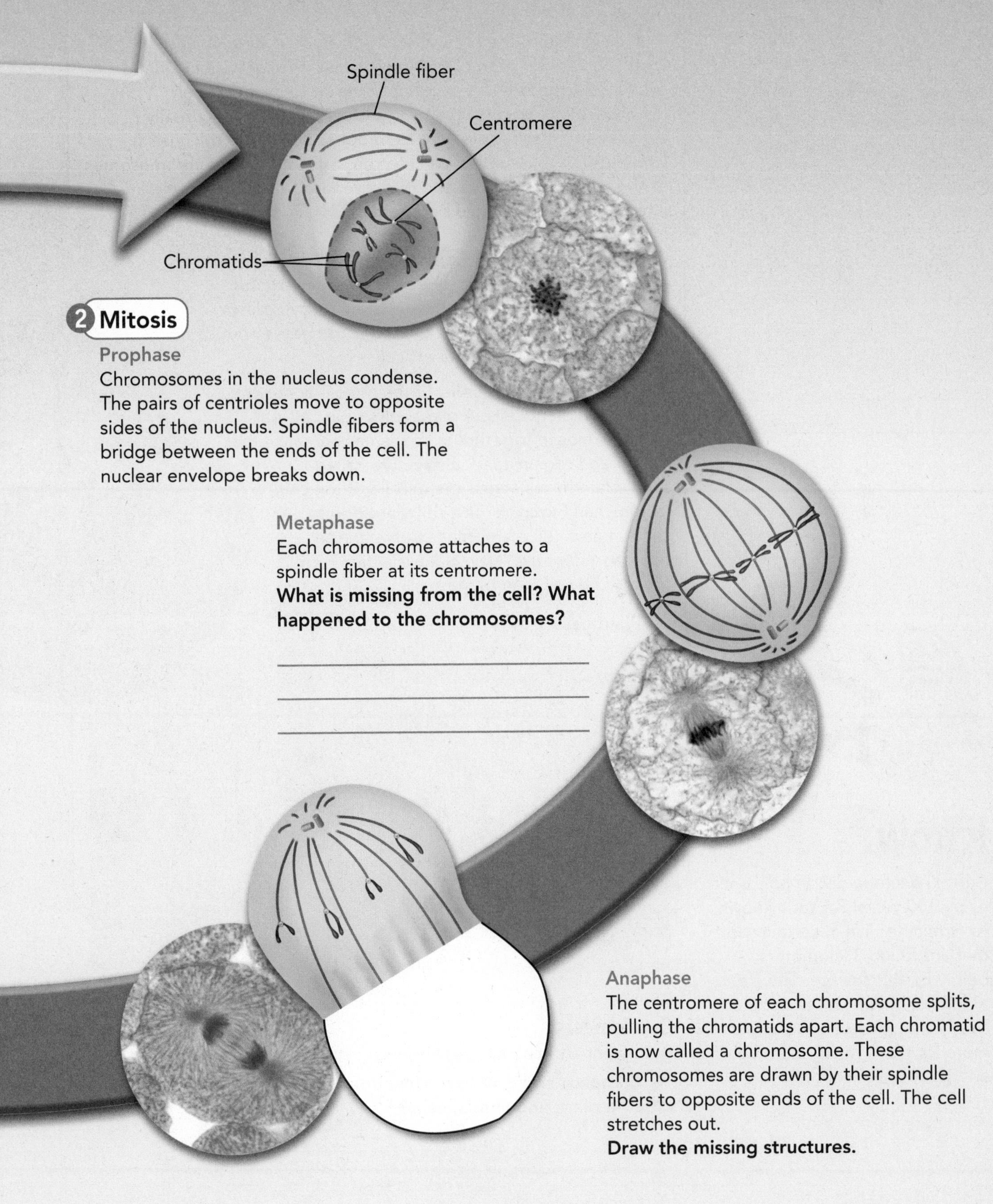

2 Mitosis

Prophase

Chromosomes in the nucleus condense. The pairs of centrioles move to opposite sides of the nucleus. Spindle fibers form a bridge between the ends of the cell. The nuclear envelope breaks down.

Metaphase

Each chromosome attaches to a spindle fiber at its centromere. **What is missing from the cell? What happened to the chromosomes?**

____

____

____

Anaphase

The centromere of each chromosome splits, pulling the chromatids apart. Each chromatid is now called a chromosome. These chromosomes are drawn by their spindle fibers to opposite ends of the cell. The cell stretches out.
Draw the missing structures.

Ask Questions Before you read details about cytokinesis, write a question that asks something you would like to learn.

____

____

____

____

____

____

____

Stage 3: Cytokinesis

The final stage of the cell cycle, which is called **cytokinesis** (sy toh kih NEE sis), completes the process of cell division. During cytokinesis, the cytoplasm divides. The structures are then distributed into each of the two new cells. Cytokinesis usually starts at about the same time as telophase. When cytokinesis is complete, each daughter cell has the same number of chromosomes as the parent cell. At the end of cytokinesis, each cell enters interphase, and the cycle begins again.

Cytokinesis in Animal Cells During cytokinesis in animal cells, the cell membrane squeezes together around the middle of the cell, as shown here. The cytoplasm pinches into two cells. Each daughter cell gets about half of the organelles of the parent cell.

Cytokinesis in Plant Cells Cytokinesis is somewhat different in plant cells. A plant cell's rigid cell wall cannot squeeze together in the same way that a cell membrane can. Instead, a structure called a cell plate forms across the middle of the cell, as shown in **Figure 5.** The cell plate begins to form new cell membranes between the two daughter cells. New cell walls then form around the cell membranes.

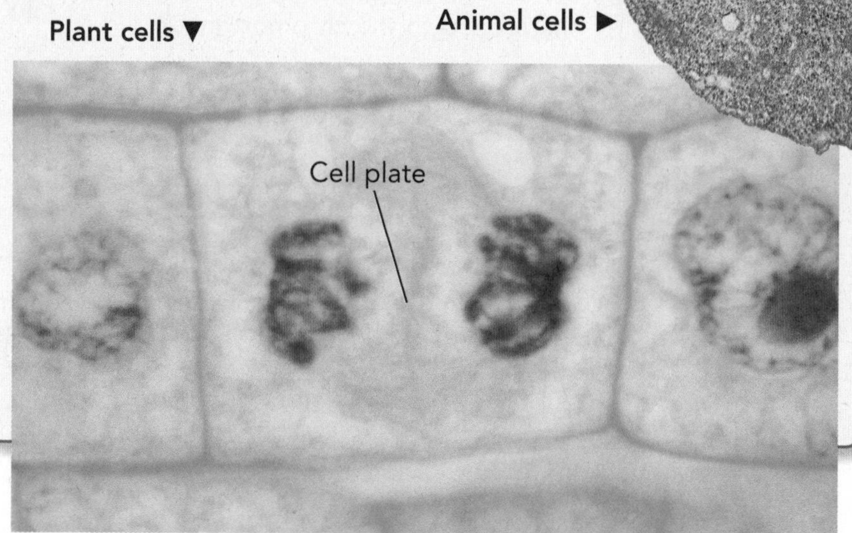

FIGURE 5

Cytokinesis

Both plant and animal cells undergo cytokinesis.

Compare and Contrast How does cytokinesis differ in plant and animal cells?

____

____

____

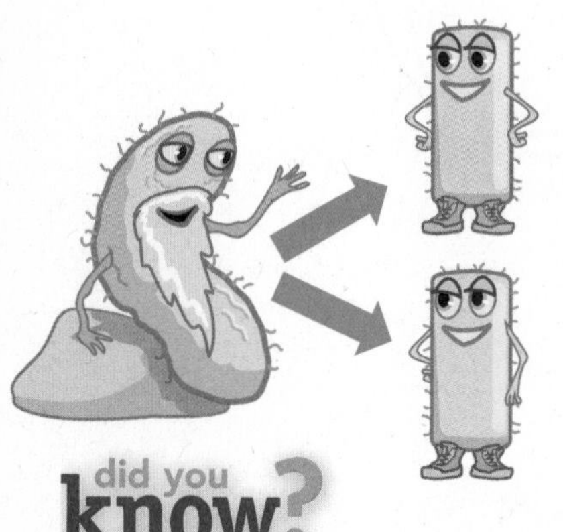

did you know?

Certain bacteria divide only once every 100 years! Bacteria known as *Firmicutes* live in certain rocks that are found 3 kilometers below Earth's surface. The life functions of *Firmicutes* occur so slowly that it takes 100 years or more for them to store enough energy to split in two.

do the math! Analyzing Data

Length of a liver cell cycle

How long does it take for a cell to go through one cell cycle? It depends on the cell. Human liver cells generally reproduce less than once per year. At other times, they can complete one cell cycle in about 22 hours, as shown in the circle graph. Study the graph and answer the following questions.

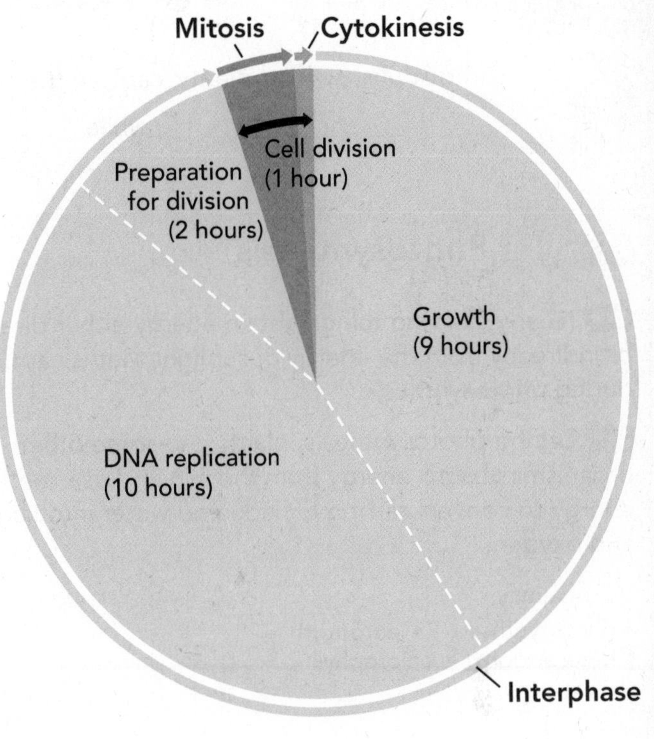

1. **Read Graphs** What do the three curved arrows outside of the circle represent?

____

2. **Read Graphs** The wedge representing growth is in which stage of the cell cycle?

____

3. **Interpret Data** About what percentage of the cell cycle is shown for DNA replication?

____

4. **Interpret Data** What stage in the cell cycle takes the shortest amount of time? How do you know?

____

Lab zone® Do the Quick Lab *Modeling Mitosis.*

Assess Your Understanding

1a. List What are the three stages of the cell cycle?

____

b. Sequence Put the following terms in correct order: anaphase, telophase, metaphase, prophase.

____

c. Predict What do you think would happen if a cell's DNA did not replicate correctly?

____

got it?

O **I get it!** Now I know that during the cell cycle ______________________________

O I need extra help with ______________________________

Go to MY SCIENCE COACH *online for help with this subject.*

CHAPTER 5

Study Guide

Autotrophs, such as plants, capture the sun's energy and make their food through ________________________, while ________________________ get energy by eating food.

LESSON 1 Photosynthesis

Nearly all living things obtain energy either directly or indirectly from the energy of sunlight that is captured during photosynthesis.

During photosynthesis, plants and some other organisms absorb energy from the sun and use the energy to convert carbon dioxide and water into sugars and oxygen.

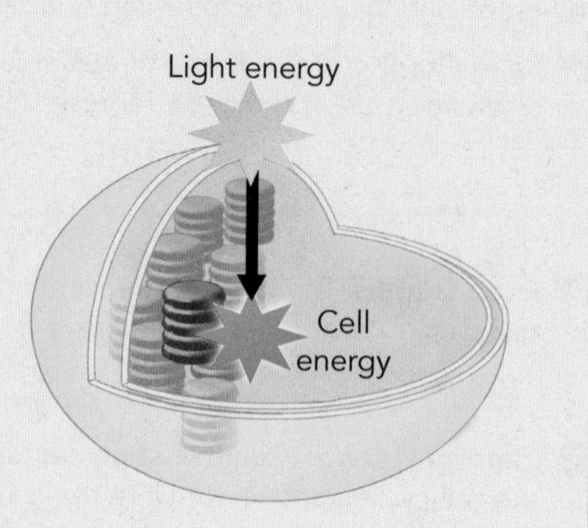

Vocabulary
- photosynthesis
- autotroph
- heterotroph
- chlorophyll

LESSON 2 Cellular Respiration

During cellular respiration, cells break down glucose and other molecules from food in the presence of oxygen, releasing energy.

During fermentation, cells release energy from food without using oxygen.

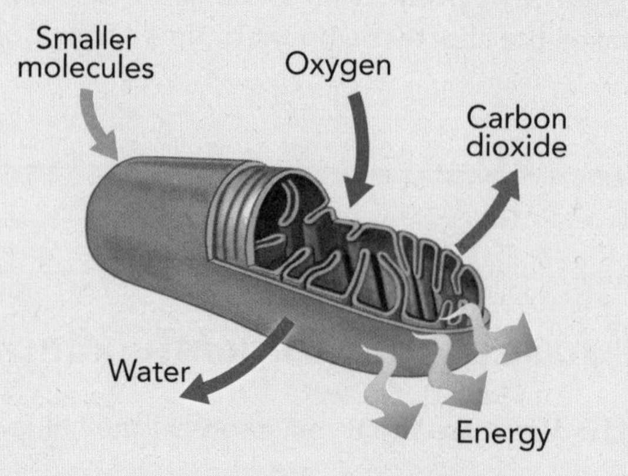

Vocabulary
- cellular respiration
- fermentation

LESSON 3 Cell Division

Cell division allows organisms to grow, repair damaged structures, and reproduce.

During the cell cycle, a cell grows, prepares for division, and divides into two new cells, which are called "daughter cells."

Vocabulary
- cell cycle
- interphase
- replication
- chromosome
- mitosis
- cytokinesis

Review and Assessment

LESSON 1 Photosynthesis

1. Which of the following organisms are autotrophs?
   a. fungi
   b. rabbits
   c. humans
   d. oak trees

2. Plants are green because of ______________________, the main photosynthetic pigment in chloroplasts.

3. **Interpret Diagrams** Fill in the missing labels in the diagram below.

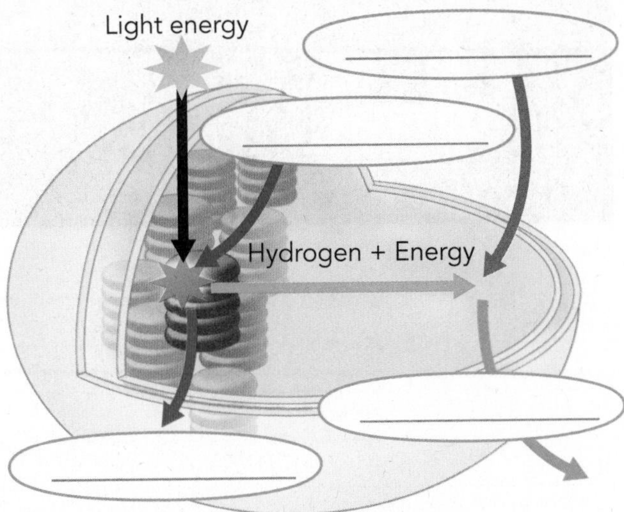

4. **Predict** Suppose a volcano threw so much ash into the air that it blocked much of the sunlight. How might this event affect the ability of animals to obtain energy to live?

5.  **Write About It** How do you get energy? Describe the path of energy from the sun to you, using at least two vocabulary terms you learned in this lesson.

LESSON 2 Cellular Respiration

6. In which organelle does cellular respiration take place?
   a. nucleus
   b. chloroplast
   c. chlorophyll
   d. mitochondrion

7. ______________________ is a process that releases energy in cells without using oxygen.

8. What is one common food that is made with the help of fermentation?

9. **Explain** Write a word equation for cellular respiration in cells.

10. **Summarize** In one or two sentences, summarize what happens during each of the two stages of cellular respiration.

11. **Apply Concepts** How is breathing related to cellular respiration?

CHAPTER 5

Review and Assessment

LESSON 3 Cell Division

12. During which phase of the cell cycle does DNA replication occur?

a. mitosis
b. division
c. interphase
d. cytokinesis

13. During _______________, a cell's nucleus divides into two new nuclei.

14. Make Generalizations Why is cell division a necessary function of living things?

____

____

____

15. Relate Cause and Effect Why is replication a necessary step in cell division?

____

____

____

16. Sequence Fill in the diagram below with descriptions of each part of the cell cycle.

Interphase
____
____
____

Mitosis
____
____
____

Cytokinesis
____
____
____

How do living things get energy?

17. All living things need energy. Use the terms *autotroph* and *heterotroph* to describe how each of the organisms in the illustration below obtains energy.

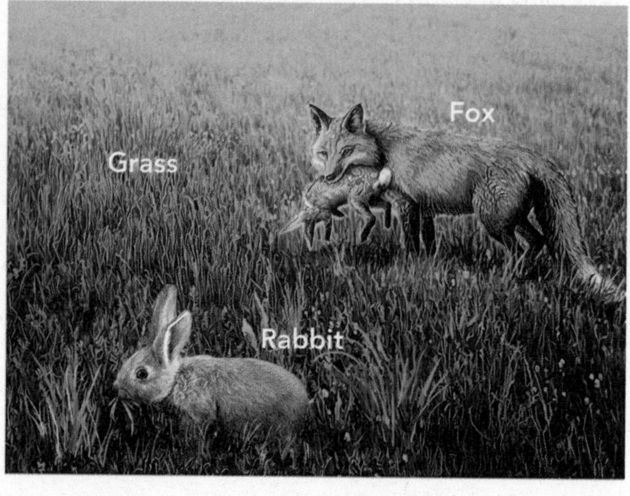

____

____

____

____

____

____

____

____

____

____

____

____

____

Virginia SOL Test Prep

Read each question and choose the best answer.

1 Choose the name and cellular process that match the organelle shown below.

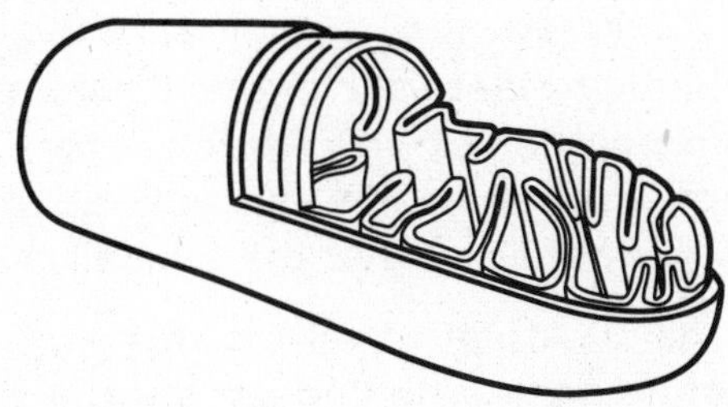

A chloroplast; cellular respiration
B mitochondrion; cellular respiration
C chloroplast; photosynthesis
D mitochondrion; photosynthesis

2 What is the result of cell division?

F one daughter cell with double the DNA of the parent cell
G two daughter cells with double the DNA of the parent cell
H one daughter cell with half the DNA of the parent cells
J two daughter cells with the same DNA as the parent cell

3 The source of energy used in photosynthesis is—

A glucose
B sunlight
C chlorophyll
D DNA

4 What is one main difference between fermentation and cellular respiration?

F Fermentation does not require oxygen, while cellular respiration does.
G Fermentation does not release energy, while cellular respiration does.
H Fermentation does not occur in animals, while cellular respiration does
J Fermentation does not depend on the sun, while cellular respiration does.

5 Which statement *best* applies to chromosomes?

A They carry out respiration.
B They consist mostly of the pigment chlorophyll.
C Their structure is visible only during interphase.
D They become visible during the mitosis stage of the cell cycle.

6 Which words *best* complete the table?

	Photosynthesis	Cellular Respiration
Raw materials	Water and carbon dioxide	**glucose and oxygen**
Products	**glucose and oxygen**	______ ______
Energy released?	**no**	**yes**

F carbon dioxide and water
G glucose and water
H oxygen and water
J glucose and carbon dioxide

Athletic Trainer

Athletic trainers at commercial gyms help people perform exercises to improve their health. But athletic trainers do more than play at the gym all day.

In reality, athletic trainers are professionals who understand the ways in which muscles and body systems work together. Many athletic trainers who work with elite athletes study biology, anatomy and physiology, or physical education in college. They are often athletes too, and may gain experience as a trainer at a commercial gym.

An athletic trainer must apply scientific discoveries to people's fitness training. For example, have you ever felt a burning sensation in your muscles after a workout? People sometimes think this feeling is caused by a buildup of lactic acid in the muscles. However, scientists think that cells use lactic acid to produce energy when glucose supplies are low. An athletic trainer may suggest that an athlete use endurance training. Endurance training helps train muscles to efficiently burn lactic acid, which improves the athlete's performance.

Athletic trainers work in an exciting and constantly changing field. As scientists learn more about human biology, athletic trainers apply these lessons. They help athletes continue to push the limits of human performance.

 LS.1j

Research It Find out about an athletic trainer, and create a profile of that person. Describe where he or she works, why he or she chose this career, and whether the trainer performs any research. Then, identify where in your community an athletic trainer might be able to help people.

WHY HEARTS Don't Get Cancer

You've probably heard of heartburn and heart attacks, and even heartbreak. But have you heard of heart cancer? Heart cancer occurs very rarely, and the tumors usually do not grow the way most cancer tumors do. So why doesn't the heart usually develop cancer? The answer may lie with cell division.

Every moment of your life, cells in your body are dividing. During cell division, a cell's genetic material is copied, and a new cell forms. However, mistakes in how genes are copied can occur during cell division. Occasionally, these mistakes can lead to certain forms of cancer.

In a healthy heart, cell division slows significantly by the time a person reaches adulthood. Cell division is slow and rare in the adult heart because the cells of the heart are active every minute of life. Therefore, heart cells do not mutate very often, so the risk of a mutation causing cancer is very low.

Present It Find out more about rare cancers. Then, create a multimedia presentation that describes why these types of cancer are uncommon. Be sure to cite your sources of information.

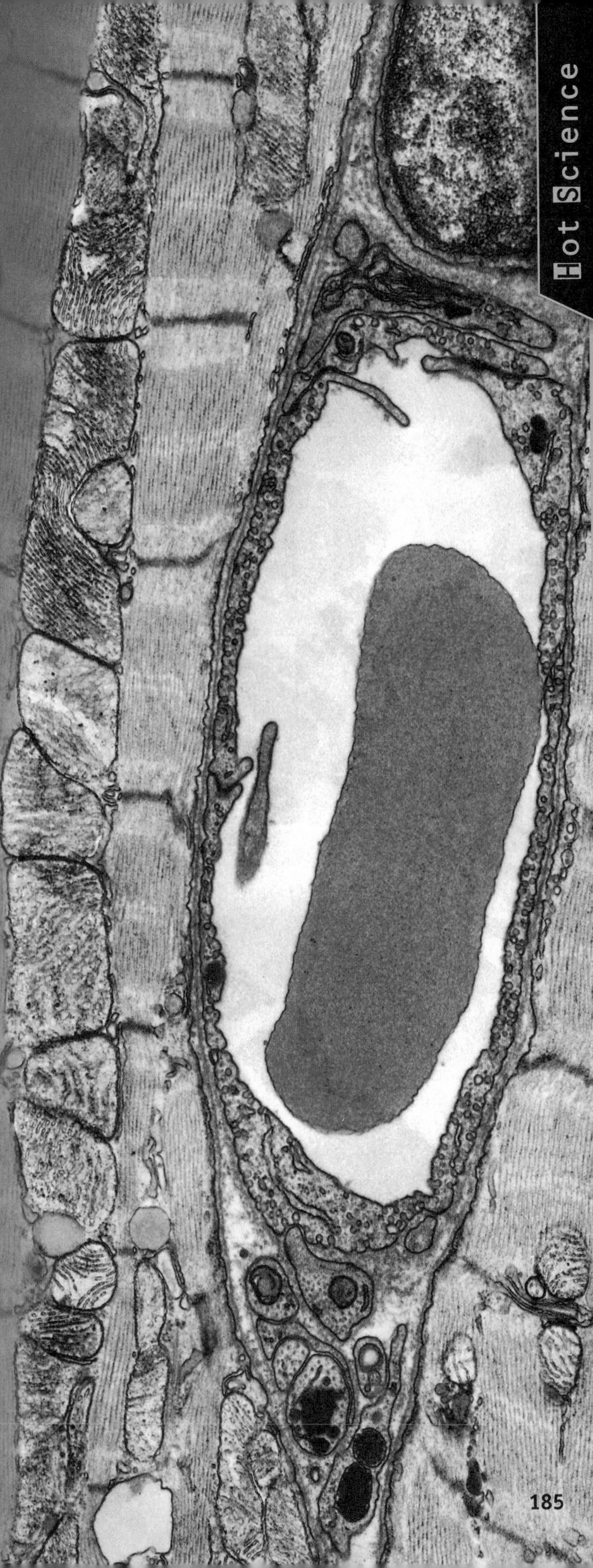

This colored transmission electron micrograph (TEM) shows muscle cells from a healthy heart. The hardworking cells in your heart rarely rest long enough for cell division to occur. ▶

WHAT MAKES THIS BABY KOALA DIFFERENT?

Why don't offspring always look like their parents?

UNTAMED SCIENCE Watch the **Untamed Science** video to learn more about heredity.

Even though this young koala, or joey, has two fuzzy ears, a long nose, and a body shaped like its mom's, you can see that the two are different. You might expect a young animal to look exactly like its parents, but think about how varied a litter of kittens or puppies can look. This joey is an albino—an animal that lacks the usual coloring in its eyes, fur, and skin.

Observe **Describe how this joey looks different from its mom.**

CHAPTER

6

Genetics: The Science of Heredity

Science Standards of Learning

LS.1a, LS.1d, LS.1h, LS.1i, LS.1j, LS.2d, LS.12b, LS.12c, LS.12d, LS.12f

CHAPTER 6

Getting Started

Check Your Understanding

1. Background Read the paragraph below and then answer the question.

Kent's cat just had six kittens. All six kittens look different from one another—and from their two parents! Kent knows each kitten is unique because cats reproduce through **sexual reproduction,** not **asexual reproduction.** Before long, the kittens will grow bigger and bigger as their cells divide through **mitosis.**

Sexual reproduction involves two parents and combines their genetic material to produce a new organism that differs from both parents.

Asexual reproduction involves only one parent and produces offspring that are identical to the parent.

During **mitosis,** a cell's nucleus divides into two new nuclei, and one copy of DNA is distributed into each daughter cell.

- In what way are the two daughter cells that form by mitosis and cell division identical?

____

MY READING WEB If you had trouble completing the question above, visit **My Reading Web** and type in ***Genetics: The Science of Heredity.***

Vocabulary Skill

Suffixes A suffix is a word part that is added to the end of a word to change its meaning. For example, the suffix *-tion* means "process of." If you add the suffix *-tion* to the verb *fertilize,* you get the noun *fertilization. Fertilization* means "the process of fertilizing." The table below lists some other common suffixes and their meanings.

Suffix	Meaning	Example
-ive	performing a particular action	recessive allele, *n.* an allele that is masked when a dominant allele is present
-ance or *-ant*	state, condition of	codominance, *n.* occurs when both alleles are expressed equally

2. Quick Check Fill in the blank with the correct suffix.

- A domin__________ allele can mask a recessive allele.

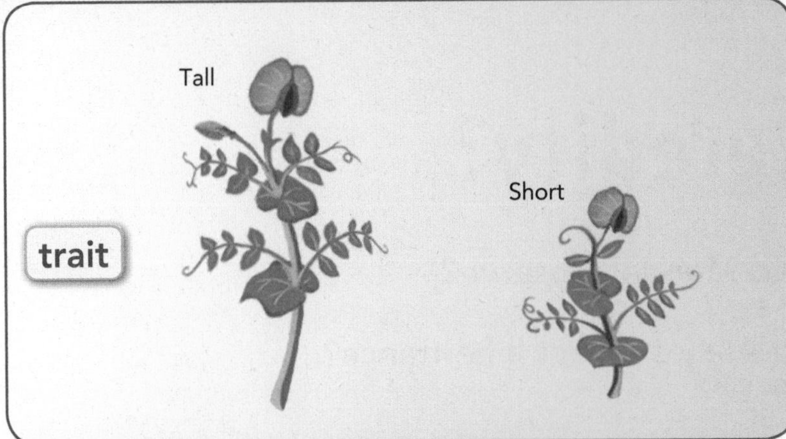

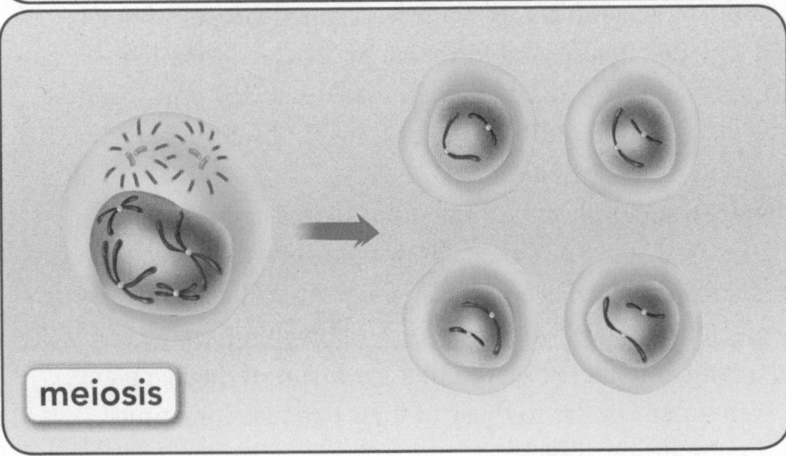

Chapter Preview

LESSON 1

- heredity
- trait
- genetics
- fertilization
- purebred
- gene
- allele
- dominant allele
- recessive allele
- hybrid

Identify Supporting Evidence
Predict

LESSON 2

- probability
- Punnett square
- phenotype
- genotype
- homozygous
- heterozygous

Identify the Main Idea
Draw Conclusions

LESSON 3

- incomplete dominance
- codominance
- multiple alleles
- polygenic inheritance

Compare and Contrast
Interpret Data

LESSON 4

- meiosis

Relate Cause and Effect
Design Experiments

> VOCAB FLASH CARDS For extra help with vocabulary, visit **Vocab Flash Cards** and type in ***Genetics: The Science of Heredity.***

What Is Heredity?

- What Did Mendel Observe?
  LS.1d, LS.12c, LS.12f
- How Do Alleles Affect Inheritance?
  LS.12b, LS.12c, LS.12f

my planet Diary

BIOGRAPHY

Almost Forgotten

When scientists make great discoveries, sometimes their work is praised, criticized, or even forgotten. Gregor Mendel was almost forgotten. He spent eight years studying pea plants, and he discovered patterns in the way characteristics pass from one generation to the next. For almost 40 years, people overlooked Mendel's work. When it was finally rediscovered, it unlocked the key to understanding heredity.

Communicate **Discuss the question below with a partner. Then write your answer.**

Did you ever rediscover something of yours that you had forgotten? How did you react?

____

____

____

PLANET DIARY Go to **Planet Diary** to learn more about heredity.

Do the Inquiry Warm-Up *What Does the Father Look Like?*

Science Standards of Learning

LS.1d Construct and use models and simulations to illustrate and explain phenomena.

LS.12c Investigate and understand genotypes and phenotypes.

LS.12f Investigate and understand the historical contributions and significance of discoveries related to genetics.

What Did Mendel Observe?

In the mid-nineteenth century, a priest named Gregor Mendel tended a garden in a central European monastery. Mendel's experiments in that peaceful garden would one day transform the study of heredity. **Heredity** is the passing of physical characteristics from parents to offspring.

Mendel wondered why different pea plants had different characteristics. Some pea plants grew tall, while others were short. Some plants produced green seeds, while others had yellow seeds. Each specific characteristic, such as stem height or seed color, is called a **trait.** Mendel observed that the forms of the pea plants' traits were often similar to those of their parents. Sometimes, however, the forms differed.

Vocabulary
- heredity • trait • genetics • fertilization
- purebred • gene • allele • dominant allele
- recessive allele • hybrid

Skills
- Reading: Identify Supporting Evidence
- Inquiry: Predict

Mendel's Experiments Mendel experimented with thousands of pea plants. Today, Mendel's discoveries form the foundation of **genetics,** the scientific study of heredity. **Figure 1** shows the parts of a pea plant's flower. The pistil produces female sex cells, or eggs. The stamens produce pollen, which contains the male sex cells, or sperm. A new organism begins to form when egg and sperm cells join in the process called **fertilization.** Before fertilization can happen in pea plants, pollen must reach the pistil of a pea flower. This process is called pollination.

Pea plants are usually self-pollinating. In self-pollination, pollen from a flower lands on the pistil of the same flower. Mendel developed a method by which he cross-pollinated, or "crossed," pea plants. **Figure 1** shows his method.

Mendel decided to cross plants that had contrasting forms of a trait—for example, tall plants and short plants. He started with purebred plants. A **purebred** organism is the offspring of many generations that have the same form of a trait. For example, purebred tall pea plants always come from tall parent plants.

FIGURE 1

Crossing Pea Plants

Mendel devised a way to cross-pollinate pea plants.

Use the diagram to answer the questions about Mendel's procedure.

1. **Observe** How does flower B differ from flower A?

______

______

2. **Infer** Describe how Mendel cross-pollinated pea plants.

______

______

______

______

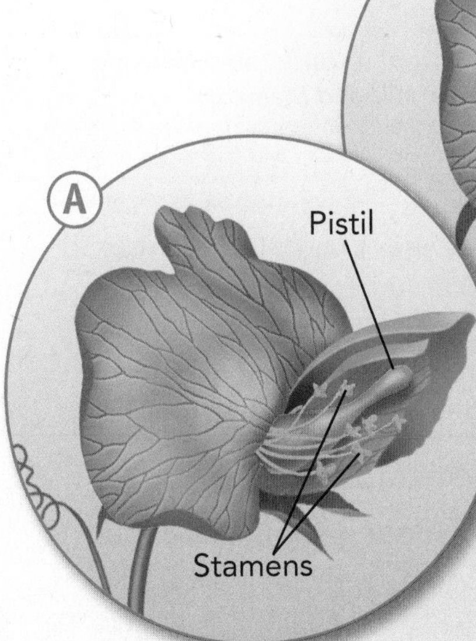

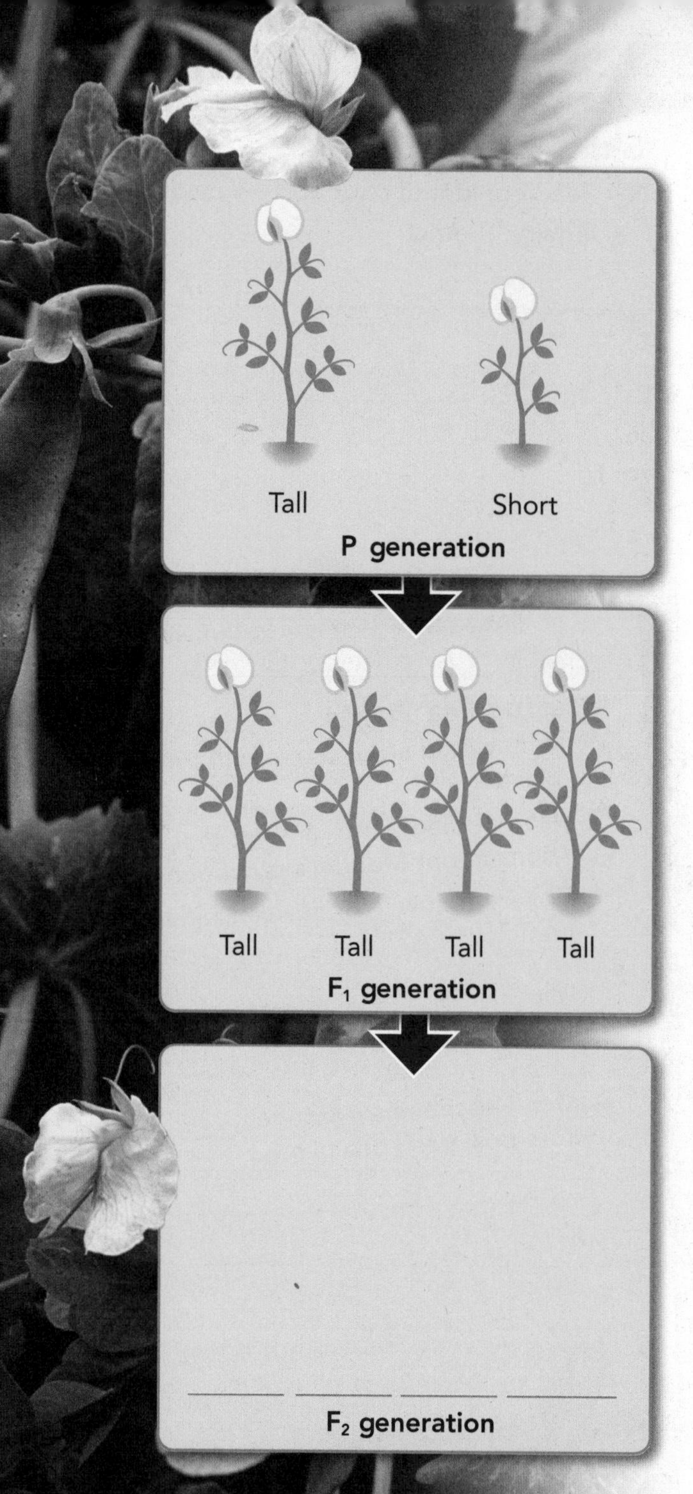

The F_1 and F_2 Offspring Mendel crossed purebred tall plants with purebred short plants. Today, scientists call these plants the parental, or P, generation. The resulting offspring are the first filial (FIL ee ul), or F_1, generation. The word *filial* comes from *filia* and *filius*, the Latin words for "daughter" and "son."

Look at **Figure 2** to see the surprise Mendel found in the F_1 generation. All the offspring were tall. The shortness trait seemed to have disappeared!

When these plants were full-grown, Mendel allowed them to self-pollinate. The F_2 (second filial) generation that followed surprised Mendel even more. He counted the plants of the F_2 generation. About three fourths were tall, while one fourth were short.

Experiments With Other Traits Mendel repeated his experiments, studying other pea-plant traits, such as flower color and seed shape. **In all of his crosses, Mendel found that only one form of the trait appeared in the F_1 generation. However, in the F_2 generation, the "lost" form of the trait always reappeared in about one fourth of the plants.**

FIGURE 2

Results of a Cross

In Mendel's crosses, some forms of a trait were hidden in one generation but reappeared in the next.

Interpret Diagrams **Draw and label the offspring in the F_2 generation.**

Do the Quick Lab *Observing Pistils and Stamens.*

Assess Your Understanding

1a. Define What happens during fertilization?

______

______

b. Compare and Contrast In Mendel's cross for stem height, how did the plants in the F_2 generations differ from the F_1 plants?

______

got it?

O **I get it!** Now I know that Mendel found that one form of a trait ______

______

______

O I need extra help with ______

Go to MY SCIENCE COACH *online for help with this subject.*

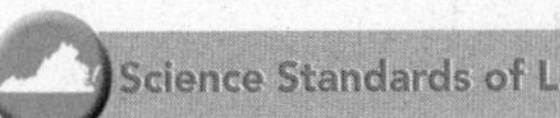

How Do Alleles Affect Inheritance?

Science Standards of Learning

LS.12b Investigate and understand the function of genes and chromosomes.

LS.12c Investigate and understand genotypes and phenotypes.

LS.12f Investigate and understand the historical contributions and significance of discoveries related to genetics.

Mendel reached several conclusions from his experimental results. He reasoned that individual factors, or sets of genetic "information," must control the inheritance of traits in peas. The factors that control each trait exist in pairs. The female parent contributes one factor, while the male parent contributes the other factor. Finally, one factor in a pair can mask, or hide, the other factor. The tallness factor, for example, masked the shortness factor.

Genes and Alleles

Today, scientists use the word **gene** to describe the factors that control a trait. **Alleles** (uh LEELZ) are the different forms of a gene. The gene that controls stem height in peas has one allele for tall stems and one allele for short stems. Each pea plant inherits two alleles—one from the egg and the other from the sperm. A plant may inherit two alleles for tall stems, two alleles for short stems, or one of each.

An organism's traits are controlled by the alleles it inherits from its parents. Some alleles are dominant, while other alleles are recessive. A **dominant allele** is one whose trait always shows up in the organism when the allele is present. A **recessive allele,** on the other hand, is hidden whenever the dominant allele is present. **Figure 3** shows dominant and recessive alleles of the traits in Mendel's crosses.

FIGURE 3

Alleles in Pea Plants

Mendel studied the inheritance of seven different traits in pea plants.

Use the table to answer the questions.

1. **Draw Conclusions** Circle the picture of each dominant form of the trait in the P generation.
2. **Predict** Under what conditions would the recessive form of one of these traits reappear?

____

____

Inheritance of Pea Plants Studied by Mendel

	Seed Shape	Seed Color	Pod Shape	Pod Color	Flower Color	Flower Position	Stem Height
P	Wrinkled X Round	Yellow X Green	Pinched X Smooth	Green X Yellow	Purple X White	Tip of stem X Side of stem	Tall X Short
F_1	Round	Yellow	Smooth	Green	Purple	Side of stem	Tall

FIGURE 4

VIRTUAL LAB Dominant and Recessive Alleles

Symbols serve as a shorthand way to identify alleles.

Complete each row of the diagram.

1. **Identify** Fill in the missing allele symbols and descriptions.
2. **Summarize** Use the word bank to complete the statements. (Terms will be used more than once.)
3. **Relate Cause and Effect** Draw the two possible ways the F_2 offspring could look.

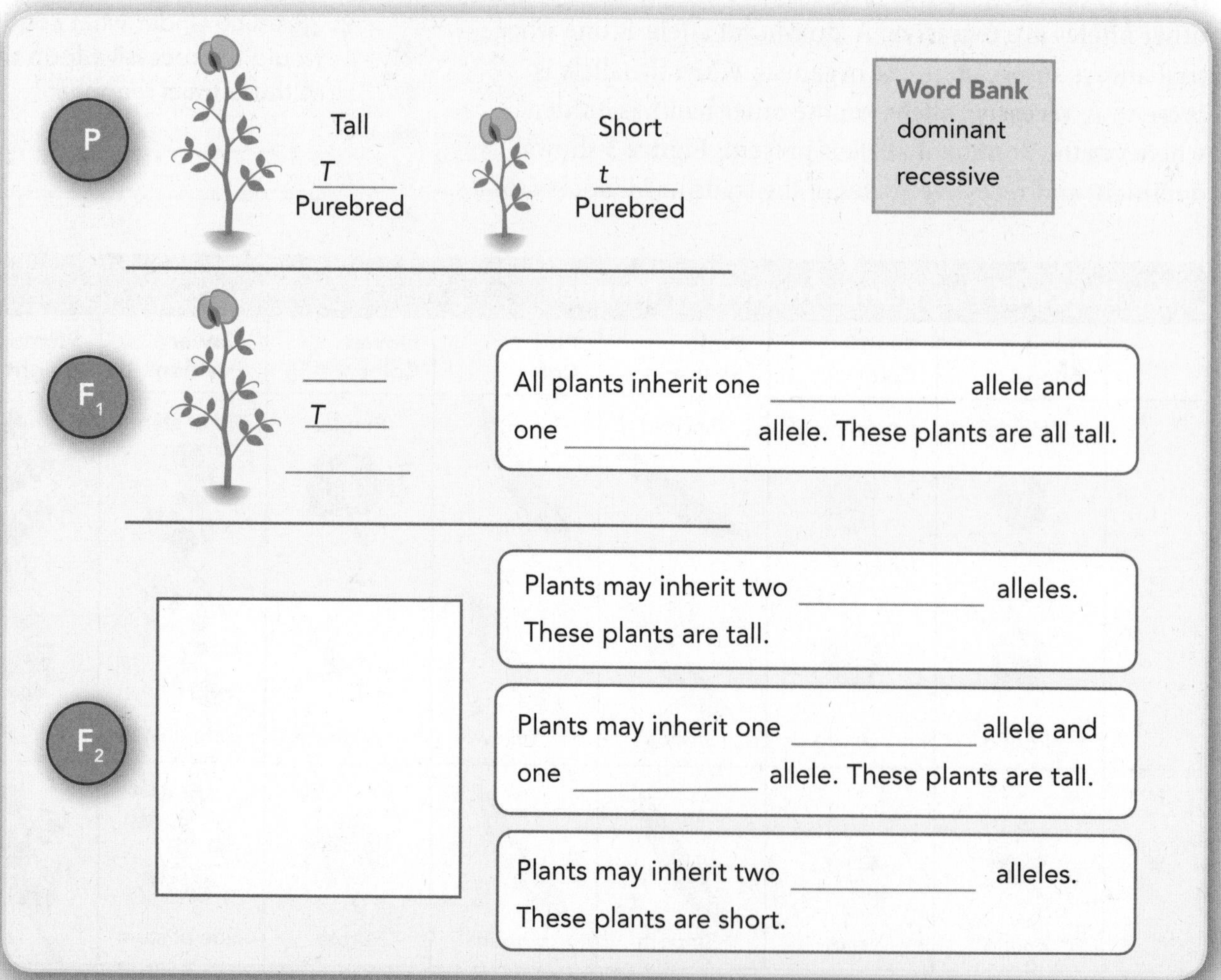

Alleles in Mendel's Crosses In Mendel's cross for stem height, the purebred tall plants in the P generation had two alleles for tall stems. The purebred short plants had two alleles for short stems. But each F_1 plant inherited one allele for tall stems and one allele for short stems. The F_1 plants are called hybrids. A **hybrid** (HY brid) organism has two different alleles for a trait. All the F_1 plants are tall because the dominant allele for tall stems masks the recessive allele for short stems.

Symbols for Alleles Geneticists, scientists who study genetics, often use letters to represent alleles. A dominant allele is symbolized by a capital letter. A recessive allele is symbolized by the lowercase version of the same letter. For example, *T* stands for the allele for tall stems, and *t* stands for the allele for short stems. When a plant has two dominant alleles for tall stems, its alleles are written as *TT*. When a plant has two recessive alleles for short stems, its alleles are written as *tt*. These plants are the P generation shown in **Figure 4.** Think about the symbols that would be used for F_1 plants that all inherit one allele for tall stems and one for short stems.

apply it!

In fruit flies, long wings are dominant over short wings. A scientist crossed a purebred long-winged fruit fly with a purebred short-winged fruit fly.

1. If W stands for long wings, write the symbols for the alleles of each parent fly.

2. **Predict** What will be the wing length of the F_1 offspring?

3. **Predict** If the scientist crosses a hybrid male F_1 fruit fly with a hybrid F_1 female, what will their offspring probably be like?

Significance of Mendel's Contribution Mendel's discovery of genes and alleles eventually changed scientists' ideas about heredity. Before Mendel, most people thought that the traits of an individual organism were simply a blend of the parents' characteristics. Mendel showed that offspring traits are determined by individual, separate alleles inherited from each parent. Unfortunately, the value of Mendel's discovery was not known during his lifetime. But when scientists in the early 1900s rediscovered Mendel's work, they quickly realized its importance. Because of his work, Mendel is often called the Father of Genetics.

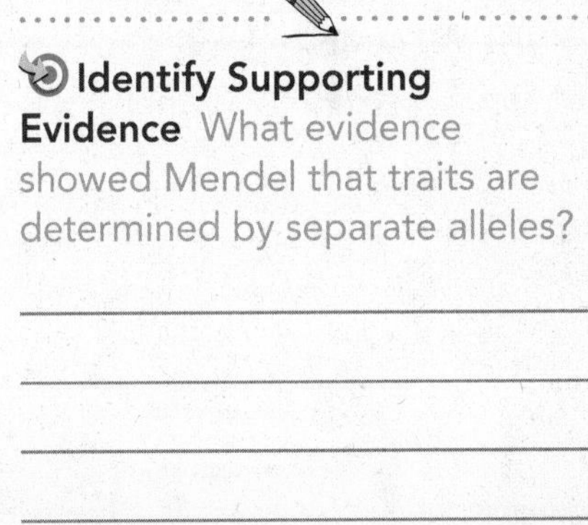

Identify Supporting Evidence What evidence showed Mendel that traits are determined by separate alleles?

Lab zone® Do the Quick Lab *Inferring the Parent Generation.*

Assess Your Understanding

2a. Relate Cause and Effect Why is a pea plant that is a hybrid for stem height tall?

b. CHALLENGE Can a short pea plant be a hybrid for the trait of stem height? Why or why not?

got it?

○ **I get it!** Now I know that an organism's traits are controlled by ______

○ I need extra help with ______

Go to **MY SCIENCE COACH** *online for help with this subject.*

Probability and Heredity

How Is Probability Related to Inheritance?
LS.1a, LS.1i, LS.12b

What Are Phenotype and Genotype?
LS.1h, LS.12b, LS.12c

my planet Diary

FIELD TRIP

Storm on the Way?

Have you ever watched a hurricane form? Weather forecasters at the National Hurricane Center (NHC) in Miami, Florida, have. From May 15 to November 30, the NHC Operations Area is staffed around the clock with forecasters. They study data from aircraft, ocean buoys, and satellites to develop computer models. These models predict the probable paths of a storm. If the probability of a certain path is high, the NHC issues a warning that helps save lives and reduce damage.

Communicate **Answer the question below. Then discuss your answer with a partner.**

Local weather forecasters often talk about the percent chance for rainfall. What do you think they mean?

PLANET DIARY Go to **Planet Diary** to learn more about probability and weather.

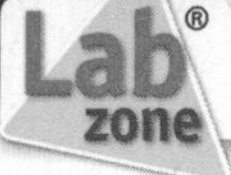

Do the Inquiry Warm-Up *What's the Chance?*

LS.1a Organize data into tables showing repeated trials and means.
LS.1i Identify, interpret, and evaluate patterns in data.
LS.12b Investigate and understand the function of genes and chromosomes.

How Is Probability Related to Inheritance?

Before the start of a football game, the team captains stand with the referee for a coin toss. The team that wins the toss chooses whether to kick or receive the ball. As the referee tosses the coin, the visiting team captain calls "heads." What is the chance that the visitors will win the toss? To answer this question, you need to understand the principles of probability.

Vocabulary
- probability
- Punnett square
- phenotype
- genotype
- homozygous
- heterozygous

Skills
- Reading: Identify the Main Idea
- Inquiry: Draw Conclusions

What Is Probability?

Each time you toss a coin, there are two possible ways it can land—heads up or tails up. **Probability** is a number that describes how likely it is that an event will occur. In mathematical terms, you can say the probability that a tossed coin will land heads up is 1 in 2. There's also a 1 in 2 probability that the coin will land tails up. A 1 in 2 probability is expressed as the fraction $\frac{1}{2}$ or as 50 percent.

The laws of probability predict what is *likely* to occur, not what *will* occur. If you toss a coin 20 times, you may expect it to land heads up 10 times and tails up 10 times. But you may get 11 heads and 9 tails, or 8 heads and 12 tails. The more tosses you make, the closer your actual results will be to those predicted by probability.

Do you think the result of one toss affects the result of the next toss? Not at all. Each event occurs independently. Suppose you toss a coin five times and it lands heads up each time. What is the probability that it will land heads up on the next toss? If you said the probability is still 1 in 2, or 50 percent, you're right. The results of the first five tosses do not affect the result of the sixth toss.

do the math!

Percentage

One way to express probability is as a percentage. A percentage is a number compared to 100. For example, 50 percent, or 50%, means 50 out of 100. Suppose you want to calculate percentage from the results of a series of basketball free throws in which 3 out of 5 free throws go through the hoop.

STEP 1 Write the comparison as a fraction.

$$3 \text{ out of } 5 = \frac{3}{5}$$

STEP 2 Calculate the number value of the fraction.

$$3 \div 5 = 0.6$$

STEP 3 Multiply this number by 100%.

$$0.6 \times 100\% = 60\%$$

Practice!

1 **Calculate** Suppose 5 out of 25 free throws go through the hoop. Write this result as a fraction.

2 **Calculate** Express your answer in Question 1 as a percentage.

Probability and Genetics How is probability related to genetics? Think back to Mendel's experiments. He carefully counted the offspring from every cross. When he crossed two plants that were hybrid for stem height (*Tt*), about three fourths of the F_2 plants had tall stems. About one fourth had short stems.

Each time Mendel repeated the cross, he observed similar results. He realized that the principles of probability applied to his work. He found that the probability of a hybrid cross producing a tall plant was 3 in 4. The probability of producing a short plant was 1 in 4. Mendel was the first scientist to recognize that the principles of probability can predict the results of genetic crosses.

Punnett Squares

A tool that can help you grasp how the laws of probability apply to genetics is called a Punnett square. A **Punnett square** is a chart that shows all the possible ways alleles can combine in a genetic cross. Geneticists use Punnett squares to see these combinations and to determine the probability of a particular outcome, or result. **In a genetic cross, the combination of alleles that parents can pass to an offspring is based on probability.**

Figure 1 shows how to make a Punnett square. In this case, the cross is between two hybrid pea plants with round seeds (*Rr*). The allele for round seeds (*R*) is dominant over the allele for wrinkled seeds (*r*). Each parent can pass either one allele or the other to an offspring. The boxes in the Punnett square show the possible combinations of alleles that the offspring can inherit.

FIGURE 1

INTERACTIVE ART **How to Make a Punnett Square**

You can use a Punnett square to find the probabilities of a genetic cross.

Follow the steps in the figure to fill in the Punnett square.

1. **Predict** What is the probability that an offspring will have wrinkled seeds?

____

2. **Interpret Tables** What is the probability that an offspring will have round seeds? Explain your answer.

____

____

____

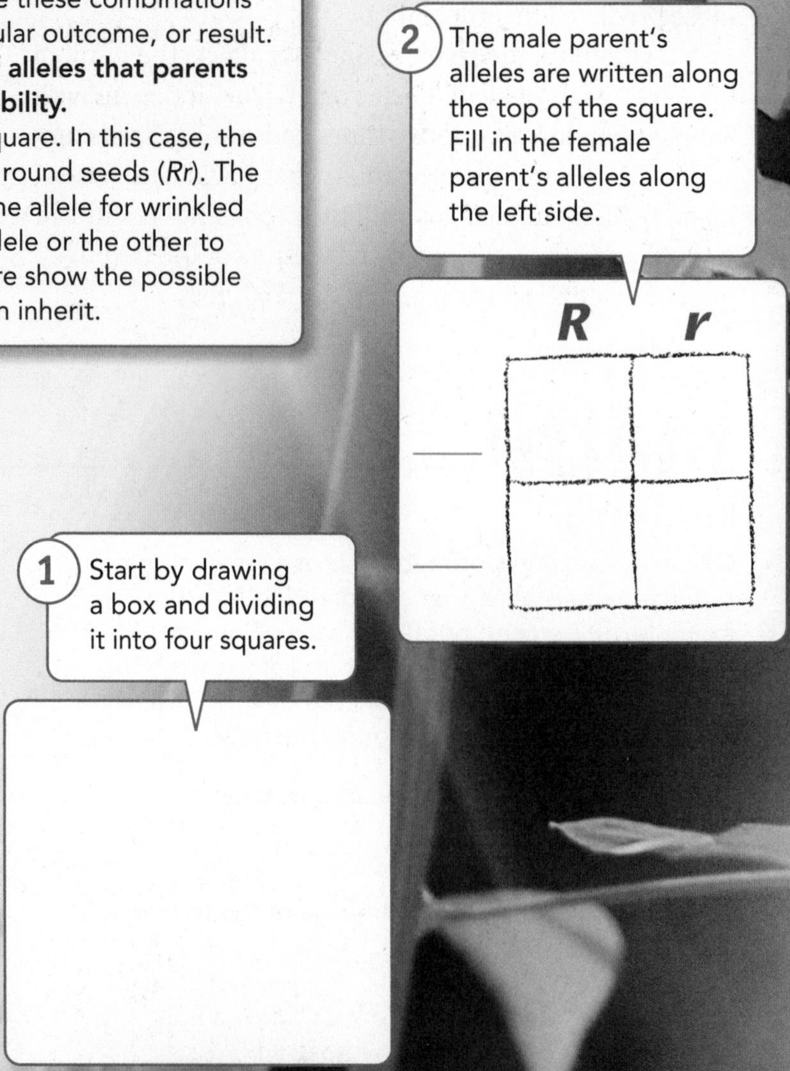

1 Start by drawing a box and dividing it into four squares.

2 The male parent's alleles are written along the top of the square. Fill in the female parent's alleles along the left side.

	R	r
___		
___		

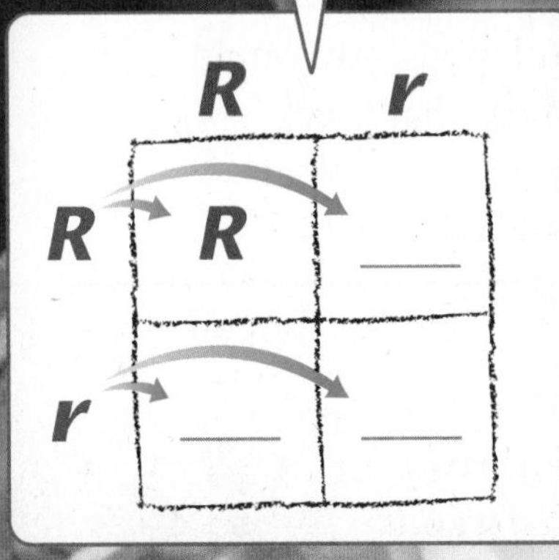

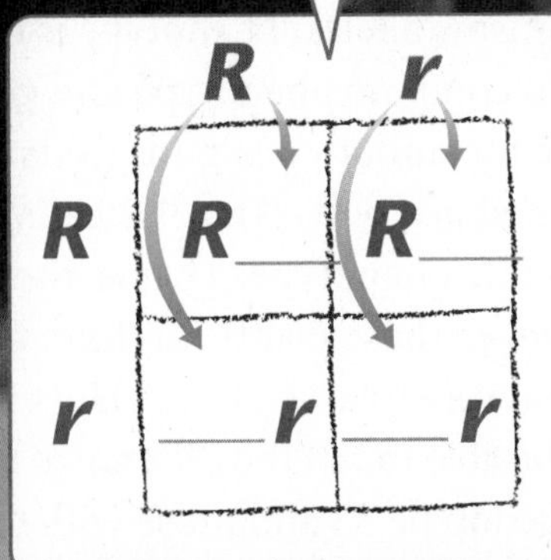

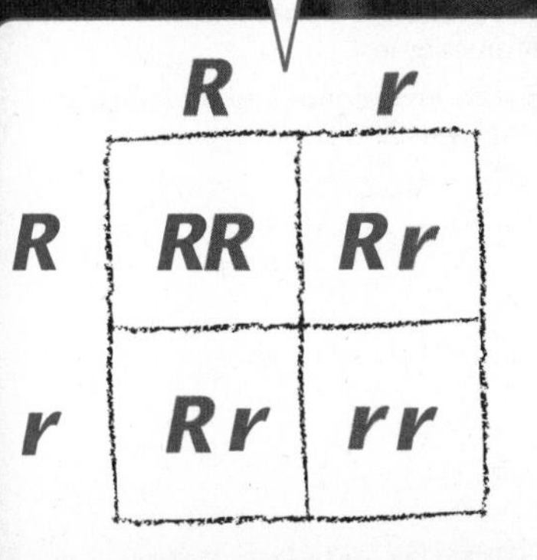

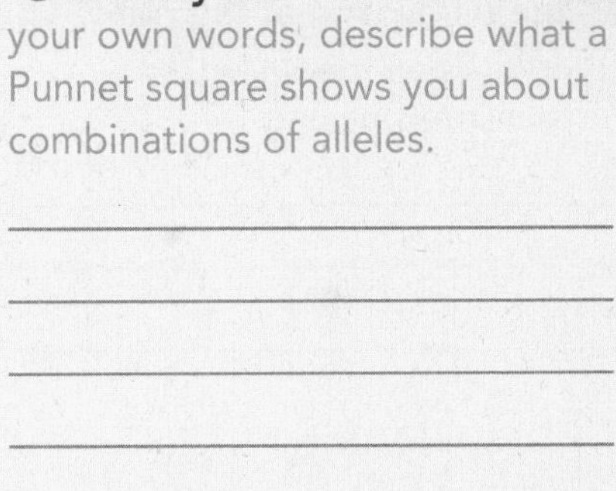

Relating Punnett Squares to Mendel Mendel did not know about alleles. But a Punnett square shows why he got the results he saw in the F_2 generations. Plants with alleles *RR* would have round seeds. So would plants with alleles *Rr*. Only plants with alleles *rr* would have wrinkled seeds.

Assess Your Understanding

1a. Review What is probability?

____

____

b. Apply Concepts What is the probability that a cross between a hybrid pea plant with round seeds and one with wrinkled seeds will produce offspring with wrinkled seeds? (Draw a Punnett square on other paper to find the answer.)

____

got it?

○ **I get it!** Now I know that the combination of alleles parents can pass to offspring ______________________

____

○ I need extra help with ______________________

Go to **MY SCIENCE COACH** *online for help with this subject.*

Science Standards of Learning

LS.1h Organize, graph, and interpret data, and use data to make predictions.

LS.12b Investigate and understand the function of genes and chromosomes.

LS.12c Investigate and understand genotypes and phenotypes.

What Are Phenotype and Genotype?

Two terms that geneticists use are **phenotype** (FEE noh typ) and **genotype** (JEE noh typ). **An organism's phenotype is its physical appearance, or visible traits. An organism's genotype is its genetic makeup, or alleles.** In other words, genotype is an organism's alleles. Phenotype is how a trait looks or is expressed.

To compare phenotype and genotype, look at **Figure 2.** The allele for smooth pea pods (*S*) is dominant over the allele for pinched pea pods (*s*). All the plants with at least one *S* allele have the same phenotype. That is, they all produce smooth pods. However, these plants can have two different genotypes—*SS* or *Ss*. If you were to look at the plants with smooth pods, you would not be able to tell the difference between those that have the genotype *SS* and those with the genotype *Ss*. The plants with pinched pods, on the other hand, would all have the same phenotype—pinched pods—as well as the same genotype—*ss*.

Vocabulary Suffixes The suffix *-ous* means "having." Circle this suffix in the highlighted terms *homozygous* and *heterozygous* in the paragraph at the right. These terms describe the organism as having

______

______

______

Geneticists use two additional terms to describe an organism's genotype. An organism that has two identical alleles for a trait is said to be **homozygous** (hoh moh ZY gus) for that trait. A smooth-pod plant that has the alleles *SS* and a pinched-pod plant with the alleles *ss* are both homozygous. An organism that has two different alleles for a trait is **heterozygous** (het ur oh ZY gus) for that trait. A smooth-pod plant with the alleles *Ss* is heterozygous. Recall that Mendel used the term *hybrid* to describe heterozygous pea plants.

FIGURE 2

Describing Inheritance

An organism's phenotype is its physical appearance. Its genotype is its genetic makeup.

Based on what you have read, answer these questions.

1. **Classify** Fill in the missing information in the table.
2. **Interpret Tables** How many genotypes are there for the smooth-pod phenotype?

______

Phenotypes and Genotypes

Phenotype	Genotype	Homozygous or Heterozygous
Smooth pods	____	______
Smooth pods	____	______
Pinched pods	____	______

apply it!

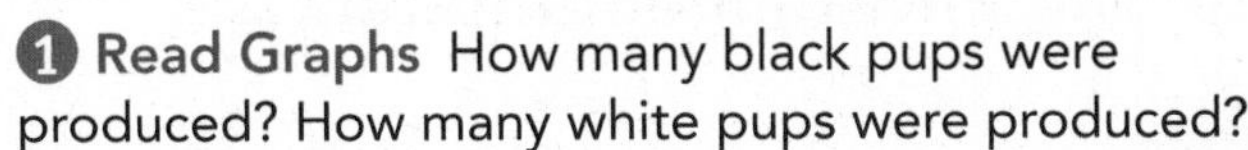

Mendel's principles of heredity apply to many other organisms. For example, in guinea pigs, black fur color (*B*) is dominant over white fur color (*b*). Suppose a pair of black guinea pigs produces several litters of pups during their lifetimes. The graph shows the phenotypes of the pups. Write a title for the graph.

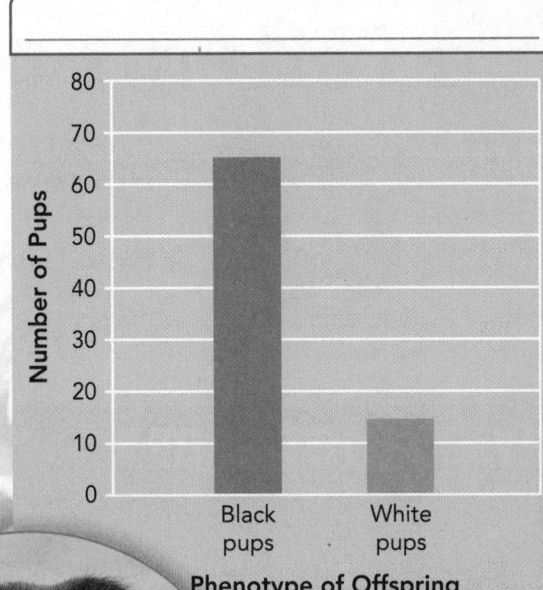

1 **Read Graphs** How many black pups were produced? How many white pups were produced?

____

2 **Infer** What are the possible genotypes of the offspring?

____

3 **Draw Conclusions** What can you conclude about the genotypes of the parent guinea pigs? Explain your answer.

____

Lab zone Do the Lab Investigation *Make the Right Call!*

Assess Your Understanding

2a. Relate Cause and Effect Explain how two organisms can have the same phenotype but different genotypes.

____

b. CHALLENGE In their lifetimes, two guinea pigs produce 40 black pups and 40 white pups. On a separate paper, make a Punnett square and find the likely genotypes of these parents.

____

got it?

○ **I get it!** Now I know that phenotype and genotype are terms that describe _______________

○ I need extra help with _______________

Go to **my science coach** *online for help with this subject.*

Patterns of Inheritance

How Are Most Traits Inherited?
LS.1i, LS.12b, LS.12c

How Do Genes and the Environment Interact?
LS.12b, LS.12c, LS.12d

my planet Diary

DISCOVERY

Cold, With a Chance of Males

Is it a male or a female? If you're a red-eared slider turtle, the answer might depend on the temperature! These slider turtles live in the calm, fresh, warm waters of the southeastern United States. For these turtles and some other reptiles, the temperature of the environment determines the sex of their offspring. At 26°C, the eggs of red-eared slider turtles all hatch as males. But at 31°C, the eggs all hatch as females. Only at about 29°C is there a 50% chance of hatching turtles of either sex.

Predict **Discuss the question below with a partner. Then write your answer.**

What do you think might happen to a population of red-eared slider turtles in a place where the temperature remains near or at 26°C?

PLANET DIARY Go to **Planet Diary** to learn more about patterns of inheritance.

Lab zone® Do the Inquiry Warm-Up *Observing Traits.*

Science Standards of Learning

LS.1i Identify, interpret, and evaluate patterns in data.

LS.12b Investigate and understand the function of genes and chromosomes.

LS.12c Investigate and understand genotypes and phenotypes.

How Are Most Traits Inherited?

The traits that Mendel studied are controlled by genes with only two possible alleles. These alleles are either dominant or recessive. Pea flower color is either purple or white. Peas are either yellow or green. Can you imagine if all traits were like this? If people were either short or tall? If cats were either black or yellow?

Studying two-allele traits is a good place to begin learning about genetics. But take a look around at the variety of living things in your surroundings. As you might guess, most traits do not follow such a simple pattern of inheritance. **Most traits are the result of complex patterns of inheritance.** Four complex patterns of inheritance are described in this lesson.

Vocabulary
- incomplete dominance
- codominance
- multiple alleles
- polygenic inheritance

Skills
- Reading: Compare and Contrast
- Inquiry: Interpret Data

Incomplete Dominance Some traits result from a pattern of inheritance known as incomplete dominance. **Incomplete dominance** occurs when one allele is only partially dominant. For example, look at **Figure 1.** The flowers shown are called snapdragons. A cross between a plant with red flowers and one with white flowers produces pink offspring.

Snapdragons with alleles *RR* produce a lot of red color in their flowers. It's no surprise that their flowers are red. A plant with two white alleles (*WW*) produces no red color. Its flowers are white. Both types of alleles are written as capital letters because neither is totally dominant. If a plant has alleles *RW*, only enough color is produced to make the flowers just a little red. So they look pink.

Codominance The chickens in **Figure 1** show a different pattern of inheritance. **Codominance** occurs when both alleles for a gene are expressed equally. In the chickens shown, neither black feathers nor white feathers are dominant. All the offspring of a black hen and a white rooster have both black and white feathers.

Here, F^B stands for the allele for black feathers. F^W stands for the allele for white feathers. The letter *F* tells you the trait is feathers. The superscripts *B* for black and *W* for white tell you the color.

FIGURE 1

Other Patterns of Inheritance

Many crosses do not follow the patterns Mendel discovered.

Apply Concepts Fill in the missing pairs of alleles.

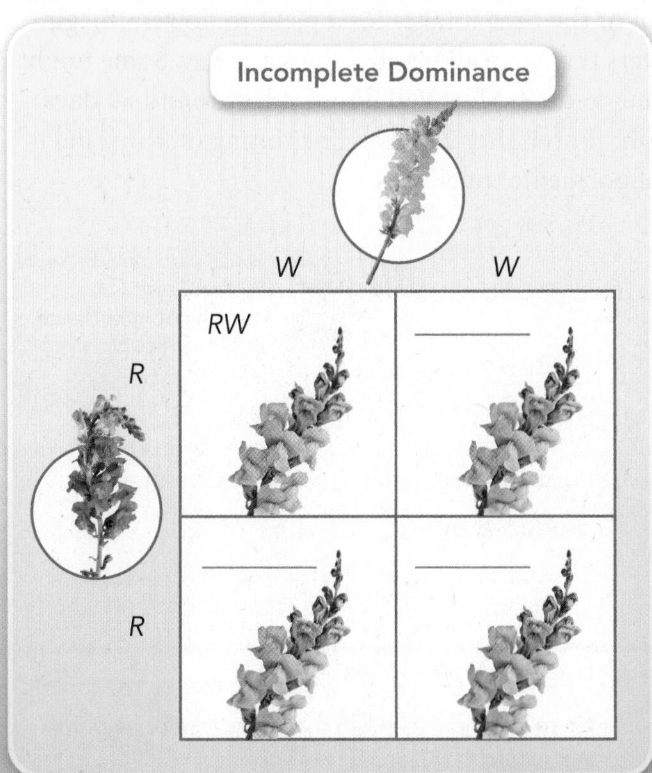

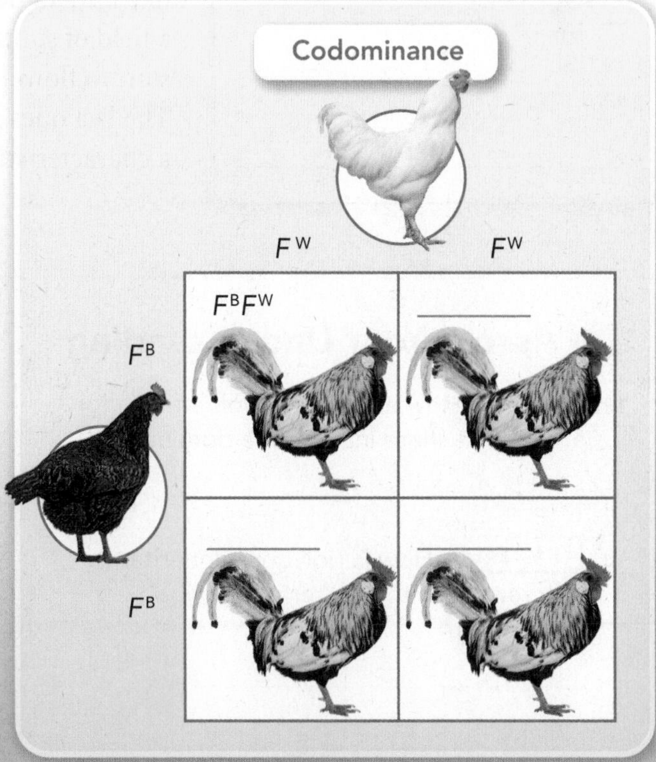

apply it!

An imaginary insect called the blingwing has three alleles for wing color: *R* (red), *B* (blue), and *Y* (yellow).

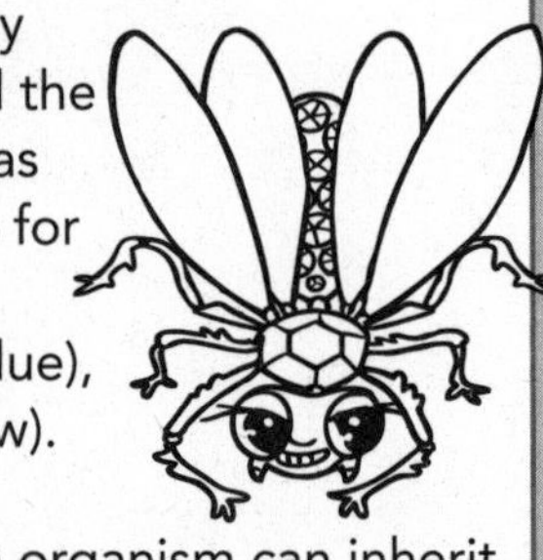

1 List If an organism can inherit only two alleles for a gene, what are the six possible allele pairs for wing color in blingwings? One answer is given.

RB, ____________________

____

2 Interpret Data Suppose wing color results from incomplete dominance. What wing color would each pair of alleles produce? One answer is given.

RB: purple ____________________

____

____

____

____

____

Multiple Alleles Some genes have **multiple alleles,** which means that three or more possible alleles determine the trait. Remember that an organism can only inherit two alleles for a gene—one from each parent. Even if there are four, five, or more possible alleles, an individual can only have two. However, more genotypes can occur with multiple alleles than with just two alleles. For example, four alleles control the color of fur in some rabbits. Depending on which two alleles a rabbit inherits, its coat color can range from brownish gray to all white.

Polygenic Inheritance The traits that Mendel studied were each controlled by a single gene. **Polygenic inheritance** occurs when more than one gene affects a trait. The alleles of the different genes work together to produce these traits.

Polygenic inheritance results in a broad range of phenotypes, like human height or the time it takes for a plant to flower. Imagine a field of sunflowers that were all planted the same day. Some might start to flower after 45 days. Most will flower after around 60 days. The last ones might flower after 75 days. The timing of flowering is a characteristic of polygenic traits.

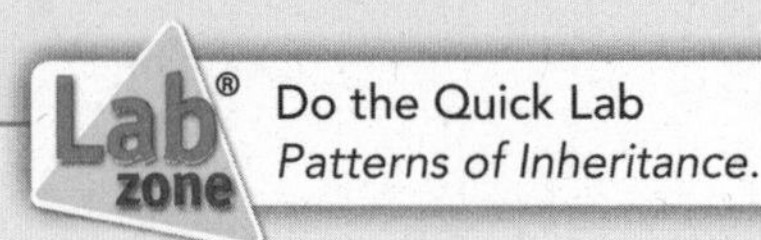

Assess Your Understanding

1a. Describe How are the symbols written for alleles that share incomplete dominance?

____

b. CHALLENGE How is polygenic inheritance different from the patterns described by Mendel?

____

____

got it?

O **I get it!** Now I know that most traits are produced by ____________________

____

____

O I need extra help with ____________________

Go to MY SCIENCE COACH *online for help with this subject.*

How Do Genes and the Environment Interact?

LS.12b Investigate and understand the functions of genes and chromosomes.

LS.12c Investigate and understand genotypes and phenotypes.

LS.12d Investigate and understand characteristics that can and cannot be inherited.

You were not born knowing how to skateboard, but maybe you can skateboard now. Many traits are learned, or acquired. Unlike inherited traits, acquired traits are not carried by genes or passed to offspring. Although inherited traits are determined by genes, they also can be affected by factors in the environment. The phenotypes you observe in an organism result both from genes and from interactions of the organism with its environment.

Inherited and Acquired Traits Humans are born with inherited traits, such as vocal cords and tongues that allow for speech. But humans are not born speaking Spanish, or Mandarin, or English. The languages that a person speaks are acquired traits. Do you have a callus on your finger from writing with your pencil? That is an acquired trait. Skills you learn and physical changes that occur, such as calluses and haircuts, are aquired traits. See if you can tell the inherited traits from the acquired traits in **Figure 2.**

FIGURE 2

Inherited or Acquired?

Which traits shown are carried in the genes, and which are not?

Classify **Identify each trait shown as inherited or acquired.**

Their heights ________

Dyed hair color ________

Fish body color ________

These hedge shapes ________

Her freckles ________

Genes and the Environment Think again about sunflowers. Genes control when the plants flower. But sunlight, temperature, soil nutrients, and water also affect a plant's flowering time. **Environmental factors can influence the way genes are expressed.** Like sunflowers, you have factors in your environment that can affect how your genes are expressed. For example, you may have inherited the ability to play a musical instrument. But without an opportunity to learn, you may never develop the skill.

Some environmental factors can change an organism's genes. For example, tobacco smoke and other pollutants can affect genes in a person's body cells in a way that may result in lung cancer and other cancers. Still other genetic changes happen by chance.

Changes in body cells cannot be passed to offspring. Only changes in the sex cells—eggs and sperm—can be passed to offspring. Not all genetic changes have negative effects. Genetic change in sex cells is an important source of life's variety.

Compare and Contrast Underline two sentences that tell how changes to genes in body cells differ from changes to genes in egg and sperm cells.

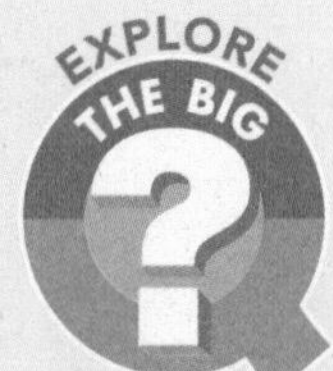

Patterns of Inheritance

Why don't offspring always look like their parents?

FIGURE 3

INTERACTIVE ART The traits you see in organisms result from their genes and from interactions of genes with the environment.

Summarize Match the terms in the word bank with the examples shown.

Word Bank	
Incomplete dominance	Dominant and recessive traits
Environmental factors	Polygenic inheritance
Multiple alleles	Codominance
Acquired traits	

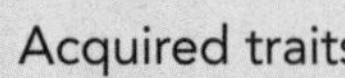

Lab zone® Do the Quick Lab *Is It All in the Genes?*

Assess Your Understanding

2a. Review Only genetic changes in (sex cells/ body cells) can be passed to offspring.

b. Describe Give one example of how environmental factors affect gene expression.

c. ANSWER THE BIG Q Why don't offspring always look like their parents?

got it?

- O **I get it!** Now I know that the environment can affect ______
- O I need extra help with ______

Go to MY SCIENCE COACH *online for help with this subject.*

Chromosomes and Inheritance

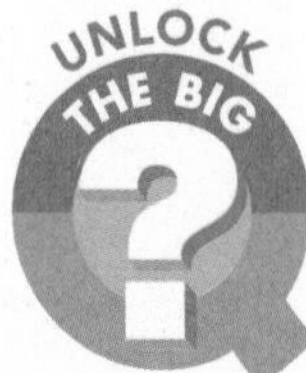

How Are Chromosomes, Genes, and Inheritance Related?
LS.12b, LS.12f

What Happens During Meiosis?
LS.1d, LS.2d, LS.12b

my planet Diary

CAREER

Chromosome Sleuth

Finding answers about how chromosomes relate to disease is one job of genetic technologists. These scientists analyze chromosomes from cells. The analysis may pinpoint genetic information that can cause disease or other health problems. In their work, genetic technologists use microscopes, computer-imaging photography, and lab skills. They report data that are used in research and in treating patients affected by genetic diseases.

Communicate Answer these questions. Then discuss Question 2 with a partner.

1. Would you like to be a genetic technologist? Why or why not?

2. If you were a genetic technologist, what would you like to research?

PLANET DIARY Go to **Planet Diary** to learn more about genetic technologists.

Lab zone® Do the Inquiry Warm-Up *Which Chromosome Is Which?*

Vocabulary
- meiosis

Skills
 Reading: Relate Cause and Effect
Inquiry: Design Experiments

How Are Chromosomes, Genes, and Inheritance Related?

Science Standards of Learning

LS.12b Investigate and understand the function of genes and chromosomes.

LS.12f Investigate and understand the historical contributions and significance of discoveries related to genetics.

Mendel's work showed that genes exist. (Remember that he called them "factors.") But scientists in the early twentieth century did not know what structures in cells contained genes. The search for the answer was something like a mystery story. The story could be called "The Clue in the Grasshopper's Cells."

At the start of the 1900s, Walter Sutton, an American geneticist, studied the cells of grasshoppers. He wanted to understand how sex cells (sperm and eggs) form. Sutton focused on how the chromosomes moved within cells during the formation of sperm and eggs. He hypothesized that chromosomes are the key to learning how offspring have traits similar to those of their parents.

Design Experiments Different types of organisms have different numbers of chromosomes, and some organisms are easier to study than others. Suppose you are a scientist studying chromosomes and you have to pick an organism from those shown below to do your work. Which one would you pick and why?

____

____

____

____

____

Skunk
50 chromosomes

Mosquito
6 chromosomes

Corn
20 chromosomes

Shrimp
90 chromosomes

Grasshopper
24 chromosomes

did you know?

The organism with the highest known number of chromosomes is a plant in the fern family. The netted adderstongue fern has more than 1,200 chromosomes!

Chromosomes and Inheritance

Sutton needed evidence to support his hypothesis. Look at **Figure 1** to see how he found this evidence in grasshopper cells. To his surprise, he discovered that grasshopper sex cells have exactly half the number of chromosomes found in grasshopper body cells.

Chromosome Pairs Sutton observed what happened when a sperm cell and an egg cell joined. The fertilized egg that formed had 24 chromosomes. It had the same number of chromosomes as each parent. These 24 chromosomes existed as 12 pairs. One chromosome in each pair came from the male parent. The other chromosome came from the female parent.

FIGURE 1

Paired Up

Sutton studied grasshopper cells through a microscope. He concluded that genes are carried on chromosomes.

Relate Text and Visuals **Answer the questions in the spaces provided.**

1 Body Cell

Each grasshopper body cell has 24 chromosomes.

2 Sex Cells

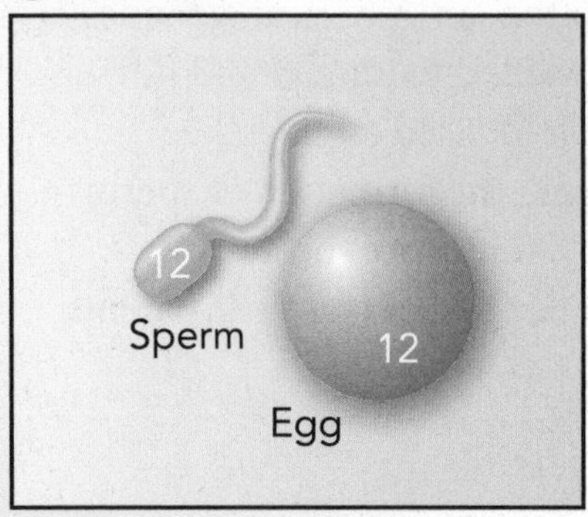

Sutton found that grasshopper sex cells each have 12 chromosomes.

1. How does the number of chromosomes in grasshopper sex cells compare to the number in body cells?

____

____

____

____

3 Fertilization

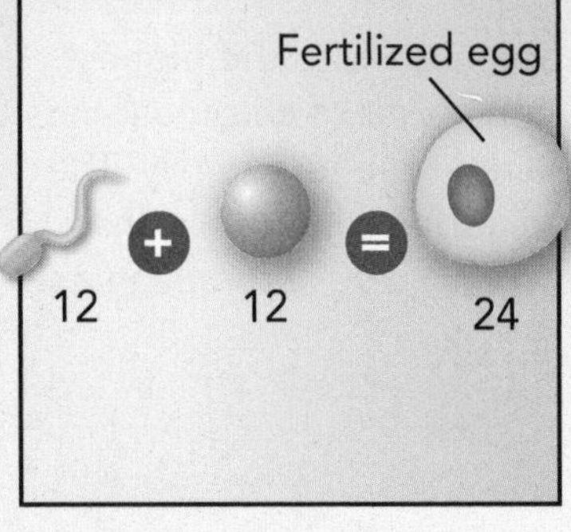

The fertilized egg cell has 24 chromosomes.

4 Grasshopper Offspring

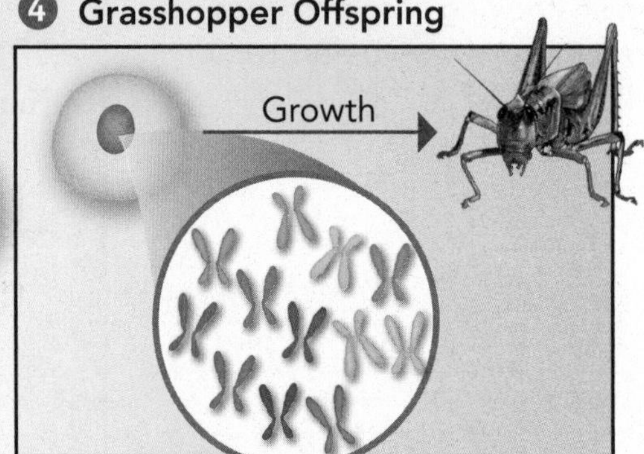

The 24 chromosomes exist as 12 pairs.

2. How is the inheritance of chromosomes similar to what you know about alleles?

____

____

____

____

Genes on Chromosomes Recall that alleles are different forms of a gene. Because of Mendel's work, Sutton knew that alleles exist in pairs in an organism. One allele comes from the female parent. The other allele comes from the male parent. Sutton realized that paired alleles are carried on paired chromosomes. His idea is now known as the chromosome theory of inheritance. **According to the chromosome theory of inheritance, genes pass from parents to their offspring on chromosomes.**

A Lineup of Genes

The body cells of humans contain 46 chromosomes that form 23 pairs. Chromosomes are made up of many genes joined together like beads on a string. Although you have only 23 pairs of chromosomes, your body cells each contain between 20,000 and 25,000 genes. Genes control traits.

Figure 2 shows a pair of chromosomes from an organism. One chromosome is from the female parent. The other chromosome is from the male parent. Notice that each chromosome has the same genes. The genes are lined up in the same order on both chromosomes. However, the alleles for some of the genes are not identical. For example, one chromosome has allele *A*, and the other chromosome has allele *a*. As you can see, this organism is heterozygous for some traits and homozygous for others.

Relate Cause and Effect Suppose gene A on the left chromosome is damaged and no longer functions. What form of the trait would show? Why?

____

____

____

____

____

FIGURE 2

A Pair of Chromosomes

Chromosomes in a pair may have different alleles for some genes and the same alleles for others.

Interpret Diagrams For each pair of alleles, tell whether the organism is homozygous or heterozygous. The first two answers are shown.

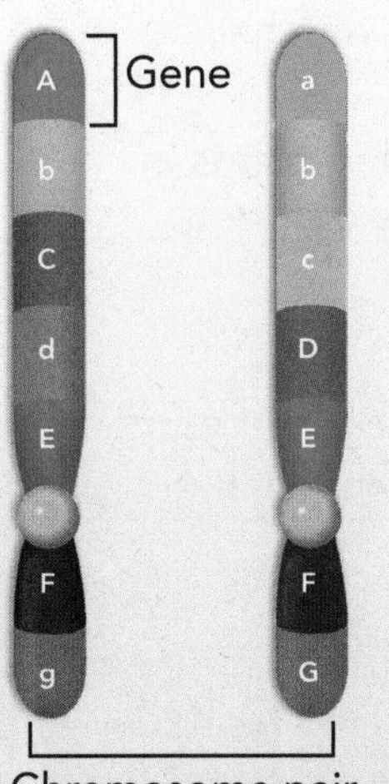

Heterozygous

Homozygous

____

____

____

____

____

Do the Quick Lab *Chromosomes and Inheritance.*

Assess Your Understanding

1a. Describe When two grasshopper sex cells join, the chromosome number in the new cell is (half/double) the number in the sex cells.

b. Summarize Describe the arrangement of genes on a pair of chromosomes.

____

____

____

c. Relate Evidence and Explanation How do Sutton's observations support the chromosome theory of inheritance?

____

____

____

____

got it?

O **I get it!** Now I know that genes are passed from parents to offspring _______________

____

O I need extra help with _______________

Go to MY SCIENCE COACH *online for help with this subject.*

Science Standards of Learning

LS.1d Construct and use models and simulations to illustrate and explain phenomena.

LS.2d Investigate and understand cell division.

LS.12b Investigate and understand the function of genes and chromosomes.

What Happens During Meiosis?

How do sex cells end up with half the number of chromosomes as body cells? The answer to this question is a form of cell division called meiosis. **Meiosis** (my OH sis) is the process by which the number of chromosomes is reduced by half as sex cells form. You can trace the events of meiosis in **Figure 3.** Here, the parent cell has four chromosomes arranged in two pairs. **During meiosis, the chromosome pairs separate into two different cells. The sex cells that form later have only half as many chromosomes as the other cells in the organism.**

FIGURE 3

ART IN MOTION **Meiosis**

During meiosis, a cell produces sex cells with half the number of chromosomes.

Interpret Diagrams Fill in the missing terms in the spaces provided, and complete the diagram.

Before Meiosis

Every chromosome in the parent cell is copied. Centromeres hold the two chromatids together.

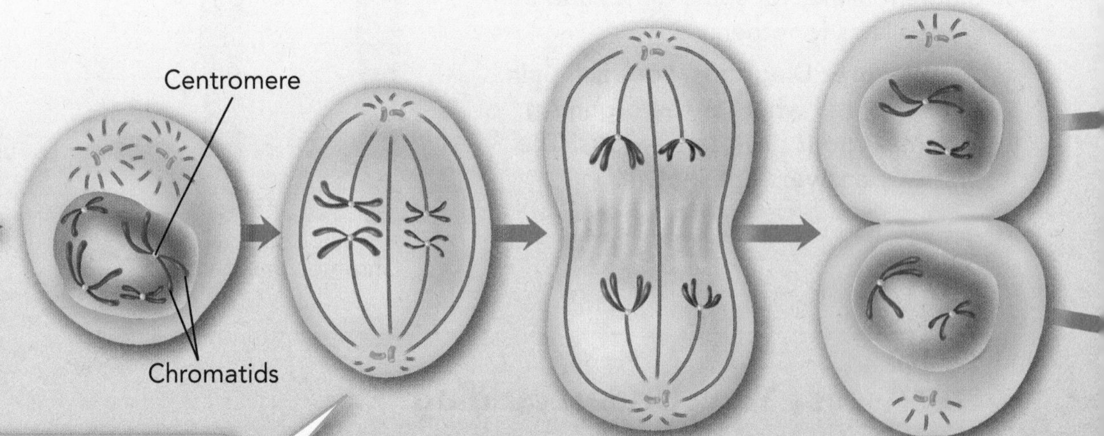

Centromere

Chromatids

1 The chromosome pairs line up in the

____

of the cell.

2 The pairs separate and move to

____

ends of the cell.

3 Two cells form. Each cell has half the original number of chromosomes. Each chromosome is still made of

____

chromatids.

During meiosis, a cell divides into two cells. Then each of these cells divides again, forming a total of four cells. The chromosomes duplicate only before the first cell division.

Each of the four sex cells shown below receives two chromosomes—one chromosome from each pair in the original cell. When two sex cells join at fertilization, the new cell that forms has the full number of chromosomes. In this case, the number is four. The organism that grows from this cell got two of its chromosomes from one parent and two from the other parent.

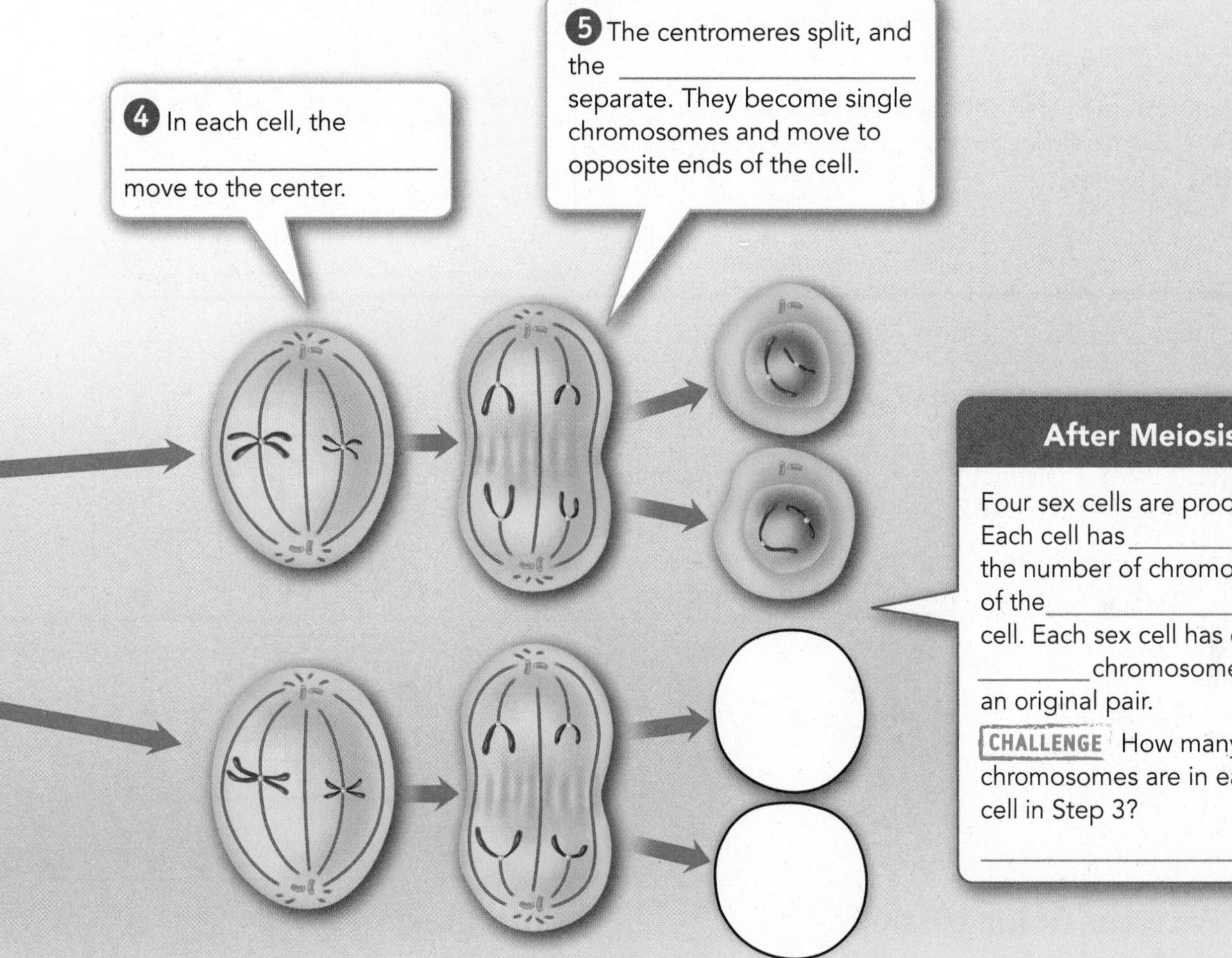

After Meiosis

Four sex cells are produced. Each cell has ______ the number of chromosomes of the ______ cell. Each sex cell has only ______ chromosome from an original pair.

CHALLENGE How many chromosomes are in each cell in Step 3?

______

Lab zone® Do the Quick Lab *Modeling Meiosis.*

Assess Your Understanding

got it?

O **I get it!** Now I know that during meiosis, the number of chromosomes ______

______

O I need extra help with ______

Go to my science COACH *online for help with this subject.*

CHAPTER 6

Study Guide

Offspring inherit different forms of genes called ________________ from each parent. Traits are affected by patterns of inheritance and interactions with the ____________________.

LESSON 1 What Is Heredity?

In all of his crosses, Mendel found that only one form of the trait appeared in the F_1 generation. However, in the F_2 generation, the "lost" form of the trait always reappeared in about one fourth of the plants.

An organism's traits are controlled by the alleles it inherits from its parents. Some alleles are dominant, while other alleles are recessive.

Vocabulary

- heredity • trait • genetics • fertilization • purebred
- gene • allele • dominant allele • recessive allele • hybrid

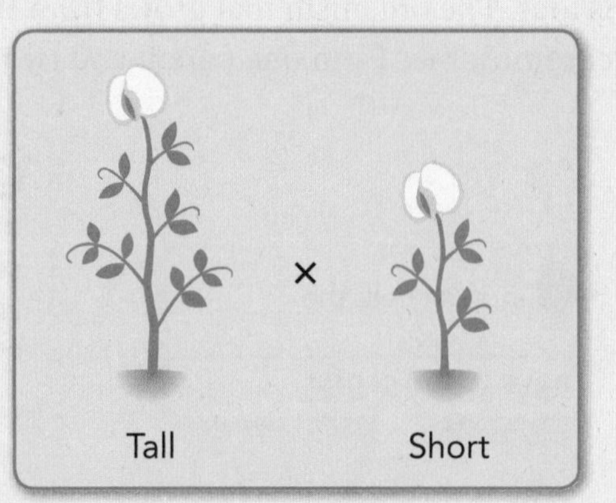

LESSON 2 Probability and Heredity

In a genetic cross, the combination of alleles that parents can pass to an offspring is based on probability.

An organism's phenotype is its physical appearance, or visible traits. An organism's genotype is its genetic makeup, or alleles.

Vocabulary

- probability • Punnett square • phenotype • genotype
- homozygous • heterozygous

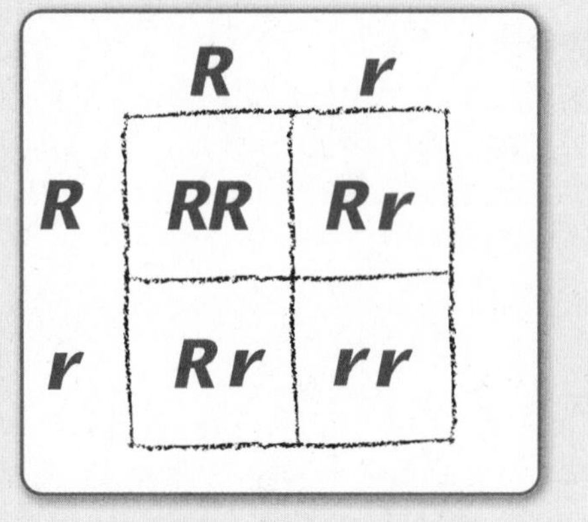

LESSON 3 Patterns of Inheritance

Most traits are the result of complex patterns of inheritance.

Environmental factors can influence the way genes are expressed.

Vocabulary

- incomplete dominance
- codominance
- multiple alleles
- polygenic inheritance

LESSON 4 Chromosomes and Inheritance

The chromosome theory of inheritance states that genes pass from parents to their offspring on chromosomes.

Meiosis produces sex cells that have half as many chromosomes as body cells.

Vocabulary

- meiosis

Review and Assessment

LESSON 1 What Is Heredity?

1. Different forms of a gene are called
   a. alleles. b. hybrids.
   c. genotypes. d. chromosomes.

2. ______________________ is the scientific study of heredity.

3. **Explain** Mendel crossed two pea plants: one with green pods and one with yellow pods. The F_1 generation all had green pods. What color pods did the F_2 generation have? Explain your answer.

4. **Predict** The plant below is purebred for height (tall). Write the alleles of this plant. In any cross for height, what kind of offspring will this plant produce? Why?

5. **Compare and Contrast** How do dominant alleles and recessive alleles differ?

6. **Write About It** Write a diary entry as if you are Gregor Mendel. You may describe any part of his experiences, experiments, or observations.

LESSON 2 Probability and Heredity

7. Which of the following represents a heterozygous genotype?
   a. *YY* b. *yy*
   c. *Yy* d. Y^HY^H

8. An organism's ______________________ is the way its genotype is expressed.

9. **Make Models** Fill in the Punnett square below to show a cross between two guinea pigs that are heterozygous for coat color. *B* is for black coat color, and *b* is for white coat color.

	_	_
_	_ _	_ _
_	_ _	_ _

10. **Interpret Tables** What is the probability that an offspring from the cross above has each of the following genotypes?
    BB ______________
    Bb ______________
    bb ______________

11. **Apply Concepts** What kind of cross might tell you if a black guinea pig is *BB* or *Bb*? Why?

12. **do the math!** A garden has 80 pea plants. Of this total, 20 plants have short stems and 60 plants have tall stems. What percentage of the plants have short stems? What percentage have tall stems?

CHAPTER

6 Review and Assessment

LESSON 3 Patterns of Inheritance

13. Which of the following terms describes a pattern of inheritance in which one allele is only partially dominant?

a. codominance

b. acquired traits

c. multiple alleles

d. incomplete dominance

14. Traits that have three or more phenotypes may be the result of ________________ alleles.

15. Compare and Contrast How is codominance different from incomplete dominance?

____

____

____

____

____

16. Relate Cause and Effect Human height is a trait with a very broad range of phenotypes. Which pattern of inheritance could account for human height? Explain your answer.

____

____

____

____

____

17. Identify Faulty Reasoning Neither of Josie's parents plays a musical instrument. Josie thinks that she won't be able to play an instrument because her parents can't. Is she right? Why or why not?

____

____

____

____

____

LESSON 4 Chromosomes and Inheritance

18. Genes are carried from parents to offspring on structures called

a. alleles.

b. chromosomes.

c. phenotypes.

d. genotypes.

19. The process of ____________ results in the formation of sex cells.

20. Summarize If an organism's body cells have 12 chromosomes, how many chromosomes will the sex cells have? Explain your answer.

____

____

____

____

____

Why don't offspring always look like their parents?

21. A species of butterfly has three alleles for wing color: blue, orange, and pale yellow. A blue butterfly mates with an orange butterfly. The following offspring result: about 25% are blue and 25% are orange. However, another 25% are speckled blue and orange, and 25% are yellow. Explain how these results could occur.

Offspring of blue butterfly and orange butterfly

____

____

____

____

Virginia SOL Test Prep

Read each question and choose the best answer.

1 The Punnett square below shows a cross between two pea plants, each with round seeds. What is the missing genotype in the empty square?

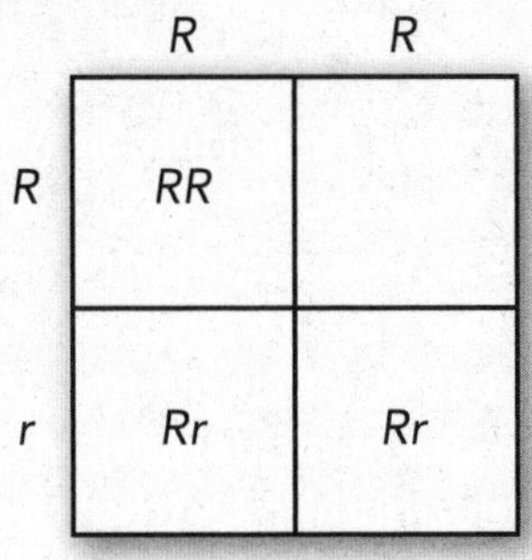

A *rr*
B *rR*
C *Rr*
D *RR*

2 A particular trait has multiple alleles: A, B, and C. How many different genotypes are possible?

F 2
G 3
H 4
J 6

3 The scientific study of heredity is called—

A meiosis
B genetics
C probability
D fertilization

4 For a particular plant, leaf texture is either fuzzy or smooth. A purebred fuzzy plant is crossed with a purebred smooth plant. All offspring are smooth. Which sentence best describes the alleles for this trait?

F Fuzzy is dominant over smooth.
G Smooth is dominant over fuzzy.
H The alleles are codominant.
J The alleles have incomplete dominance.

5 Which of the following traits is acquired?

A the number of petals that grow in a plant's flowers
B the wing shape of a wild bird
C the ability of some gorillas to use sign language
D a cheetah's ability to run faster than any other land animal

6 During meiosis, a cell with 12 chromosomes produces four sex cells with how many chromosomes each?

F 3
G 6
H 12
J 48

7 Janet painted her nails pink. Her new nail color is an example of—

A an acquired trait
B a dominant trait
C a recessive trait
D codominance

Nature vs. Nurture

In 1990, the Monterey Bay Aquarium in Monterey, California, released a young otter into the wild. Wildlife rehabilitators at the aquarium raised the otter and taught her how to find food. But, because she was used to receiving food and affection from people at the aquarium, she did not know to avoid other humans. After the otter pestered some local divers, she had to be returned to live at the aquarium.

So, which behaviors do animals learn, and which behaviors "just come naturally"? Actually, the line between inherited behaviors and learned behaviors is rarely clear. Although wild otters are naturally shy around humans, the otter at the Monterey Bay Aquarium had learned to expect food and affection from humans. As a result, wildlife rehabilitators commonly use puppets or animal costumes to keep the animals they care for from becoming too familiar with humans.

▼ This photograph shows a pair of otters, one of the species wildlife rehabilitators try to reintroduce into the wild.

Design It Choose a species, such as deer, otter, or panda, that is sometimes raised in captivity and returned to the wild. Design a rehabilitation activity to help orphaned animals learn a skill that they will need to survive in the wild. Explain the features of your rehabilitation activity to your class.

LS.1d, LS.1j, LS.12d

Seeing Spots

You would probably recognize a Dalmatian if you saw one—Dalmatians typically have white coats with distinctive black or brown spots. Spots are a defining characteristic of the Dalmatian breed. These spots can be large or small, but all Dalmatians have them.

In Dalmatians, spots are a dominant trait. When two Dalmatians breed, each parent contributes a gene for spots. The trait for spots is controlled by one set of genes with only two possible alleles. No matter how many puppies are in a litter, they will all develop spots.

But what if a Dalmatian breeds with another dog that isn't a Dalmatian? While the puppies won't develop the distinctive Dalmatian pattern, they will have spots, because the allele for spots is dominant. Some puppies will have many tiny spots and some will have large patches! Dalmatians, like leopards, cannot change their spots.

Newborn Dalmatian puppies are white—their spots develop when the puppies are about a week old. ▼

Predict It! Dalmatians' spots may be black or liver (brown), but never both on the same dog. Liver is a recessive allele. Use a Punnett square to predict the color of the spots on the offspring of a liver Dalmatian and a black Dalmatian with a recessive liver allele. Display your prediction on a poster.

LS.1a, LS.1d, LS.1h, LS.1j, LS.12b

WHY IS THIS LOBSTER BLUE?

THE BIG ?

What does DNA do?

American lobsters are usually dark green in color. But, most people see only red lobsters. Lobsters turn red after they have been cooked. The chance of finding a blue lobster is about one in a million.

Infer **Why might a lobster have a blue shell?**

UNTAMED SCIENCE Watch the **Untamed Science** video to learn more about DNA.

DNA: The Code of Life

Science Standards of Learning

LS.1d, LS.1h, LS.1i, LS.1j, LS.12a, LS.12b, LS.12f, LS.13a

CHAPTER

7 Getting Started

Check Your Understanding

1. **Background** Read the paragraph below and then answer the question.

> Leo's sister likes to joke that Leo inherited his dad's **genes** for playing the piano. Leo knows that **heredity** may not be that simple. But there are other **traits**—like the widow's peak on his forehead—that he did inherit from his father.

A segment of DNA on a chromosome that codes for a specific trait is a **gene.**

Heredity is the passing of traits from parent to offspring.

A **trait** is a characteristic that an organism can pass on through its genes.

- Why couldn't Leo inherit his dad's piano skills?

____

____

MY READING WEB If you had trouble completing the question above, visit **My Reading Web** and type in ***DNA: The Code of Life.***

Vocabulary Skill

Latin Word Parts Some vocabulary in this chapter contains word parts with Latin origins. Look at the Latin words below, and the example derived from each word.

Latin Word	Meaning of Latin Word	Example
mutare	to change	mutation, *n.* any change in the DNA of a gene or chromosome
tumere	to swell	tumor, *n.* a mass of abnormal cells that develops when cells divide and grow uncontrollably

2. **Quick Check The meaning of the Latin word *mutare* appears in the definition of *mutation.* Circle the word in both places that it appears in the table above.**

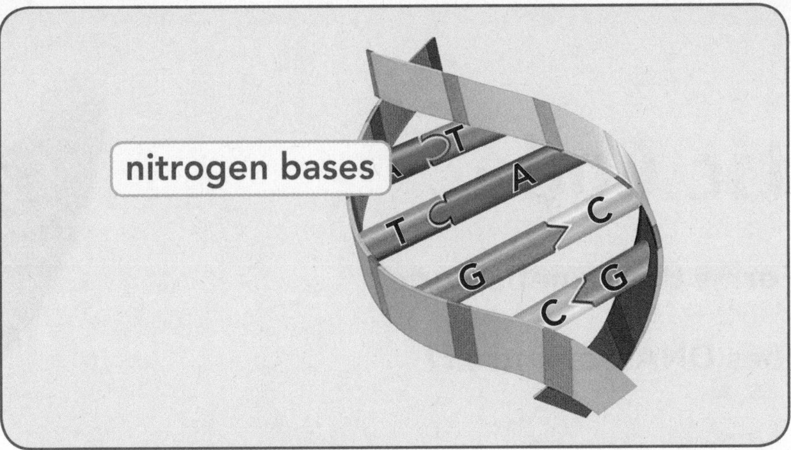

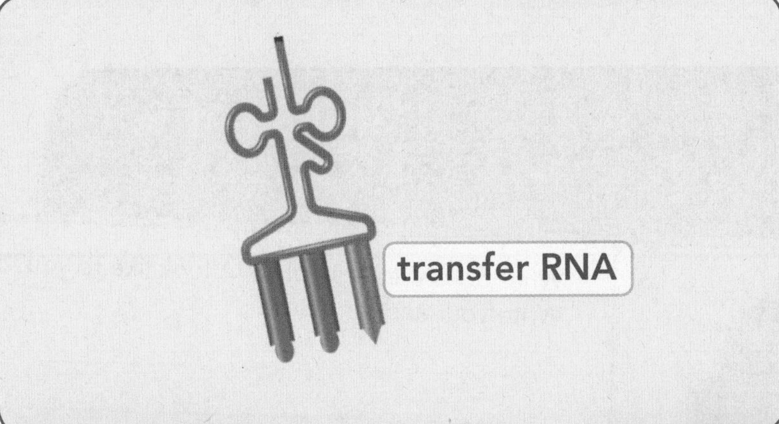

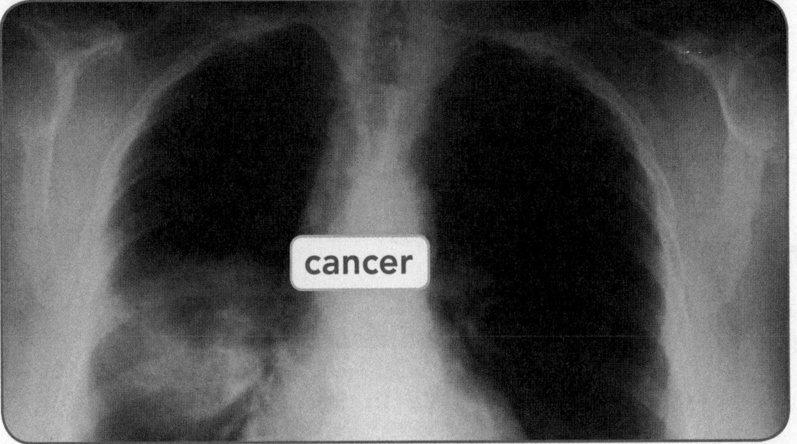

Chapter Preview

LESSON 1
- nitrogen bases
- DNA replication

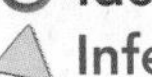 **Identify the Main Idea**
△ **Infer**

LESSON 2
- messenger RNA
- transfer RNA

Summarize
△ **Design Experiments**

LESSON 3
- mutation
- cancer
- tumor
- chemotherapy

Relate Cause and Effect
△ **Calculate**

 For extra help with vocabulary, visit **Vocab Flash Cards** and type in ***DNA: The Code of Life.***

The Genetic Code

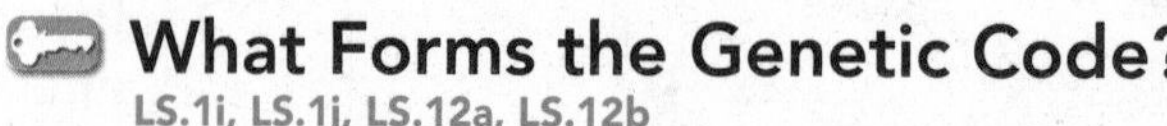

my planet Diary

BIOGRAPHY

DNA Debut

In 1951, English scientist Rosalind Franklin discovered that DNA could exist in a dry form and a wet form. Franklin made an image of the wet form of DNA by exposing it to X-rays. The X-rays bounced off the atoms in the DNA to make the image. The image (see the background on the next journal page) was so clear that it helped scientists understand the structure of DNA for the first time. Her discovery was important for figuring out how genetic information is passed from parent to offspring. Franklin's contribution to science was not only in her research, but also in that she succeeded at a time when many people thought women shouldn't be scientists.

PLANET DIARY Go to **Planet Diary** to learn more about the genetic code.

What does the X-ray of DNA look like to you? Write your answer below.

____

____

____

____

Lab zone Do the Inquiry Warm-Up *Can You Crack the Code?*

Vocabulary
- nitrogen bases
- DNA replication

Skills
 Reading: Identify the Main Idea
Inquiry: Infer

What Forms the Genetic Code?

It took almost 100 years after the discovery of DNA for scientists to figure out that it looks like a twisted ladder. When James Watson and Francis Crick published the structure of DNA in 1953, they added another clue to how traits are passed from parent to offspring. DNA contains the genetic information for cells to make proteins. Proteins determine a variety of traits, from hair color to an organism's ability to digest food.

Science Standards of Learning

LS.1i Identify, interpret, and evaluate patterns in data.
LS.1j Use current applications to reinforce life science concepts.
LS.12a Investigate and understand the structure and role of DNA.
LS.12b Investigate and understand the function of genes and chromosomes.

The Structure of DNA

Parents pass traits to offspring through chromosomes. Chromosomes are made of DNA and proteins and are located in a cell's nucleus. Look at **Figure 1.** The twisted ladder structure of DNA is also known as a "double helix." The sides of the double helix are made up of sugar molecules called deoxyribose, alternating with phosphate molecules. The name DNA, or deoxyribonucleic acid (DEE ahk see ry boh noo klee ik), comes from this structure.

The rungs of DNA are made of nitrogen bases. **Nitrogen bases** are molecules that contain nitrogen and other elements. DNA has four kinds of nitrogen bases: adenine (AD uh neen), thymine (THY meen), guanine (GWAH neen), and cytosine (SY tuh seen). The capital letters *A, T, G,* and *C* are used to represent the bases.

FIGURE 1
ART IN MOTION **Genetic Structures**
Hummingbirds, like all organisms, contain all of the genetic structures below.
Sequence Put the structures in order from largest to smallest by writing the numbers two through five in the blank circles.

1

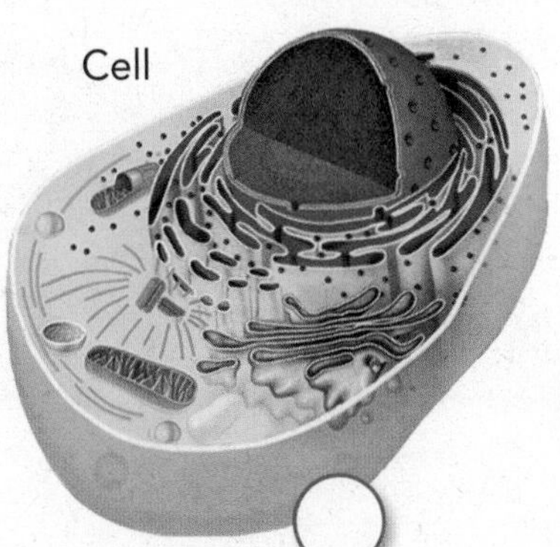

Nitrogen bases
C A C G T G A T C

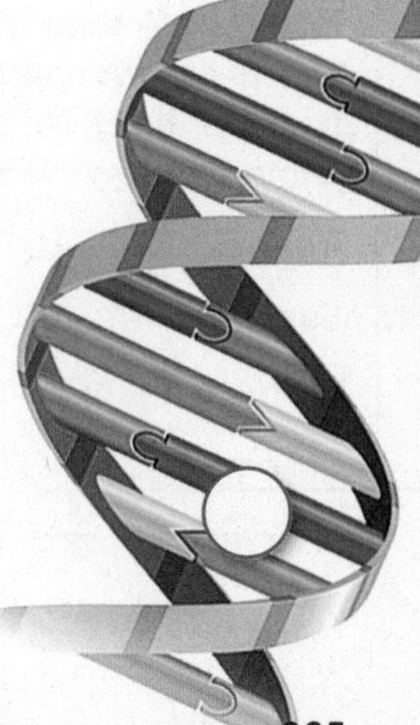

Identify the Main Idea Underline the sentence that explains the role of genes in making proteins.

Chromosomes, Genes, and DNA

In **Figure 2,** you can see the relationship among chromosomes, genes, and DNA. A gene is a section of a DNA molecule that contains the information to code for one specific protein. A gene is made up of a series of bases in a row. The bases in a gene are arranged in a specific order—for example, ATGACGTAC. A single gene on a chromosome may contain anywhere from several hundred to a million or more of these bases. Each gene is located at a specific place on a chromosome.

Because there are so many possible combinations of bases and genes, each individual organism has a unique set of DNA. DNA can be found in all of the cells of your body except for red blood cells. DNA can be found in blood samples, however, because white blood cells do contain DNA.

FIGURE 2

Chromosomes and Genes

Humans have between 20,000 and 25,000 genes on their chromosomes. The corals that make up ocean reefs are thought to have as many as 25,000 genes too!

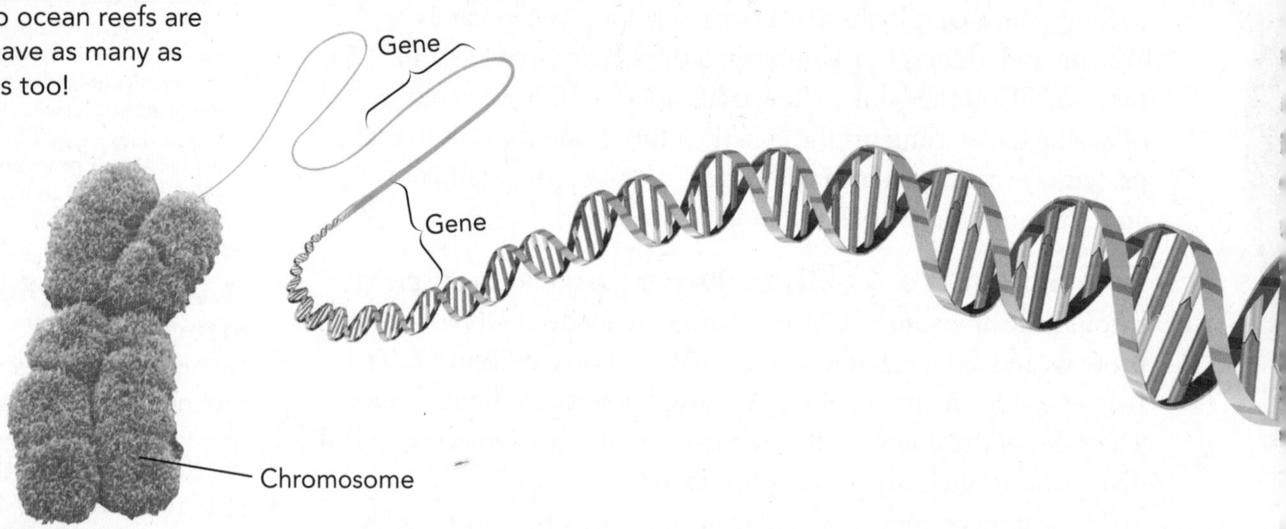

Gene

Gene

Chromosome

apply it!

Can you help solve the crime?

Someone robbed a jewelry store. The robber's DNA was extracted from skin cells found on the broken glass of a jewelry case. The police collected DNA samples from three suspects. The letters below represent the sequences of nitrogen bases in the DNA. Based on the DNA found at the crime scene, circle the DNA of the guilty suspect.

Robber: GACCAGTTAGCTAAGTCT

Suspect 1: TAGCTGA

Suspect 2: GACGAGT

Suspect 3: CTAAGTC

1 **Explain** Why can you solve crimes using DNA?

2 **Infer** Could the police have used blood on the broken glass to test for DNA? Why or why not?

Order of the Bases

A gene contains the code that determines the structure of a protein. **The order of the nitrogen bases along a gene forms a genetic code that specifies what type of protein will be produced.** Remember that proteins are long-chain molecules made of individual amino acids. In the genetic code, a group of three DNA bases codes for one specific amino acid. For example, the three-base sequence CGT (cytosine-guanine-thymine) always codes for the amino acid alanine. The order of the three-base code units determines the order in which amino acids are put together to form a protein.

did you know?

If you took all the DNA from the cells in the average adult human body and stretched it out, it would reach to the sun and back again multiple times!

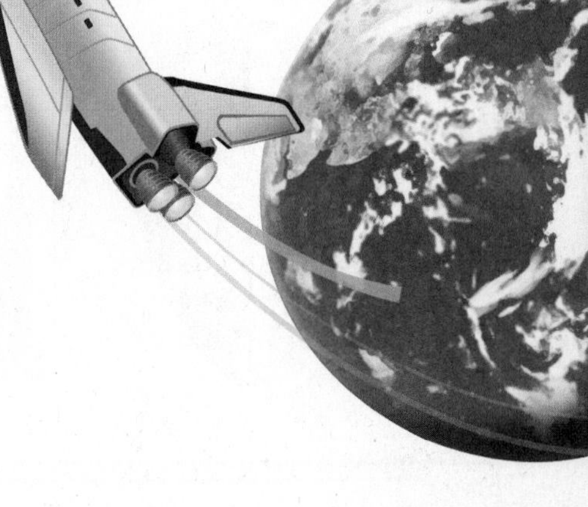

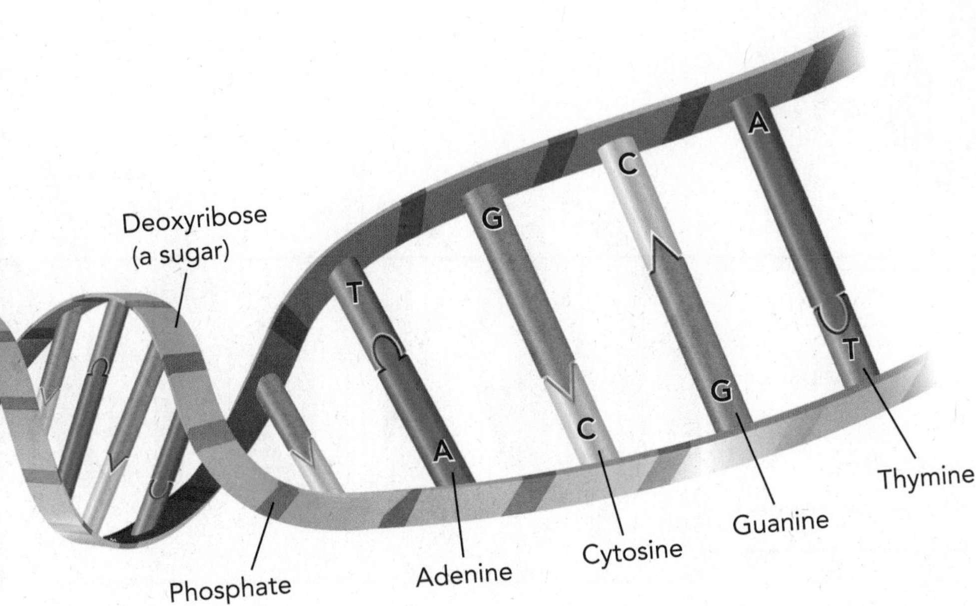

FIGURE 3

DNA Bases

Notice the pattern in the DNA bases.

Interpret Diagrams **Which base always pairs with cytosine?**

____

____

Do the Lab Investigation *Guilty or Innocent?*

Assess Your Understanding

1a. Identify These letters represent the nitrogen bases on one strand of DNA: GGCTATCCA. What letters would form the other strand of the helix?

____

b. Explain How can a parent pass a trait such as eye color to its offspring?

____

____

____

got it?

O **I get it!** Now I know that the genetic code of nitrogen bases specifies ______________________

____

____

O I need extra help with ______________________

____

Go to MY SCIENCE COACH *online for help with this subject.*

FIGURE 4

INTERACTIVE ART DNA Replication

Without DNA replication, daughter cells could not carry out their life functions.

Interpret Diagrams Fill in the missing bases on the strands of DNA. Then complete the sentences below.

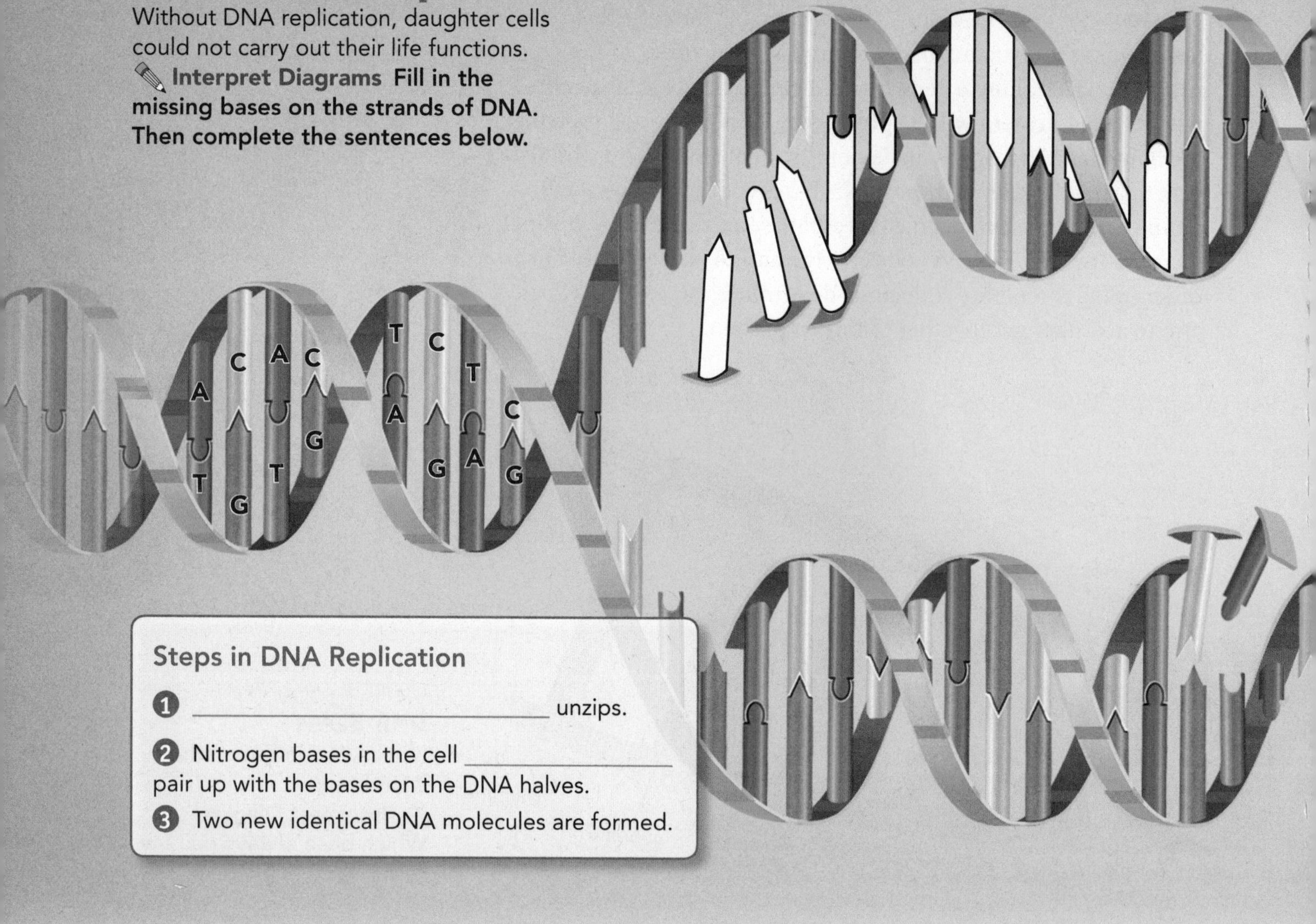

Steps in DNA Replication

1. ______________________ unzips.
2. Nitrogen bases in the cell ______________ pair up with the bases on the DNA halves.
3. Two new identical DNA molecules are formed.

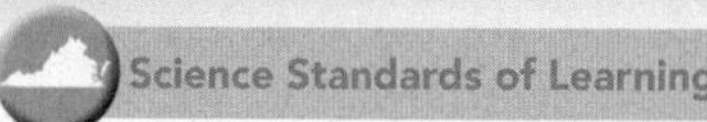

LS.1d Construct and use models and simulations to illustrate and explain phenomena.

LS.1i Identify, interpret, and evaluate patterns in data.

LS.12a Investigate and understand the structure and role of DNA.

How Does DNA Copy Itself?

Two new cells, or daughter cells, result when a cell divides. To ensure that each daughter cell has the genetic information it needs to carry out its activities, DNA copies itself. **DNA replication** is the process in which an identical copy of a DNA strand is formed for a new cell. Replication is very important, since daughter cells need a complete set of DNA to survive.

DNA replication begins when the two sides of a DNA molecule unwind and separate, like a zipper unzipping, between the nitrogen bases. Next, nitrogen bases in the nucleus pair up with the bases on each half of the DNA. **Because of the way the nitrogen bases pair up, the order of the bases in each new DNA strand exactly matches the order in the original DNA strand.** This pattern is key to understanding how DNA replication occurs. Adenine always pairs with thymine, while guanine always pairs with cytosine. At the end of replication, two identical DNA molecules are formed.

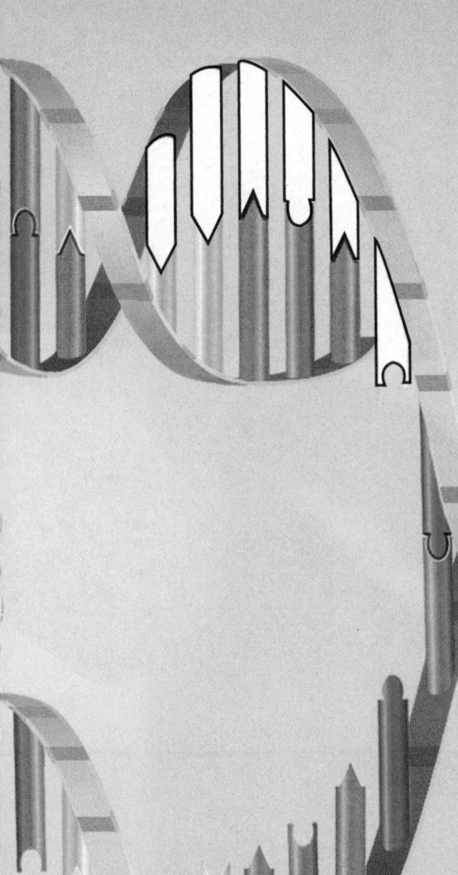

FIGURE 5

Magnified Strand of DNA

A photograph of DNA replication is taken through an electron microscope.

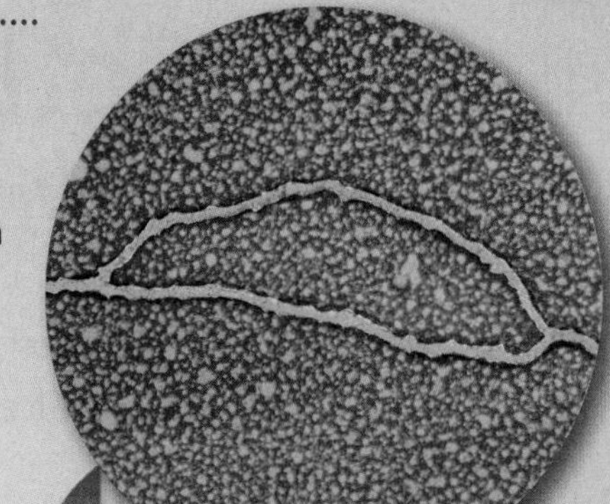

Do the Quick Lab *Modeling the Genetic Code.*

Assess Your Understanding

2a. Review The (nitrogen base pattern/ number of genes/size of DNA) determines how DNA is replicated.

b. Describe Where in the cell does DNA replication take place?

____

c. CHALLENGE What do you think would happen if the DNA code in a daughter cell did not match the code in the parent cell?

____

got it?

O **I get it!** Now I know that DNA replication is the process in which ______________________

O I need extra help with ______________________

Go to my science coach *online for help with this subject.*

LESSON 2

How Cells Make Proteins

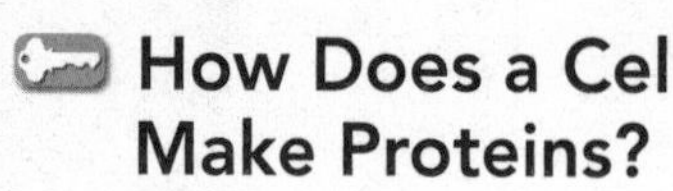

How Does a Cell Make Proteins?
LS.1d, LS.12a

my planet Diary

DISCOVERY

Dinosaur Chicken?

In 2007, a 68-million-year-old dinosaur protein was discovered by Harvard scientists. The protein, called *collagen,* was extracted from the soft tissue of a *Tyrannosaurus rex* that died in Montana. Collagen is an important component of bone. The protein from the dinosaur is similar to protein found in modern-day chickens, supporting the connection between dinosaurs and birds. With this discovery, scientists have more evidence that these two species are related.

Communicate **Discuss the question with a group of classmates. Write your answer below.**

What other information about the two species would you want to compare? ________________________________

____

PLANET DIARY Go to **Planet Diary** to learn more about how cells make proteins.

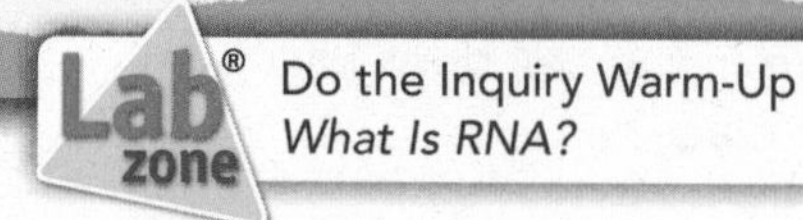

Do the Inquiry Warm-Up *What Is RNA?*

Science Standards of Learning

LS.1d Construct and use models and simulations to illustrate and explain phenomena.

LS.12a Investigate and understand the structure and role of DNA.

How Does a Cell Make Proteins?

The production of proteins in a cell is called protein synthesis. **During protein synthesis, the cell uses information from a gene on a chromosome to produce a specific protein.** Proteins help determine the size, shape, color, and other traits of an organism by triggering cellular processes. The protein code passes from parent to offspring through DNA, resulting in inherited traits.

Vocabulary
messenger RNA
transfer RNA

Skills
Reading: Summarize
Inquiry: Design Experiments

The Structure of Proteins Proteins are made up of molecules called amino acids, as shown in **Figure 1.** Although there are only 20 amino acids, cells can combine them in different ways to form thousands of different proteins. You can think of the 20 amino acids as being like the 26 letters of the alphabet. Those 26 letters can form thousands of words. The letters you use and their order determine the words you form. A change in just one letter, for example, from *rice* to *mice*, creates a new word. Similarly, a change in the type or order of amino acids can result in a different protein.

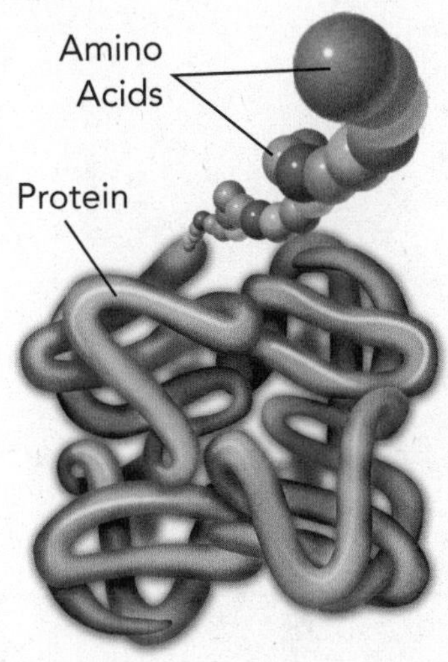

FIGURE 1
Proteins
Proteins help determine what you look like.
Interpret Diagrams Complete the sentence. Proteins are made of folded and bundled chains of

____

____

The Role of RNA Protein synthesis takes place in the cytoplasm outside the cell's nucleus. The chromosomes are found inside the nucleus, so a messenger must carry the genetic code from the DNA inside the nucleus to the cytoplasm. This genetic messenger is called RNA, or ribonucleic acid (ry boh noo KLEE ik).

Although both RNA and DNA are nucleic acids, they have some differences. RNA has only one strand and contains a different sugar molecule than DNA. Another difference is in the nitrogen bases. Like DNA, RNA contains adenine, guanine, and cytosine. However, instead of thymine, RNA contains uracil (YOOR uh sil).

Types of RNA Two types of RNA take part in protein synthesis. **Messenger RNA** (mRNA) copies the message from DNA in the nucleus and carries the message to the ribosome in the cytoplasm. **Transfer RNA** (tRNA) carries amino acids to the ribosome and adds them to the growing protein.

apply it!

RNA

DNA

While working in the lab, your assistant accidentally mixes one beaker of DNA into a beaker containing RNA. You need to separate the molecules before doing your experiments.

Design Experiments How could you test each molecule to determine if it was DNA or RNA? ________________________________

____

____

____

____

Protein Synthesis

What does DNA do?

FIGURE 2

INTERACTIVE ART The steps of protein synthesis are shown in the numbered boxes. Notice that the bases in the steps align with the bases in the summary chart on the far right.

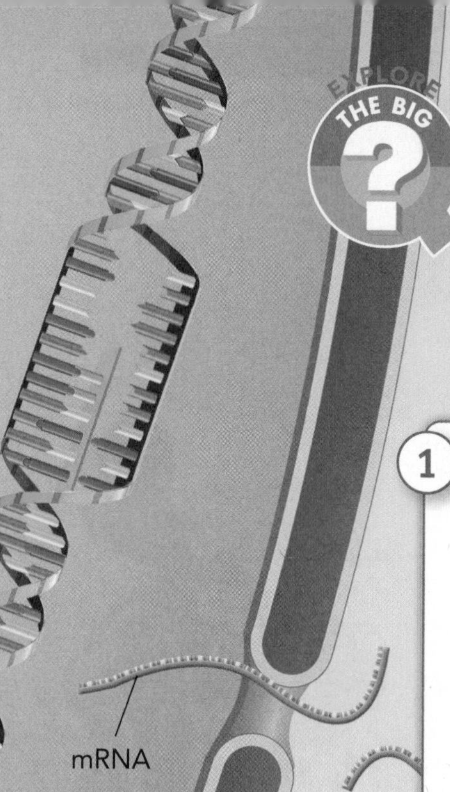

1 mRNA Enters the Cytoplasm

DNA unzips between its base pairs. Then one of the strands of DNA directs the production of a strand of mRNA. To form the RNA strand, RNA bases pair up with the DNA bases. The process is similar to DNA replication. Cytosine always pairs with guanine. However, uracil, not thymine, pairs with adenine. The mRNA leaves the nucleus and enters the cytoplasm.

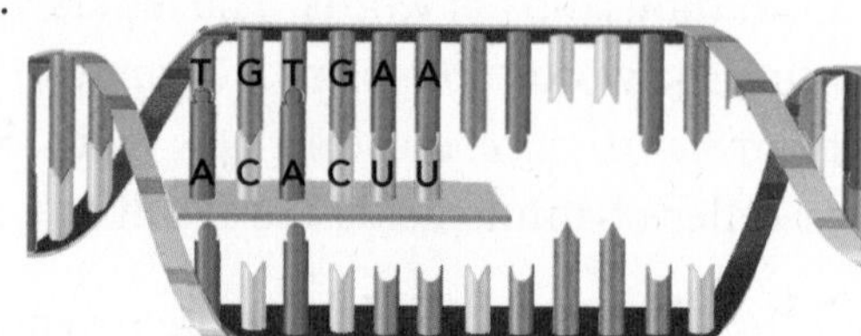

2 Ribosomes Attach to mRNA

A ribosome attaches to mRNA in the cytoplasm. On the ribosome, the mRNA provides the code for the protein that will be made. In the cytoplasm, specific amino acids are attached to specific molecules of tRNA.

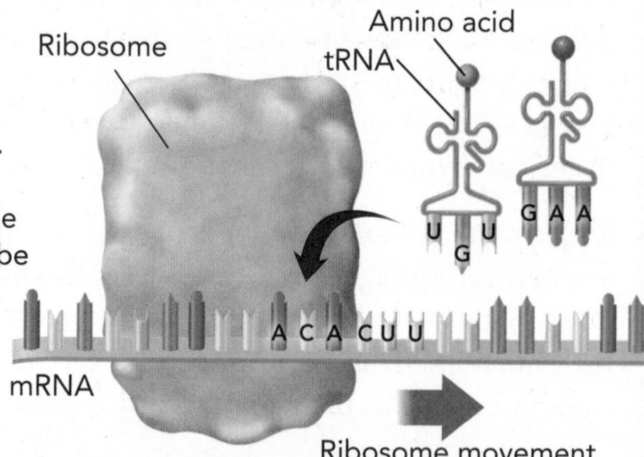

3 tRNA Attaches to mRNA

Molecules of tRNA and their amino acids attach to the mRNA. The bases on tRNA "read" the message and pair with bases on mRNA.

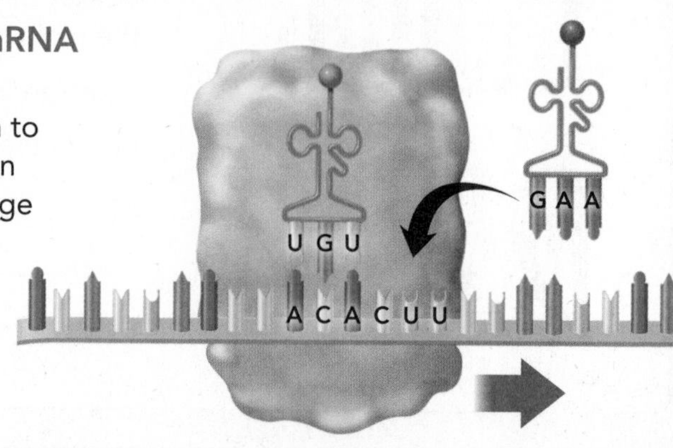

4 Amino Acids Join in the Ribosome

Transfer molecules attach one at a time to the ribosome and continue to read the message. The amino acids are linked together and form a growing chain. The order of the amino acids is determined by the order of the three-base codes on the mRNA.

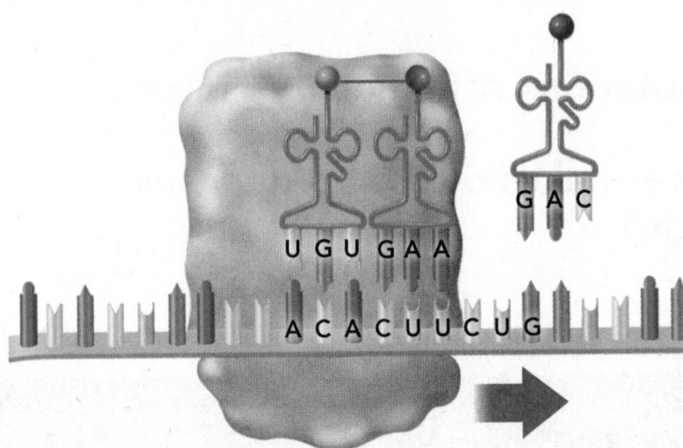

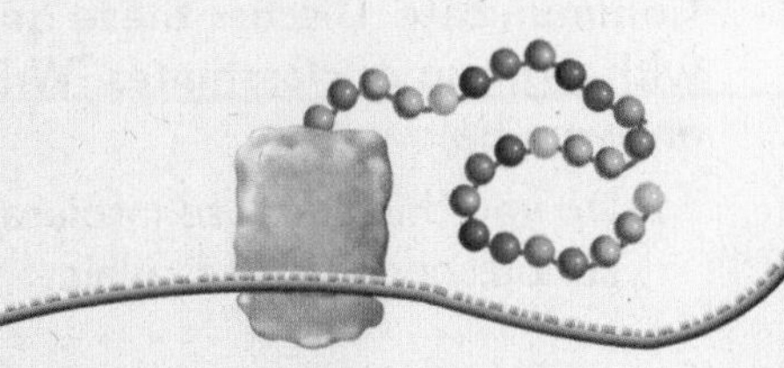

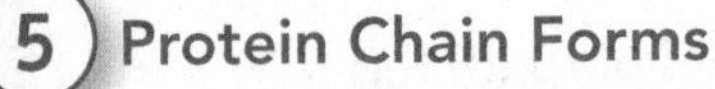

5 Protein Chain Forms

As the ribosome continues to move along the mRNA adding amino acids, the protein grows. Once an amino acid is added, the tRNA is released and picks up another amino acid of the same kind. The protein continues to grow until the ribosome reaches a three-base code that signals it to stop. The protein is then released.

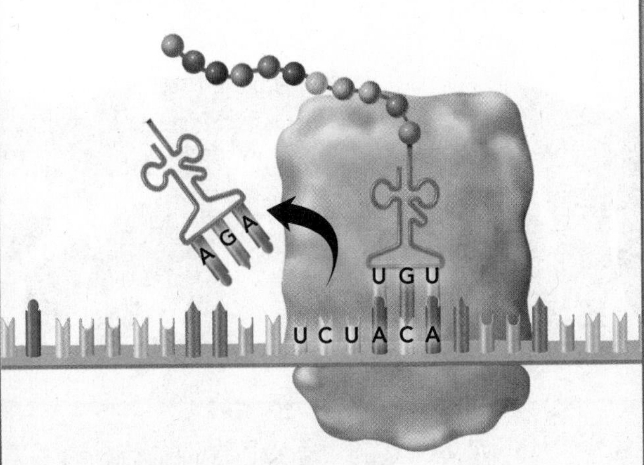

Summarize The chart below summarizes protein synthesis. Read the chart and fill in the blank labels.

DNA: T G T G A A

_________: A C A C U U

_________: U G U G A A

Protein: Amino acid | Amino acid

Lab zone Do the Quick Lab *Modeling Protein Synthesis.*

Assess Your Understanding

1a. Review (Messenger RNA/Transfer RNA) carries the genetic information in DNA from the nucleus to the cytoplasm.

b. ANSWER THE BIG Q What does DNA do?

____

____

____

____

got it?

O **I get it!** I now know that protein synthesis is the process in which _______________

____

____

____

O I need extra help with _______________

____

Go to **MY SCIENCE COACH** *online for help with this subject.*

Virginia

LESSON 3

Mutations

How Can Mutations Affect an Organism?
LS.12a, LS.13a

How Is Cancer Related to Mutations and the Cell Cycle?
LS.13a

my planet Diary

Dairy DNA

Every mammal, from mice to monkeys to whales, drinks milk as a baby. But humans are the only mammals that can digest milk and other dairy products throughout their lifetime. Humans have a mutation (a change in DNA) that allows their bodies to break down lactose, a sugar in dairy products. However, not all people can digest dairy products. Many people are lactose intolerant, meaning their bodies cannot break down lactose. Lactose-intolerant people have the original DNA without the mutation. While many other mutations are considered harmful, this mutation is helpful to humans. And just think—ice cream might never have been invented if humans couldn't break down lactose!

MISCONCEPTION

Communicate Discuss these questions with a group of classmates. Write your answers below.

1. Do you think lactose intolerance is a serious condition? Explain.

____

____

2. Do you think people with this condition can *never* have milk?

____

____

____

PLANET DIARY Go to **Planet Diary** to learn more about mutations.

Do the Inquiry Warm-Up *Oops!*

Vocabulary
- mutation
- cancer
- tumor
- chemotherapy

Skills
- Reading: Relate Cause and Effect
- Inquiry: Calculate

How Can Mutations Affect an Organism?

Some traits are not inherited from parent organisms. Traits can also be a result of a change in DNA. A **mutation** is any change in the DNA of a gene or chromosome. For example, instead of the base sequence AAG, the DNA might have the sequence ACG. **Mutations can cause a cell to produce an incorrect protein during protein synthesis. As a result, the organism's trait may be different from what it normally would be.**

If a mutation occurs in a body cell, such as a skin cell, the mutation will not be passed on to the organism's offspring. But if a mutation occurs in a sex cell (egg or sperm), the mutation can be passed on to an offspring and affect the offspring's traits.

Types of Mutations Some mutations are the result of small changes in an organism's DNA. For example, a base pair may be added, a base pair may be substituted for another, or one or more bases may be deleted from a section of DNA. These types of mutations can occur during the DNA replication process. Other mutations may occur when chromosomes don't separate correctly during the formation of sex cells. When this type of mutation occurs, a cell can end up with too many or too few chromosomes. The cell can also end up with extra segments of chromosomes.

Science Standards of Learning

LS.12a Investigate and understand the structure and role of DNA.

LS.13a Investigate and understand relationships of mutation, adaptation, natural selection, and extinction.

Vocabulary Latin Word Origins *Mutation* comes from the Latin word *mutare*, meaning "to change." How can mutations change an organism's traits?

FIGURE 1

Mutations

The types of mutations of DNA include deletion, addition, and substitution.

Interpret Diagrams Circle the added base pair on the third piece of DNA. Fill in the nitrogen bases on the fourth piece of DNA to illustrate a substitution.

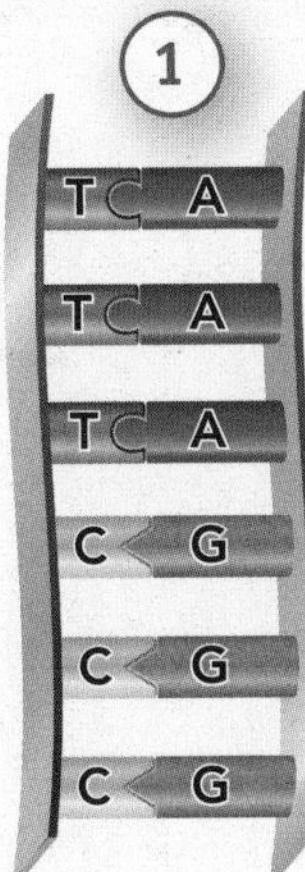

Original DNA sequence

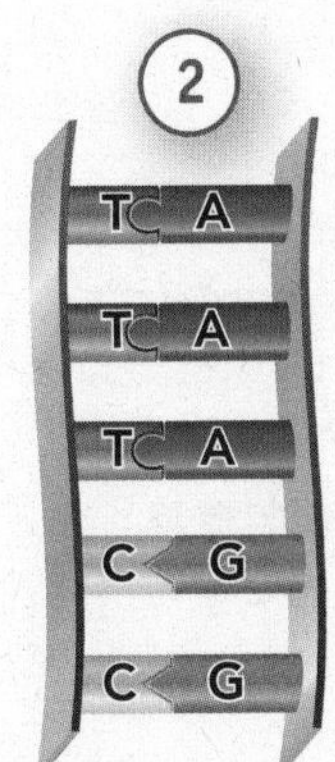

One base pair is removed (deletion).

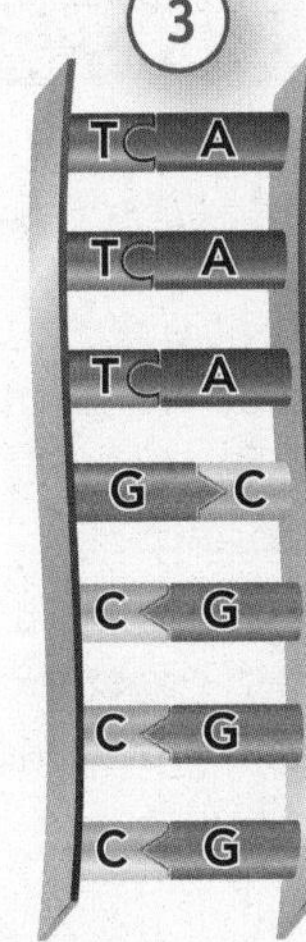

One base pair is added (addition).

One base pair is switched for another (substitution).

Effects of Mutations Mutations introduce changes in an organism. Mutations can be harmful, helpful, or neither harmful nor helpful. A mutation is harmful if it reduces the organism's chances for survival and reproduction. Harmful mutations can have negative effects on a species population by reducing the number of individuals that can reproduce. Helpful mutations can benefit a species population by allowing more individuals to reproduce.

Whether a mutation is harmful or not depends partly on the organism's environment. The mutation that led to this alligator's white color would probably be harmful to it in the wild. A white alligator is more visible to its prey. This alligator may find it difficult to catch prey and may not get enough food to survive. A white alligator in a zoo has the same chance for survival as a green alligator because it does not hunt. In a zoo, the mutation neither helps nor harms the alligator.

Helpful mutations increase an organism's ability to survive and reproduce. Mutations have allowed some bacteria that are harmful to humans to become resistant to drugs. The drugs do not kill the bacteria with the mutations, so they continue to survive and reproduce.

FIGURE 2

Review Check the phrase that best completes the sentence.

VIRTUAL LAB **Alligator Mutation**

A white alligator does not blend into its natural habitat, but this color change may be a beneficial mutation for an organism if it

- ○ reduces its chances for survival.
- ○ increases its chances for survival.
- ○ decreases its chances for reproduction.

Assess Your Understanding

1a. Explain Mutations that occur in body cells (can/cannot) be passed on to offspring. Mutations that occur in sex cells (can/cannot) be passed on to offspring.

b. Apply Concepts Drug resistance in bacteria is a beneficial mutation for the bacteria, but how can it be harmful for humans?

____

____

____

____

Lab zone Do the Quick Lab *Effects of Mutations.*

got it?

O **I get it!** Now I know that mutations affect an organism's traits by ______________________________

____

O I need extra help with ______________________________

____

Go to MY SCIENCE COACH *online for help with this subject.*

How Is Cancer Related to Mutations and the Cell Cycle?

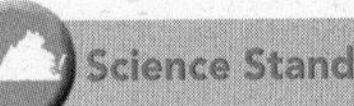

Science Standards of Learning

LS.13a Investigate and understand relationships of mutation, adaptation, natural selection, and extinction.

Did you know cancer is not just one disease? There are more than 100 types of cancer, and they can occur in almost any part of the body. Cancer affects many people around the world, regardless of age, race, or gender. Cancers are often named for the place in the body where they begin. For example, lung cancer begins in lung tissues, as shown in **Figure 3.**

What Is Cancer?

Cancer is a disease in which cells grow and divide uncontrollably, damaging the parts of the body around them. Cancer cells are like weeds in a garden. Weeds can overrun a garden by robbing plants of the space, sunlight, and water they need. Similarly, cancer cells can overrun normal cells.

Different factors work together in determining if a person gets cancer. Because of their inherited traits, some people are more likely than others to develop certain cancers. A woman with a mother or grandmother who had breast cancer has an increased chance of developing breast cancer herself. Some substances in the environment may also lead to cancer, like the tar in cigarettes or ultraviolet light from the sun or tanning beds. People who have a high-fat diet may also be more likely to develop cancer.

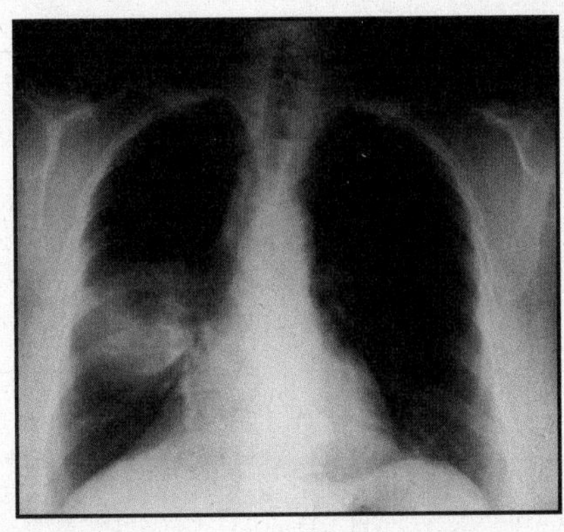

FIGURE 3

Lung Tumor X-Ray

Tumors can be visible in X-rays.

Interpret Photos Circle the tumor in the X-ray above.

do the math!

You may have noticed labels like SPF 15 on your sunscreen. *SPF* stands for "sun protection factor," and the number lets you know how long the sunscreen works. For example, a person who burns in the sun after 10 minutes could use sunscreen with an SPF of 15 and stay in the sun for as long as 150 minutes ($10 \times 15 = 150$). This time can vary greatly and sunscreen should be reapplied often to prevent damaging sunburns.

Sunscreen Strength Over Time

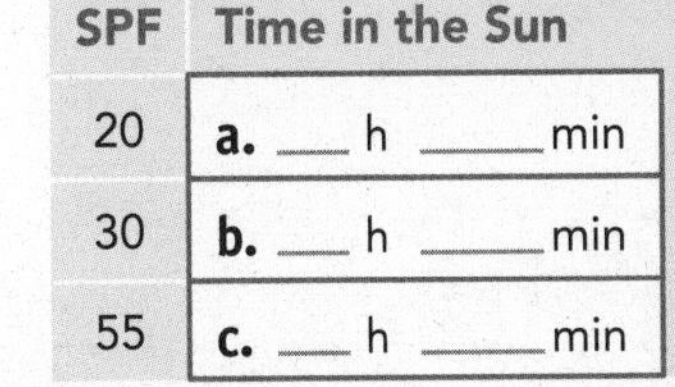

SPF	Time in the Sun
20	**a.** ___ h _____ min
30	**b.** ___ h _____ min
55	**c.** ___ h _____ min

1. Fill in the table with the length of time for sun protection each SPF rating offers for someone who burns in 10 minutes without sunscreen.

2. **Calculate** At the beach, you put on SPF 25 at 8:00 A.M. and your friend puts on SPF 15 at 9:00 A.M. You both would burn in 10 minutes without sunscreen. Who should reapply their sunscreen first? When?

____

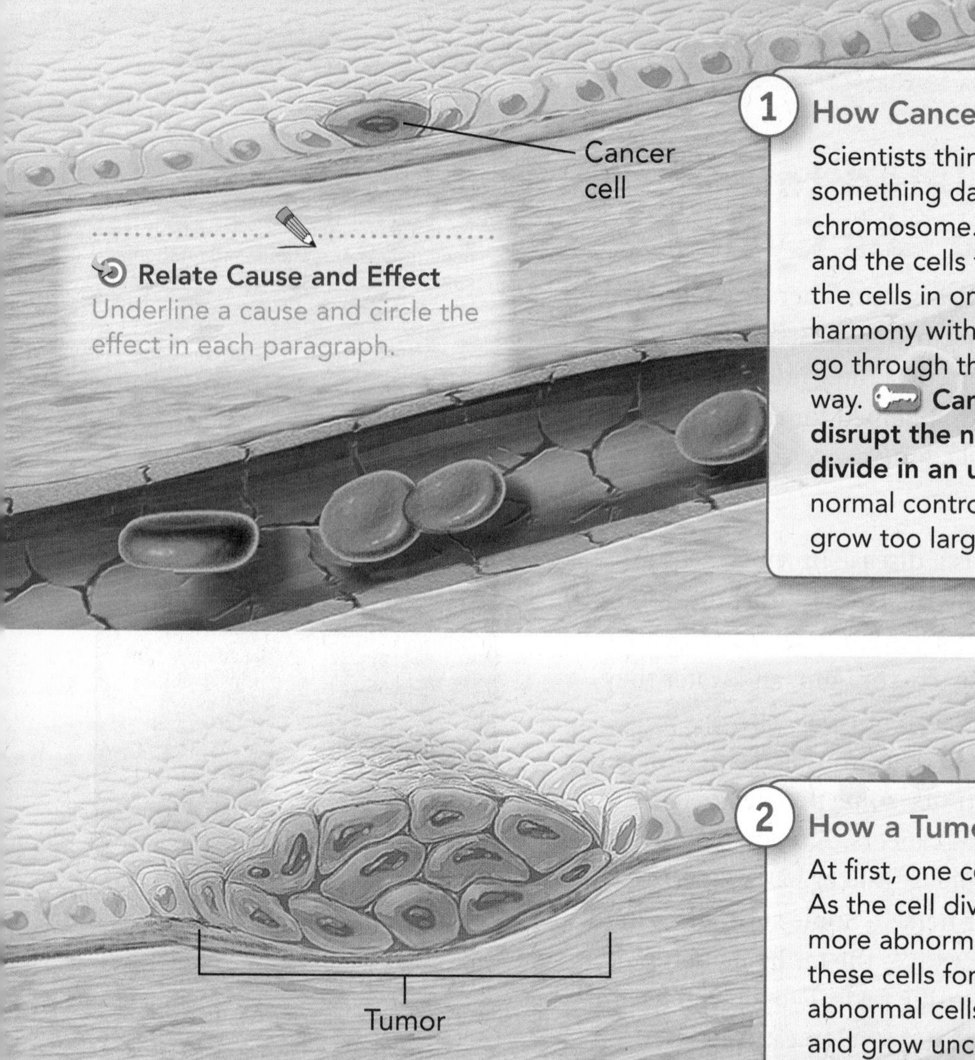

Relate Cause and Effect
Underline a cause and circle the effect in each paragraph.

1 How Cancer Begins

Scientists think that cancer begins when something damages a portion of the DNA in a chromosome. The damage causes a mutation and the cells function abnormally. Normally, the cells in one part of the body live in harmony with the cells around them. Cells that go through the cell cycle divide in a controlled way. **Cancer begins when mutations disrupt the normal cell cycle, causing cells to divide in an uncontrolled way.** Without the normal controls on the cell cycle, the cells may grow too large and divide too often.

2 How a Tumor Forms

At first, one cell develops in an abnormal way. As the cell divides over and over, more and more abnormal cells are produced. In time, these cells form a tumor. A **tumor** is a mass of abnormal cells that develops when cells divide and grow uncontrollably.

3 How Cancer Spreads

Tumors often take years to grow to a noticeable size. During that time, the cells become more and more abnormal as they continue to divide. Some of the cancerous cells may break off from the tumor and enter the bloodstream. In this way, the cancer can spread to other areas of the body.

How Cancer Is Treated People with cancer can undergo a variety of treatments. Treatments include surgery, radiation, and drugs that destroy the cancer cells.

When cancer is detected before it has spread to other parts of the body, surgery is usually the best treatment. If doctors can completely remove a cancerous tumor, the person may be cured. If the cancer cells have spread or the tumor cannot be removed, doctors may use radiation. Radiation treatment uses beams of high-energy waves. The beams are more likely to destroy the fast-growing cancer cells than normal cells.

Chemotherapy is another treatment option. **Chemotherapy** is the use of drugs to treat a disease. Cancer-fighting drugs are carried throughout the body by the bloodstream. The drugs can kill cancer cells or slow their growth. Many of these drugs, however, destroy some normal cells as well, producing nausea and other side effects patients often experience with chemotherapy treatments.

Scientists are continuing to look for new ways to treat cancer. If scientists can better understand how the cell cycle is controlled, they may find ways to stop cancer cells from multiplying.

apply it!

Drugs are one cancer treatment option.

1 If you were a cancer researcher working on a cure, would you want to design a chemotherapy drug that would speed up the cell cycle or slow it down? Why?

____

2 CHALLENGE Based on what you have learned about cancer and chemotherapy, explain why you think cancer patients who are treated with chemotherapy drugs can lose their hair.

____

Do the Quick Lab *What Happens When There Are Too Many Cells?*

Assess Your Understanding

2a. List What are the options for treating cancer?

____

b. Draw Conclusions Based on the fact that people can get cancer regardless of their genetics, what are some things you can do to lower your risk of getting cancer?

____

got it?

O **I get it!** Now I know that cancer is related to mutations and the cell cycle because _______________

O I need extra help with _______________

Go to **MY SCIENCE COACH** *online for help with this subject.*

CHAPTER 7

Study Guide

DNA passes information to ____________________ which passes the information to ____________________, the source of amino acids that make up ____________________.

LESSON 1 The Genetic Code

The order of the nitrogen bases along a gene forms a genetic code that specifies what type of protein will be produced.

Because of the way the nitrogen bases pair up, the order of the bases in each new DNA strand exactly matches the order in the original DNA strand.

Vocabulary

- nitrogen bases
- DNA replication

LESSON 2 How Cells Make Proteins

During protein synthesis, the cell uses information from a gene on a chromosome to produce a specific protein.

Vocabulary

- messenger RNA
- transfer RNA

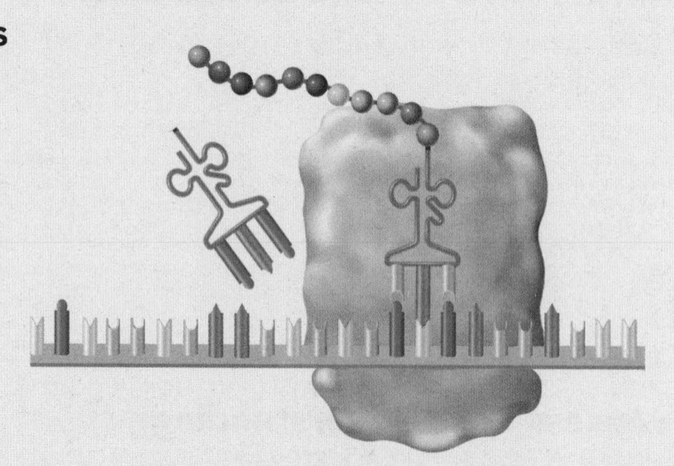

LESSON 3 Mutations

Mutations can cause a cell to produce an incorrect protein during protein synthesis. As a result, the organism's trait may be different from what it normally would be.

Cancer begins when mutations disrupt the normal cell cycle, causing cells to divide in an uncontrolled way.

Vocabulary

- mutation
- cancer
- tumor
- chemotherapy

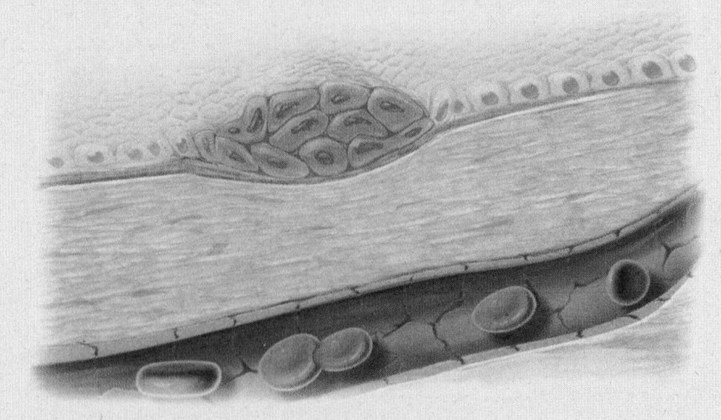

Review and Assessment

LESSON 1 The Genetic Code

1. DNA has four bases: A, C, G, and T. The base A always pairs with ________, and C always pairs with _______.
   a. A, C b. C, G
   c. C, T d. T, G

2. A ____________ is a section of DNA within a chromosome that codes for a specific protein.
   a. double helix
   b. ribosome
   c. gene
   d. amino acid

3. **Draw Conclusions** How does the pairing of the nitrogen bases in a DNA molecule make sure that a replicated strand is exactly the same as the original strand?

4. **Interpret Diagrams** A DNA molecule is shaped like a double helix. Label the structures of the molecule. Draw in the missing bases and label each base with its code letter.

LESSON 2 How Cells Make Proteins

5. Proteins are made up of molecules called
   a. RNA. b. ribosomes.
   c. nitrogen bases. d. amino acids.

6. ______________________ carries the information from the genetic code out of the nucleus and into the cytoplasm.

7. **Form Operational Definitions** During protein synthesis, what is the role of transfer RNA?

8. **Apply Concepts** What is the relationship among a DNA molecule, messenger RNA, and a protein?

9. **Write About It** Scientists can insert a gene for green fluorescent protein (GFP), which comes from jellyfish, into another organism, such as a flatworm. Explain the process that would then result in the flatworm producing GFP.

CHAPTER 7

Review and Assessment

LESSON 3 Mutations

10. A mass of cancer cells is called a

a. tumor.
b. chromosome.
c. mutation.
d. phenotype.

11. A mutation is a change in ________________.

12. Interpret Diagrams Circle the mutation shown in the illustration below.

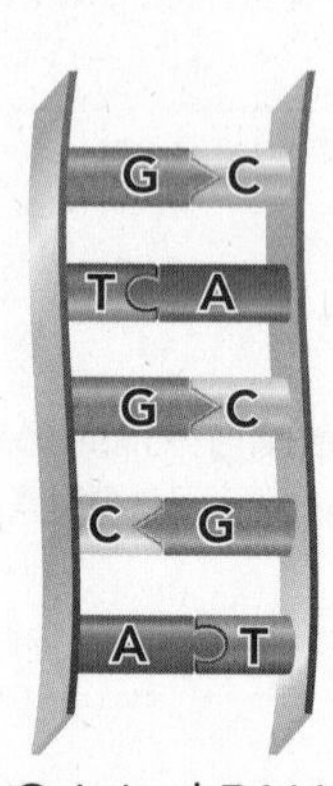

Original DNA

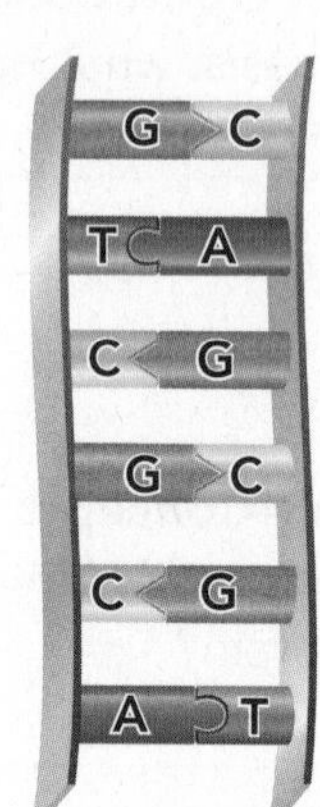

After mutation

13. Relate Cause and Effect What is the relationship between the cell cycle and cancer?

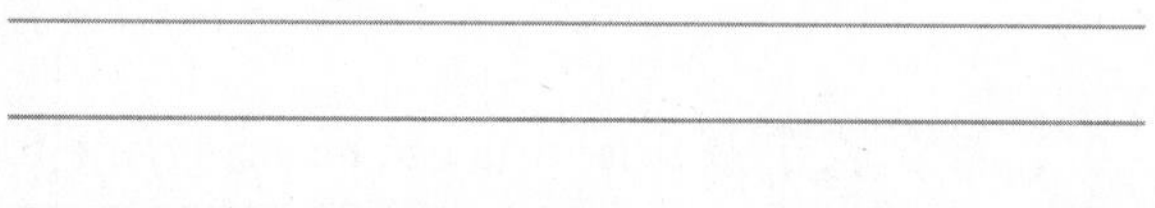

14. Apply Concepts How can cancer spread from one part of the body to another?

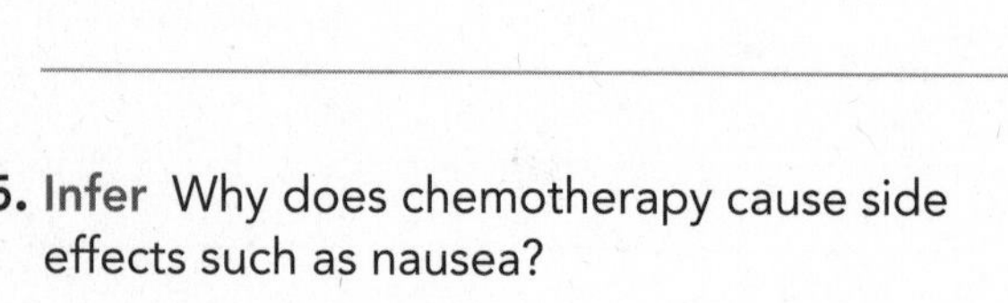

15. Infer Why does chemotherapy cause side effects such as nausea?

What does DNA do?

16. The ribosome in the diagram will start to build a protein by linking amino acids. Use what you know about how cells make proteins to fill in the missing letters of the bases in the messenger RNA strand. Then, on the blank strand below, write the DNA code that made the messenger RNA.

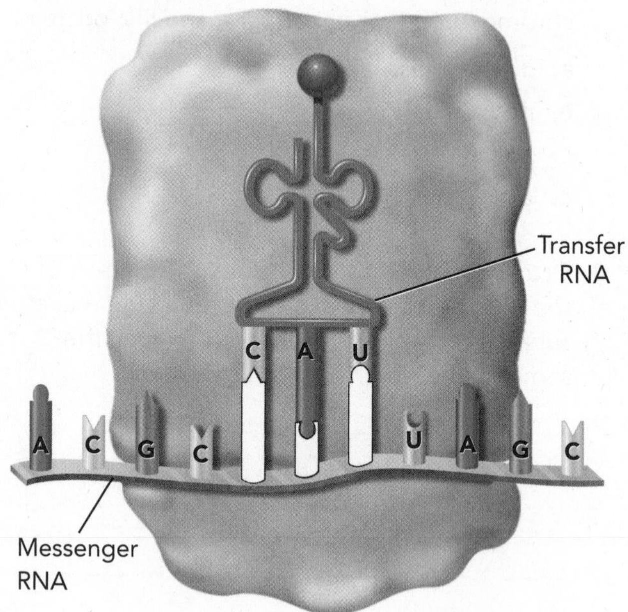

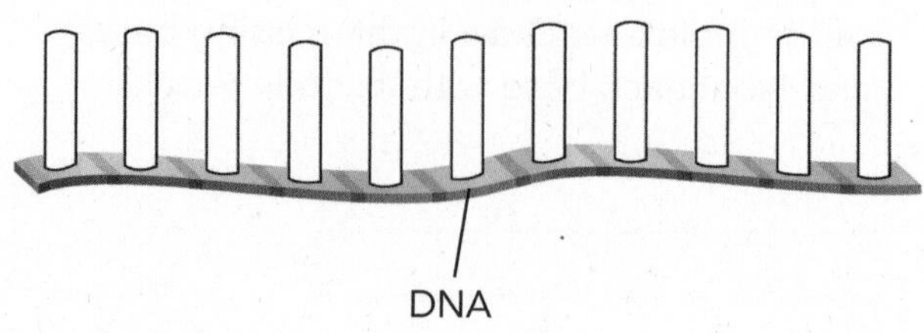

Virginia SOL Test Prep

Read each question and choose the best answer.

1 Select the correct group of words to match the numbered circles in the image.

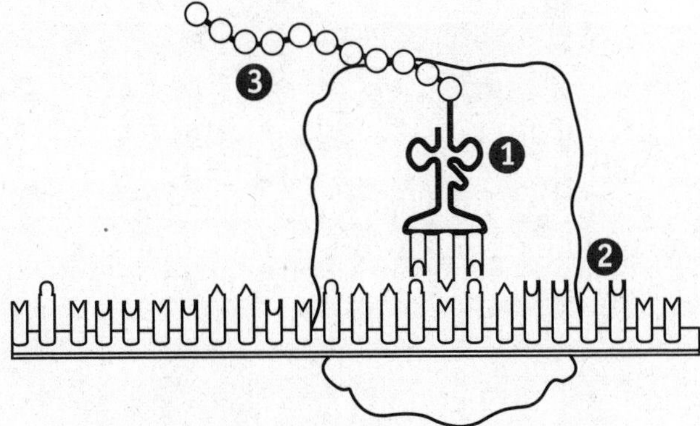

A (1) tRNA, (2) mRNA, (3) amino acids
B (1) mRNA, (2) protein, (3) DNA
C (1) DNA, (2) tRNA , (3) amino acids
D (1) protein, (2) mRNA, (3) tRNA

2 The main function of messenger RNA is—

F it adds amino acids to a growing protein chain
G it carries the information necessary for protein synthesis
H it carries the information necessary for DNA replication
J it carries information that causes deletions and other mutations

3 What is the sequence of events that results in the growth of a tumor?

A cancer, mutation, disrupted cell cycle, tumor
B disrupted cell cycle, protein change, mutation, tumor
C mutation, disrupted cell cycle, cancer, tumor
D DNA, cancer, mutation, tumor

4 Imagine a new medication that slows the cell cycle. How would this medication likely affect cancer?

F It might slow the rate of mutations.
G It might slow blood flow to the tumor.
H It might slow the division of cancerous cells.
J It might slow the effectiveness of chemotherapy.

5 When DNA replicates, the new strand is __________ the original strand.

A similar to
B larger than
C different from
D identical to

6 The drawing below shows half of a DNA molecule. Which set of bases would form the other half?

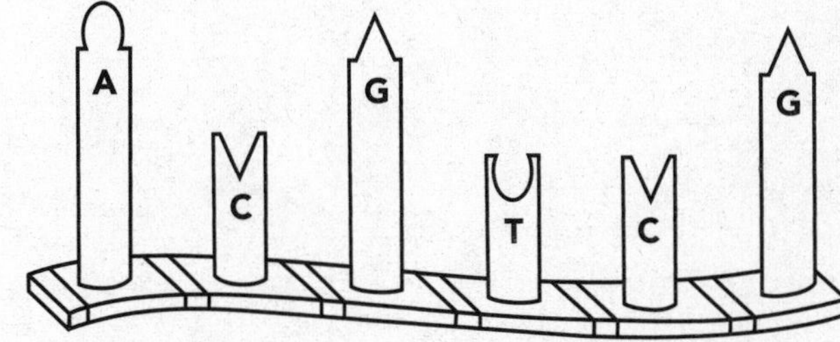

F GCTGCA
G AGCCGT
H TGCAGC
J ACGTCG

SCIENCE MATTERS

Hot Science

The Frozen Zoo

In addition to habitat loss, gorillas in Africa are threatened by the trade in bushmeat. Bushmeat is meat that comes from killing wild animals, such as gorillas. Catching people who sell gorilla meat is difficult because gorilla meat looks like other types of meat that are legal. Fortunately, researchers at the Frozen Zoo are developing genetic tools to catch people who sell gorilla meat.

The Frozen Zoo is a resource center that stores biological material to aid in the conservation of threatened and endangered animals. Researchers at the Frozen Zoo are building a database of genetic material from gorillas. They hope that this database will help conservation officers identify gorilla meat by using DNA barcoding. DNA barcoding is a method that uses a short DNA sequence, found in a cell's mitochondria, to identify an organism as belonging to a particular species.

Students at High Tech High in San Diego recently used DNA barcoding to identify samples of beef, ostrich meat, and turkey meat. Students in New York have also used this tool to identify the fish in their sushi. Now, researchers would like to teach this technique to conservation officers in Nigeria, where gorillas are severely threatened by the trade in bushmeat.

▲ Western Lowland Gorillas are one of the species that is most at risk from illegal hunting and the sale of bushmeat.

▼ Preserved DNA from many animals, including the Western Lowland Gorillas, is kept at the Frozen Zoo.

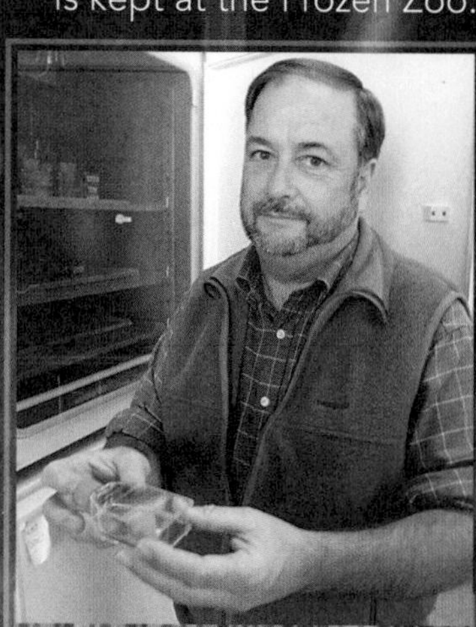

Research It Find out more about the Frozen Zoo. How do researchers use the biological material stored there? Create a concept map that shows the main ways that the Frozen Zoo aids in the conservation of threatened and endangered animals.

LS.1h, LS.1j, LS.12a, LS.12f

Technology and Society

The DNA mutations that cause cancer happen deep inside cells, where we can't see them, but that doesn't mean we are helpless. About one third of all cancer deaths in the United States are linked to poor diet and lack of exercise. A diet rich in fruits and vegetables reduces your cancer risk. So does regular exercise. Sunscreen or protective clothing can reduce the damage to DNA caused by sunlight when outdoors. And smoking is the largest cause of preventable cancer deaths in the world—by avoiding smoking and secondhand smoke, you are doing your cells a favor!

For existing cancer cases, scientists are using DNA studies to create treatments for specific types of cancers and even specific individuals! Scientists are also developing drugs that repair the damaged DNA.

Write About It Create a poster explaining one thing your classmates can do to reduce their risk of cancer. Use facts and other appropriate information to persuade your classmates.

Kids Doing Science

Do restaurant menus always tell the truth? High school students Kate Stoeckle and Louisa Strauss asked themselves this question while eating sushi in New York City. They decided to identify the fish in their sushi. Kate and Louisa gathered 60 fish samples from local restaurants and grocery stores. They sent the samples to a lab that used DNA barcoding to test the samples.

The tests showed that 25 percent of the samples were mislabeled! Often, inexpensive fish was labeled as more expensive fish. For example, a sample labeled "red snapper" was actually Atlantic cod. Another sample was from an endangered fish.

In the future, DNA barcoding could be done by using a handheld device. Such a device might look similar to a supermarket barcode scanner. Then, anyone could quickly solve a DNA mystery at the dinner table or beyond!

Research It Find out more about DNA barcoding. Identify a question you could answer by using this technology. Describe how you could use DNA barcoding to answer your question.

HOW CAN SCIENTISTS IDENTIFY HUMAN REMAINS?

How can genetic information be used?

These forensic scientists are putting together the skeletons of war victims. They can determine the age, sex, height, and ancestry of each body by examining bones. But that does not identify who the person was. Other scientists work to determine the identities of the victims.

Develop Hypotheses How do you think a scientist might figure out a person's identity from bones?

UNTAMED SCIENCE Watch the **Untamed Science** video to learn more about genetic technology.

Virginia

CHAPTER 8

Human Genetics and Genetic Technology

Science Standards of Learning

LS.1d, LS.1h, LS.1j, LS.12b, LS.12c, LS.12e, LS.12f

CHAPTER

8 Getting Started

Check Your Understanding

1. **Background** Read the paragraph below and then answer the question.

> Abdul has a white mouse named Pug. Both of Pug's parents had black fur, but they each had one **allele** for white fur and one allele for black fur. Because the **dominant allele** is for black fur, there was only a 25 percent **probability** that Pug would have white fur.

An **allele** is a different form of a gene.

The trait determined by a **dominant allele** always shows up in an organism if the allele is present.

Probability is a number that describes how likely it is that an event will occur.

- What is the probability that Pug's parents would have an offspring with black fur? ______________________________

MY READING WEB If you had trouble completing the question above, visit **My Reading Web** and type in ***Human Genetics and Genetic Technology.***

Vocabulary Skill

High-Use Academic Words High-use academic words are words that are used frequently in classrooms. Look for the words below as you read this chapter.

Word	Definition	Example
normal	*adj.* usual; typical, expected	It is *normal* to feel nervous about going to a new school.
resistant	*adj.* capable of preventing something from happening	The fabric stays clean easily because it is *resistant* to stains.

2. **Quick Check** **Choose the word that best completes each sentence.**

- Some bacteria are ______________________________ to common antibiotic medicines, so they are not killed by them.
- A ____________________ body temperature in a human is about 37°C.

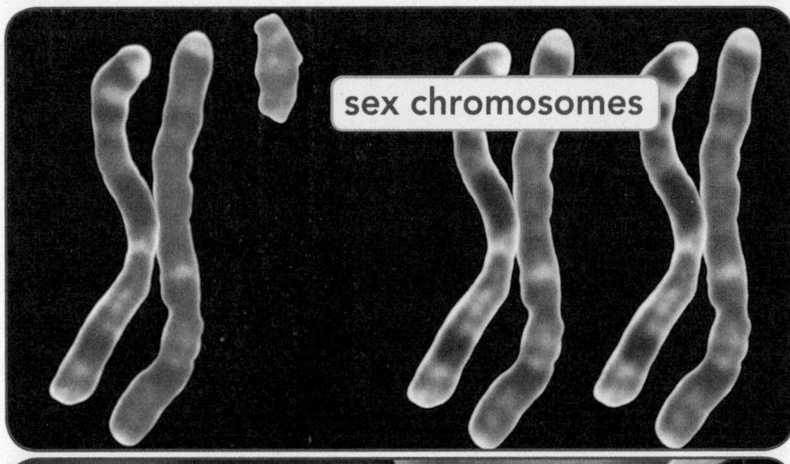

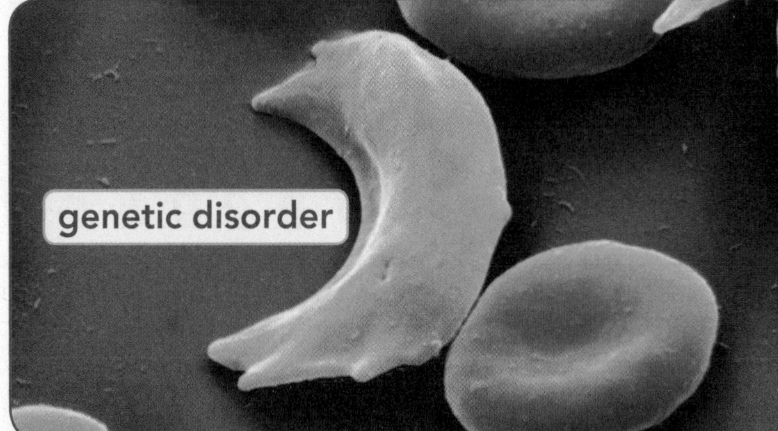

Chapter Preview

LESSON 1

- sex chromosomes
- sex-linked gene
- carrier

Relate Cause and Effect

Infer

LESSON 2

- genetic disorder
- pedigree
- karyotype

Outline

Make Models

LESSON 3

- selective breeding
- inbreeding
- hybridization
- clone
- genetic engineering
- gene therapy

Ask Questions

Draw Conclusions

LESSON 4

- genome
- ethics

Summarize

Communicate

VOCAB FLASH CARDS For extra help with vocabulary, visit **Vocab Flash Cards** and type in ***Human Genetics and Genetic Technology.***

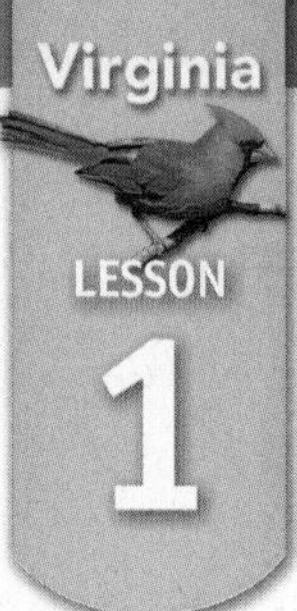

Human Inheritance

UNLOCK THE BIG Q

What Are Some Patterns of Human Inheritance?
LS.12b, LS.12c

What Are the Functions of the Sex Chromosomes?
LS.12b, LS.12c

my planet Diary for Virginia

BLOG

Posted by: KP

Location: Warrenton, Virginia

Everyone in the world has inherited traits from their grandparents or parents. Traits are physical characteristics of your appearance such as eye color, hair color and skin tone. I have inherited traits from my parents too. I have deep brown eyes and reddish brown hair from my mother. I inherited athletic skills and my smile from my dad. You have inherited traits from your parents. Which ones have you inherited?

Write your answer below.

What characteristics do you have that resemble those of your relatives?

PLANET DIARY Go to **Planet Diary** to learn more about human inheritance.

Lab zone® Do the Inquiry Warm-Up *How Tall Is Tall?*

Science Standards of Learning

LS.12b Investigate and understand the function of genes and chromosomes.

LS.12c Investigate and understand genotypes and phenotypes.

What Are Some Patterns of Human Inheritance?

Look at the other students in your classroom. Some people have curly hair; others have straight hair. Some people are tall, some are short, and many others are in between. You'll probably see eyes of many different colors, ranging from pale blue to dark brown. The different traits you see are determined by a variety of inheritance patterns. **Some human traits are controlled by single genes with two alleles, and others by single genes with multiple alleles. Still other traits are controlled by many genes that act together.**

Vocabulary

- sex chromosomes
- sex-linked gene
- carrier

Skills

- Reading: Relate Cause and Effect
- Inquiry: Infer

Single Genes With Two Alleles A number of human traits, such as a dimpled chin or a widow's peak, are controlled by a single gene with either a dominant or a recessive allele. These traits have two distinctly different physical appearances, or phenotypes.

Single Genes With Multiple Alleles Some human traits are controlled by a single gene that has more than two alleles. Such a gene is said to have multiple alleles—three or more forms of a gene that code for a single trait. Even though a gene may have multiple alleles, a person can carry only two of those alleles. This is because chromosomes exist in pairs. Each chromosome in a pair carries only one allele for each gene. Recall that an organism's genetic makeup is its genotype. The physical characteristics that result are called the organism's phenotype.

Human blood type is controlled by a gene with multiple alleles. There are four main blood types—A, B, AB, and O. Three alleles control the inheritance of blood types. The allele for blood type A is written as I^A. The allele for blood type B is written as I^B. The allele for blood type A and the allele for blood type B are codominant. This means that both alleles for the gene are expressed equally. A person who inherits an I^A allele from one parent and an I^B allele from the other parent will have type AB blood. The allele for blood type O—written as i—is recessive. **Figure 1** shows the different allele combinations that result in each blood type.

FIGURE 1

Inheritance of Blood Type

The table below shows which combinations of alleles result in each human blood type.

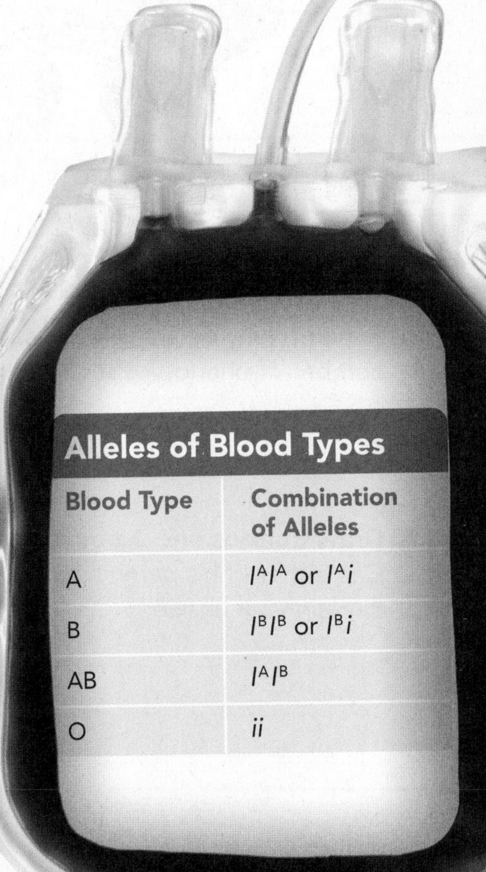

Alleles of Blood Types

Blood Type	Combination of Alleles
A	I^AI^A or I^Ai
B	I^BI^B or I^Bi
AB	I^AI^B
O	ii

Use what you have learned about blood types and **Figure 1** to answer the following questions.

1. **Interpret Tables** Genotypes are listed in the (left/right) column of the table, while phenotypes are on the (left/right).

2. **Infer** Why are there more genotypes than phenotypes for blood types?

___

___

___

___

___

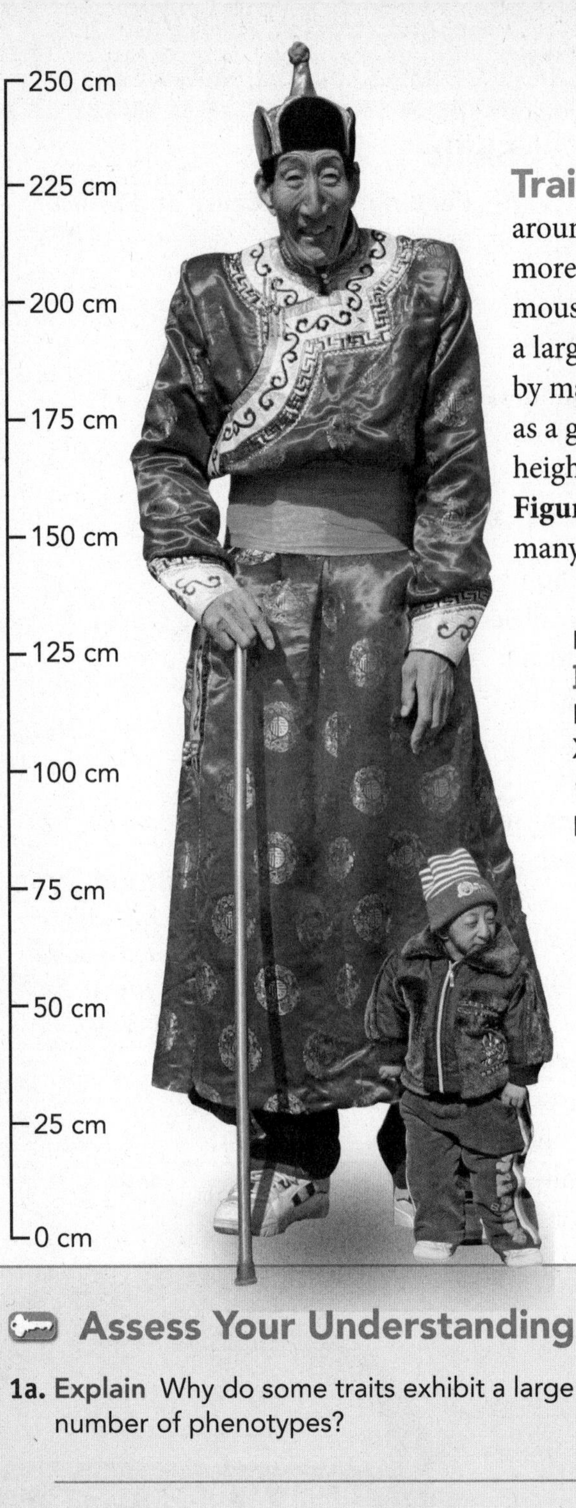

Traits Controlled by Many Genes If you look around your classroom, you'll see that height in humans has more than two distinct phenotypes. In fact, there is an enormous variety of phenotypes for height. Some human traits show a large number of phenotypes because the traits are controlled by many genes. The alleles of the different genes act together as a group to produce a single trait. At least four genes control height in humans. You can see the extreme range of heights in **Figure 2.** Skin color is another human trait that is controlled by many genes.

FIGURE 2

Extreme Heights

Human heights are known to range from the tall Bao Xishun, at 236 cm, to the short He Pingping, at 76 cm.

On the scale, mark your height and the heights of Bao Xishun and He Pingping.

1. **Calculate** How many times taller are you than He Pingping?

____

2. **Predict** Do you think Bao Xishun's parents are also tall? Why?

____

____

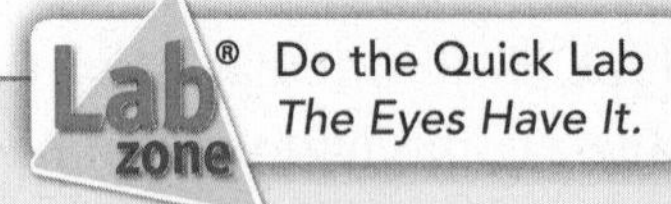

Do the Quick Lab *The Eyes Have It.*

Assess Your Understanding

1a. Explain Why do some traits exhibit a large number of phenotypes?

____

____

b. Draw Conclusions Aaron has blood type O. Can either of his parents have blood type AB? Explain your answer.

____

____

____

____

____

____

got it?

O **I get it!** Now I know that some human traits are controlled by _______________

____

____

____

____

O I need extra help with _______________

____

____

Go to **MY SCIENCE COACH** *online for help with this subject.*

What Are the Functions of the Sex Chromosomes?

Science Standards of Learning

LS.12b Investigate and understand the function of genes and chromosomes.

LS.12c Investigate and understand genotypes and phenotypes.

The body cells of humans contain 23 chromosome pairs, or 46 chromosomes. The **sex chromosomes** are one of the 23 pairs of chromosomes in each body cell. **The sex chromosomes carry genes that determine a person's sex as being either male or female. They also carry genes that determine other traits.**

Girl or Boy?

The sex chromosomes are the only chromosome pair that do not always match. Girls have two sex chromosomes that match. The two chromosomes are called X chromosomes. Boys have two sex chromosomes that do not match. They have an X chromosome and a Y chromosome. The Y chromosome is much smaller than the X chromosome. To show the size difference, the sex chromosomes in **Figure 3** have been stained and magnified.

Sex Chromosomes and Fertilization

When egg cells and sperm cells form, what happens to the sex chromosomes? Since both of a female's sex chromosomes are X chromosomes, all eggs carry one X chromosome. Males, however, have two different sex chromosomes. Therefore, half of a male's sperm cells carry an X chromosome, while half carry a Y chromosome.

When a sperm cell with an X chromosome fertilizes an egg, the egg has two X chromosomes. The fertilized egg will develop into a girl. When a sperm with a Y chromosome fertilizes an egg, the egg has one X chromosome and one Y chromosome. The fertilized egg will develop into a boy.

FIGURE 3

Male or Female?

The father's chromosome determines the sex of his child.

Using the genotypes given for the mother and father, complete the Punnett square to show their child's genotype and phenotype.

1. **Calculate** What is the probability that the child will be a girl? A boy?

____

____

2. **Interpret Diagrams** What sex will the child be if a sperm with a Y chromosome fertilizes an egg? _______________

Relate Cause and Effect Underline the cause of sex-linked traits in males and circle the effect of the traits.

Sex-Linked Genes

The genes for some human traits are carried on the sex chromosomes. Genes found on the X and Y chromosomes are often called **sex-linked genes** because their alleles are passed from parent to child on a sex chromosome. Traits controlled by sex-linked genes are called sex-linked traits. One sex-linked trait is red-green colorblindness. A person with this trait cannot see the difference between red and green. Normal vision is dominant, while colorblindness is recessive.

FIGURE 4

VIRTUAL LAB **X and Y Chromosomes**

The human X chromosome is larger and carries more genes than the human Y chromosome.

Recall that a Y chromosome is smaller than an X chromosome. Females have two X chromosomes, but males have one X chromosome and one Y chromosome. These chromosomes have different genes.

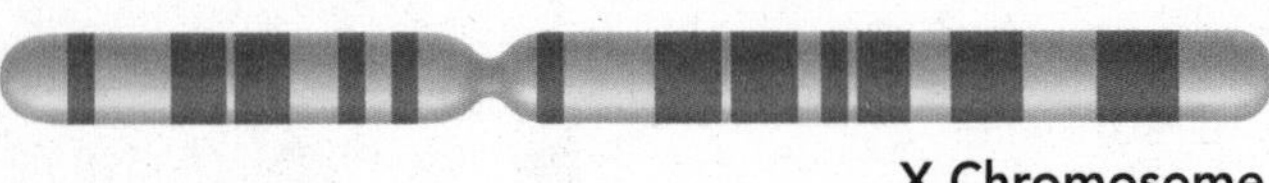

Most of the genes on the X chromosome are not on the Y chromosome. So an allele on an X chromosome may have no corresponding allele on a Y chromosome.

Like other genes, sex-linked genes can have dominant and recessive alleles. In females, a dominant allele on an X chromosome will mask a recessive allele on the other X chromosome. But in males, there is usually no matching allele on the Y chromosome to mask the allele on the X chromosome. As a result, any allele on the X chromosome—even a recessive allele—will produce the trait in a male who inherits it. This means that males are more likely than females to express a sex-linked trait that is controlled by a recessive allele. Individuals with colorblindness may have difficulty seeing the numbers in **Figure 5.** Test your vision below.

FIGURE 5

Colorblindness

Most colorblind individuals have difficulty seeing red and green.

Communicate **Working with a partner, look at the circles. Write the number you see in the space below each circle.**

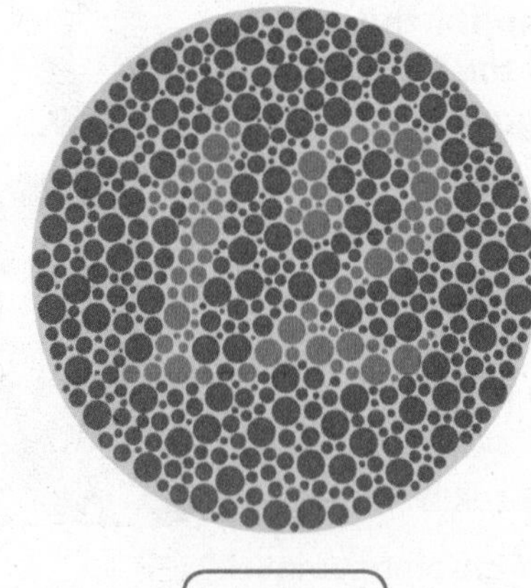

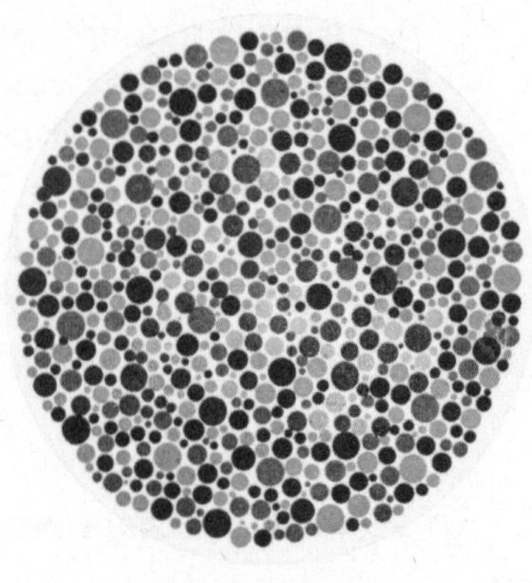

Inheritance of Colorblindness

Inheritance of Colorblindness Colorblindness is a trait controlled by a recessive allele on the X chromosome. Many more males than females have red-green colorblindness. You can understand why this is the case by examining the Punnett square in **Figure 6.** Both parents have normal color vision. Notice that the mother carries the dominant allele for normal vision (X^C) and the recessive allele for colorblindness (X^c). A **carrier** is a person who has one recessive allele for a trait and one dominant allele. A carrier of a trait controlled by a recessive allele does not express the trait. However, the carrier can pass the recessive allele on to his or her offspring. In the case of sex-linked traits, only females can be carriers because they are the only ones who can carry two alleles for the trait.

Key
- ○ Female; does not have trait nor is a carrier
- □ Male; does not have trait nor is a carrier
- ◐ or ◧ Carrier for trait
- ● or ■ Has trait

FIGURE 6

Colorblindness Punnett Square

Red-green colorblindess is a sex-linked trait.

Using the parents' information and the key, complete the Punnett square.

1. **Identify** Complete the Punnett square by filling in the child's genotype, sex, and phenotype. For each child, draw the correct shape, and color it in to match the key.
2. **Calculate** What is the probability that this couple will have a colorblind child?

   ____

3. **Apply Concepts** What allele combination would a daughter need to inherit to be colorblind?

   ____

Father normal vision □

Mother carrier ◐

	X^C	Y
X^C	X^CX^C ○ Female normal vision	
X^c		

Lab zone Do the Lab Investigation *How Are Genes on the Sex Chromosomes Inherited?*

Assess Your Understanding

2a. Review What is the sex of a person who is a carrier for colorblindness?______________

b. CHALLENGE Mary and her mother are both colorblind. Is Mary's father colorblind, too? How do you know?

____

____

____

____

____

got it?

O **I get it!** Now I know that the functions of the sex chromosomes are ______________________________

____

____

O I need extra help with ______________________________

____

Go to MY SCIENCE COACH *online for help with this subject.*

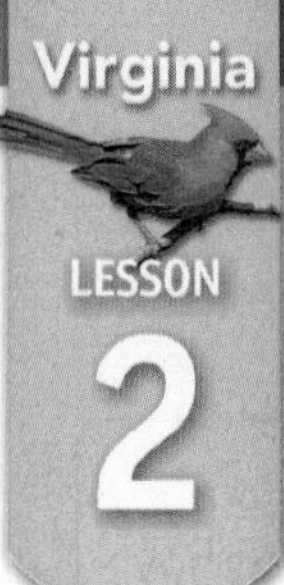

LESSON 2

Human Genetic Disorders

How Are Genetic Disorders Inherited in Humans?
LS.12b, LS.12c

How Are Genetic Disorders Traced, Diagnosed, and Treated?
LS.1d, LS.1j, LS.12b, LS.12c

my planet Diary

DISCOVERY

Doggie Diagnosis

Maybe you have a dog or know someone who does. Did you know that dogs and humans can have some of the same health problems? It is not uncommon for dogs to have cancer, diabetes, allergies, epilepsy, and eye diseases. Scientists are studying the genes and genetic mutations that cause diseases in dogs in the hopes of better understanding human diseases. Most diseases in dogs are caused by a mutation on one gene. In humans, the mutations can be on multiple genes. The genes that cause diseases in dogs are much easier to find than those in humans. So far, scientists are looking into the genes that cause blindness, cancer, and spinal cord disorders in dogs.

Communicate Discuss the questions with a classmate. Then write your answers.

1. Why are scientists studying dog genes to understand human diseases?

2. In what other ways could studying dog diseases be beneficial?

PLANET DIARY Go to **Planet Diary** to learn more about human genetic disorders.

German shepherds can have a form of cancer similar to breast cancer in humans.

Dachshunds and humans can both suffer from blindness.

Golden retrievers can have cancer that affects the blood vessels.

Lab zone Do the Inquiry Warm-Up *How Many Chromosomes?*

Vocabulary
- genetic disorder
- pedigree
- karyotype

Skills
- Reading: Outline
- Inquiry: Make Models

How Are Genetic Disorders Inherited in Humans?

Science Standards of Learning

LS.12b Investigate and understand the function of genes and chromosomes.

LS.12c Investigate and understand genotypes and phenotypes.

Many of the athletes who compete in the Special Olympics have disabilities that result from genetic disorders. A **genetic disorder** is an abnormal condition that a person inherits through genes or chromosomes. **Some genetic disorders are caused by mutations in the DNA of genes. Other disorders are caused by changes in the overall structure or number of chromosomes.** In this lesson, you will learn about some common genetic disorders.

Cystic Fibrosis Cystic fibrosis is a genetic disorder in which the body produces abnormally thick mucus in the lungs and intestines. The thick mucus fills the lungs, making it hard for the affected person to breathe. Cystic fibrosis occurs when two mutated alleles are inherited, one from each parent. The mutation causes three bases to be removed from a DNA molecule.

Sickle-Cell Disease Sickle-cell disease is caused by a mutation that affects hemoglobin. Hemoglobin is a protein in red blood cells that carries oxygen. The red blood cells of people with the disease have a sickle, or crescent, shape. Sickle-shaped red blood cells cannot carry as much oxygen as normal cells and also clog blood vessels. The allele for the sickle-cell trait (*S*) is codominant with the normal allele (*A*). A person with one normal allele and one sickle-cell allele (*AS*) will produce both normal hemoglobin and abnormal hemoglobin. This person usually does not have symptoms of the disease. He or she has enough normal hemoglobin to carry oxygen to cells. A person with two sickle-cell alleles (*SS*) will have the disease.

FIGURE 1

Sickle-Cell Disease

In a person with sickle-cell disease, red blood cells can become sickle-shaped instead of round.

Predict A man has sickle-cell disease. His wife does not have the disease, but is heterozygous for the sickle-cell trait. Use the parents' information to fill in the Punnett square. What is the probability that their child will have sickle-cell disease?

____

	___	___
___	___	___
___	___	___

Outline After you read this section, make an outline on a separate sheet of paper that includes the different types of genetic disorders. Use the red headings to help you organize your outline.

Hemophilia Hemophilia is a genetic disorder in which a person's blood clots very slowly or not at all. People with the disorder do not produce enough of one of the proteins needed for normal blood clotting. The danger of internal bleeding from small bumps and bruises is very high. Hemophilia is caused by a recessive allele on the X chromosome. Because hemophilia is a sex-linked disorder, it occurs more frequently in males than in females.

Down Syndrome In Down syndrome, a person's cells have an extra copy of chromosome 21. Instead of a pair of chromosomes, a person with Down syndrome has three copies. Down syndrome most often occurs when chromosomes fail to separate properly during meiosis, when sex cells (egg and sperm) form. People with Down syndrome have some degree of intellectual disability. Heart defects are also common, but can be treated.

FIGURE 2

INTERACTIVE ART **Hemophilia**

Hemophilia occurs more often in males than in females.

Cross a carrier female, X^HX^h, with a healthy male, X^HY, and fill in the Punnett square.

1. **Calculate** What percentage of the offspring
   would be normal?__________
   would be carriers? __________
   would have hemophilia? __________
2. CHALLENGE To have a daughter with hemophilia, the father must have the disorder (X^hY) and the mother must have one of two genotypes. What are they?
   ____

	___	___
___	___	___
___	___	___

Lab zone® Do the Quick Lab *What Went Wrong?*

Assess Your Understanding

1a. Explain Which of the two major causes of genetic disorders is responsible for Down syndrome?

____

b. Infer Why is hemophilia more common in males?

____

got it?

O **I get it!** Now I know that the two major causes of genetic disorders are __________

O I need extra help with __________

Go to MY SCIENCE COACH *online for help with this subject.*

How Are Genetic Disorders Traced, Diagnosed, and Treated?

Years ago, only Punnett squares were used to predict whether a child might have a genetic disorder. **Today, doctors use tools such as pedigrees, karyotypes, and genetic testing to trace and diagnose genetic disorders. People with genetic disorders are helped through medical care, education, and job training.**

Science Standards of Learning

LS.1d Construct and use models and simulations to illustrate and explain phenomena.

LS.1j Use current applications to reinforce life science concepts.

LS.12b Investigate and understand the function of genes and chromosomes.

LS.12c Investigate and understand genotypes and phenotypes.

Pedigrees Suppose that you are interested in tracing the occurrence of a trait through several generations of a family. What would you do? A **pedigree** is a chart or "family tree" that tracks which members of a family have a particular trait. The trait in a pedigree can be an ordinary trait, such as eye color, or a genetic disorder. The pedigree shown below is for albinism, a condition in which a person's skin, hair, and eyes lack normal coloring.

apply it!

This pedigree shows the inheritance of the allele for albinism in three generations of a family.

1 Interpret Diagrams Circle the place in the pedigree that shows an albino male.

Key

- ○ Female; does not have trait nor is a carrier
- □ Male; does not have trait nor is a carrier
- ◐ or ◧ Carrier for trait
- ● or ■ Has trait

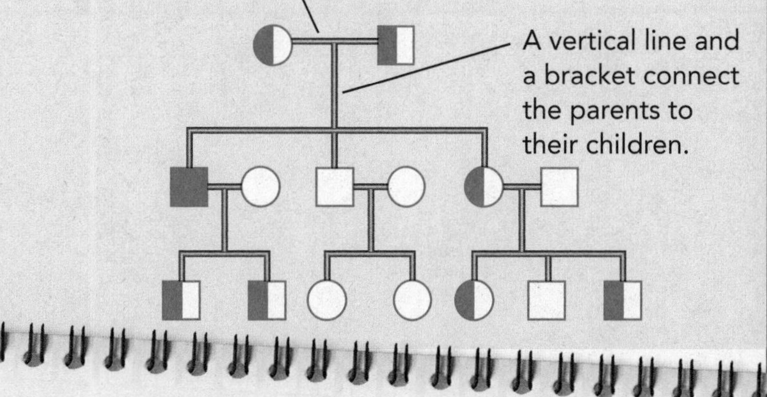

2 Make Models Using what you have learned about pedigrees and pedigree symbols, construct a two-generation pedigree for sickle-cell disease, starting with parents who are both carriers, *AS* × *AS*. (*Hint:* Construct Punnett squares on a separate sheet of paper to determine the possible genotypes of the offspring.)

Karyotypes To detect a chromosomal disorder such as Down syndrome, doctors examine karyotypes. A **karyotype** (KA ree uh typ) is a picture of all the chromosomes in a person's cell. Look at **Figure 3.** As you can see, the chromosomes in a karyotype are arranged in pairs. A karyotype can reveal whether a person has the correct number of chromosomes in his or her cells.

FIGURE 3

Karyotypes

Look at the karyotypes below. One is a normal karyotype and the other is an abnormal karyotype.

Working with a classmate, compare the two karyotypes.

1. **Interpret Photos** What numbered set of chromosomes are the most different between the karyotypes? ____________

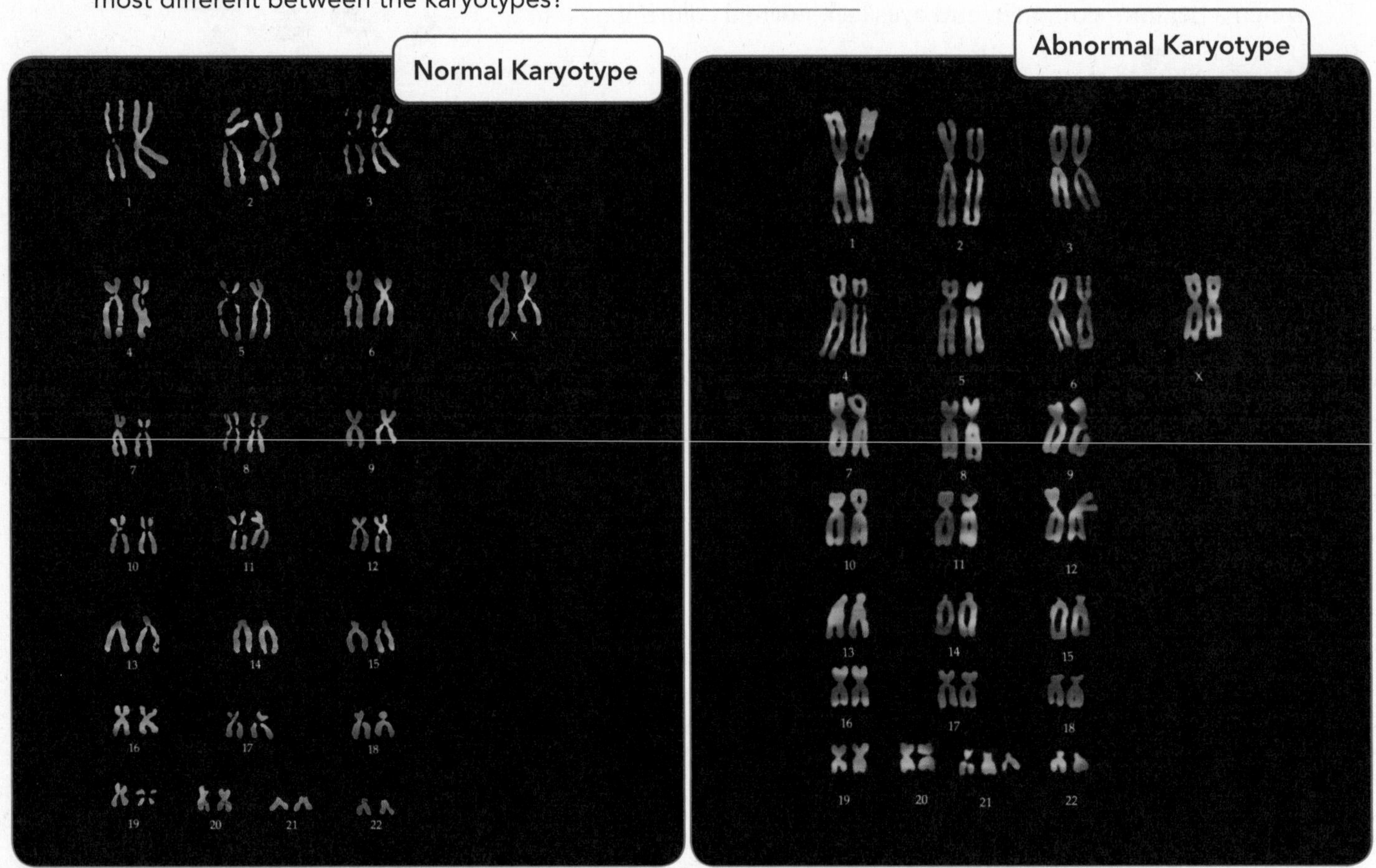

2. **Draw Conclusions** What can you conclude about the individual with the abnormal karyotype? Use evidence to support your answer.

____

____

____

____

Genetic Counseling A couple that has a family history of a genetic disorder may turn to a genetic counselor for advice. Genetic counselors help couples understand their chances of having a child with a particular genetic disorder. Genetic counselors also help couples prepare for having children with a disorder. Karyotypes, pedigree charts, and Punnett squares assist genetic counselors in their work.

With advances in technology, new tests have been developed to screen for genetic disorders. Genetic tests examine genes, DNA, enzymes, and proteins to see if an individual has a genetic disorder or carries a gene for a genetic disorder. Whether or not the person develops the disease also depends on many other genetic factors, environmental conditions, and lifestyle.

did you know?

Malaria is an infectious disease that kills more than a million people a year. This disease is transmitted to people when they are bitten by an infected mosquito. However, people who have the gene that causes sickle-cell disease are less likely to develop malaria.

Dealing With Genetic Disorders People with genetic disorders face serious challenges, but they can be helped. Medical treatments help people with the symptoms of some disorders. For example, physical therapy helps remove mucus from the lungs of people with cystic fibrosis. People with sickle-cell disease take folic acid, a vitamin, to help their bodies manufacture red blood cells. Because of education and job training programs, adults with Down syndrome can find work in banks, restaurants, and other places. Most genetic disorders do not prevent people from living active, productive lives.

FIGURE 4
Genetic Disorders
These athletes have Down syndrome, a genetic disorder.

List **Name two types of programs that benefit individuals with Down syndrome.**

______

______

______

Do the Quick Lab *Family Puzzle.*

Assess Your Understanding

got it?

O **I get it!** Now I know that genetic disorders are traced, diagnosed, and treated by ______

O I need extra help with ______

Go to MY SCIENCE COACH *online for help with this subject.*

Advances in Genetics

How Can Organisms Be Produced With Desired Traits?

LS.1h, LS.1j, LS.12e

my planet Diary

FUN FACT

Zorses and Zedonks

Most people can tell the difference between a zebra and a horse. But would you be able to tell the difference between a zorse and a zedonk? Both types of animals are zebroids, or zebra hybrids. These animals result when a zebra mates with a horse or a donkey. Zebroids do not usually occur in nature. They generally result when people cross them on purpose. People may have first crossed zebras and horses in an effort to develop disease-resistant transportation animals for use in Africa. Zebras are resistant to African sleeping sickness. It was hoped that zorses, the offspring of zebras and horses, would have this resistance.

Communicate Discuss these questions with a classmate. Write your answers below.

1. Why may zebras and horses have been first crossed by people?

2. If zebras and horses do not usually mate in nature, should people intentionally cross them? Why or why not?

PLANET DIARY Go to **Planet Diary** to learn more about advances in genetics.

Do the Inquiry Warm-Up *What Do Fingerprints Reveal?*

Vocabulary
- selective breeding
- inbreeding
- hybridization
- clone
- genetic engineering
- gene therapy

Skills
- Reading: Ask Questions
- Inquiry: Draw Conclusions

How Can Organisms Be Produced With Desired Traits?

Science Standards of Learning

LS.1h Organize, graph, and interpret data, and use data to make predictions.

LS.1j Use current applications to reinforce life science concepts.

LS.12e Investigate and understand genetic engineering and its applications.

Unless you are an identical twin, your DNA is different from everyone else's. Because of advances in genetics, DNA evidence can show many things, such as family relationships or the ability to produce organisms with desirable traits.  **Selective breeding, cloning, and genetic engineering are three different methods for developing organisms with desired traits.**

Selective Breeding The process of selecting organisms with desired traits to be parents of the next generation is called **selective breeding.** Thousands of years ago, in what is now Mexico, the food that we call corn was developed in this way. Every year, farmers saved seeds from the healthiest plants that produced the best food. In the spring, they planted only those seeds. This process was repeated over and over. In time, farmers developed plants that produced better corn. People have used selective breeding with many types of plants and animals. Two techniques for selective breeding are inbreeding and hybridization.

Ask Questions Before you read this lesson, preview the red headings. In the graphic organizer below, ask a question for each heading. As you read, write answers to your questions.

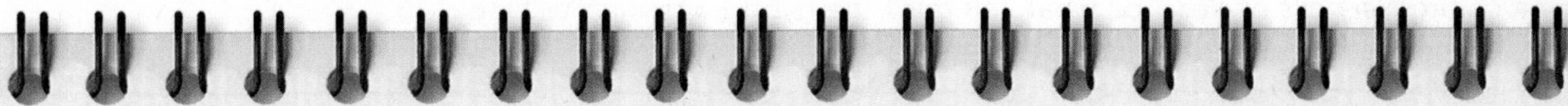

Question	Answer
What is selective breeding?	Selective breeding is

Vocabulary **High-Use Academic Words** Use the word *resistant* to explain how hybridization can be useful.

____

____

____

____

____

____

Inbreeding The technique of **inbreeding** involves crossing two individuals that have similar desirable characteristics. Suppose a male and a female golden retriever are both friendly and have the same coloring. Their offspring will probably also have those qualities. Inbreeding produces organisms that are genetically very similar. When inbred organisms are mated, the chance of their offspring inheriting two recessive alleles increases. This can lead to genetic disorders. For example, inherited hip problems are common in golden retrievers and other types of inbred dogs.

Hybridization In **hybridization** (hy brid ih ZAY shun), breeders cross two genetically different individuals. Recall that a hybrid organism has two different alleles for a trait. The hybrid organism that results is bred to have the best traits from both parents. For example, a farmer might cross corn that produces many kernels with corn that is resistant to disease. The farmer is hoping to produce a hybrid corn plant with both of the desired traits. Roses and other types of flowers are also commonly crossed.

apply it!

Since the late eighteenth century, gardeners and plant breeders have used hybridization to develop roses with certain characteristics.

1 Observe Look at each rose below. One characteristic for each flower is given to you. List any other observable characteristics you see.

2 Draw Conclusions Based on the characteristics of the two roses, draw with colored pencils or describe what you think the hybrid offspring will look like. Name the flower and list its characteristics.

Parent A	Parent B	Hybrid name: ____________
fragrant	survives cold temperatures	____________
____________	____________	____________
____________	____________	____________
____________	____________	____________

do the math!

Changing Rice Production

This data table shows how worldwide rice production changed between 1965 and 2005. New hybrid varieties of rice plants are one factor that has affected the amount of rice produced.

Year	Yield
1965	2.04
1970	2.38
1975	2.52
1980	2.75
1985	3.26
1990	3.53
1995	3.66
2000	3.89
2005	4.09

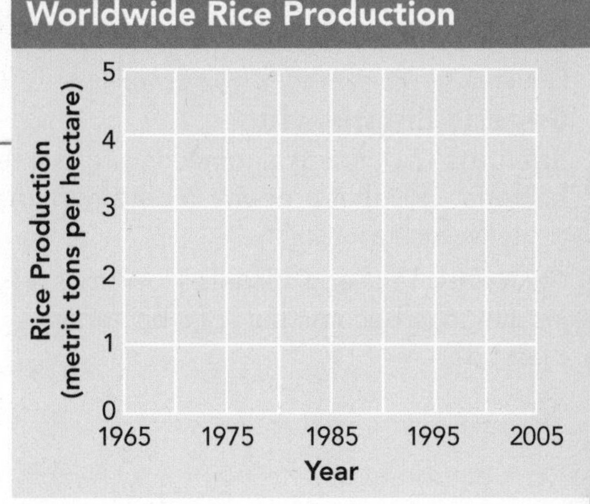

1 Graph Plot the data from the table and draw a line graph.

2 Interpret Data What is the approximate difference between rice production in 1965 and 2005? ____________________

3 CHALLENGE What other factors might help account for the difference in rice production between 1965 and 2005?

____

____

____

Cloning For some organisms, such as the dog shown in **Figure 1,** a technique called cloning can be used to produce offspring with desired traits. A **clone** is an organism that has exactly the same genes as the organism from which it was produced. It isn't hard to clone some kinds of plants such as African violets. Just cut a stem from one plant and put the stem in soil. Water it, and soon you will have a whole new plant. The new plant is genetically identical to the plant from which the stem was cut.

Genetic Engineering Geneticists have developed another powerful technique for producing organisms with desired traits. In this process, called **genetic engineering,** genes from one organism are transferred into the DNA of another organism. Genetic engineering can produce medicines and improve food crops.

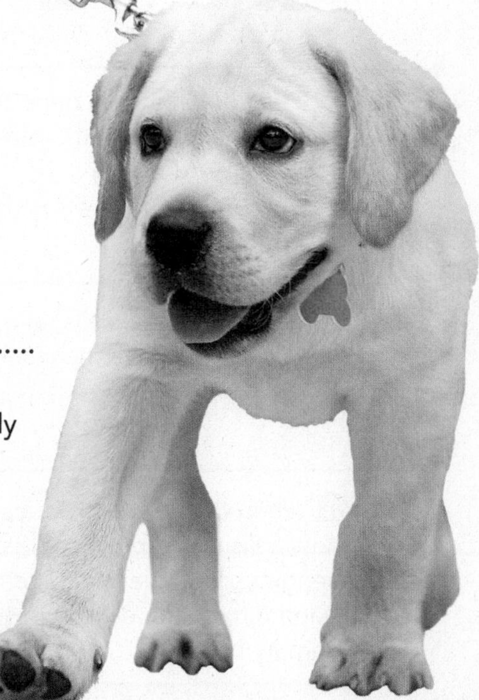

FIGURE 1

Cloning

This puppy, Lancelot Encore, is thought to be the first commercially cloned puppy in the United States. His owners paid $150,000 to have him cloned in South Korea.

Make Judgments Would you pay $150,000 to clone a pet? Why or why not?

____

____

FIGURE 2

Genetic Engineering

Scientists use genetic engineering to create bacterial cells that produce important human proteins such as insulin.

Relate Text and Visuals How does a human insulin gene become part of a bacterium's plasmid?

____

____

____

____

____

____

____

1 Small rings of DNA, or plasmids, can be found in some bacterial cells.

2 Scientists remove the plasmid. An enzyme cuts open the plasmid and removes the human insulin gene from its chromosome.

3 The human insulin gene attaches to the open ends of the plasmid to form a closed ring.

4 Some bacterial cells take up the plasmids that have the insulin gene.

5 When the cells reproduce, the new cells will contain copies of the "engineered" plasmid. The foreign gene directs the cells to produce human insulin.

Genetic Engineering in Bacteria One type of bacterium is genetically engineered to produce a human protein called insulin. Many people with diabetes need insulin injections. Bacteria have a single DNA molecule in the cytoplasm. Some bacterial cells also contain small circular pieces of DNA called plasmids. You can see how scientists insert the DNA for the human insulin gene into the plasmid of a bacterium in **Figure 2.** Once the gene is inserted into the plasmid, the bacterial cell and all of its offspring will contain this human gene. As a result, the bacteria produce the protein that the human gene codes for—in this case, insulin. Because bacteria can reproduce quickly, large amounts of insulin can be produced in a short time.

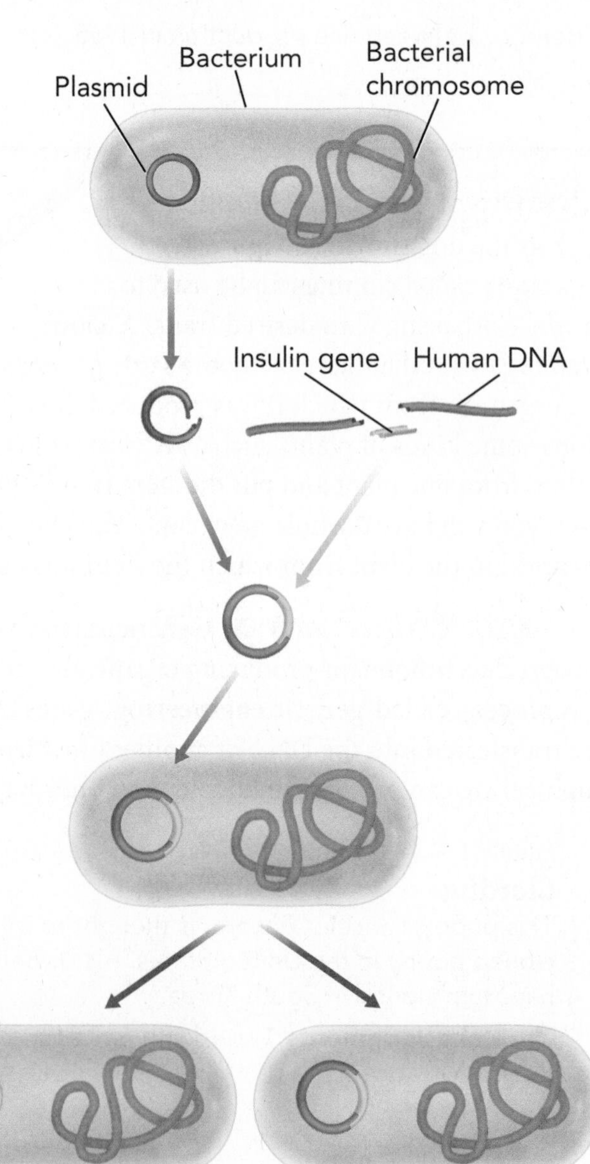

Genetic Engineering in Other Organisms

Scientists can also use genetic engineering techniques to insert genes into animals. For example, human genes can be inserted into the cells of cows. The cows then produce milk containing the human protein coded by the gene. Scientists have used this technique to produce the blood-clotting protein needed by people with hemophilia.

Genes have also been inserted into the cells of plants, such as tomatoes and rice. Some of the genes enable the plants to survive in cold temperatures or in poor soil. Other genetically engineered crops can resist insect pests or contain more nutrients.

Gene Therapy Someday it may be possible to use genetic engineering to correct some genetic disorders in humans. This process, called **gene therapy,** will involve inserting copies of a gene directly into a person's cells. For example, doctors may be able to treat hemophilia by replacing the defective allele on the X chromosome. The inserted gene would provide the body the correct instructions to clot blood normally.

Concerns About Genetic Engineering Some people are concerned about the long-term effects of genetic engineering. For example, some people think that genetically engineered crops may not be entirely safe. People fear that these crops may harm the environment or cause health problems in humans. To address such concerns, scientists are studying the effects of genetic engineering.

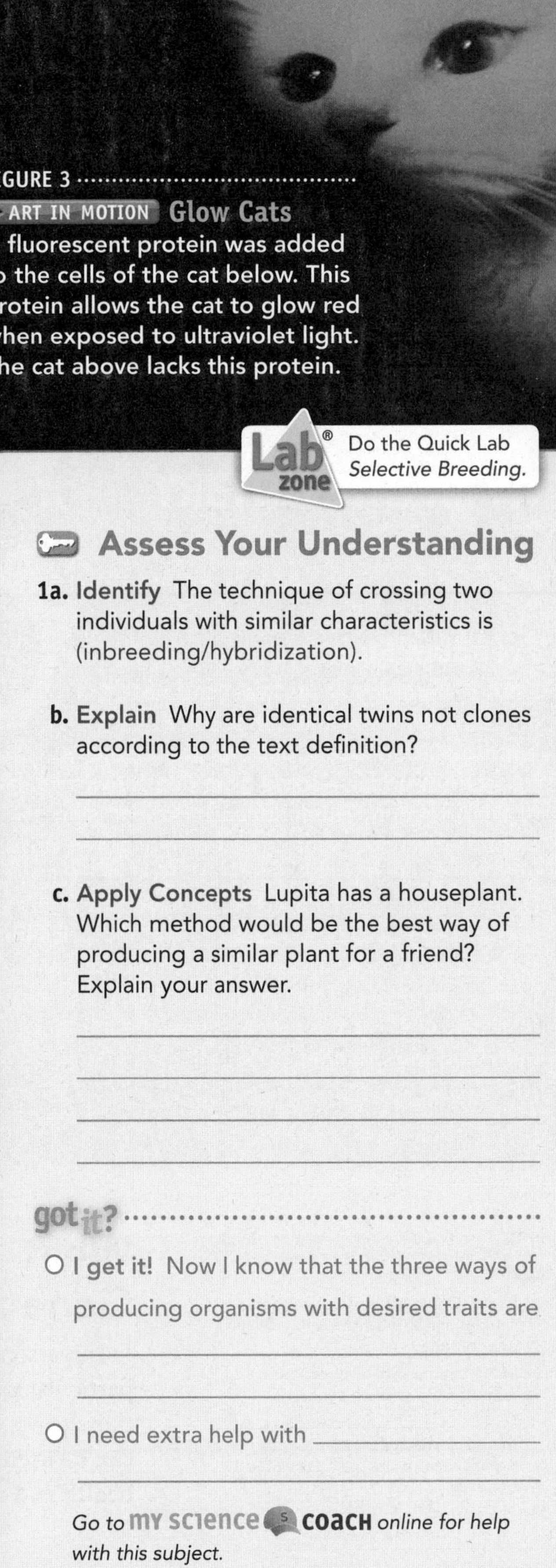

FIGURE 3

ART IN MOTION **Glow Cats**

A fluorescent protein was added to the cells of the cat below. This protein allows the cat to glow red when exposed to ultraviolet light. The cat above lacks this protein.

Lab zone® Do the Quick Lab *Selective Breeding.*

Assess Your Understanding

1a. Identify The technique of crossing two individuals with similar characteristics is (inbreeding/hybridization).

b. Explain Why are identical twins not clones according to the text definition?

____

____

c. Apply Concepts Lupita has a houseplant. Which method would be the best way of producing a similar plant for a friend? Explain your answer.

____

____

____

____

got it?

O **I get it!** Now I know that the three ways of producing organisms with desired traits are ______________________________

____

O I need extra help with ______________________________

____

Go to **MY SCIENCE COACH** *online for help with this subject.*

Using Genetic Information

What Are Some Uses of Genetic Information?
LS.1d, LS.1j, LS.12f

my planet Diary

TECHNOLOGY

Freedom Fighters

DNA technology saves lives, and not just through medicine. Since 1992, hundreds of innocent people have been freed from prison—some from death row—thanks to DNA testing. The Innocence Project is an organization that uses DNA testing to free prisoners who were wrongfully convicted. First, a sample of DNA is obtained from evidence saved from the crime scene. Then, a sample is taken from the prisoner. Laboratory procedures allow scientists to compare the two samples. If the prisoner's DNA is different from the DNA at the crime scene, the evidence may help free the prisoner.

Infer If the DNA from the crime scene matches the DNA from the prisoner, what might that suggest?

PLANET DIARY Go to **Planet Diary** to learn more about using genetic information.

Do the Inquiry Warm-Up *Using Genetic Information.*

LS.1d Construct and use models and simulations to illustrate and explain phenomena.
LS.1j Use current applications to reinforce life science concepts.
LS.12f Investigate and understand the historical contributions and significance of discoveries related to genetics.

What Are Some Uses of Genetic Information?

Each person's genes contain unique information about that particular person's growth and development. If we could "read" those genes, think of all we could learn! **Genetic information can be used positively to identify individuals and to learn about health and disease, or negatively to discriminate against people.**

Vocabulary
- genome
- ethics

Skills
- Reading: Summarize
- Inquiry: Communicate

Human Genome Project

Imagine trying to crack a code that is six billion letters long. That's exactly what scientists working on the Human Genome Project did. An organism's full set of DNA is called its **genome.** The main goal of the Human Genome Project was to identify the DNA sequence of the entire human genome. In 2003, the project was completed. Scientists continue to research the functions of the tens of thousands of human genes.

DNA Fingerprinting

DNA technology used in the Human Genome Project can also identify people and show whether people are related. DNA from a person's cells is broken down into small pieces, or fragments. Selected fragments are used to produce a pattern called a DNA fingerprint. Except for identical twins, no two people have exactly the same DNA fingerprint.

Genetic "fingerprints" can tie a person to the scene of a crime or prevent the wrong person from going to jail. They also can be used to identify skeletal remains. Today, soldiers and sailors give blood and saliva samples so their DNA fingerprints can be saved. DNA records can be used to identify the bodies of unknown soldiers or civilians.

apply it!

DNA fingerprints are stored in national DNA databases such as the Combined DNA Index System (CODIS). Databases contain the genetic information from crime scenes, convicted offenders, and missing persons. Law enforcement uses these databases to see if the DNA they have collected matches a known sample.

Communicate Discuss the following statement with a partner. Identify the pros and cons related to the statement.
Each citizen of the United States should have his or her DNA fingerprint added to the national databases.

Pros: ______________________________

____

Cons: ______________________________

____

Summarize What is the main purpose of the Genetic Information Nondiscrimination Act?

Genetic Discrimination As it becomes easier to obtain genetic information, there are concerns about who can access that information. There are concerns about how it can be used, too. For example, soldiers provide the government with a DNA sample for identification. It could be possible for the government to use their DNA in other ways such as in criminal cases or paternity suits. **Ethics** is the study of principles about what is right and wrong, fair and unfair. Using genetic information in an ethical way means using it in a way that is fair and just.

The Genetic Information Nondiscrimination Act (GINA) was signed into law in 2008. This act makes it illegal for health insurance companies and employers to discriminate against individuals based on genetic information. It also makes it illegal for insurance companies and employers to ask or tell individuals that they must have a genetic test done.

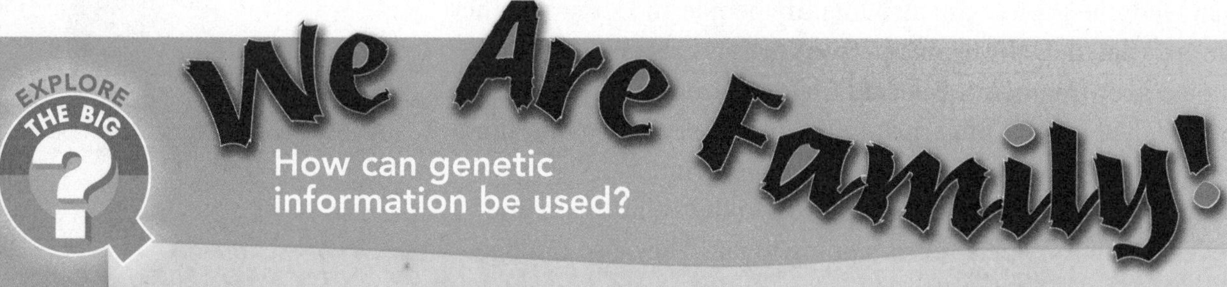

We Are Family!

How can genetic information be used?

FIGURE 1

INTERACTIVE ART You have been assigned to develop a family pedigree. Several members of this family have a hairline that comes to a point on their forehead. This characteristic, called a widow's peak, is a dominant trait.

Complete these tasks.

1. **Make Models** Draw and label this family's pedigree that shows how children may have inherited a widow's peak from their parents.

Genetic Privacy Doctors are expected to protect patients' privacy by not revealing their medical information. Patients' medical records may include information such as their medical history and their family's medical history. This information could indicate if a patient is at risk for developing a disease or mental illness. Details about a person's lifestyle may also be included in medical records. Doctors may record if a person drinks alcohol, smokes, or participates in sports that are dangerous.

If a patient has a genetic condition, the patient's relatives are likely at risk, too. Should other family members have the right to know? Or should a patient's medical records be kept private?

2. **Summarize** What tools and techniques would you use if you wanted to know what your chances were of inheriting a genetic disease from a family member?

3. **Evaluate the Impact on Society** If you learn that you have inherited a particular trait or genetic disease, who would you want to know? For each group of people listed, mark whether or not you think they should have the right to access your personal genetic information. Then explain why in the space below.

Immediate family members Yes / No

Your principal and teachers Yes / No

Do the Quick Lab *Extraction in Action.*

Assess Your Understanding

1a. Define What is a genome?

b. CHALLENGE Do you think it is ethical for doctors to share a patient's medical records? Explain.

c. ANSWER THE BIG ? How can genetic information be used?

got it?

○ **I get it!** Now I know that there are positive and negative ways of using genetic information such as

○ I need extra help with

Go to **MY SCIENCE COACH** *online for help with this subject.*

CHAPTER 8

Study Guide

Genetic information can be used to ______________________________,
______________________________, and ______________________________.

LESSON 1 Human Inheritance

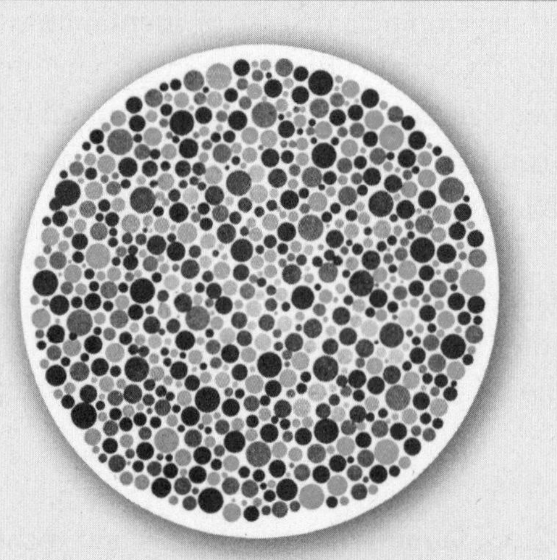

Some human traits are controlled by single genes with two alleles, and others by single genes with multiple alleles. Still other traits are controlled by many genes that act together.

The sex chromosomes carry genes that determine whether a person is male or female. They also carry genes that determine other traits.

Vocabulary

• sex chromosomes • sex-linked gene • carrier

LESSON 2 Human Genetic Disorders

Some genetic disorders are caused by mutations in the DNA of genes. Other disorders are caused by changes in the overall structure or number of chromosomes.

Today, doctors use tools such as pedigrees, karyotypes, and genetic testing to help trace and diagnose genetic disorders. People with genetic disorders are helped through medical care, education, and job training.

Vocabulary

• genetic disorder • pedigree • karyotype

LESSON 3 Advances in Genetics

Selective breeding, cloning, and genetic engineering are three methods for developing organisms with desired traits.

Vocabulary

- selective breeding
- inbreeding
- hybridization
- clone
- genetic engineering
- gene therapy

LESSON 4 Using Genetic Information

Genetic information can be used positively to identify individuals and to learn about health and disease, or negatively to discriminate against people.

Vocabulary

• genome • ethics

Review and Assessment

LESSON 1 Human Inheritance

1. Which human trait is controlled by a single gene with multiple alleles?
   a. height **b.** dimples
   c. skin color **d.** blood type

2. Colorblindness is carried on the X chromosome and is more common in males than in females because it is a ______________________
____

3. **Compare and Contrast** Describe the main differences between the inheritance patterns for a dimpled chin and for height.
____
____
____
____
____
____
____
____

4. **Interpret Data** Complete the Punnett square below to show the possible genotypes for the offspring of a colorblind mother and a father with normal vision. Circle the genotypes that would produce colorblind offspring.

	___	___
___	___	___
___	___	___

LESSON 2 Human Genetic Disorders

5. Which of the following would most likely be used to diagnose Down syndrome?
   a. a pedigree **b.** a karyotype
   c. a Punnett square **d.** a blood-clotting test

6. Cystic fibrosis and hemophilia are two examples of ______________________

7. **Make Generalizations** What information is shown by a karyotype?
____
____

8. **Relate Cause and Effect** How does the cause of cystic fibrosis differ from the cause of Down syndrome?
____
____
____
____
____
____

9. **Interpret Diagrams** The pedigree chart below shows the inheritance of sickle-cell disease. Circle all the individuals on the chart who have the disease. Draw a square around individuals who are carriers.

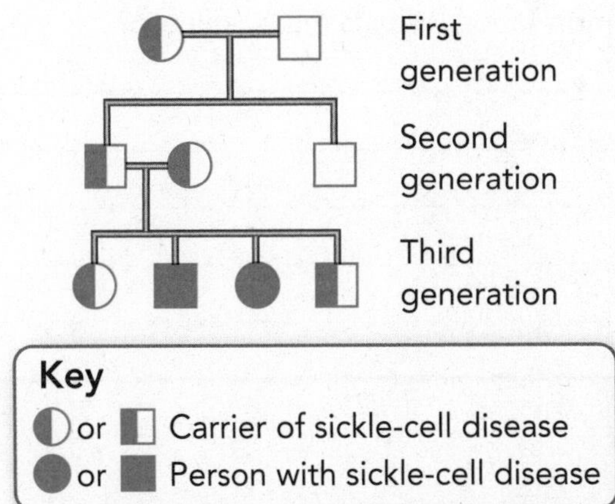

CHAPTER 8

Review and Assessment

LESSON 3 Advances in Genetics

10. An organism that has the same genes as the organism that produced it is called a

a. clone. b. hybrid.
c. genome. d. pedigree.

11. Inbreeding and hybridization are two different types of ______________________

12. Write About It Suppose that you are giving a presentation about genetic engineering to a group of people who are not familiar with the topic. Write a short speech that includes a definition of genetic engineering, a description of how it is used, and an explanation of some of the concerns about its use.

LESSON 4 Using Genetic Information

13. Genetic fingerprinting is a tool that is used in

a. gene therapy. b. selective breeding.
c. cloning. d. identification.

14. An organism's ______________ is its full set of DNA.

15. **Apply Concepts** Around the globe, people are discussing the ethical use of genetic information. Why is this a concern?

How can genetic information be used?

16. Genetic information can be applied in healthcare, agriculture, forensics, and many other fields. Using at least three vocabulary terms from this chapter, describe a situation in which genetic information such as this karyotype could have either a positive or negative impact on your daily life. Explain your reasoning.

Read each question and choose the best answer.

1 This Punnett square shows the possible genotypes for the offspring of a colorblind father and a mother who is a carrier. If this couple has a daughter, what is the probability that she will be colorblind?

	X^c	Y
X^C	X^CX^c	X^CY
X^c	X^cX^c	X^cY

A 0 percent
B 25 percent
C 50 percent
D 100 percent

2 Inserting a human gene into a bacterial plasmid is an example of—

F inbreeding
G selective breeding
H DNA fingerprinting
J genetic engineering

3 What was the main goal of the Human Genome Project?

A to clone a human
B to identify the sequence of the human genome
C to protect the genetic privacy of individuals
D to collect the genetic fingerprints of all humans

4 Which of the following is a selective breeding technique?

F cloning
G forensics
H inbreeding
J gene therapy

5 How is human blood type inherited?

A through a sex-linked gene
B through a single gene with multiple alleles
C through many genes, which produce many possible combinations of genes and alleles
D through a single gene with two alleles, one that is dominant and one that is recessive

6 Sasha's mother has sickle-cell disease. Her father does not have the disease and is not a carrier. Sasha has one brother and one sister. Which of the following must be true?

F Sasha and her sister have the disease. Her brother does not have the disease and is not a carrier.
G Sasha, her sister, and her brother are all carriers.
H Sasha, her sister, and her brother all have the disease.
J Sasha and her sister do not have the disease and are not carriers. Her brother has the disease.

7 Which of the following is a picture of all the chromosomes in a person's cell?

A karyotype
B pedigree
C hybridization
D genome

Museum of Science | TECH & DESIGN

MINI BUT MIGHTY

On TV crime shows, cases are solved in one hour. In real life, lab results may take weeks or months. Who knows how many more criminals could be caught if the lab techniques could be improved?

Scientists have recently developed technology that can run the same genetic tests that a lab can. "Lab-on-a-chip" devices are small and portable. They can usually produce results within an hour, right where the sample is taken. Scientists hope that one day, the units will be as small as a USB flash drive and affordable for everyone. Doctors could then diagnose and treat patients more quickly. Scientists at a crime scene could also get the answers they need almost immediately!

Analyze It Can you imagine any risks of a lab-on-a-chip? Do research about this new technology with its costs and benefits in mind. Make a presentation to your class on the impacts this device may have.

LS.1j, LS.12f

Museum of Science

CODIS:
THE DNA DATABASE

Genetic evidence is one of the most powerful tools that investigators can use to solve a crime. A genetic fingerprint is the unique information stored in a piece of each person's DNA. Forensic investigators use a computer program called the Combined DNA Index System (CODIS) to identify suspects by using their DNA fingerprint. CODIS compares DNA fingerprints that are stored in databases across the country. These DNA fingerprints can be used to link different crime scenes or to identify a suspect. CODIS has also been used to prove that convicted criminals are innocent.

CODIS has been used in more than 79,000 criminal investigations. However, the system is limited by the amount of information in the databases. Many law enforcement agencies do not have enough people to analyze all of the genetic samples gathered from crime scenes. As a result, the CODIS system is incomplete. As more information is added to the system, the technology will become more and more useful.

Write About It Find out more about how genetic evidence is used to investigate crimes. Then, write a short detective story to explain how a forensic investigator uses genetic technologies to solve a burglary.

LS.1j, LS.12f

▲ DNA samples can be collected at a crime scene and analyzed at a lab. Then, the analysis can be entered into a database to make the information available to CODIS.

The DNA from a human hair, like the one shown in this photomicrograph, can be used as evidence in criminal cases. ▶

DOES THIS FISH HAVE LEGS?

How do life forms change over time?

This is not your average fish. Besides having bright red lips, the rosy-lipped batfish is a poor swimmer. Instead of using its pectoral fins for swimming, the batfish uses them to crawl along the seafloor.

Develop Hypotheses **How do you think the batfish's leglike fins help it survive?**

UNTAMED SCIENCE Watch the **Untamed Science** video to learn more about adaptations.

Change Over Time

Science Standards of Learning

LS.1a, LS.1c, LS.1d, LS.1f, LS.1g, LS.1i, LS.1j, LS.4d, LS.11a, LS.13a, LS.13b, LS.13c

CHAPTER

9 Getting Started

Check Your Understanding

1. **Background** Read the paragraph below and then answer the question.

> Last fall, Jerome collected more than 100 seeds from a single sunflower in his garden. In the spring, he planted all the seeds. He was not surprised that the new plants all varied in many **traits.** Jerome knows that, because of **sexual reproduction,** each plant's **DNA** is different.

A **trait** is a characteristic that an organism passes to offspring through its genes.

Sexual reproduction results in offspring that are genetically different from each parent.

DNA is genetic material that carries information about an organism and is passed from parent to offspring.

- How are the plants' different traits related to sexual reproduction?

____

____

MY READING WEB If you had trouble completing the question above, visit **My Reading Web** and type in ***Change Over Time.***

Vocabulary Skill

Identify Multiple Meanings Familiar words may mean something else in science. Look at the different meanings of the words below.

Word	Everyday Meaning	Scientific Meaning
theory	*n.* a guess **Example:** Sue has a theory that soccer is harder to play than basketball.	*n.* a well-tested concept that explains a wide range of observations **Example:** The cell theory says that all organisms are made of cells.
adaptation	*n.* a change in an individual's behavior **Example:** Talia's adaptation to her new school was hard, but she did it.	*n.* a trait that helps an individual survive and reproduce **Example:** Fur is an adaptation to cold.

2. **Quick Check** **Circle the sentence that uses the scientific meaning of the word *theory.***
   - Evolutionary *theory* describes change over time.
   - Do you have a *theory* about why Sarah is a vegetarian?

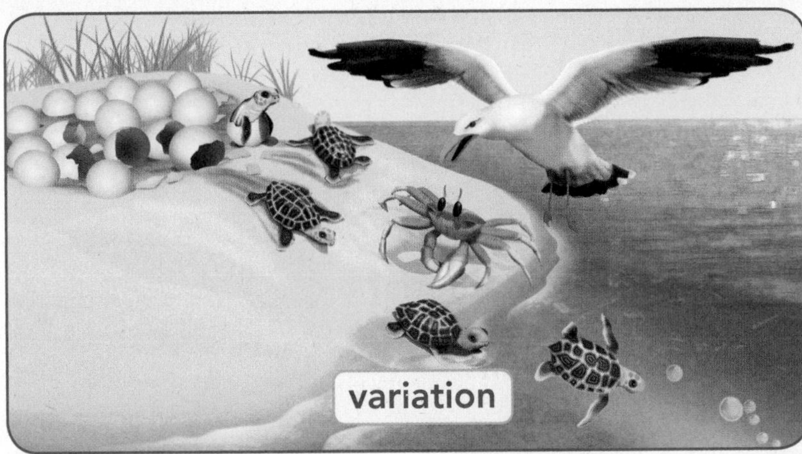

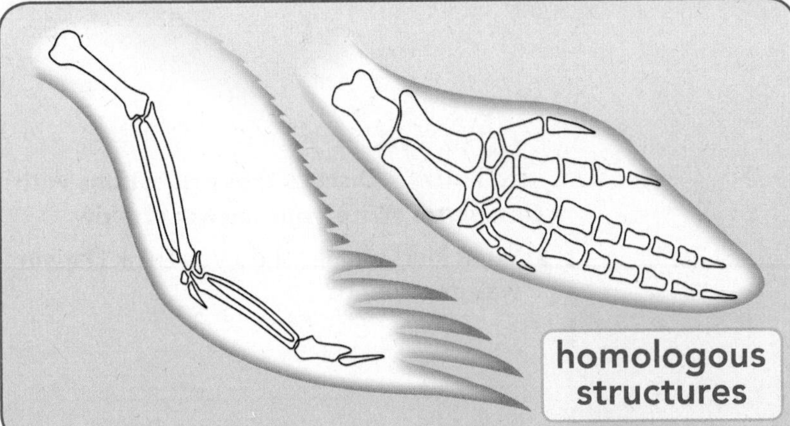

Chapter Preview

LESSON 1

- species
- fossil
- adaptation
- evolution
- scientific theory
- natural selection
- variation

Relate Cause and Effect
Develop Hypotheses

LESSON 2

- homologous structures

Identify the Main Idea
Communicate

LESSON 3

- gradualism
- punctuated equilibrium

Compare and Contrast
Make Models

VOCAB FLASH CARDS For extra help with vocabulary, visit **Vocab Flash Cards** and type in ***Change Over Time.***

Darwin's Theory

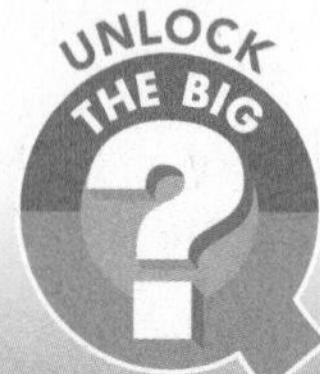

What Was Darwin's Hypothesis?
LS.1d, LS.4d, LS.13a, LS.13b, LS.13c

What Is Natural Selection?
LS.1a, LS.1d, LS.1f, LS.1i, LS.1j, LS.13a, LS.13c

my planet Diary

VOICES FROM HISTORY

Charles Darwin

In 1839, Charles Darwin published his book *The Voyage of the Beagle.* Read the following excerpt about an animal Darwin encountered while in the Galápagos Islands.

The inhabitants believe that these animals are absolutely deaf; certainly they do not overhear a person walking close behind them. I was always amused when overtaking one of these great monsters, as it was quietly pacing along, to see how suddenly, the instant I passed, it would draw in its head and legs, and uttering a deep hiss fall to the ground with a heavy sound, as if struck dead. I frequently got on their backs, and then giving a few raps on the hinder part of their shells, they would rise up and walk away; — but I found it very difficult to keep my balance.

Communicate **Discuss these questions with a classmate. Write your answers below.**

1. What kind of animal do you think Darwin was describing?

2. Describe your reaction to an unusual animal that you may have seen at a zoo, at an aquarium, or in a pet store. What was your first impression of the animal?

PLANET DIARY Go to **Planet Diary** for more information about Charles Darwin.

Do the Inquiry Warm-Up *How Do Living Things Vary?*

Vocabulary
- species
- fossil
- adaptation
- evolution
- scientific theory
- natural selection
- variation

Skills
- Reading: Relate Cause and Effect
- Inquiry: Develop Hypotheses

What Was Darwin's Hypothesis?

In 1831, the British ship HMS *Beagle* set sail from England on a five-year trip around the world. Charles Darwin was on board. Darwin was a naturalist—a person who observes and studies the natural world.

Diversity Darwin was amazed by the diversity of living things that he saw during the voyage. He wondered why they were so different from those in England. Darwin saw insects that looked like flowers. He also observed sloths, slow-moving animals that spent much of their time hanging in trees. Today, scientists know that organisms are even more diverse than Darwin thought. In fact, scientists have identified more than 1.6 million species of organisms on Earth. A **species** is a group of similar organisms that can mate with each other and produce fertile offspring. The exact number of species is unknown because many areas of Earth have not yet been studied.

Fossils Darwin saw fossils of animals that had died long ago. A **fossil** is the preserved remains or traces of an organism that lived in the past. Darwin was puzzled by some of the fossils he observed. For example, he saw fossils that resembled the bones of living sloths but were much larger in size. He wondered what had happened to the ancient, giant ground sloths. See **Figure 1**.

Science Standards of Learning

LS.1d Construct and use models and simulations to illustrate and explain phenomena.

LS.4d Investigate and understand characteristics that define a species.

LS.13a Investigate and understand relationships of mutation, adaptation, natural selection, and extinction.

LS.13b Investigate and understand evidence of evolution of different species in fossil record.

LS.13c Investigate and understand how environmental influences, as well as genetic variation, can lead to diversity of organisms.

FIGURE 1

Sloth Similarities

Darwin thought that the fossil bones of the giant ground sloths (left) resembled the bones of modern-day sloths (above).

Observe List two similarities that you notice between the two sloths.

Similarities

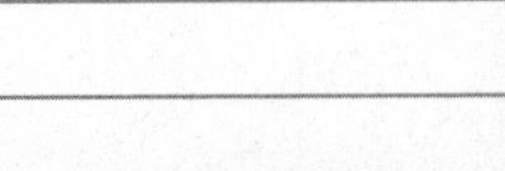

did you know?

The Galápagos penguin is the northernmost penguin in the world! It lives on the equator and is kept cool by ocean currents. The Galápagos penguin is the rarest penguin species and is endangered.

Galápagos Organisms The *Beagle* made many stops along the Atlantic and Pacific coasts of South America. From the Pacific coast, the ship traveled west to the Galápagos Islands. Darwin observed many unusual life forms there. He compared organisms from the Galápagos Islands to organisms that lived elsewhere. He also compared organisms living on the different islands.

Comparisons to South American Organisms Darwin discovered many similarities between Galápagos organisms and those found in South America. Many of the birds and plants on the islands resembled those on the mainland. However, he also noted important differences between the organisms. For instance, you can see differences between island and mainland iguanas in **Figure 2.**

Darwin became convinced that species do not always stay the same. Instead, he thought species could change and even produce new species over time. Darwin began to think that maybe the island species were somehow related to South American species. Perhaps, he thought, the island species had become different from their mainland relatives over time.

FIGURE 2

Comparing Iguanas

The iguanas on the Galápagos Islands have large claws that allow them to grip slippery rocks so they can feed on seaweed.

The iguanas on the mainland have smaller claws that allow them to climb trees so they can eat leaves.

Infer The color of each iguana is an adaptation to its

- ○ food.
- ○ habitat.
- ○ predators.
- ○ climate.

Explain your answer.

____

____

____

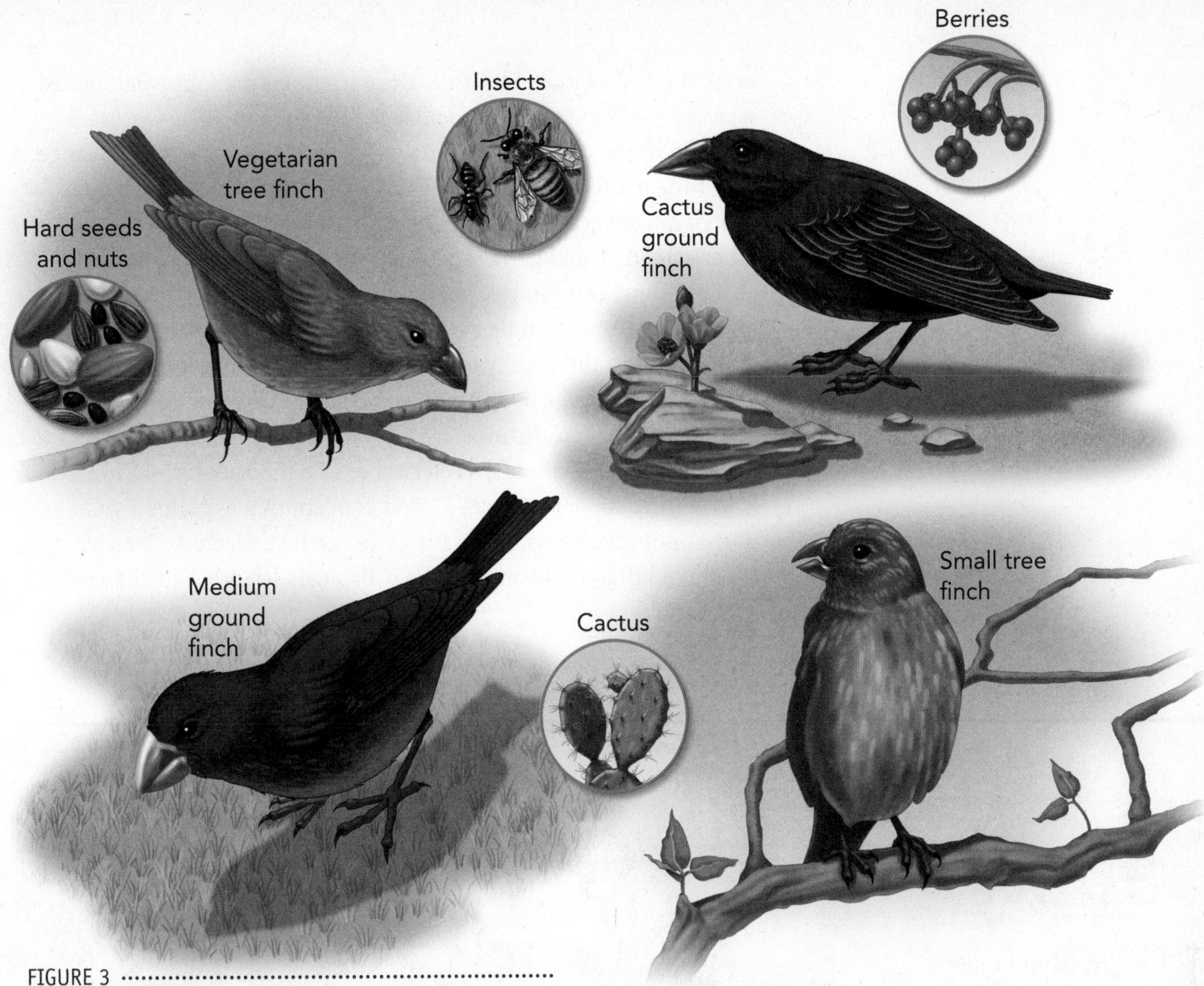

FIGURE 3

INTERACTIVE ART **Galápagos Finches**

The structure of each bird's beak is an adaptation to the type of food the bird eats. Birds with long, pointed, sharp beaks pick at cacti. Those with short, thick beaks crush seeds. Birds with narrow, pointed beaks grasp insects. Those with short, hooked beaks tear open fruit.

Interpret Diagrams Look at the different beak structures. Draw a line from each finch to the type of food you think it eats.

Comparisons Among the Islands Darwin also discovered many differences among organisms on the different Galápagos Islands. For example, the tortoises on one island had dome-shaped shells. Those on another island had saddle-shaped shells. A government official in the islands told Darwin that he could tell which island a tortoise came from just by looking at its shell.

Adaptations Birds were also different from one island to the next. Look at **Figure 3.** When Darwin returned to England, he learned that the different birds were all finches. Darwin concluded that the finch species were all related to a single ancestor species that came from the mainland. Over time, different finches developed different beak shapes and sizes that were well suited to the food that they ate. Beak shape is an example of an **adaptation,** a trait that increases an organism's ability to survive and reproduce.

Vocabulary **Identify Multiple Meanings** Write a sentence using the everyday meaning of the word *adapt*.

Darwin's Hypothesis Darwin thought about what he had seen during his voyage on the *Beagle*. By this time, Darwin was convinced that organisms change over time. The process of change over time is called **evolution.** Darwin, however, wanted to know *how* organisms change. Over the next 20 years, he consulted with other scientists and gathered more information. Based on his observations, Darwin reasoned that plants or animals that arrived on the Galápagos Islands faced conditions that were different from those on the nearby mainland. **Darwin hypothesized that species change over many generations and become better adapted to new conditions.**

Darwin's ideas are often referred to as a theory of evolution. A **scientific theory** is a well-tested concept that explains a wide range of observations. From the evidence he collected, Darwin concluded that organisms on the Galápagos Islands had changed over time.

apply it!

The first labradoodle dog was bred in 1989. A labradoodle is a cross between a standard poodle and a Labrador retriever. The poodle is very smart and has fur that sheds very little. The poodle may be less irritating for people allergic to dogs. Labradors are gentle, easily trained, and shed seasonally.

Standard poodle　Labrador retriever　Labradoodle

1 **Make Generalizations** Why do you think people breed these two dogs together?

____

____

2 **Develop Hypotheses** Would you expect the first labradoodle puppies to be the same as puppies produced several generations later? Explain.

____

____

Artificial Selection Darwin studied the offspring of domesticated animals that were produced by artificial selection in an effort to understand how evolution might occur. In artificial selection, only the organisms with a desired characteristic, such as color, are bred. Darwin himself had bred pigeons with large, fan-shaped tails. By repeatedly allowing only those pigeons with many tail feathers to mate, Darwin produced pigeons with two or three times the usual number of tail feathers. Darwin thought that a process similar to artificial selection might happen in nature. But he wondered what natural process selected certain traits.

FIGURE 4

Artificial Selection

The pigeons that Darwin bred were all descended from the rock dove (left). Pigeons can be bred for characteristics such as color, beak shape, wingspan, and feather patterns.

Describe If you were to breed an animal, what would it be and what traits would you want it to have?

____

____

____

Lab zone® Do the Quick Lab *Bird Beak Adaptations.*

Assess Your Understanding

1a. List Make a list of three observations that Darwin made during the *Beagle's* voyage.

____

____

____

b. Describe An adaptation is a trait that increases an organism's ability to ____________ and ____________

c. Develop Hypotheses How does artificial selection support Darwin's hypothesis?

____

____

____

____

____

got it?

○ **I get it!** Now I know that Darwin's hypothesis was ______________________________

____

○ I need extra help with ______________________________

Go to MY SCIENCE COACH *online for help with this subject.*

Science Standards of Learning

LS.1a Organize data into tables showing repeated trials and means.
LS.1d Construct and use models and simulations to illustrate and explain.
LS.1f Identify dependent variables, independent variables, and constants.
LS.1i Identify, interpret, and evaluate patterns in data.
LS.1j Use current applications to reinforce life science concepts.
LS.13a Investigate and understand relationships of mutation, adaptation, natural selection, and extinction.
LS.13c Investigate and understand how environmental influences, as well as genetic variation, can lead to diversity of organisms.

What Is Natural Selection?

In 1858, Darwin and Alfred Russel Wallace, another British biologist, both proposed the same explanation for how evolution occurs. The next year, Darwin described his explanation in his book *The Origin of Species.* In this book, Darwin proposed that evolution occurs by means of natural selection. **Natural selection** is the process by which individuals that are better adapted to their environment are more likely to survive and reproduce more than other members of the same species. Darwin identified factors that affect the process of natural selection: overproduction, variation, and competition. **Figure 5** shows how natural selection might happen in a group of sea turtles.

Overproduction Darwin knew that most species produce far more offspring than can possibly survive. In many species, so many offspring are produced that there are not enough resources—food, water, and living space—for all of them.

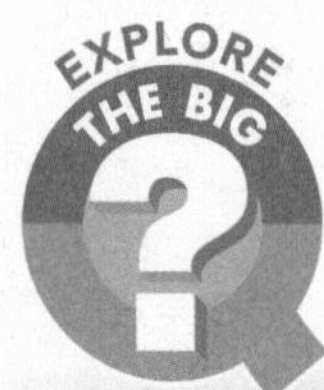

Factors That Affect Natural Selection

How do life forms change over time?

FIGURE 5

REAL-WORLD INQUIRY Overproduction, variation, and competition are factors that affect the process of natural selection.

Summarize Examine the sequence below that shows how natural selection could affect a group of sea turtles over time. Label each factor in the illustration and write a brief caption explaining what is occurring.

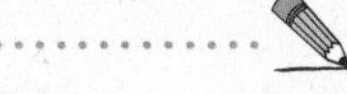

Variation Members of a species differ from one another in many of their traits. Any difference between individuals of the same species is called a **variation.** For example, sea turtles may differ in color, size, the ability to swim quickly, and shell hardness.

Competition Since food, space, and other resources are limited, the members of a species must compete with one another to survive. Competition does not always involve physical fights between members of a species. Instead, competition is usually indirect. For example, some turtles may not find enough to eat. A slower turtle may be caught by a predator, while a faster turtle may escape. Only a few turtles will survive to reproduce.

Selection Darwin observed that some variations make individuals better adapted to their environment. Those individuals are more likely to survive and reproduce. Their offspring may inherit the helpful characteristic. The offspring, in turn, will be more likely to survive and reproduce, and pass the characteristic to their offspring. After many generations, more members of the species will have the helpful characteristic.

In effect, the environment selects organisms with helpful traits to become parents of the next generation. **Darwin proposed that, over a long time, natural selection can lead to change. Helpful variations may accumulate in a species, while unfavorable ones may disappear.**

Relate Cause and Effect
Fill in the graphic organizer to identify the factors that cause natural selection.

Causes	Effect
Overproduction	Natural selection
______	
______	

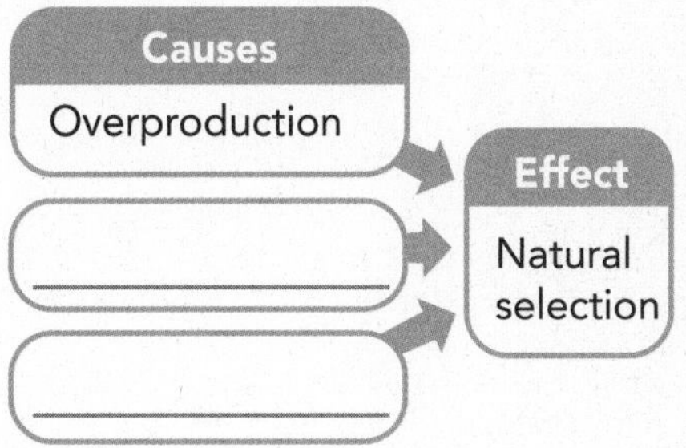

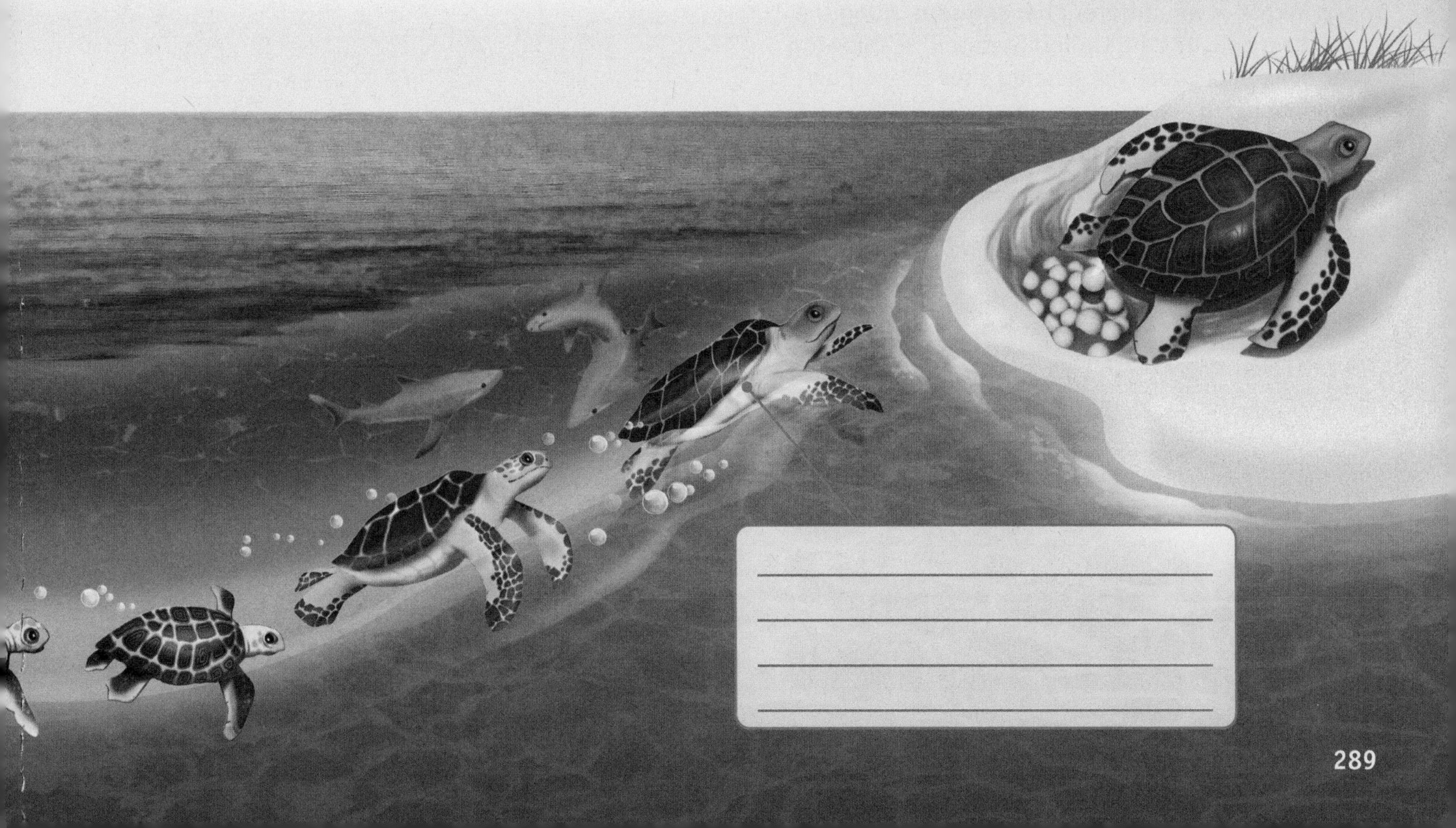

Environmental Change A change in the environment can affect an organism's ability to survive and therefore lead to natural selection. For example, monkey flowers are plants that do not normally grow in soil that has a high concentration of copper. However, because of genetic variation, some varieties of monkey flower now grow near copper mines. In **Figure 6** you can see how natural selection might have resulted in monkey flowers that can grow in copper-contaminated soil.

Genes and Natural Selection Without variations, all the members of a species would have the same traits and the same chance of surviving and reproducing. But where do variations come from? How are they passed on from parents to offspring?

Darwin could not explain what caused variations or how they were passed on. As scientists later learned, variations can result from changes in genes and the shuffling of different forms of genes when egg and sperm join. Genes, such as those for hair color and height, are passed from parents to their offspring. Only traits that are inherited, or controlled by genes that are passed on to offspring, can be acted upon by natural selection.

do the math!

The typical clutch size, or number of eggs, a loggerhead sea turtle can lay at once is around 113. Even with producing so many offspring, the loggerhead sea turtle is endangered in many areas. Suppose that scientists counted the number of eggs laid at seven different nesting sites along the southeast coast of the United States. The following year, scientists check the nesting sites to see how many offspring survived and returned.

Loggerhead Sea Turtle Data

Site	A	B	C	D	E	F	G
Clutch Size	114	103	121	118	107	103	104
Returning Turtles	45	35	55	53	40	66	38

1. **Calculate** Determine the mean for the clutch sizes of the seven nesting sites in the table. ________ How does the mean compare to the typical clutch size for loggerheads? ____________________

2. **Interpret Data** Do you think clutch size influences the survival rates of the offspring? Use the data to support your answer.

3. CHALLENGE Hypothesize why Site F had the largest number of returning turtles.

Monkey flowers grow successfully in healthy, unpolluted soil.

Copper seeps into the soil around the copper mine. Most monkey flowers cannot grow in this polluted soil, and they begin to die.

Some monkey flowers have genetic variations that allow them to survive and reproduce in copper-contaminated soil.

____
____
____
____

FIGURE 6

Environmental Change

When copper contaminated the soil surrounding the monkey flowers, the environment changed. Due to a genetic variation, some varieties of monkey flower are now able to survive in that soil.

Draw Conclusions In the last circle, draw what you think the area will look like in ten years' time. Write a caption describing what has taken place.

Do the Lab Investigation *Nature at Work.*

Assess Your Understanding

2a. Define A variation is any (similarity/difference) between individuals of the same species.

b. ANSWER THE BIG Q How do life forms change over time?

____
____
____

c. Relate Cause and Effect Explain how unfavorable traits can disappear in a species.

____
____
____
____
____

got it?

O **I get it!** Now I know that natural selection occurs _______________
____
____

O I need extra help with _______________

Go to MY SCIENCE COACH *online for help with this subject.*

Virginia

LESSON 2

Evidence of Evolution

What Evidence Supports Evolution?

LS.1a, LS.1d, LS.1i, LS.1j, LS.13a, LS.13b

my planet Diary

DISCOVERY

Moving On Up

In 2004, researchers on Ellesmere Island, Nunavut, in the Canadian Arctic, found a fossil that provides information about when fish first came onto land. The fossil, called *Tiktaalik,* is 375 million years old. *Tiktaalik* has characteristics of both fish and four-legged animals. Like other fish, it has fins. However, the fins have interior bones that helped push the animal up in the shallow waters close to shore to find food. The discovery of *Tiktaalik* has provided new fossil evidence to help scientists understand the relationship between marine vertebrates and land vertebrates.

Communicate Discuss these questions with a partner. Write your answers below.

1. Do you think the discovery of *Tiktaalik* is important to understanding evolution? Why?

2. Do you think *Tiktaalik* spent most of its time on land or in water? Why?

PLANET DIARY Go to **Planet Diary** to learn more about fossil evidence.

Researcher from Ellesmere Island

This model of *Tiktaalik* shows what it may have looked like 375 million years ago.

Do the Inquiry Warm-Up *How Can You Classify a Species?*

Vocabulary
- homologous structures

Skills
- Reading: Identify the Main Idea
- Inquiry: Communicate

What Evidence Supports Evolution?

Science Standards of Learning

LS.1a Organize data into tables showing repeated trials and means.
LS.1d Construct and use models and simulations to illustrate and explain phenomena.
LS.1i Identify, interpret, and evaluate patterns in data.
LS.1j Use current applications to reinforce life science concepts.
LS.13a Investigate and understand relationships of mutation, adaptation, natural selection, and extinction.
LS.13b Investigate and understand evidence of evolution of different species in fossil record.

Since Darwin's time, scientists have found a great deal of evidence that supports the theory of evolution. **Fossils, patterns of early development, similar body structures, and similarities in DNA and protein structures all provide evidence that organisms have changed over time.**

Fossils By examining fossils, scientists can infer the structures of ancient organisms. Fossils show that, in many cases, organisms that lived in the past were very different from organisms alive today. The millions of fossils that scientists have collected are called the fossil record. The fossil record provides clues about how and when new species evolved and how organisms are related.

Similarities in Early Development Scientists also infer evolutionary relationships by comparing the early development of different organisms. For example, the organisms in **Figure 1** look similar during the early stages of development. All four organisms have a tail. They also have a row of tiny slits along their throats. The similarities suggest that these vertebrate species are related and share a common ancestor.

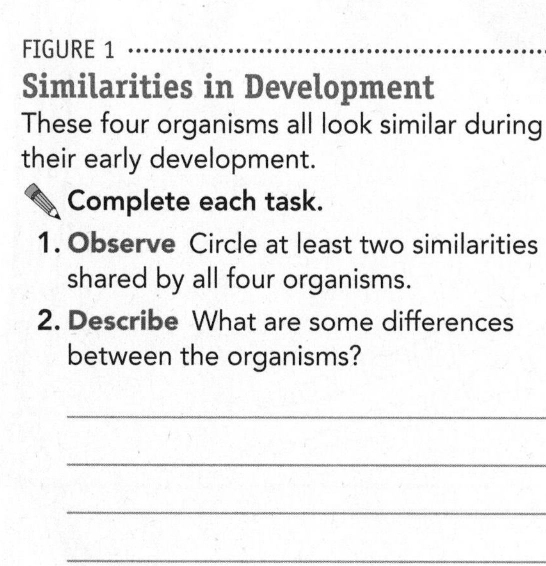

FIGURE 1

Similarities in Development

These four organisms all look similar during their early development.

Complete each task.

1. **Observe** Circle at least two similarities shared by all four organisms.
2. **Describe** What are some differences between the organisms?

____

____

____

____

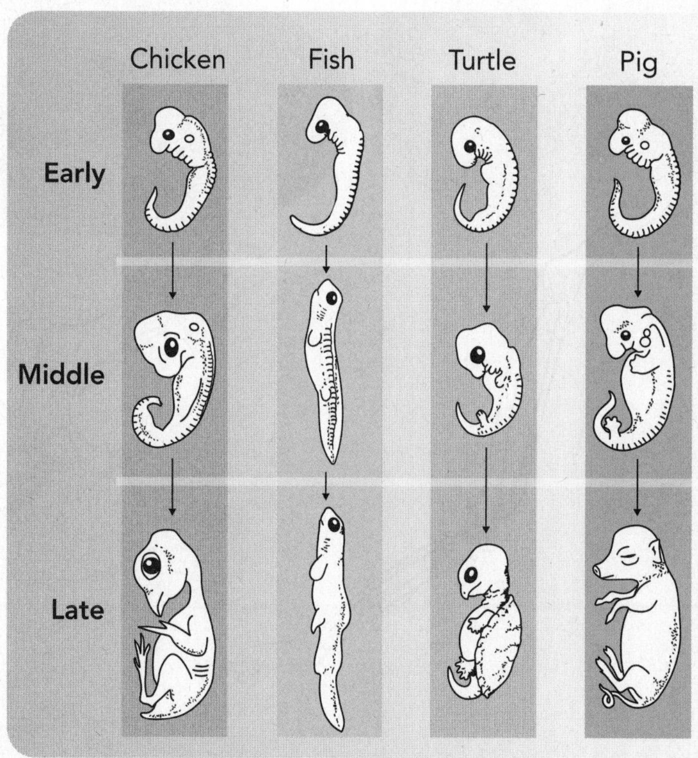

Similarities in Body Structure

Similarities in Body Structure An organism's body structure is its basic body plan, which in vertebrates includes how its bones are arranged. Fishes, amphibians, reptiles, birds, and mammals all have an internal skeleton with a backbone. This similarity provides evidence that these animal groups all evolved from a common ancestor.

Identify the Main Idea Describe the main idea on this page.

Similar structures that related species have inherited from a common ancestor are known as **homologous structures** (hoh MAHL uh gus). In **Figure 2,** you can see some examples of homologous structures. These include a bird's wing, a dolphin's flipper, and a dog's leg.

Sometimes fossils show structures that are homologous with structures in living species. For example, scientists have recently found fossils of ancient whalelike creatures. The fossils show that the ancestors of today's whales had legs and walked on land. This evidence supports other evidence that whales and other vertebrates share a common ancestor that had a skeleton with a backbone.

FIGURE 2

INTERACTIVE ART **Homologous Structures**

The bones in a bird's wing, a dolphin's flipper, and a dog's leg have similar structures.

Interpret Diagrams Use the drawing of the dog's leg as a guide. Color in the matching bones in the bird's wing and the dolphin's flipper with the appropriate colors.

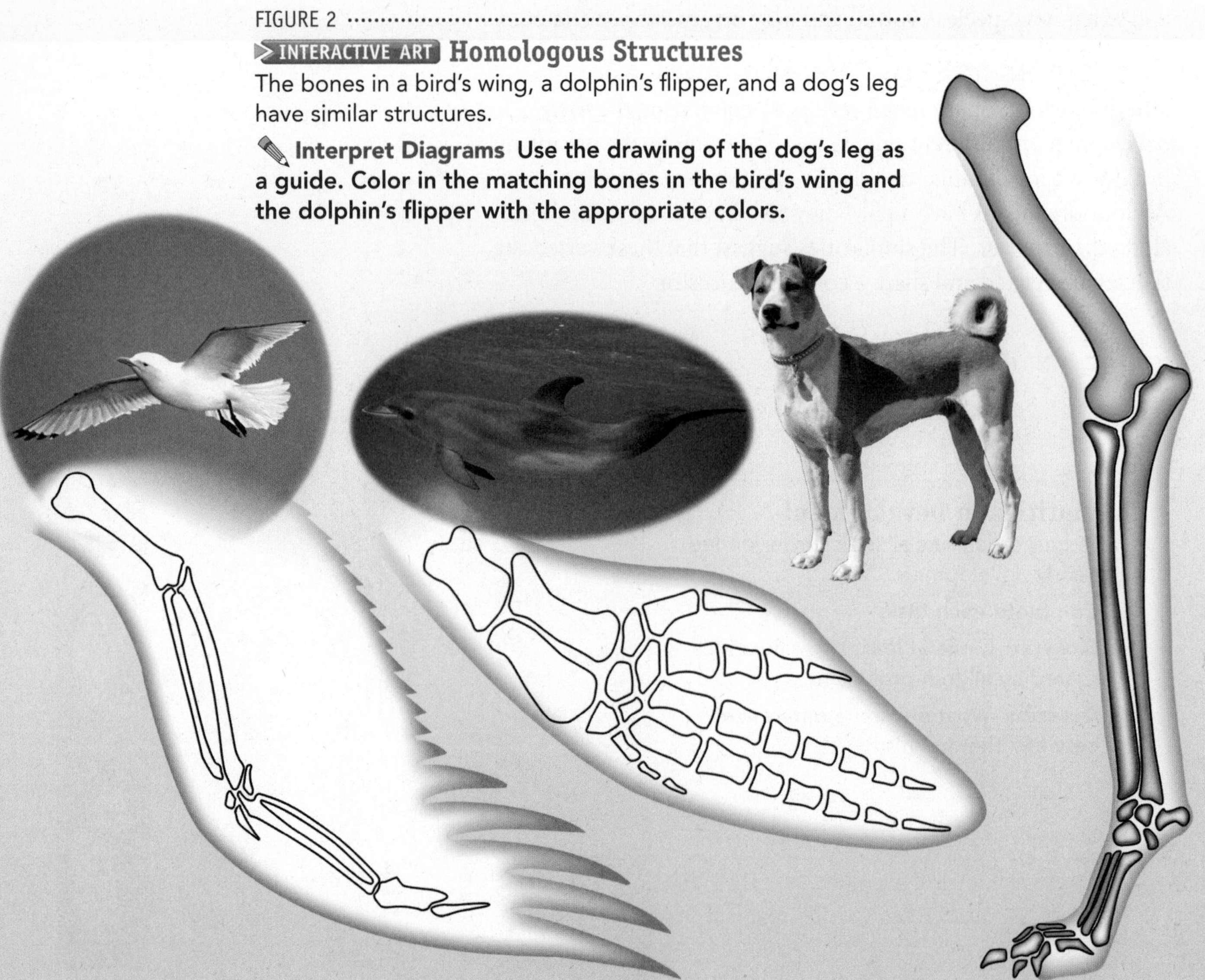

Similarities in DNA and Protein Structure

Similarities in DNA and Protein Structure Why do some species have similar body structures and development patterns? Scientists infer that the species inherited many of the same genes from a common ancestor.

Recall that genes are segments of DNA. Scientists compare the sequence of nitrogen bases in the DNA of different species to infer how closely related the two species are. The more similar the DNA sequences, the more closely related the species are. The DNA bases along a gene specify what type of protein will be produced. Therefore, scientists can also compare the order of amino acids in a protein to see how closely related two species are.

In most cases, evidence from DNA and protein structure has confirmed conclusions based on fossils, embryos, and body structure. For example, DNA comparisons show that dogs are more similar to wolves than to coyotes. Scientists had already reached this conclusion based on similarities in the structure and development of these three species.

apply it!

The table shows the sequence of amino acids in one region of a protein, cytochrome c, for five different animals. Each letter corresponds to a different amino acid in the protein.

Section of Cytochrome *c* Protein in Animals

Animal	Amino Acid Position in the Sequence											
	39	40	41	42	43	44	45	46	47	48	49	50
Horse	N	L	H	G	L	F	G	R	K	T	G	Q
Donkey	N	L	H	G	L	F	G	R	K	T	G	Q
Rabbit	N	L	H	G	L	F	G	R	K	T	G	Q
Snake	N	L	H	G	L	F	G	R	K	T	G	Q
Turtle	N	L	N	G	L	I	G	R	K	T	G	Q

1. **Interpret Tables** Which species is most distantly related to the horse? ______________

2. **Communicate** Explain how amino acid sequences provide information about evolutionary relationships among organisms.

____

____

____

____

____

Do the Quick Lab *Finding Proof.*

Assess Your Understanding

1a. Define ______________________ structures are structurally similar body parts in related species.

b. CHALLENGE Insects and birds both have wings. What kinds of evidence might show whether or not insects and birds are closely related? Explain.

____

____

____

____

got it?

○ **I get it!** Now I know that the theory of evolution is supported by evidence that includes ____

____

____

____

○ I need extra help with ______________________

Go to MY SCIENCE COACH *online for help with this subject.*

Rate of Change

How Do New Species Form?
LS.13c

What Patterns Describe the Rate of Evolution?
LS.1d, LS.13b

my planet Diary

Crickets, Maggots, and Flies, Oh My!

A male cricket chirps to attract a mate. Unfortunately, chirping also attracts a parasitic fly. Parasitic flies listen for chirping crickets. When a cricket is located, a female fly deposits larvae onto the cricket's back. The larvae, or maggots, burrow into the cricket. The maggots come out seven days later, killing the cricket in the process. Parasitic flies reduced the cricket population on the Hawaiian island of Kauai between 1991 and 2001. By 2003, the cricket population on Kauai had increased. The male crickets were silent! In about 20 cricket generations, the crickets had evolved into an almost silent population.

Do the Inquiry Warm-Up *Making a Timeline.*

FUN FACT

Communicate **Discuss these questions with a classmate. Write your answers below.**

1. Why do you think the crickets on Kauai evolved so quickly?

____

2. If most of the male crickets can no longer chirp, how do you think it might affect the size of the cricket population?

____

PLANET DIARY Go to **Planet Diary** to learn more about evolution.

Science Standards of Learning

LS.13c Investigate and understand how environmental influences, as well as genetic variation, can lead to diversity of organisms.

How Do New Species Form?

Natural selection explains how variations can lead to changes in a species. But how could an entirely new species form? **A new species can form when a group of individuals remains isolated from the rest of its species long enough to evolve different traits that prevent reproduction.** Isolation, or complete separation, occurs when some members of a species become cut off from the rest of the species. One way this can happen is when a natural barrier, such as a river, separates group members.

Vocabulary
- gradualism
- punctuated equilibrium

Skills
- Reading: Compare and Contrast
- Inquiry: Make Models

FIGURE 1

Kaibab and Abert's Squirrels

The Kaibab squirrel (left) and the Abert's squirrel (right) have been isolated from each other for a long time. Eventually, this isolation may result in two different species.

Identify What conditions might differ from one side of the Grand Canyon to the other that would cause the squirrels to be different colors?

____

____

____

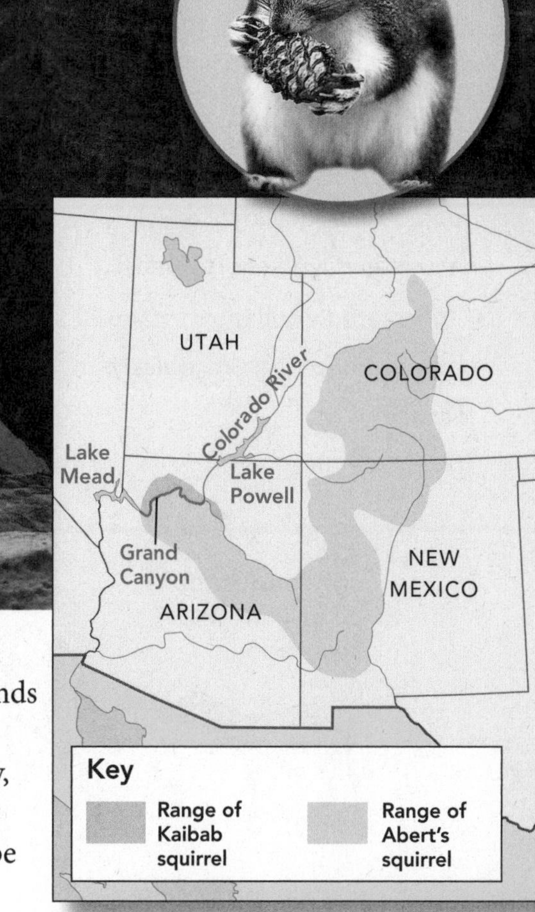

As you can see in **Figure 1,** the populations of Kaibab and Abert's squirrels are separated by the Grand Canyon. The two kinds of squirrels are the same species, but they have slightly different characteristics. For example, the Kaibab squirrel has a black belly, while Abert's squirrel has a white belly. It is possible that one day these squirrels will become so different that they will no longer be able to mate with each other and will become separate species.

Do the Quick Lab *Large-Scale Isolation.*

Assess Your Understanding

got it?

O **I get it!** Now I know that new species form when _______________

____

O I need extra help with _______________

Go to MY SCIENCE COACH *online for help with this subject.*

Science Standards of Learning

LS.1d Construct and use models and simulations to illustrate and explain phenomena.

LS.13b Investigate and understand evidence of evolution of different species in fossil record.

What Patterns Describe the Rate of Evolution?

The fossil record has provided scientists with a lot of important information about past life on Earth. For example, scientists have found many examples of the appearance of new species as older species vanish. Sometimes the new species appear rapidly, and at other times they are the result of more gradual change. **Scientists have developed two patterns to describe the pace of evolution: gradualism and punctuated equilibrium.**

Compare and Contrast Identify the similarity and the key differences between gradualism and punctuated equilibrium.

- Both describe the ________________
- Gradualism states that evolution occurs (quickly/slowly) and (steadily/in short bursts).
- Punctuated equilibrium states that evolution occurs (quickly/slowly) over__________ periods of time.

Gradual Change

Some species in the fossil record seem to change gradually over time. **Gradualism** involves small changes that add up to major changes over a long period of time. Since the time scale of the fossil record involves hundreds, thousands, or even millions of years, there is plenty of time for gradual changes to produce new species. The fossil record contains many examples of species that are intermediate between two others. One example is the horse relative, *Merychippus*, shown in **Figure 2.** Many such intermediate forms seem to be the result of gradual change.

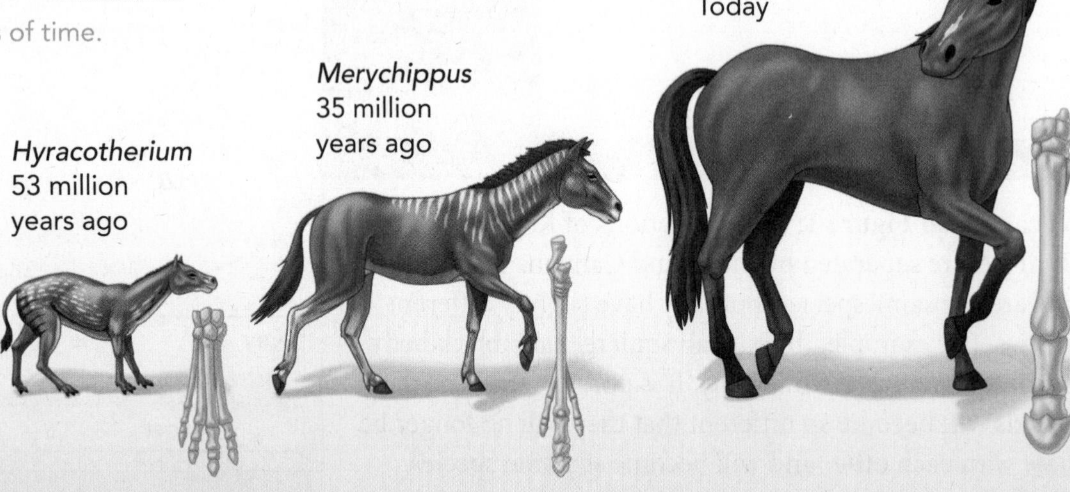

FIGURE 2

ART IN MOTION **Horse Evolution**

Horses left a rich and detailed fossil record of their evolution. Many intermediate forms have been found between modern horses and their four-toed ancestors. *Merychippus* is shown here.

Answer these questions.

1. **List** Name two differences between the horses.

____

____

2. CHALLENGE How could the evolution of the shape of the leg and the number of toes have benefited *Equus*?

____

____

____

Rapid Change Scientists have also found that many species remain almost unchanged during their existence. Then, shortly after they become extinct, related species often appear in the fossil record. This pattern, in which species evolve during short periods of rapid change and then don't change much, is called **punctuated equilibrium.** Today most scientists think that evolution can occur rapidly at some times, and more gradually at others.

Two patterns that describe the rate of evolution are modeled at the right.

Make Models **Look at the shells in the key. For each pattern, decide if—and at what point—each shell belongs on the timelines. Using colored pencils, draw and color in the shells at their correct locations to show how they have evolved over time.**

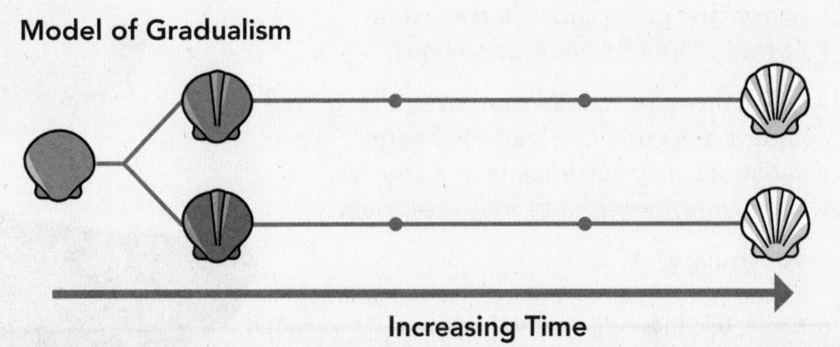

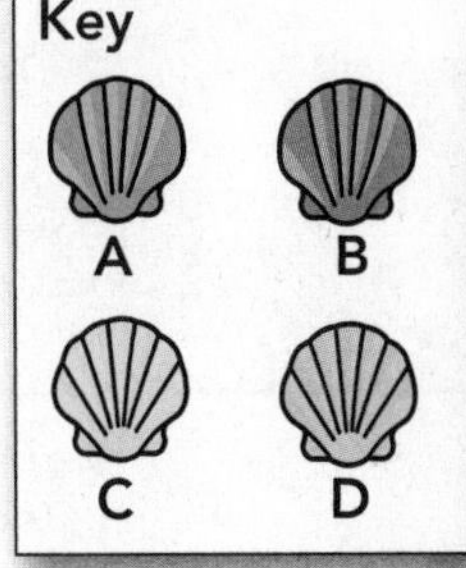

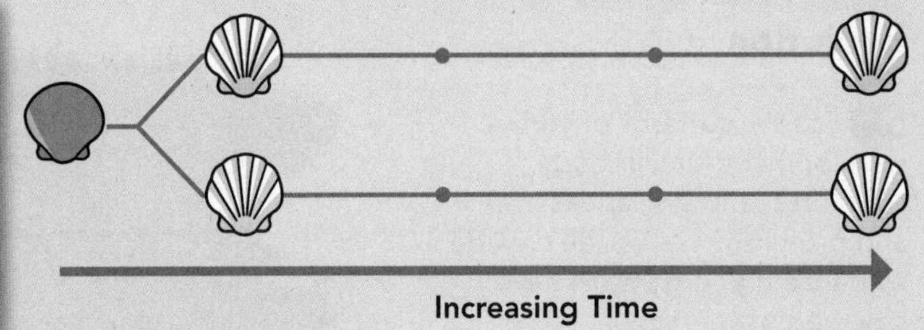

Do the Quick Lab *Slow or Fast?*

Assess Your Understanding

1a. Identify The ________________ has given scientists information about past life on Earth.

b. Infer Why are fossils of intermediate life forms likely to be rare if the pattern of punctuated equilibrium explains how evolution occurs?

____

____

____

____

got it?

○ **I get it!** Now I know that two patterns of evolution are ____

____

____

○ I need extra help with ____

____

Go to **my science coach** *online for help with this subject.*

CHAPTER 9

Study Guide

Living things change over time, or ______________________, through a process called ______________________

LESSON 1 Darwin's Theory

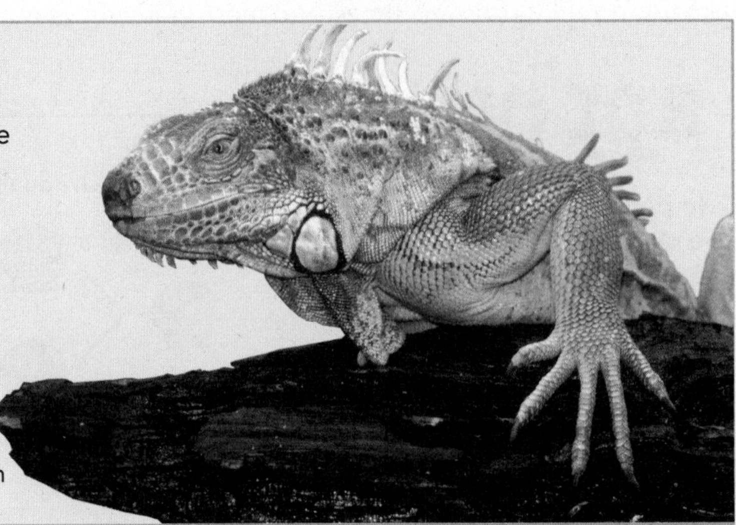

Darwin hypothesized that species change over many generations and become better adapted to new conditions.

Darwin proposed that, over a long time, natural selection can lead to change. Helpful variations may accumulate in a species, while unfavorable ones may disappear.

Vocabulary

- species
- fossil
- adaptation
- evolution
- scientific theory
- natural selection
- variation

LESSON 2 Evidence of Evolution

Fossils, patterns of early development, similar body structures, and similarities in DNA and protein structures all provide evidence that organisms have changed over time.

Vocabulary

- homologous structures

LESSON 3 Rate of Change

A new species can form when a group of individuals remains isolated from the rest of its species long enough to evolve different traits that prevent reproduction.

Scientists have developed two patterns to describe the pace of evolution: gradualism and punctuated equilibrium.

Vocabulary

- gradualism
- punctuated equilibrium

Review and Assessment

LESSON 1 Darwin's Theory

1. A trait that helps an organism to survive and reproduce is called a(n)
   - **a.** variation.
   - **b.** adaptation.
   - **c.** species.
   - **d.** selection.

2. Two organisms that can mate and produce fertile offspring are members of the same ______________

3. **Infer** Why are Darwin's ideas classified as a scientific theory?

4. **Apply Concepts** What is one factor that affects natural selection? Give an example.

5. **Compare and Contrast** Identify one similarity and one difference between natural selection and artificial selection.

6. **Write About It** You are a reporter in the 1800s interviewing Charles Darwin about his theory of evolution. Write three questions you would ask him. Then write answers that Darwin might have given.

LESSON 2 Evidence of Evolution

7. Similar structures that related species have inherited from a common ancestor are called
   - **a.** adaptations.
   - **b.** fossils.
   - **c.** ancestral structures.
   - **d.** homologous structures.

8. The more ______________ the DNA sequences between two organisms are, the more closely related the two species are.

9. **Draw Conclusions** Look at the drawing, at the right, of the bones in a crocodile's leg. Do you think that crocodiles share a common ancestor with birds, dolphins, and dogs? Support your answer with evidence.

Crocodile

10. **Make Judgments** What type of evidence is the best indicator of how closely two species are related? Explain your answer.

CHAPTER 9

Review and Assessment

LESSON 3 Rate of Change

11. The pattern of evolution that involves short periods of rapid change is called
    - **a.** adaptation.
    - **b.** gradualism.
    - **c.** isolation.
    - **d.** punctuated equilibrium.

12. ______________________ involves tiny changes in a species that slowly add up to major changes over time.

13. **Apply Concepts** A population of deer lives in a forest. Draw a picture that illustrates how a geographic feature could isolate this deer population into two separate groups. Label the geographic feature.

14. **Develop Hypotheses** Describe the conditions that could cause these two groups of deer to become separate species over time.

APPLY THE BIG Q How do life forms change over time?

15. Suppose that over several years, the climate in an area becomes much drier than it was before. How would plants, like the ones shown below, be affected? Using the terms *variation* and *natural selection,* predict what changes you might observe in the plants as a result of this environmental change.

Virginia SOL Test Prep

Read each question and choose the best answer.

1 The illustration below has no title. Which of the following titles would *best* describe the concept shown in this drawing?

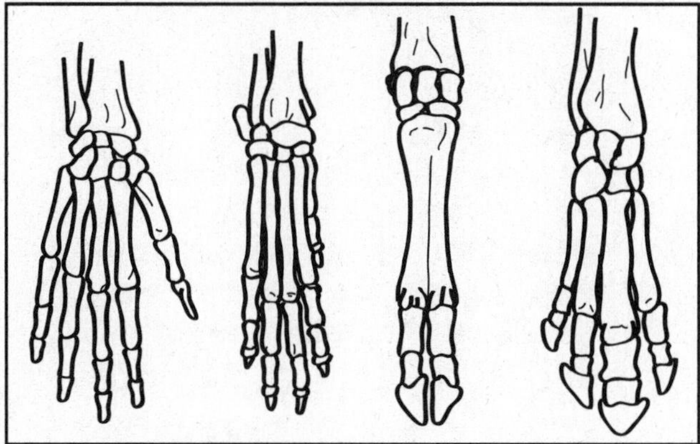

A Wrist Bone Adaptations
B Similarities in Wrist Bone Development
C Evolutionary Change Through Gradualism
D Homologous Structures in Four Animals

2 The process by which individuals that are better adapted to their environment are more likely to survive and reproduce than other members of the same species is called—

F natural selection
G evolution
H competition
J overproduction

3 Which of the following is the *best* example of an adaptation that helps organisms survive in their environment?

A green coloring in lizards living on gray rocks
B a thick coat of fur on animals that live in the desert
C an extensive root system in desert plants
D thin, delicate leaves on plants in a cold climate

4 Which of the following sets of factors did Darwin identify as affecting natural selection?

F adaptations, gradualism, and evolution
G overproduction, variation, and competition
H adaptations, traits, and variations
J predation, competition, and mutualism

5 Evolution that occurs slowly is described by the pattern of—

A natural selection
B homologous structures
C gradualism
D punctuated equilibrium

6 This drawing shows variations in wing size within a species of fly. In which situation would natural selection favor flies with the smallest wings?

F Flies with smaller wings can escape predators more frequently.
G Flies with smaller wings can reproduce more easily.
H Flies with smaller wings can find food faster.
J Flies with smaller wings have fewer unfavorable traits that can be passed on to offspring.

7 Which of the following *best* describes punctuated equilibrium?

A gradual change
B short periods of rapid change followed by little change
C constant rapid change
D no change

SCIENCE MATTERS

Science and Society

The Incredible Shrinking Fish

For years, fishers have followed a simple rule: keep the big fish and release the small fish. This practice aims to keep fish populations stable by allowing young fish to reach reproductive age. However, a scientist named David Conover thinks that this practice of throwing back small fish might be affecting the evolution of fish species.

Not all small fish are young. Like humans, adult fish come in different sizes. Conover hypothesized that removing the largest fish from fish populations might result in populations of smaller fish because smaller adult fish would survive to reproduce more often than larger adult fish. To test this hypothesis, Conover's team divided a population of 6,000 fish into different groups. Over four generations, the scientists selectively removed 90 percent of the fish in each group before they could reproduce.

The results showed that over just a few generations, selection pressures can influence not only the size of fish, but also the health of fish populations. Currently, Conover is researching ways to change fishing regulations so fish populations can recover.

▲ The practice of commercial fishing may be leading to populations of smaller and smaller fish.

This diagram shows how Dr. Conover and his team set up and performed their experiment. It also shows the results. ▶

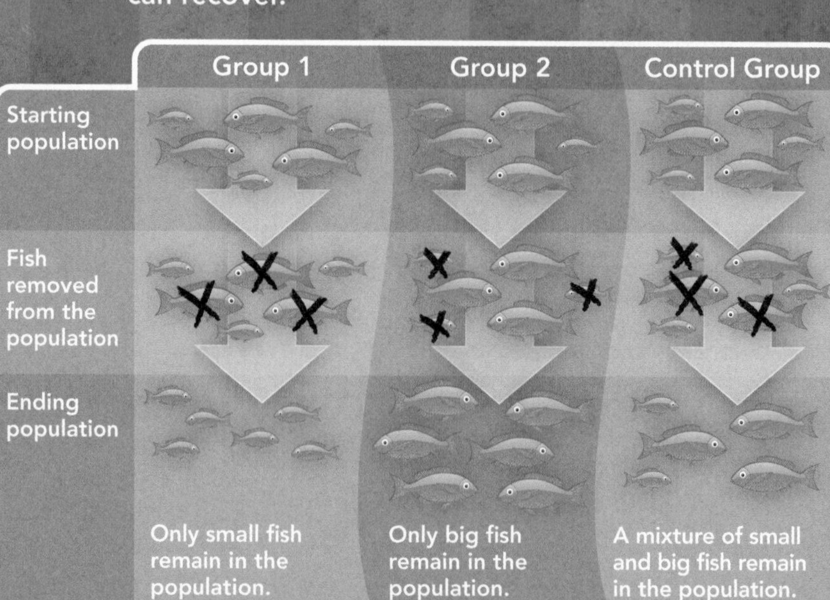

Design It If current policies are causing the average size of fish to decrease, what is the best way to help fish populations recover? Design an experiment that would test your method for helping fish populations recover.

LS.1g, LS.1j, LS.11a, LS.13a

WALKING WHALES?

If you could visit Earth 50 million years ago, you would see many amazing sights. One of the strangest things you might see is the ancestor of modern whales—walking on land!

For years, scientists have thought that whales evolved from land-dwelling mammals. About 50 million years ago, the ancestors of modern whales had four legs and were similar to large dogs. Over 50 million years, whales evolved to become the giant marine mammals we recognize today. However, scientists have had difficulty finding fossils of whales that show how this dramatic change occurred. These missing links could reveal how whales lost their legs.

Now, several new discoveries are helping scientists fill in the blanks in the evolutionary history of whales. A fossil whale skeleton discovered in Washington State has a pelvis with large cuplike sockets. These sockets likely held short legs that enabled the whale to move on land. Other whale fossils, found in Alabama, include large hind limbs that probably helped the animials swim. Researchers have also discovered the gene mutation that could have been responsible for whales losing their legs about 35 million years ago.

Design It Find out more about the evolutionary history of whales. How is a whale flipper similar to a bat wing and a human hand? Design and draw a poster to scale (using a metric ruler and/or meter stick) that shows the evolutionary history of whales.

LS.1c, LS.1d, LS.13a, LS.13b, LS.13c

Over 50 million years, whales evolved from a species of doglike land mammals to the aquatic giants we know today.

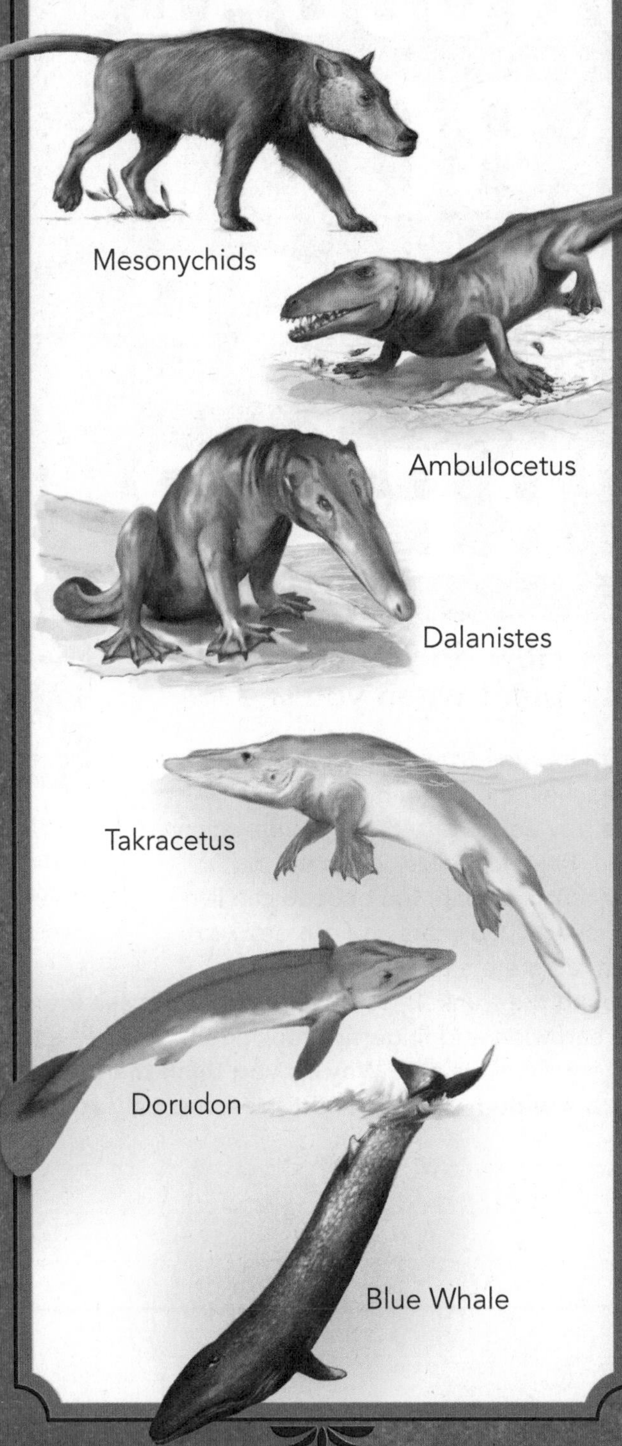

WHAT'S UNUSUAL ABOUT THESE TREES?

How do you know a plant when you see it?

With its wide trunk and short stubby branches, the baobab tree looks like a sweet potato or an upside-down tree. Seen for miles across the dry African savannah, the baobab can live for over 1,000 years and can grow to over 23 meters high and 27 meters around the trunk. It would take about 18 teenagers with arms spread wide and fingertips touching to encircle a tree that wide!

Draw Conclusions **Why do you think the baobab tree has such a wide trunk and short branches only at the very top?**

UNTAMED SCIENCE Watch the **Untamed Science** video to learn more about plants.

Plants

Science Standards of Learning

LS.1d, LS.1h, LS.1i, LS.1j, LS.2a, LS.3a, LS.3b, LS.4a, LS.4b, LS.4c, LS.5a, LS.5b, LS.5c, LS.10a, LS.11a, LS.11b, LS.11d, LS.11e

CHAPTER

10 Getting Started

Check Your Understanding

1. **Background** Read the paragraph below and then answer the question.

Rahim and Malika were in the park after school. "Plants are such cool **organisms,**" said Rahim. "Can you imagine if humans had green **pigment** in their skin?" "Yeah," said Malika. "If we were **autotrophs,** I'd never have to get up early to pack my lunch!"

An **organism** is a living thing.

A **pigment** is a colored chemical compound that absorbs light.

An **autotroph** is an organism that makes its own food.

- Give an example of an autotrophic organism that has green pigment.

____

____

MY READING WEB If you had trouble completing the question above, visit **My Reading Web** and type in ***Plants.***

Vocabulary Skill

Greek Word Origins Many science words come to English from ancient Greek. Learning the Greek word parts can help you understand some of the vocabulary in this chapter.

Greek Word Part	Meaning	Example Word
chloros	pale green	chloroplast, *n.* green cellular structure in which photosynthesis occurs
petalon	leaf	petal, *n.* colorful, leaflike flower structure

2. **Quick Check** ***Chlorophyll*** **is a pigment found in plants. Which part of the word** ***chlorophyll*** **tells you that it is a green pigment?**

____

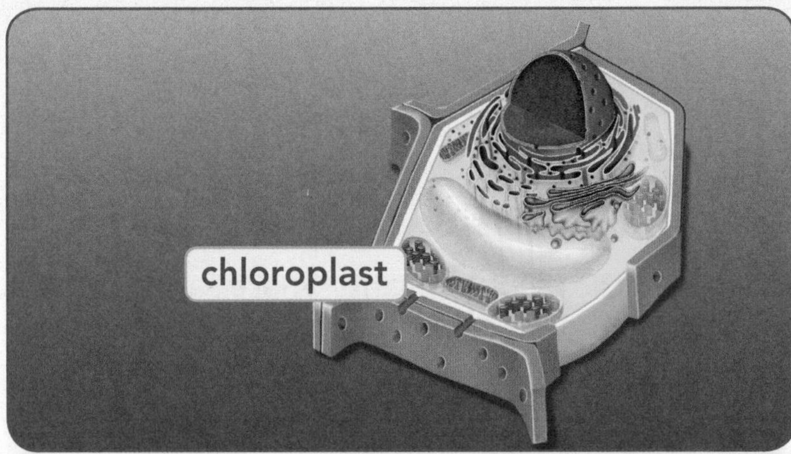

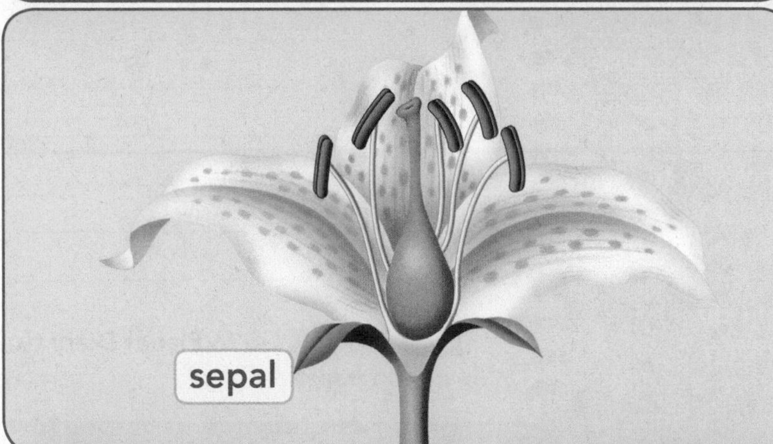

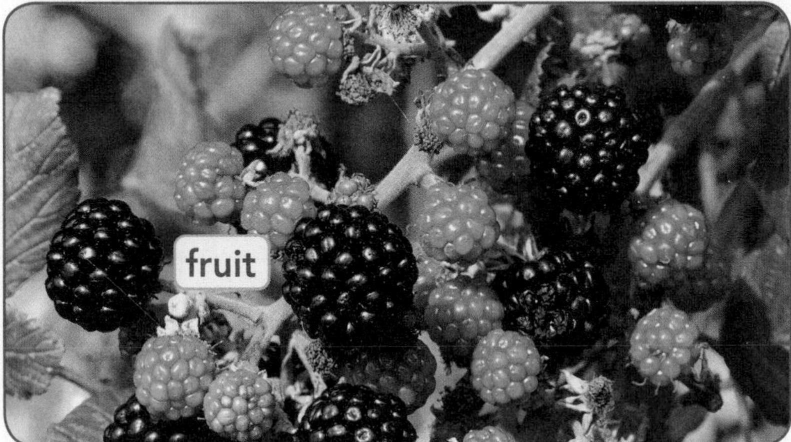

Chapter Preview

LESSON 1

- chlorophyll • photosynthesis
- tissue • chloroplast • vacuole
- cuticle • vascular tissue

Compare and Contrast
Predict

LESSON 2

- nonvascular plant • rhizoid
- vascular plant • phloem
- xylem • frond • pollen • seed
- gymnosperm • angiosperm
- cotyledon • monocot
- dicot

Outline
Communicate

LESSON 3

- root cap • cambium • stoma
- transpiration • embryo
- germination • flower
- pollination • sepal • petal
- stamen • pistil • ovary

Relate Cause and Effect
Observe

LESSON 4

- sporophyte • gametophyte
- annual • biennial • perennial
- fertilization • zygote
- cone • ovule • fruit

Summarize
Infer

LESSON 5

- tropism • hormone
- auxin • photoperiodism
- critical night length
- short-day plant • long-day plant
- day-neutral plant • dormancy

Relate Text and Visuals
Draw Conclusions

LESSON 6

- peat

Identify the Main Idea
Pose Questions

What Is a Plant?

What Characteristics Do All Plants Share?
LS.2a, LS.5a, LS.5b

What Do Plants Need to Live Successfully on Land?
LS.1d, LS.1h, LS.1i, LS.1j, LS.2a

my planet Diary

PROFILE

How Does Your Garden Grow?

Students at The Hilldale School in Daly City, California, get to play in the dirt during class. The students planted and maintain a garden filled with native species. Native plants, or plants that have been in an area for a long time, can struggle to survive if new plants are introduced. This creates problems for the insects, animals, and other organisms that rely on the native plants. The students spent three months removing nonnative plants before creating a garden that will help local organisms right outside their school.

Communicate Discuss the question with a group of classmates. Write your answer below.

Describe a plant project you would like to do at your school.

____

____

____

____

____

____

____

PLANET DIARY Go to **Planet Diary** to learn more about plants.

Do the Inquiry Warm-Up *What Do Leaves Reveal About Plants?*

LS.2a Investigate and understand cell structure and organelles.

LS.5a Investigate and understand energy transfer between sunlight and chlorophyll.

LS.5b Investigate and understand transformation of water and carbon dioxide into sugar and oxygen in photosynthesis.

What Characteristics Do All Plants Share?

Which organisms were the ancestors of today's plants? In search of answers, biologists studied fossils, the traces of ancient life forms preserved in rock and other substances. The oldest plant fossils are about 400 million years old. These fossils show that even at that early date, plants already had many adaptations for life on land.

Vocabulary
- chlorophyll • photosynthesis • tissue • chloroplast
- vacuole • cuticle • vascular tissue

Skills
- Reading: Compare and Contrast
- Inquiry: Predict

Better clues to the origin of plants came from comparing the chemicals in modern plants to those in other organisms. Biologists studied a pigment called chlorophyll. **Chlorophyll** (KLAWR uh fil) is a green pigment found in the chloroplasts of plants, algae, and some bacteria. Land plants and green algae contain the same forms of chlorophyll. Further comparisons of genetic material clearly showed that plants and green algae are very closely related. Today, green algae are classified as plants.

Members of the plant kingdom share several characteristics. **Nearly all plants are autotrophs, organisms that produce their own food. With the exception of some green algae, all plants contain many cells. In addition, all plant cells are surrounded by cell walls.**

Compare and Contrast How do you think the ancient environment of the leaf in the fossil differed from that of the modern leaf in the pictures below?

Plants Are Autotrophs

You can think of a typical plant as a sun-powered, food-making factory. Sunlight provides the energy for this food-making process, called **photosynthesis.** During photosynthesis, a plant uses carbon dioxide gas and water to make food and oxygen.

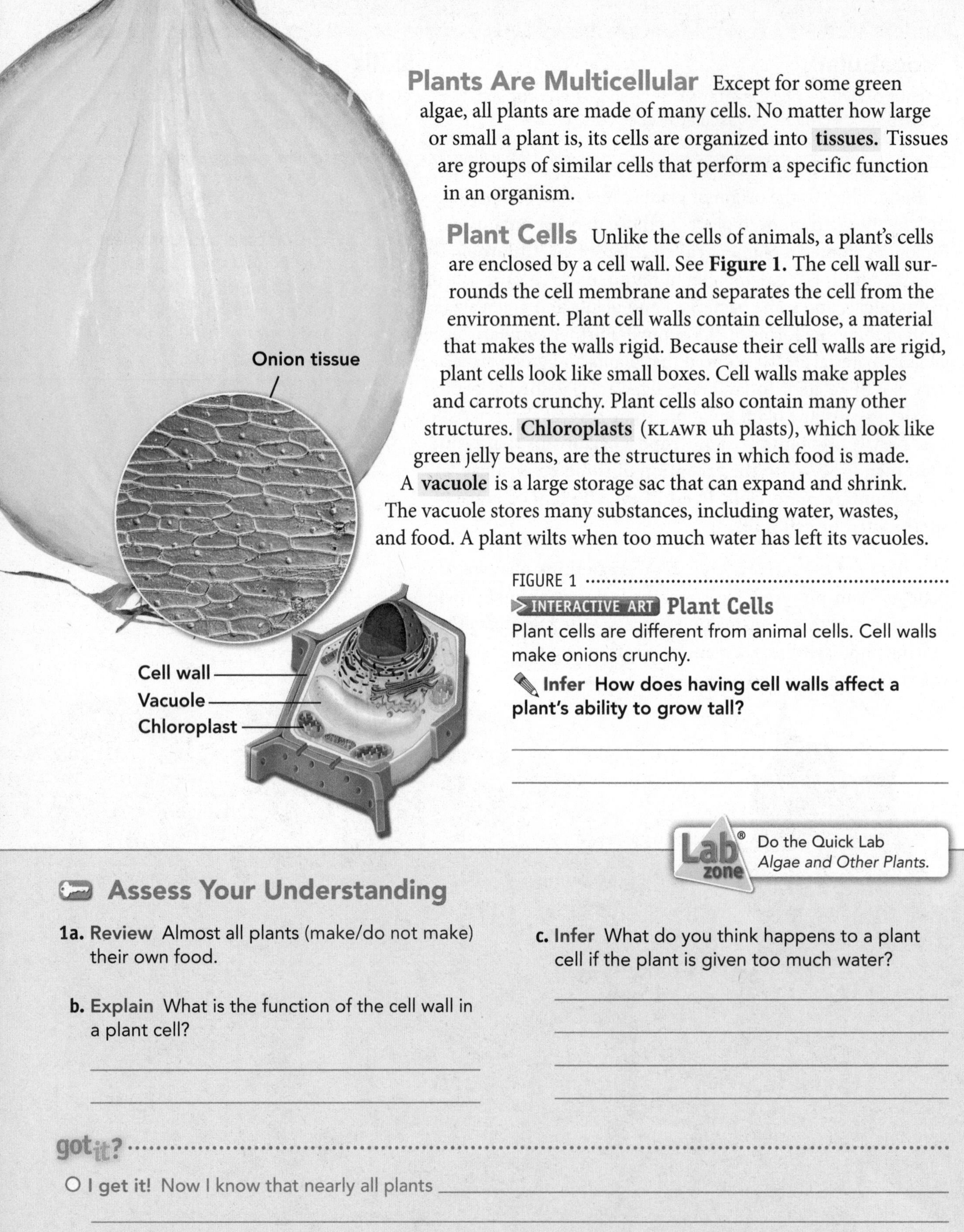

Plants Are Multicellular Except for some green algae, all plants are made of many cells. No matter how large or small a plant is, its cells are organized into **tissues.** Tissues are groups of similar cells that perform a specific function in an organism.

Plant Cells Unlike the cells of animals, a plant's cells are enclosed by a cell wall. See **Figure 1.** The cell wall surrounds the cell membrane and separates the cell from the environment. Plant cell walls contain cellulose, a material that makes the walls rigid. Because their cell walls are rigid, plant cells look like small boxes. Cell walls make apples and carrots crunchy. Plant cells also contain many other structures. **Chloroplasts** (KLAWR uh plasts), which look like green jelly beans, are the structures in which food is made. A **vacuole** is a large storage sac that can expand and shrink. The vacuole stores many substances, including water, wastes, and food. A plant wilts when too much water has left its vacuoles.

FIGURE 1

INTERACTIVE ART **Plant Cells**

Plant cells are different from animal cells. Cell walls make onions crunchy.

Infer How does having cell walls affect a plant's ability to grow tall?

Lab zone® Do the Quick Lab *Algae and Other Plants.*

Assess Your Understanding

1a. Review Almost all plants (make/do not make) their own food.

b. Explain What is the function of the cell wall in a plant cell?

c. Infer What do you think happens to a plant cell if the plant is given too much water?

got it?

○ **I get it!** Now I know that nearly all plants

○ I need extra help with

Go to MY SCIENCE COACH *online for help with this subject.*

What Do Plants Need to Live Successfully on Land?

Imagine multicellular algae floating in the ocean. The algae obtain water and other materials directly from the water around them. They are held up toward the sunlight by the water. Now imagine plants living on land. What adaptations would help them meet their needs without water all around them? **For plants to survive on land, they must have ways to obtain water and other nutrients from their surroundings, retain water, support their bodies, transport materials, and reproduce.**

Science Standards of Learning

LS.1d Construct and use models and simulations to illustrate and explain phenomena.

LS.1h Organize, graph, and interpret data, and use data to make predictions.

LS.1i Identify, interpret, and evaluate patterns in data.

LS.1j Use current applications to reinforce life science concepts.

LS.2a Investigate and understand cell structure and organelles.

Obtaining Water and Other Nutrients

Recall that all organisms need water to survive. Obtaining water is easy for algae because water surrounds them. To live on land, plants need adaptations for obtaining water from the soil. One adaptation is the way the plant produces its roots, as shown in **Figure 2.** Plants must also have ways of obtaining other nutrients from the soil.

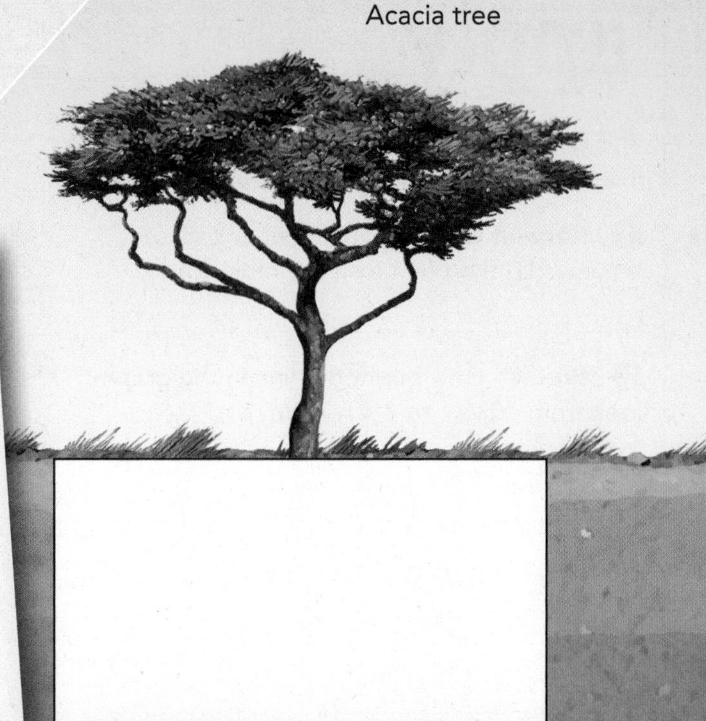

FIGURE 2

Getting Water in the Desert

The saguaro cactus and the acacia tree both live in deserts with limited water. Saguaro roots spread out horizontally. When it rains, the roots quickly absorb water over a wide area. Acacia trees in the Negev Desert of Israel get their water from deep underground instead of at the surface.

Interpret Diagrams **Draw the roots of the acacia tree. Then describe how the growth of the roots differs between the plants.**

______

______

______

FIGURE 3

Waterproof Leaves

The waxy cuticle of many leaves, like the one below, looks shiny under light.

Retaining Water When there is more water in plant cells than in the air, the water leaves the plant and enters the air. The plant could dry out if it cannot hold onto water. One adaptation that helps a plant reduce water loss is a waxy, waterproof layer called the **cuticle.** You can see the cuticle on the leaf in **Figure 3.**

Support A plant on land must support its own body. It's easier for small, low-growing plants to support themselves. In larger plants, the food-making parts must be exposed to as much sunlight as possible. Cell walls and tissue strengthen and support the large bodies of these plants.

Transporting Materials A plant needs to transport water, minerals, food, and other materials from one part of its body to another. In general, water and minerals are taken up by the bottom part of the plant, while food is made in the top part. But all of the plant's cells need water, minerals, and food.

In small plants, materials can simply move from one cell to the next. Larger plants need a more efficient way to transport materials from one part of the plant to another. These plants have vascular tissue for transporting materials. **Vascular tissue** is a system of tubelike structures inside a plant through which water, minerals, and food move. See vascular tissue in action in **Figure 4.**

apply it!

This graph shows how much water a plant loses during the day. Give the graph a title.

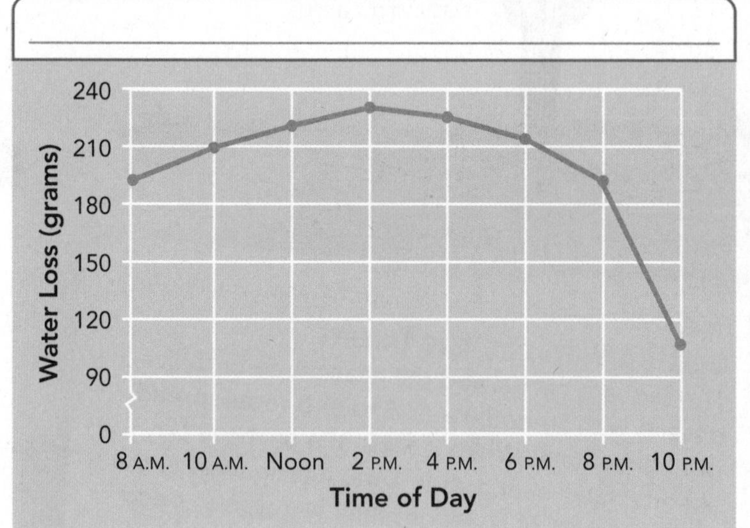

1 **Interpret Graphs** During what part of the day did the plant lose the most water?

2 **Predict** How might the line in the graph look from 10 P.M. to 8 A.M.? Why?

3 CHALLENGE Do you think this graph would be the same for plants all around the world? Why?

Reproduction For algae and some other plants, reproduction can only occur if there is water in the environment. This is because the sperm cells of these plants swim through the water to the egg cells. Land plants need to have adaptations that make reproduction possible in dry environments.

FIGURE 4

Colorful Carnations

These three carnations were left overnight in glasses of water. Blue dye was added to the glass in the middle. The stem of the flower on the right was split in half. Part of the stem was placed in water with blue dye and the other part was placed in water with red dye.

Draw Conclusions Why did the flowers in the glasses with dye change color?

Lab zone Do the Quick Lab *Local Plant Diversity.*

Assess Your Understanding

2a. Define What is a cuticle?

b. Apply Concepts Describe the pros and cons of being a tall land plant.

got it?

O **I get it!** Now I know that to live on land, plants need to ______

O I need extra help with ______

Go to **MY SCIENCE COACH** *online for help with this subject.*

Classifying Plants

- What Are the Characteristics of Nonvascular Plants? LS.4c
- What Are the Characteristics of Seedless Vascular Plants? LS.1j, LS.4c
- What Are the Characteristics of Seed Plants? LS.1h, LS.1i, LS.4c

my planet Diary

CAREER

The Moss Is Greener on the Other Side

Tired of mowing the lawn? Never want to pull out another weed? Hire a moss landscaper! Landscapers design beautiful yards, usually planting trees, flowers, bushes, and grasses. These plants need a lot of care. Moss doesn't. Moss grows in the shade where other plants can't.

Landscapers can use moss to cover an entire yard if the conditions are right. Mosses are also better for the environment. People don't have to put toxic chemicals on their moss lawns to kill weeds or keep it green.

Write your answer below.

Do you think people should use moss instead of grass for their lawns? Why?

PLANET DIARY Go to **Planet Diary** to learn more about plant classification.

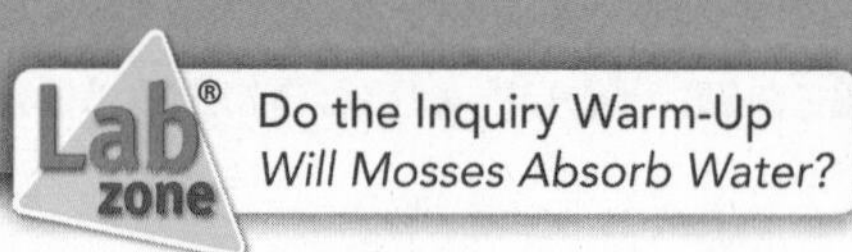

Lab® zone Do the Inquiry Warm-Up *Will Mosses Absorb Water?*

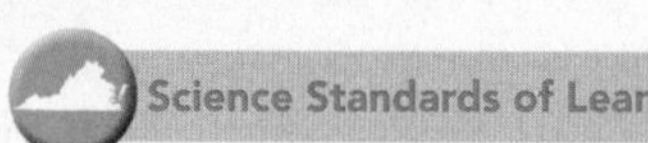

Science Standards of Learning

LS.4c Investigate and understand distinguishing characteristics of major plant divisions.

What Are the Characteristics of Nonvascular Plants?

Plants that lack vascular tissue for transporting materials are known as **nonvascular plants.** **Nonvascular plants are low-growing, have thin cell walls, and do not have roots for absorbing water from the ground.** Instead, they obtain water and materials directly from their surroundings. The materials then pass from one cell to the next. This means that materials do not travel far or quickly. This slow method helps explain why most nonvascular plants live in damp, shady places. The thin cell walls are why these plants cannot grow more than a few centimeters tall.

Vocabulary

- nonvascular plant • rhizoid • vascular plant • phloem
- xylem • frond • pollen • seed • gymnosperm
- angiosperm • cotyledon • monocot • dicot

Skills

- Reading: Outline
- Inquiry: Communicate

Mosses Have you ever seen mosses growing in the cracks of a sidewalk or in a shady spot? With more than 10,000 species, mosses are by far the most diverse group of nonvascular plants.

If you were to look closely at a moss, you would see a plant that looks something like **Figure 1.** Structures that look like tiny leaves grow off a small, stemlike structure. Thin, rootlike structures called **rhizoids** anchor the moss and absorb water and nutrients. Moss grows a long, slender stalk with a capsule at the end. The capsule contains spores for reproduction.

FIGURE 1

Moss Structure

Diagrams can be easier to read than photographs, but photographs are more realistic.

Relate Diagrams and Photos **Label the capsule, stalk, and leaflike structure in the photo. Draw lines from your labels to the structure itself, like in the diagram below.**

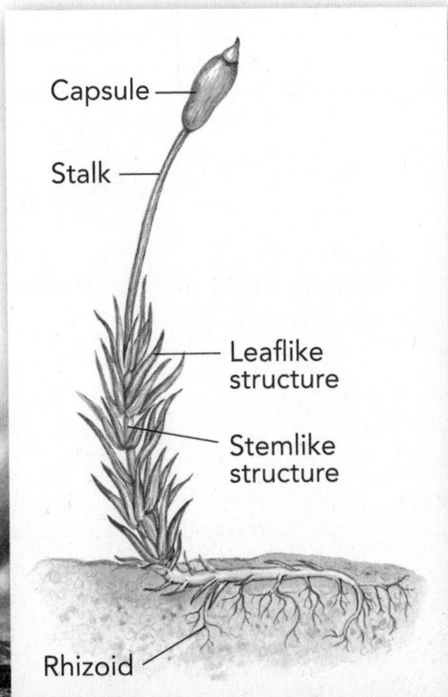

Liverwort ▲

Liverworts and Hornworts

Liverworts and Hornworts Liverworts and hornworts are two other groups of nonvascular plants. There are more than 8,000 species of liverworts. This group of plants is named for the shape of the plant's body, which looks somewhat like a human liver. *Wort* is an old English word for "plant." Liverworts are often found growing as a thick crust on moist rocks or soil along the sides of a stream. There are fewer than 100 species of hornworts. If you look closely at a hornwort, you can see slender, curved structures that look like horns growing out of the plant. Unlike mosses or liverworts, hornworts are seldom found on rocks or tree trunks. Instead, hornworts usually live in moist soil, often mixed in with grass plants.

Outline Fill in the table to the right with what you have learned about liverworts and hornworts.

Hornwort ▶

Nonvascular Plants

Plant	Identifiable Physical Characteristic	Where Found
Mosses	Fuzzy appearance	Shady spots, rocks, tree trunks
Liverworts		
Hornworts		

Lab zone Do the Quick Lab *Masses of Mosses.*

Assess Your Understanding

1a. Review (Vascular tissues/Rhizoids) anchor moss and absorb water and nutrients.

b. Explain Why are most nonvascular plants short?

c. Compare and Contrast How are liverworts and hornworts different?

got it?

○ **I get it!** Now I know the characteristics of nonvascular plants are

○ I need extra help with

Go to MY SCIENCE COACH *online for help with this subject.*

What Are the Characteristics of Seedless Vascular Plants?

Science Standards of Learning

LS.1j Use current applications to reinforce life science concepts.

LS.4c Investigate and understand distinguishing characteristics of major plant divisions.

If you could have walked through the ancient forests that existed long before the dinosaurs lived, they would have looked very strange to you. You might have recognized the mosses and liverworts that carpeted the moist soil, but you would have seen very tall, odd-looking trees. Among the trees grew huge, tree-sized ferns. Other trees resembled giant sticks with leaves up to one meter long. The odd-looking plants in the ancient forests are the ancestors of the ferns, clubmosses, and horsetails of today. **Ferns, club mosses, and horsetails share two characteristics. They have vascular tissue and they do not produce seeds. Instead of seeds, these plants reproduce by releasing spores.**

Vascular Tissue

Ancient trees were vascular plants. **Vascular plants** are plants with true vascular tissue. Vascular plants can grow tall because their vascular tissue provides an effective way of transporting materials throughout the plant. The vascular tissue also strengthens the plants' bodies. You can see vascular tissue in **Figure 2.** The cells making up the vascular tissue have strong cell walls. Imagine a handful of drinking straws bundled together with rubber bands. The bundle of straws is stronger and more stable than a single straw would be. Arranged similarly, the strong, tubelike structures in vascular plants give the plants strength and stability.

There are two types of vascular tissue. **Phloem** (FLOH um) is the vascular tissue through which food moves. After food is made in the leaves, it enters the phloem and travels to other parts of the plant. Water and minerals, on the other hand, travel in the vascular tissue called **xylem** (ZY lum). The roots absorb water and minerals from the soil. These materials enter the root's xylem and move upward into the stems and leaves.

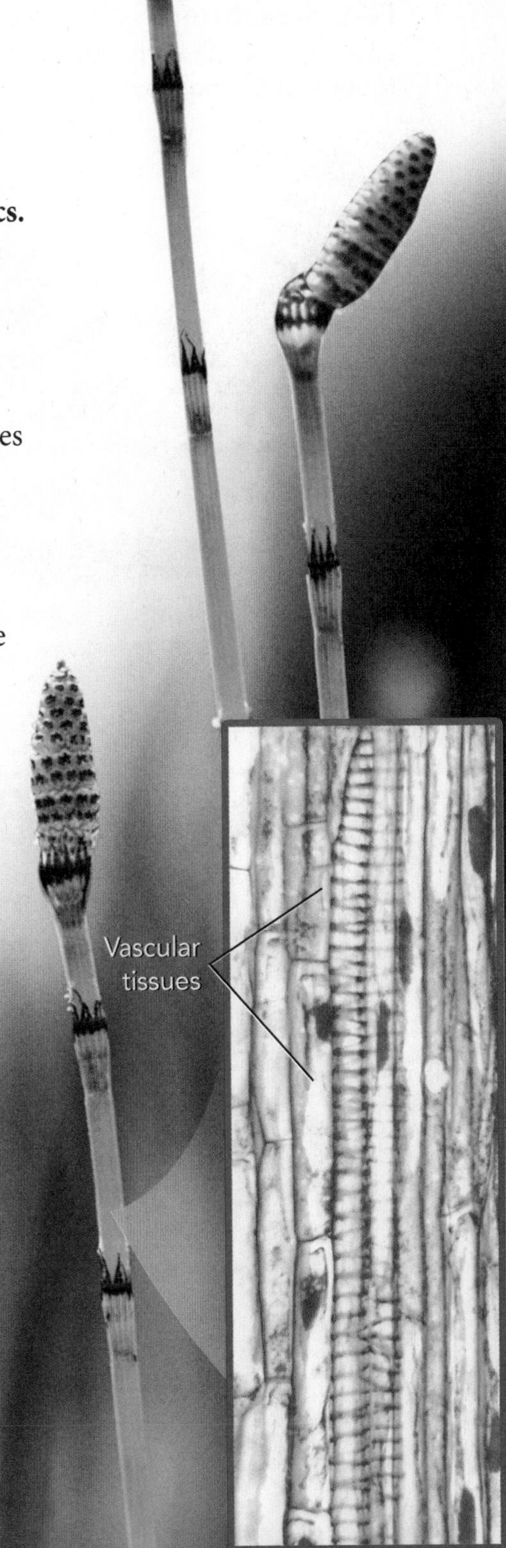

FIGURE 2

Vascular Tissue

Vascular plants have xylem and phloem.

Identify In the text, underline the roles of vascular tissue.

Ferns

Ferns There are more than 12,000 species of ferns alive today. They range in size from tiny plants about the size of this letter *M* to tree ferns that grow up to five meters tall. Ferns thrive in shaded areas with moist soil. Some remain green year-round while others turn brown in the fall and regrow in spring.

FIGURE 3

Fern Structure

Like other plants, ferns have roots, stems, and leaves.

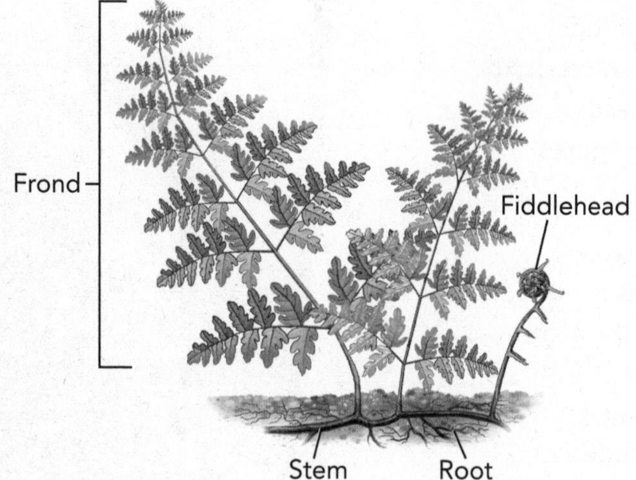

The Structure of Ferns Like other vascular plants, ferns have stems, roots, and leaves. The stems of most ferns are underground. Leaves grow upward from the top of the stems, while roots grow downward from the bottom of the stems. Water and nutrients enter the root's vascular tissue and travel through the tissue into the stems and leaves.

Figure 3 shows a fern's structure. Notice that the fern's leaves, or **fronds,** are divided into many smaller parts that look like small leaves. The upper surface of each frond is coated with a cuticle that helps the plant retain water. In many ferns, the developing leaves are coiled at first. Because they resemble the top of a violin, these young leaves are often called fiddleheads. Fiddleheads uncurl as they mature.

apply it!

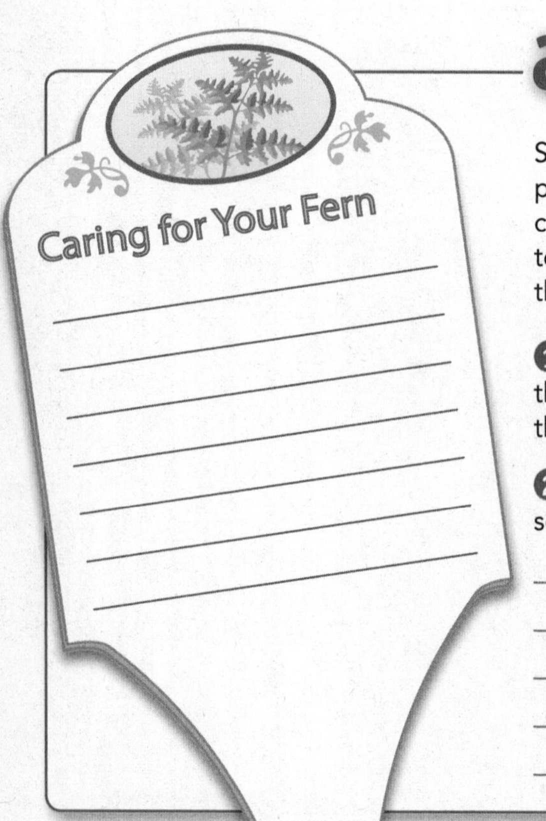

Suppose you ran a flower shop that sold cut flowers and potted plants. You have just received a shipment of potted ferns and several customers are interested in purchasing them. Before they are ready to be sold, you need to make sure your customers can take care of the ferns so they won't regret their purchase.

1 **Communicate** On the tag at left, write the care instructions that will be given to your customers who buy potted ferns. Include the conditions that the fern needs for light and water.

2 **CHALLENGE** Florists recommend not putting plants like ferns in south- or west-facing windows. Why?

Club Mosses and Horsetails Like ferns, club mosses and horsetails have true stems, roots, and leaves. However, there are relatively few species of club mosses and horsetails alive today.

Do not be confused by the name *club moss*. Unlike true mosses, club mosses have vascular tissue. You may be familiar with the club moss in **Figure 4.** The plant, which looks a little like a small branch of a pine tree, is sometimes called ground pine or princess pine. Club mosses usually grow in moist woodlands and near streams.

There are about 30 species of horsetails on Earth today. The whorled pattern of growth somewhat resembles the appearance of a horse's tail. The stems contain silica, a gritty substance also found in sand. During colonial times, Americans used the plants to scrub their pots and pans. Another common name for horsetails is scouring brushes.

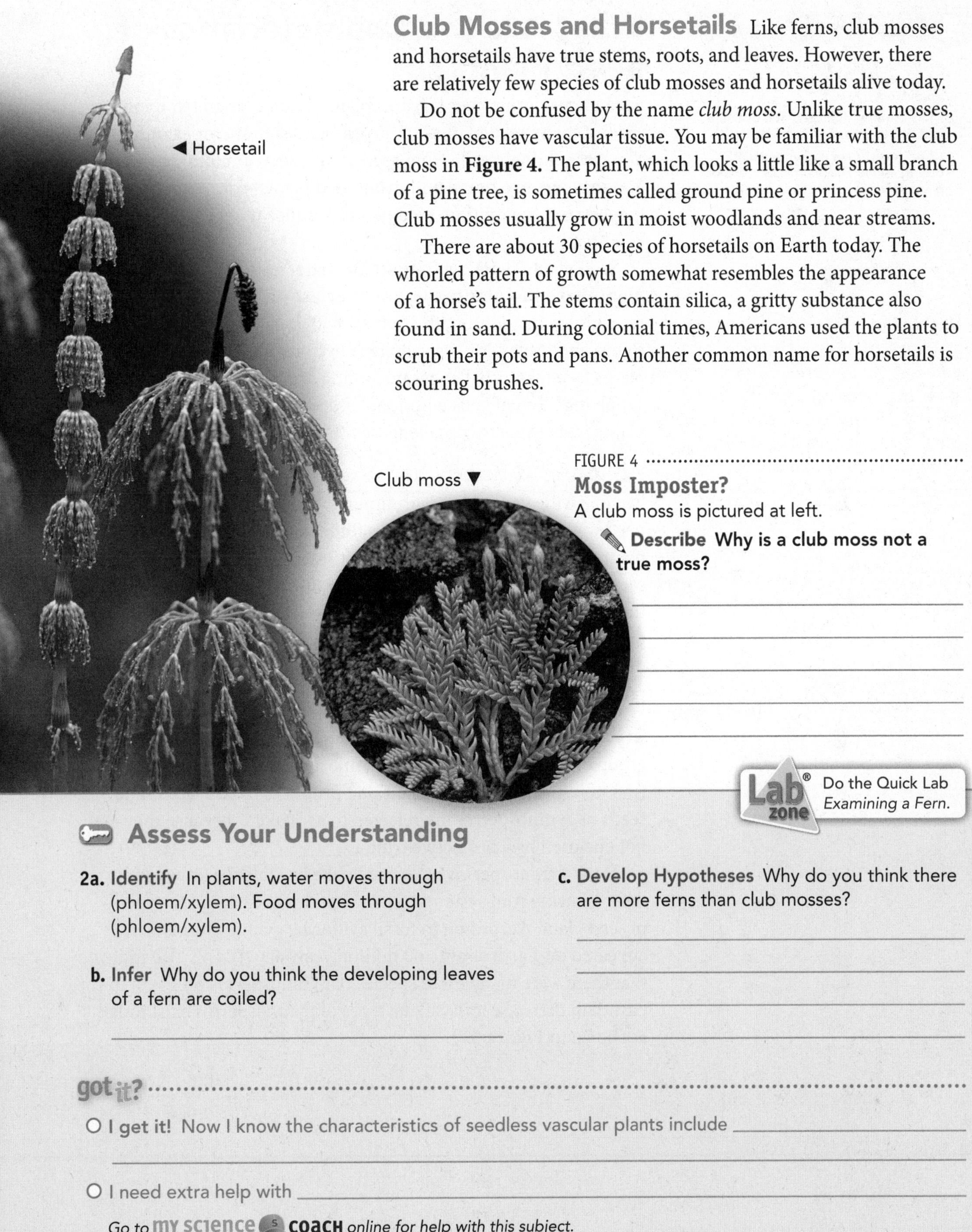

FIGURE 4

Moss Imposter?

A club moss is pictured at left.

Describe Why is a club moss not a true moss?

____

Lab zone® Do the Quick Lab *Examining a Fern.*

Assess Your Understanding

2a. Identify In plants, water moves through (phloem/xylem). Food moves through (phloem/xylem).

b. Infer Why do you think the developing leaves of a fern are coiled?

____

c. Develop Hypotheses Why do you think there are more ferns than club mosses?

____

got it?

O **I get it!** Now I know the characteristics of seedless vascular plants include ______________________________

O I need extra help with ______________________________

Go to MY SCIENCE COACH *online for help with this subject.*

Science Standards of Learning

LS.1h Organize, graph, and interpret data, and use data to make predictions.

LS.1i Identify, interpret, and evaluate patterns in data.

LS.4c Investigate and understand distinguishing characteristics of major plant divisions.

Vocabulary Greek Word Origins The word *gymnosperm* comes from the Greek words *gumnos*, meaning "naked," and *sperma*, meaning "seed." Why are the seeds of gymnosperms considered to be naked?

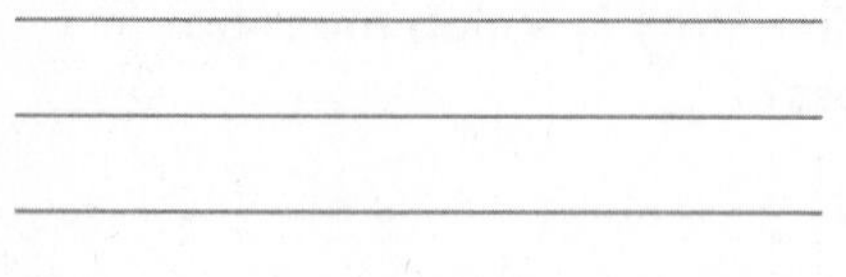

What Are the Characteristics of Seed Plants?

Seed plants outnumber seedless plants by more than ten to one. You eat many seed plants—rice, peas, and squash, for example. You wear clothes made from seed plants, such as cotton and flax. You may live in a home built from seed plants—oak, pine, or maple trees. In addition, seed plants produce much of the oxygen you breathe.

Seed plants share two important characteristics. **Seed plants have vascular tissue, and they use pollen and seeds to reproduce.** In addition, the bodies of all seed plants have roots, stems, and leaves. Most seed plants live on land. Recall that land plants face many challenges, including standing upright and supplying all their cells with food and water. Like ferns, seed plants meet these two challenges with vascular tissue.

Pollen and Seeds

Unlike seedless plants, seed plants can live in a wide variety of environments. Recall that seedless plants need water in their surroundings for fertilization to occur. Seed plants do not need water for sperm to swim to the eggs. Instead, seed plants produce **pollen,** tiny structures that contain the cells that will later become sperm cells. Pollen deliver sperm cells directly near the eggs. After sperm cells fertilize the eggs, seeds develop. A **seed** is a structure that contains a young plant inside a protective covering. Seeds protect the young plant from drying out.

Gymnosperms

The giant sequoia trees belong to the group of seed plants known as gymnosperms. A **gymnosperm** (JIM noh spurm) is a seed plant that produces naked seeds. The seeds of gymnosperms are referred to as "naked" because they are not enclosed by a protective fruit.

Many gymnosperms have needlelike or scalelike leaves and deep-growing root systems. Gymnosperms are the oldest type of seed plant. According to fossil evidence, gymnosperms first appeared on Earth about 360 million years ago. Fossils also indicate that there were many more species of gymnosperms on Earth in the past than there are today. Four types of gymnosperms exist today, as shown in **Figure 5.**

GYMNOSPERM	DESCRIPTION/FUNCTION
Cycads 	About 175 million years ago, the majority of plants were cycads (SY kadz). Today, cycads grow mainly in tropical and subtropical areas. Cycads look like palm trees with cones that can grow as large as a football!
Conifers	Conifers (KAHN uh furz), or cone-bearing plants, are the largest and most diverse group of modern gymnosperms. Most conifers are evergreens, meaning they keep their leaves or needles year-round.
Ginkgoes 	Ginkgoes (GING kohz) also grew hundreds of millions of years ago. Today, only one species, *Ginkgo biloba*, exists. It probably survived because the Chinese and Japanese cared for it in their gardens. Today, ginkgo trees are planted along city streets because they can tolerate air pollution.
Gnetophytes 	Gnetophytes (NEE tuh fyts) live in hot deserts and in tropical rain forests. Some are trees, some are shrubs, and others are vines. The *Welwitschia* (shown at left) of West Africa can live for more than 1,000 years!

FIGURE 5

Types of Gymnosperms

The chart describes the four main groups of gymnosperms.

Answer these questions.

1. **Name** Which group of gymnosperms has the most species?

____

2. **Apply Concepts** What could have happened to the ecosystem the *Ginkgo biloba* tree lived in if the tree had become extinct?

____

Angiosperms You probably associate the word *flower* with a sweet-smelling plant growing in a garden. You certainly wouldn't think of something that smells like rotting meat. That's exactly what the corpse flower, or rafflesia, smells like. This flower, which grows in Asia, produces a meat smell, which attracts flies that spread the flower's pollen. You won't be seeing rafflesia in your local florist shop any time soon! Rafflesia belongs to the group of seed plants known as angiosperms (AN jee uh spurmz). **Angiosperms,** or flowering plants, share two important characteristics. First, they produce flowers. Second, in contrast to gymnosperms, which produce uncovered seeds, angiosperms produce seeds that are enclosed in fruits.

Angiosperms live almost everywhere on Earth. They grow in frozen areas in the Arctic, tropical jungles, and barren deserts. A few angiosperms, such as mangrove trees, live at the ocean's edge.

Types of Angiosperms Angiosperms are divided into two major groups: monocots and dicots. "Cot" is short for cotyledon (kaht uh LEED un). The **cotyledon,** or seed leaf, provides food for the embryo. *Mono-* means "one" and *di-* means "two." **Monocots** are angiosperms that have only one seed leaf. Grasses, including corn, wheat, and rice, and plants such as lilies and tulips, are monocots. **Dicots,** on the other hand, produce seeds with two seed leaves. Dicots include plants such as roses and violets, as well as dandelions. Both oak and maple trees are dicots, as are food plants such as beans and apples. **Figure 6** shows the characteristics of monocots and dicots.

FIGURE 6

VIRTUAL LAB **Monocots and Dicots**

Use the table below to find your answers.

Interpret Photos Label the rafflesia (top) and the other flowers on this page as *monocots* or *dicots*.

Characteristics of Monocots and Dicots

	Seeds	Leaves	Flowers	Stems	Roots
Monocots	Single cotyledon	Parallel veins	Floral parts often in multiples of 3	Vascular tissue bundles scattered throughout stem	Many roots spread out
Dicots	Two cotyledons	Branched veins	Floral parts often in multiples of 4 or 5	Vascular tissue bundles arranged in a ring	One main root

Use the graph of known plant species to answer the questions.

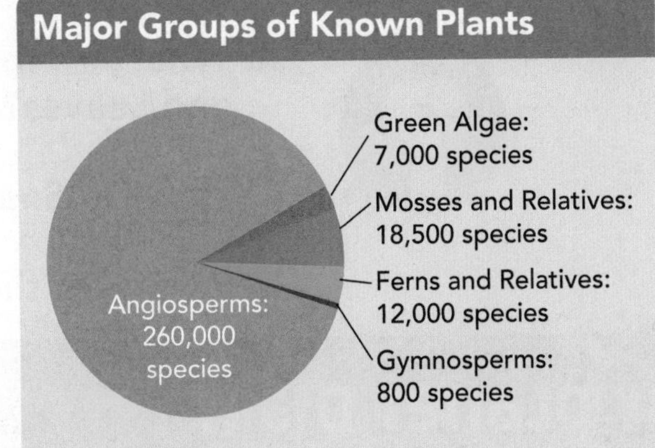

1 **Interpret Graphs** Which plant group has the fewest species?

____

2 **Calculate** Figure out the percentage that each of the following plant groups represents. Round your answer to the nearest tenth.

Green algae _______________

Ferns and relatives _______________

Angiosperms _______________

3 CHALLENGE Why do you think angiosperms are the largest group?

____

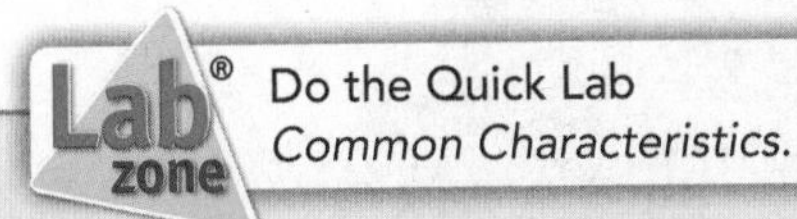

Assess Your Understanding

3a. Define What are pollen?

____

b. Draw Conclusions Why do you think angiosperms enclose their seeds in fruits?

____

got it?

O **I get it!** Now I know the characteristics of seed plants include _______________

O I need extra help with _______________

Go to MY SCIENCE COACH *online for help with this subject.*

Plant Structures

- What Are the Functions of Roots, Stems, and Leaves? LS.3a, LS.3b, LS.5a
- How Do Seeds Become New Plants? LS.1d, LS.3a, LS.3b
- What Are the Structures of a Flower? LS.1d, LS.3a, LS.3b

my planet Diary

SCIENCE STATS

Plant Giants

- The aroid plant (as shown here) on the island of Borneo in Asia has leaves that can grow three meters long! These are the largest undivided leaves on Earth!
- The rafflesia flower can grow up to one meter wide and weigh seven kilograms.
- The jackfruit can weigh up to 36 kilograms. That's the world's largest fruit that grows on trees!

Write your answer below.

Why do you think the aroid plant has such big leaves?

____

____

____

PLANET DIARY Go to **Planet Diary** to learn more about plant structures.

Do the Inquiry Warm-Up *Which Plant Part Is It?*

LS.3a Investigate and understand cells, tissues, organs, and systems.

LS.3b Investigate and understand patterns of cellular organization and their relationship to life processes in living things.

LS.5a Investigate and understand energy transfer between sunlight and chlorophyll.

What Are the Functions of Roots, Stems, and Leaves?

Each part of a plant plays an important role in its structure and function. Roots, stems, and leaves are just three structures we will look into further.

Roots Have you ever tried to pull a dandelion out of the soil? It's not easy, is it? That is because most roots are good anchors. Roots have three main functions. **Roots anchor a plant in the ground, absorb water and minerals from the soil, and sometimes store food.** The more root area a plant has, the more water and minerals it can absorb.

Vocabulary

- root cap • cambium • stoma • transpiration
- embryo • germination • flower • pollination
- sepal • petal • stamen • pistil • ovary

Skills

- Reading: Relate Cause and Effect
- Inquiry: Observe

Types of Roots The two main types of root systems are shown in **Figure 1.** A fibrous root system consists of many similarly sized roots that form a dense, tangled mass. Plants with fibrous roots take a lot of soil with them when you pull them out of the ground. Lawn grass, corn, and onions have fibrous root systems. In contrast, a taproot system has one long, thick main root. Many smaller roots branch off the main root. A plant with a taproot system is hard to pull out of the ground. Carrots, dandelions, and cacti have taproots.

FIGURE 1

Root Systems and Structure

There are two main root systems with many structures.

Interpret Photos Label the taproot *T* and the fibrous roots *F*.

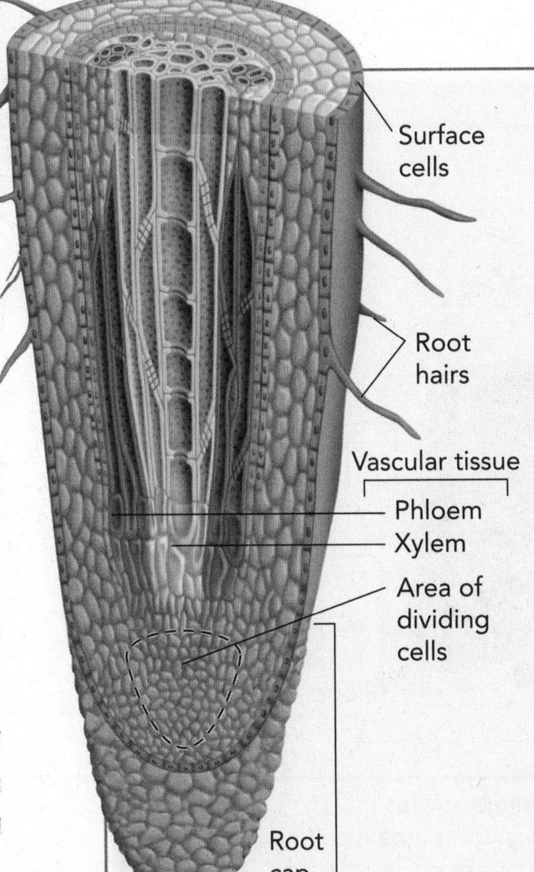

Root Structure

In **Figure 2,** you can see the structure of a typical root. The tip of the root is rounded and is covered by the root cap. The **root cap** protects the root from injury as the root grows through the soil. Behind the root cap are the cells that divide to form new root cells.

Root hairs grow out of the root's surface. These tiny hairs can enter the spaces between soil particles, where they absorb water and minerals. The root hairs also help to anchor the plant in the soil.

Locate the vascular tissue in the center of the root. The water and nutrients that are absorbed from the soil quickly move into the xylem. From there, these substances are transported upward to the plant's stems and leaves. Phloem transports food manufactured in the leaves to the root. The root tissues then use the food for growth or store it for future use by the plant.

FIGURE 2

Root Structure

Roots have many structures.

Define What is the function of the root cap?

____

____

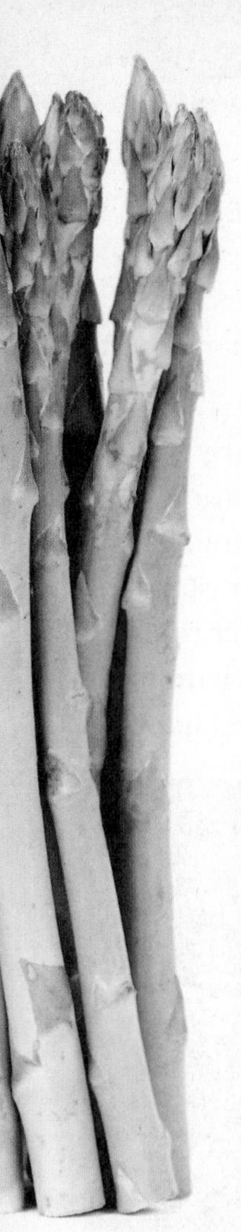

Stems The stem of a plant has two main functions. **The stem carries substances between the plant's roots and leaves. The stem also provides support for the plant and holds up the leaves so they are exposed to the sun.** In addition, some stems, such as those of asparagus, store food.

The Structure of a Stem Stems can be either woody or herbaceous (hur BAY shus). Woody stems are hard and rigid, such as in maple trees. Herbaceous stems contain no wood and are often soft. Plants with herbaceous stems include daisies, ivy, and asparagus (pictured left).

Herbaceous and woody stems consist of phloem and xylem tissue as well as many other supporting cells. As you can see in **Figure 3,** a woody stem contains many layers of tissue. The outermost layer is bark. Bark includes an outer protective layer and an inner layer of living phloem, which transports food through the stem. Next is a layer of cells called the **cambium** (KAM bee um), which divides to produce new phloem and xylem. It is xylem that makes up most of what you call "wood." Sapwood is active xylem that transports water and minerals through the stem. The older, darker, heartwood is inactive but provides support.

FIGURE 3

Stem Structure

The woody stem of a tree contains many different structures.

Interpret Diagrams Label the active xylem and phloem on the tree trunk below.

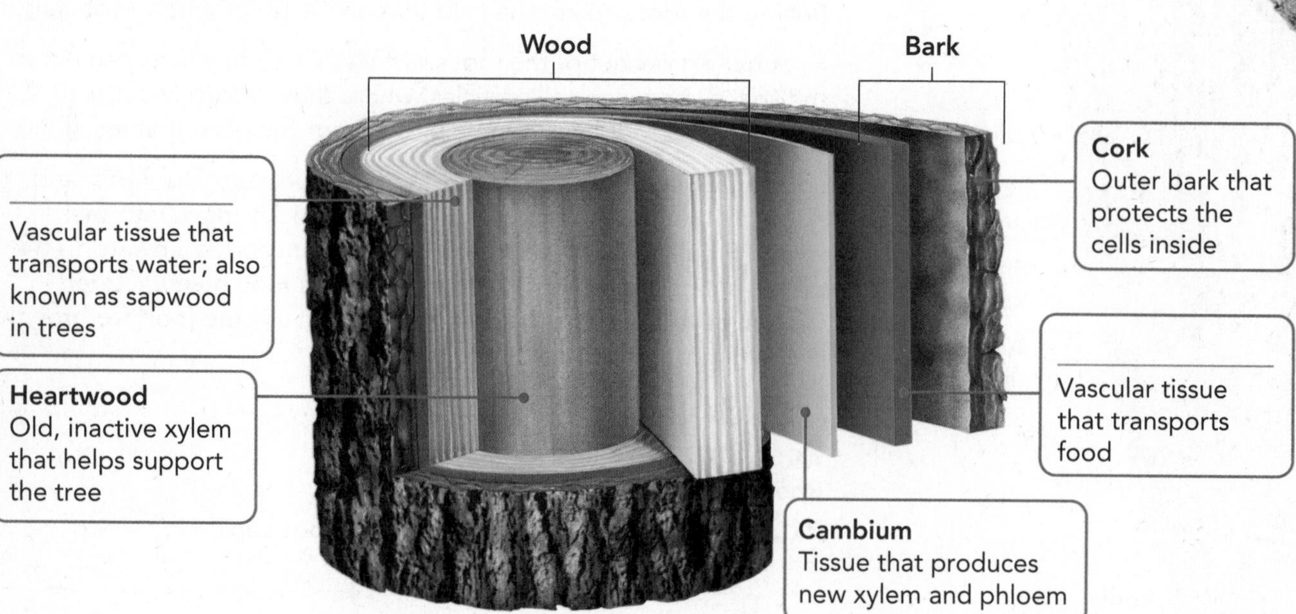

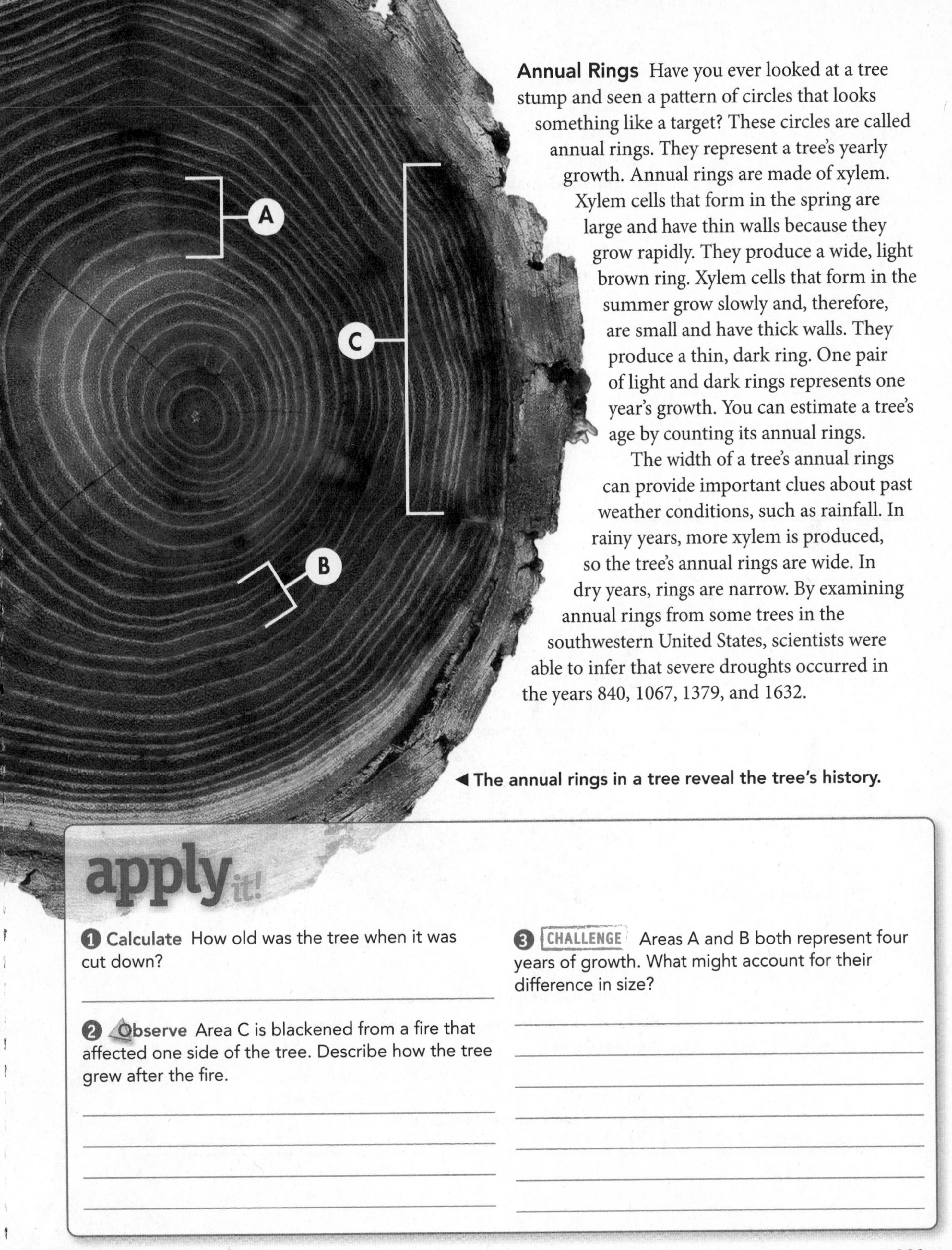

Annual Rings Have you ever looked at a tree stump and seen a pattern of circles that looks something like a target? These circles are called annual rings. They represent a tree's yearly growth. Annual rings are made of xylem. Xylem cells that form in the spring are large and have thin walls because they grow rapidly. They produce a wide, light brown ring. Xylem cells that form in the summer grow slowly and, therefore, are small and have thick walls. They produce a thin, dark ring. One pair of light and dark rings represents one year's growth. You can estimate a tree's age by counting its annual rings.

The width of a tree's annual rings can provide important clues about past weather conditions, such as rainfall. In rainy years, more xylem is produced, so the tree's annual rings are wide. In dry years, rings are narrow. By examining annual rings from some trees in the southwestern United States, scientists were able to infer that severe droughts occurred in the years 840, 1067, 1379, and 1632.

◀ **The annual rings in a tree reveal the tree's history.**

apply it!

1 **Calculate** How old was the tree when it was cut down?

2 **Observe** Area C is blackened from a fire that affected one side of the tree. Describe how the tree grew after the fire.

3 CHALLENGE Areas A and B both represent four years of growth. What might account for their difference in size?

Vocabulary Greek Word Origins The Greek word *stoma* means "mouth." How are the stomata of a plant like mouths?

Leaves Leaves vary greatly in size and shape. Pine trees have needle-shaped leaves. Birch trees have small rounded leaves with jagged edges. Regardless of their shape, leaves play an important role in a plant. **Leaves capture the sun's energy and carry out the food-making process of photosynthesis.**

The Structure of a Leaf If you were to cut through a leaf and look at the edge under a microscope, you would see the structures in **Figure 4.** The leaf's top and bottom surface layers protect the cells inside. Between the layers of cells are veins that contain xylem and phloem.

The surface layers of the leaf have small openings, or pores, called **stomata** (stoh MAH tuh; *singular* stoma). The stomata open and close to control when gases enter and leave the leaf. When the stomata are open, carbon dioxide enters the leaf, and oxygen and water vapor exit.

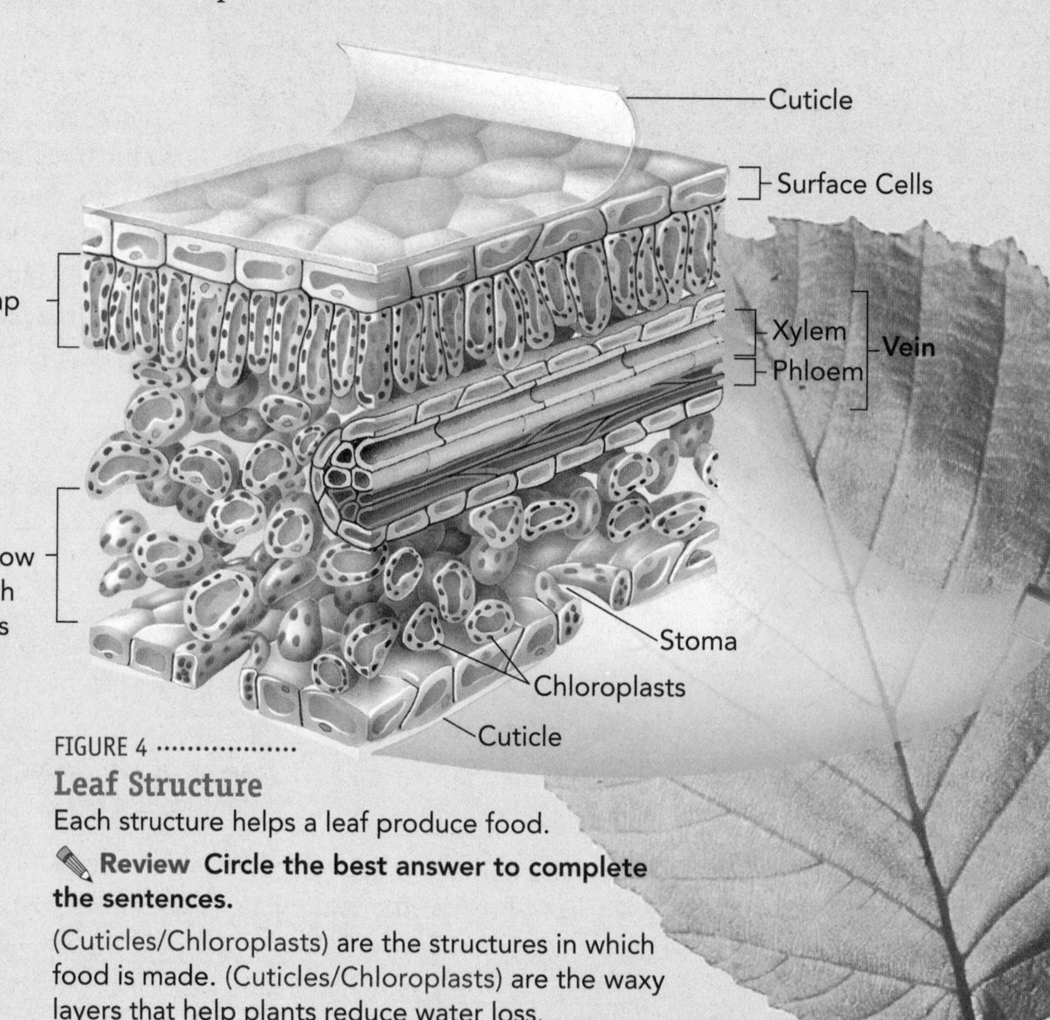

FIGURE 4

Leaf Structure

Each structure helps a leaf produce food.

Review Circle the best answer to complete the sentences.

(Cuticles/Chloroplasts) are the structures in which food is made. (Cuticles/Chloroplasts) are the waxy layers that help plants reduce water loss.

The Leaf and Photosynthesis The structure of a leaf is ideal for carrying out photosynthesis. The cells that contain the most chloroplasts are located near the leaf's upper surface, where they get the most light. The chlorophyll in the chloroplasts traps the sun's energy.

Carbon dioxide enters the leaf through open stomata. Water, which is absorbed by the plant's roots, travels up the stem to the leaf through the xylem. During photosynthesis, sugar and oxygen are produced from the carbon dioxide and water. Oxygen passes out of the leaf through the open stomata. The sugar enters the phloem and then travels throughout the plant.

Controlling Water Loss Because such a large area of a leaf is exposed to the air, water can quickly evaporate from a leaf into the air. The process by which water evaporates from a plant's leaves is called **transpiration.** A plant can lose a lot of water through transpiration. A corn plant, for example, can lose almost 4 liters of water on a hot summer day. Without a way to slow down the process of transpiration, a plant would shrivel up and die.

Fortunately, plants have ways to slow down transpiration. One way plants retain water is by closing the stomata. The stomata often close when leaves start to dry out.

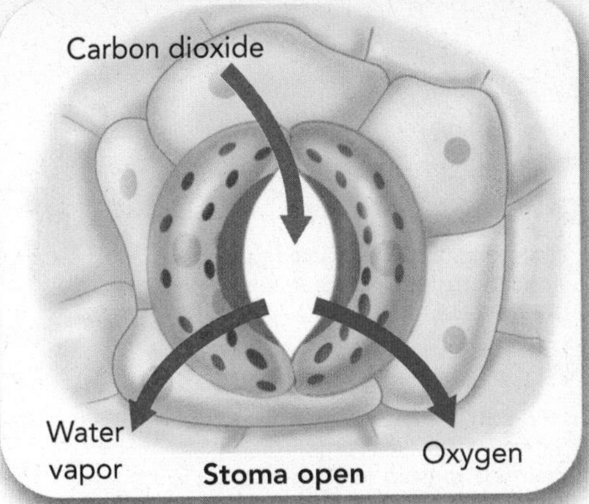

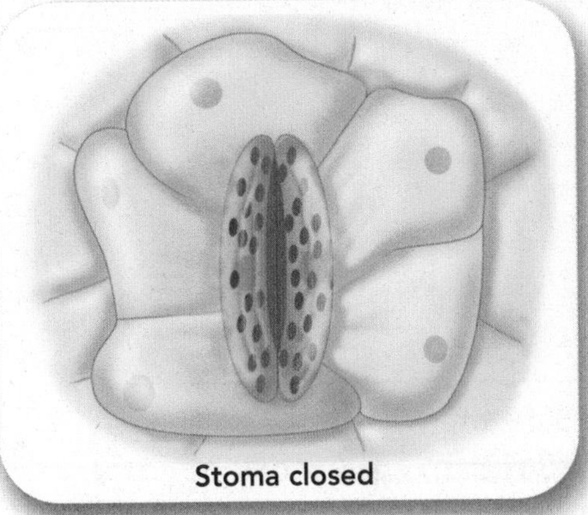

FIGURE 5

Stomata

Stomata can slow water loss.

Name What three substances enter and leave a plant through stomata?

____

____

Do the Lab Investigation *Investigating Stomata.*

Assess Your Understanding

1a. List What are the functions of a stem?

____

____

____

____

____

b. Infer If you forget to water a houseplant for a few days, would its stomata be open or closed? Why?

____

____

____

got it?

○ **I get it!** Now I know that roots, stems, and leaves perform functions like ______________________

____

○ I need extra help with ______________________

Go to **MY SCIENCE COACH** *online for help with this subject.*

Science Standards of Learning

LS.1d Construct and use models and simulations to illustrate and explain phenomena.

LS.3a Investigate and understand cells, tissues, organs, and systems.

LS.3b Investigate and understand patterns of cellular organization and their relationship to life processes in living things.

How Do Seeds Become New Plants?

Many plants begin their life cycle as a seed. You can follow the cycle from seed to plant in **Figure 6.** All seeds share important similarities. **Inside a seed is a partially developed plant. If a seed lands in an area where conditions are favorable, the plant sprouts out of the seed and begins to grow.**

Seed Structure A seed has three main parts—an embryo, stored food, and a seed coat. The young plant that develops from the zygote, or fertilized egg, is called the **embryo.** The embryo already has the beginnings of roots, stems, and leaves. In the seeds of most plants, the embryo stops growing when it is quite small. When the embryo begins to grow again, it uses the food stored in the seed until it can make its own food by photosynthesis. In all seeds, the embryo has one or more seed leaves, or cotyledons. In some seeds, food is stored in the cotyledons. In others, food is stored outside the embryo.

The outer covering of a seed is called the seed coat. The seed coat acts like plastic wrap, protecting the embryo and its food from drying out. This allows a seed to remain inactive for a long time. In many plants, the seeds are surrounded by a structure called a fruit.

FIGURE 6

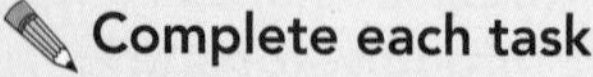

Story of a Seed

Read the text on this page and the next page. Then complete the activities about seeds becoming new plants.

Complete each task.

1. **Review** On the diagram, label the seed's embryo, cotyledons, and seed coat.

Stem and root

Stored food

Seed Dispersal After seeds form, they are usually scattered. The scattering of seeds is called seed dispersal. Seeds can be dispersed in many different ways. When animals eat fruit, the seeds inside the fruit pass through the animal's digestive system and are deposited in new areas. Other seeds are enclosed in barblike structures that hook onto fur or clothing. The seeds fall off in a new area. Water also disperses seeds that fall into oceans and rivers. Wind disperses lightweight seeds, such as those of dandelions and maple trees. Some plants eject their seeds. The force scatters the seeds in many directions. A seed that is dispersed far from its parent plant has a better chance of survival. Far away, a seed does not have to compete with its parent for light, water, and nutrients.

Relate Cause and Effect Underline a cause of seed dispersal and circle its effect in the text on this page.

Germination After a seed is dispersed, it may remain inactive for a while before it germinates. **Germination** (jur muh NAY shun) occurs when the embryo begins to grow again and pushes out of the seed. Germination begins when the seed absorbs water. Then the embryo uses stored food to begin to grow. The roots first grow downward. Then its stem and leaves grow upward.

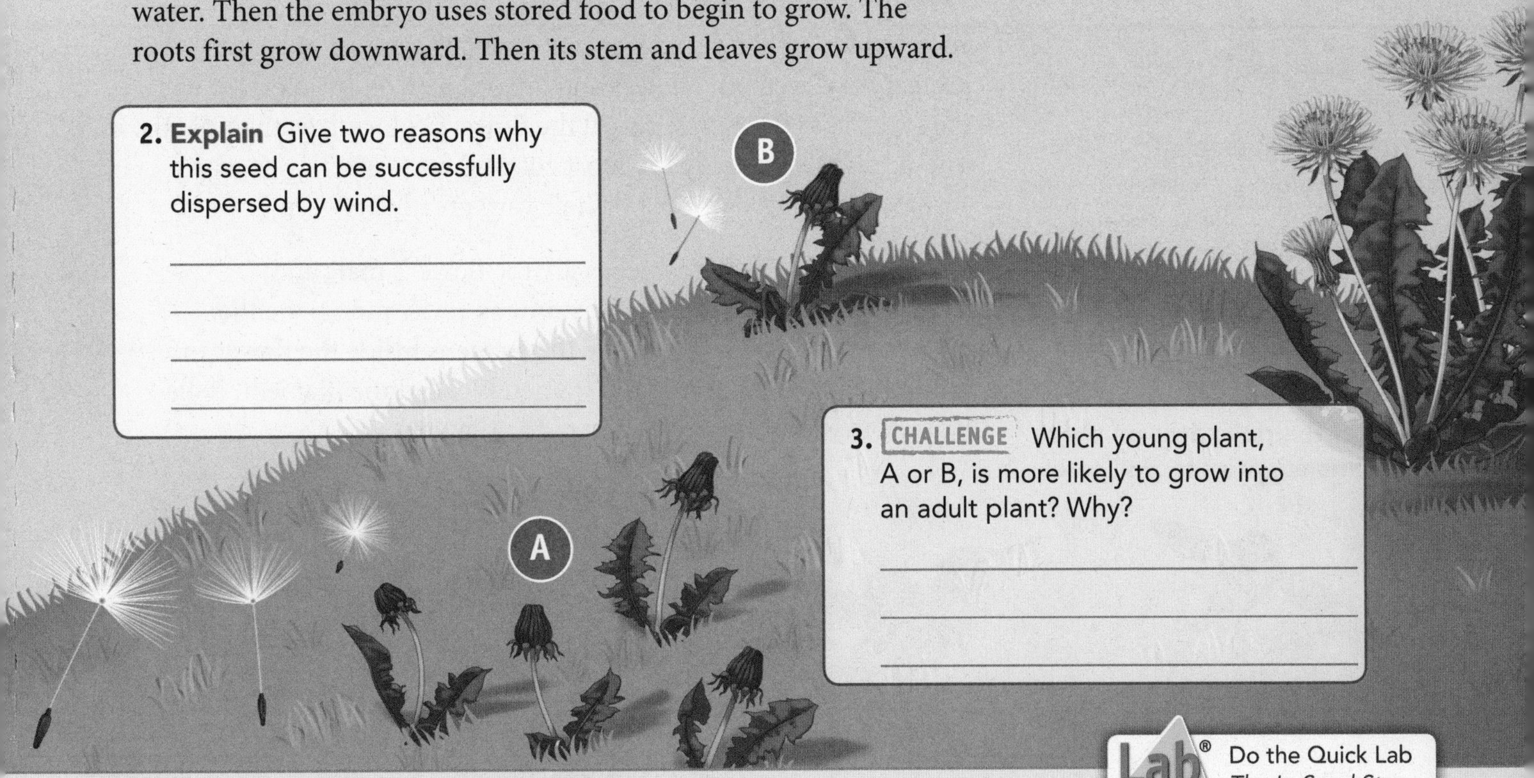

2. **Explain** Give two reasons why this seed can be successfully dispersed by wind.

____

____

____

____

B

A

3. CHALLENGE Which young plant, A or B, is more likely to grow into an adult plant? Why?

____

____

____

Lab zone® Do the Quick Lab *The In-Seed Story.*

Assess Your Understanding

got it?

○ **I get it!** Now I know that a seed becomes a new plant when _______________

____

○ I need extra help with _______________

Go to MY SCIENCE COACH *online for help with this subject.*

Science Standards of Learning

LS.1d Construct and use models and simulations to illustrate and explain phenomena.

LS.3a Investigate and understand cells, tissues, organs, and systems.

LS.3b Investigate and understand patterns of cellular organization and their relationship to life processes in living things.

What Are the Structures of a Flower?

Flowers come in all sorts of shapes, sizes, and colors. But, despite their differences, all flowers have the same function—reproduction. A **flower** is the reproductive structure of an angiosperm. **A typical flower contains sepals, petals, stamens, and pistils.**

The colors and shapes of most flower structures and the scents produced by most flowers attract insects and other animals. These organisms ensure that pollination occurs. **Pollination** is the transfer of pollen from male reproductive structures to female reproductive structures. Pollinators, such as those shown in **Figure 7,** include birds, bats, and insects such as bees and flies. As you read, keep in mind that some flowers lack one or more of the parts. For example, some flowers have only male reproductive parts, and some flowers do not have petals.

Sepals and Petals

When a flower is still a bud, it is enclosed by leaflike structures called **sepals** (SEE pulz). Sepals protect the developing flower and are often green in color. When the sepals fold back, they reveal the flower's colorful, leaflike **petals.** The petals are generally the most colorful parts of a flower. The shapes, sizes, and number of petals vary greatly between flowers.

Stamens

Within the petals are the flower's male and female reproductive parts. The **stamens** (STAY munz) are the male reproductive parts. Locate the stamens inside the flower in **Figure 8.** The thin stalk of the stamen is called the filament. Pollen is made in the anther, at the top of the filament.

FIGURE 7

Pollinator Matchup

Some pollinators are well adapted to the plants they pollinate. For example, the long tongue of the nectar bat helps the bat reach inside the agave plant, as shown below.

Apply Concepts **Write the letter of the pollinator on the plant it is adapted to pollinate.**

Pistils The female parts, or **pistils** (PIS tulz), are found in the center of most flowers, as shown in **Figure 8.** Some flowers have two or more pistils; others have only one. The sticky tip of the pistil is called the stigma. A slender tube, called a style, connects the stigma to a hollow structure at the base of the flower. This hollow structure is the **ovary,** which protects the seeds as they develop. An ovary contains one or more ovules.

FIGURE 8

INTERACTIVE ART **Structures of a Typical Flower**

Flowers have many structures.

Relate Text and Visuals

Use the word bank to fill in the missing labels.

_______ are the small, leaflike parts of a flower. They protect the developing flower.

_______ are usually the most colorful parts of a flower. Pollinators are attracted by their color and scent.

_______ are the male reproductive parts of a flower. Pollen is produced in the anther, at the top of the stalklike filament.

_______ are the female reproductive parts of a flower. They consist of a sticky stigma, a slender tube called the style, and a hollow structure called the ovary at the base.

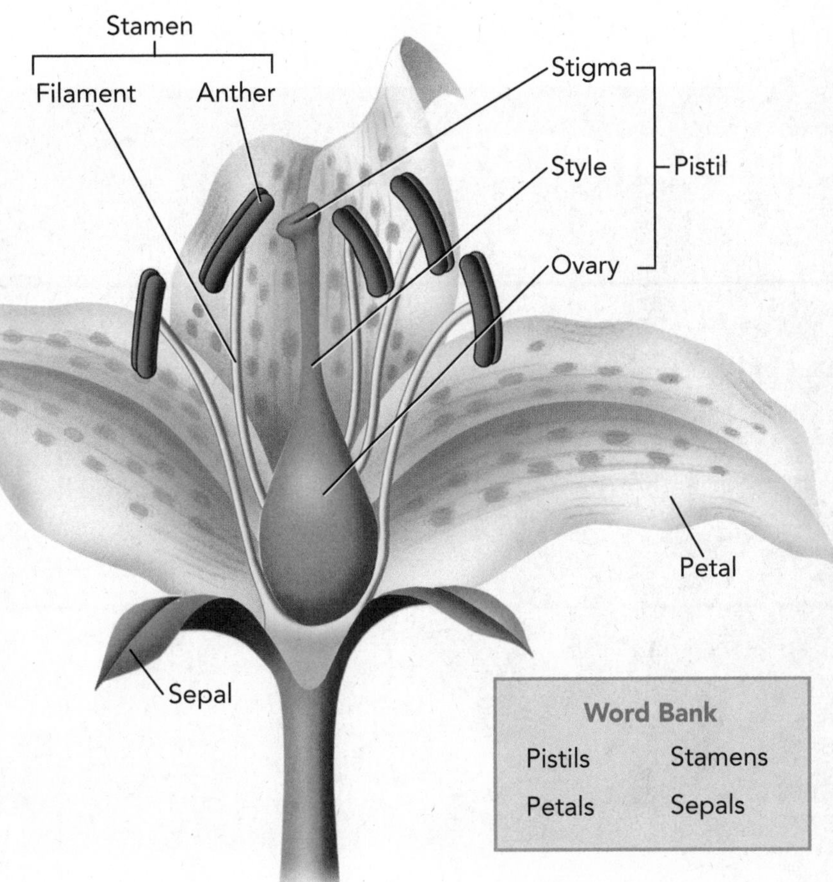

Word Bank

Pistils	Stamens
Petals	Sepals

Lab zone Do the Quick Lab *Modeling Flowers.*

Assess Your Understanding

got it?

○ **I get it!** Now I know that the structures of a flower include _______

○ I need extra help with _______

Go to MY SCIENCE COACH *online for help with this subject.*

Plant Reproduction

What Are the Stages of a Plant Life Cycle?
LS.1d, LS.4a, LS.4b, LS.4c

How Do Plants Reproduce?
LS.1d, LS.4b, LS.4c

my planet Diary

FUN FACT

If Trees Could Talk

Suppose you had been alive during the ancient Egyptian Empire, the Middle Ages, the American Revolution, and both World Wars. Think of the stories you could tell! Bristlecone pine trees can be this old. In 1964, a student got permission to cut down one of these trees. He counted the tree rings to see how old the tree was, and discovered it was 4,900 years old. He had just cut down the oldest living thing in the world! Today, Bristlecone pine forests are protected.

Write your answer below.
What could you learn from a 5,000-year-old tree?

____
____
____
____
____

PLANET DIARY Go to **Planet Diary** to learn more about plant reproduction.

Do the Inquiry Warm-Up *Make the Pollen Stick.*

Science Standards of Learning

LS.1d Construct and use models and simulations to illustrate and explain phenomena.
LS.4a Investigate and understand distinguishing characteristics of domains of organisms.
LS.4b Investigate and understand distinguishing characteristics of kingdoms of organisms.
LS.4c Investigate and understand distinguishing characteristics of major plant divisions.

What Are the Stages of a Plant's Life Cycle?

Like other living things, plants develop and reproduce through life stages. **Plants have complex life cycles that include two different stages, the sporophyte stage and the gametophyte stage.** In the **sporophyte** (SPOH ruh fyt) stage, the plant produces spores. The spore develops into the plant's other stage, called the gametophyte. In the **gametophyte** (guh MEE tuh fyt) stage, the plant produces two kinds of sex cells: sperm cells and egg cells. See **Figure 1.**

Vocabulary

• sporophyte • gametophyte • annual • biennial • perennial • fertilization • zygote • cone • ovule • fruit

Skills

Reading: Summarize
Inquiry: Infer

FIGURE 1

Plant Life Cycle

All plants go through two stages in their life cycle.

Interpret Diagrams Label the sporophyte and gametophyte stages.

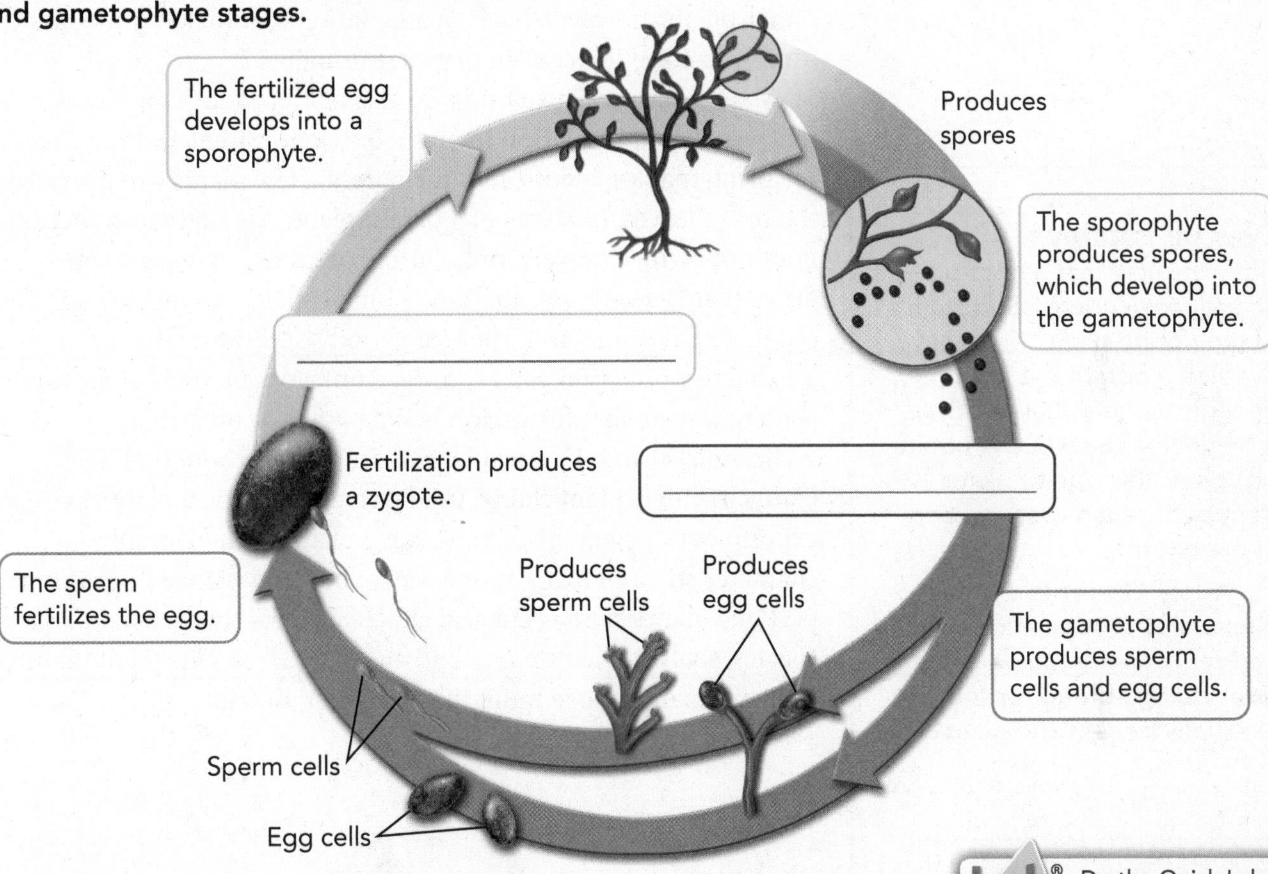

Angiosperms are classified based on the length of their life cycles. Flowering plants that complete a life cycle within one growing season are called **annuals.** Annuals include marigolds, petunias, wheat, and cucumbers. Angiosperms that complete their life cycle in two years are called **biennials** (by EN ee ulz). In the first year, biennials germinate and grow roots, very short stems, and leaves. During their second year, biennials lengthen their stems, grow new leaves, and then produce flowers and seeds. Parsley, celery, and foxglove are biennials. Flowering plants that live for more than two years are called **perennials.** Most perennials flower every year.

Lab zone® Do the Quick Lab *Plant Life Cycles.*

Assess Your Understanding

got it?

○ **I get it!** Now I know that the stages of a plant's life cycle include ____________

○ I need extra help with ____________

Go to my science coach *online for help with this subject.*

Science Standards of Learning

LS.1d Construct and use models to illustrate and explain phenomena.

LS.4b Investigate and understand distinguishing characteristics of kingdoms of organisms.

LS.4c Investigate and understand distinguishing characteristics of major plant divisions.

How Do Plants Reproduce?

Plants reproduce in different ways depending on their structures and the environment they live in. **All plants undergo sexual reproduction that involves fertilization.** **Fertilization** occurs when a sperm cell unites with an egg cell. The fertilized egg is called a **zygote.** For algae and some plants, fertilization can only occur if there is water in the environment. This is because the sperm cells of these plants swim through the water to the egg cells. Other plants, however, have an adaptation that makes it possible for fertilization to occur in dry environments.

Many plants can also undergo asexual reproduction. Recall that asexual reproduction includes only one parent and produces offspring that are identical to the parent. New plants can grow from the roots, leaves, or stems of a parent plant. Asexual reproduction does not involve flowers, pollination, or seeds, so it can happen faster than sexual reproduction. A single plant can quickly spread out in an environment if there are good conditions. However, asexual reproduction can reproduce unfavorable traits since there is no new genetic information being passed to offspring.

Scientists can take advantage of asexual reproduction in plants. A single plant can be used to create identical plants for experiments. Scientists can also copy plants with favorable characteristics. Grafting is one way of copying plants. In grafting, part of a plant's stem is cut and attached to another related plant species, such as a lemon tree and an orange tree. The plant matures and can then produce more than one kind of fruit.

FIGURE 2

Eyes on Potatoes

Did you know that a potato is actually the underground stem of the potato plant? If you have ever left a potato out long enough, you may have noticed it beginning to sprout. A potato can grow new potato plants from buds called eyes, as seen in this photo.

Apply Concepts Potato plants also produce flowers and reproduce sexually. How does being able to reproduce asexually benefit the plant?

apply it!

A citrus farmer was able to graft a lemon tree branch onto an orange tree. Now the same tree produces lemons and oranges! The farmer plans to use branches from the same lemon trees to create other combined fruit trees.

1 **Review** The farmer used the lemon tree's ability to (sexually/asexually) reproduce.

2 **Infer** Name at least one negative effect of using the same lemon tree to create new trees the farmer should know about.

____

____

3 CHALLENGE Why might the public be opposed to using this method to create new fruit trees?

____

____

Nonvascular and Seedless Vascular Plants

Mosses, liverworts, hornworts, ferns, club mosses, and horsetails need to grow in moist environments. This is because the plants release spores into their surroundings, where they grow into gametophytes. When the gametophytes produce egg cells and sperm cells, there must be enough water available for the sperm to swim toward the eggs.

For example, the familiar fern, with its visible fronds, is the sporophyte stage of the plant. On the underside of mature fronds, spores develop in tiny spore cases. Wind and water can carry the spores great distances. If a spore lands in moist, shaded soil, it develops into a gametophyte. Fern gametophytes are tiny plants that grow low to the ground.

Spore cases on the fronds of a fern

Gymnosperms You can follow the process of gymnosperm reproduction in **Figure 3.**

1 **Cone Production**

Most gymnosperms have reproductive structures called **cones.** Cones are covered with scales. Most gymnosperms produce two types of cones: male cones and female cones. Usually, a single plant produces both male and female cones. In some types of gymnosperms, however, individual trees produce either male cones or female cones. A few gymnosperms produce no cones.

2 **Pollen Production and Ovule Development**

(A) Male cones produce pollen grains. Cells in the pollen will mature into sperm cells. (B) The female gametophyte develops in structures called ovules. An **ovule** (OH vyool) is a structure that contains an egg cell. Female cones contain at least one ovule at the base of each scale. The ovule later develops into the seed.

3 **Egg Production**

Two egg cells form inside each ovule on the female cone.

4 **Pollination**

The transfer of pollen from a male reproductive structure to a female reproductive structure is called pollination. In gymnosperms, wind often carries the pollen from the male cones to the female cones. The pollen collect in a sticky substance produced by each ovule.

5 **Fertilization**

Once pollination has occurred, the ovule closes and seals in the pollen. The scales also close, and a sperm cell fertilizes an egg cell inside each ovule. The zygote then develops into the embryo part of the seed.

6 **Seed Development**

Female cones remain on the tree while the seeds mature. As the seeds develop, the female cone increases in size. It can take up to two years for the seeds of some gymnosperms to mature. Male cones, however, usually fall off the tree after they have shed their pollen.

7 **Seed Dispersal**

When the seeds are mature, the scales open. The wind shakes the seeds out of the cone and carries them away. Only a few seeds will land in suitable places and grow into new plants.

FIGURE 3

Gymnosperm Reproduction Cycle

The reproduction cycle of a gymnosperm is shown at right.

Complete each task.

1. **Identify** Underline the sentence(s) on this page that use the vocabulary terms *cone* and *ovule.*
2. **Describe** What is the relationship between cones and ovules?

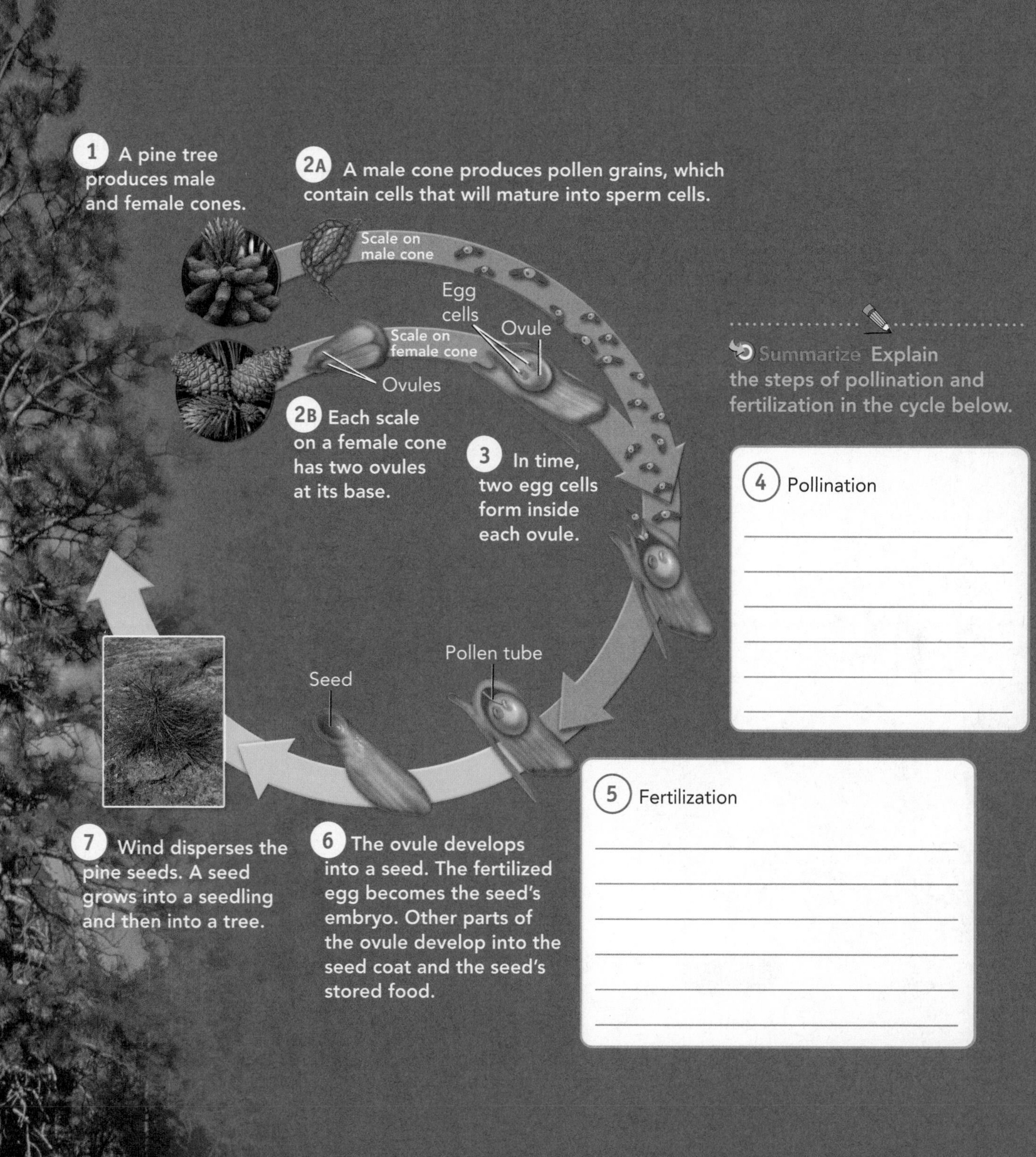

Summarize Explain the steps of pollination and fertilization in the cycle below.

4 Pollination

____

____

____

____

____

5 Fertilization

____

____

____

____

____

FIGURE 4

Angiosperm Reproduction

Reproduction in angiosperms begins with flowers.

Relate Text and Visuals Look back at the plant life and gymnosperm reproduction cycles in this lesson. What do the yellow and purple colors of the arrows represent?

____

____

____

____

____

Angiosperms You can follow angiosperm reproduction in **Figure 4.** First, pollen fall on a flower's stigma. In time, the sperm cell and egg cell join together in the flower's ovule. The zygote develops into the embryo part of the seed.

Pollination A flower is pollinated when a grain of pollen falls on the stigma. Some angiosperms are pollinated by the wind, but most rely on other organisms. When an organism enters a flower to obtain food, it becomes coated with pollen. Some of the pollen can drop onto the flower's stigma as the animal leaves. The pollen can also be brushed onto the stigma of the next flower the animal visits.

Fertilization If the pollen fall on the stigma of a similar plant, fertilization can occur. A sperm cell joins with an egg cell inside an ovule within the ovary at the base of the flower. The zygote then begins to develop into the seed's embryo. Other parts of the ovule develop into the rest of the seed.

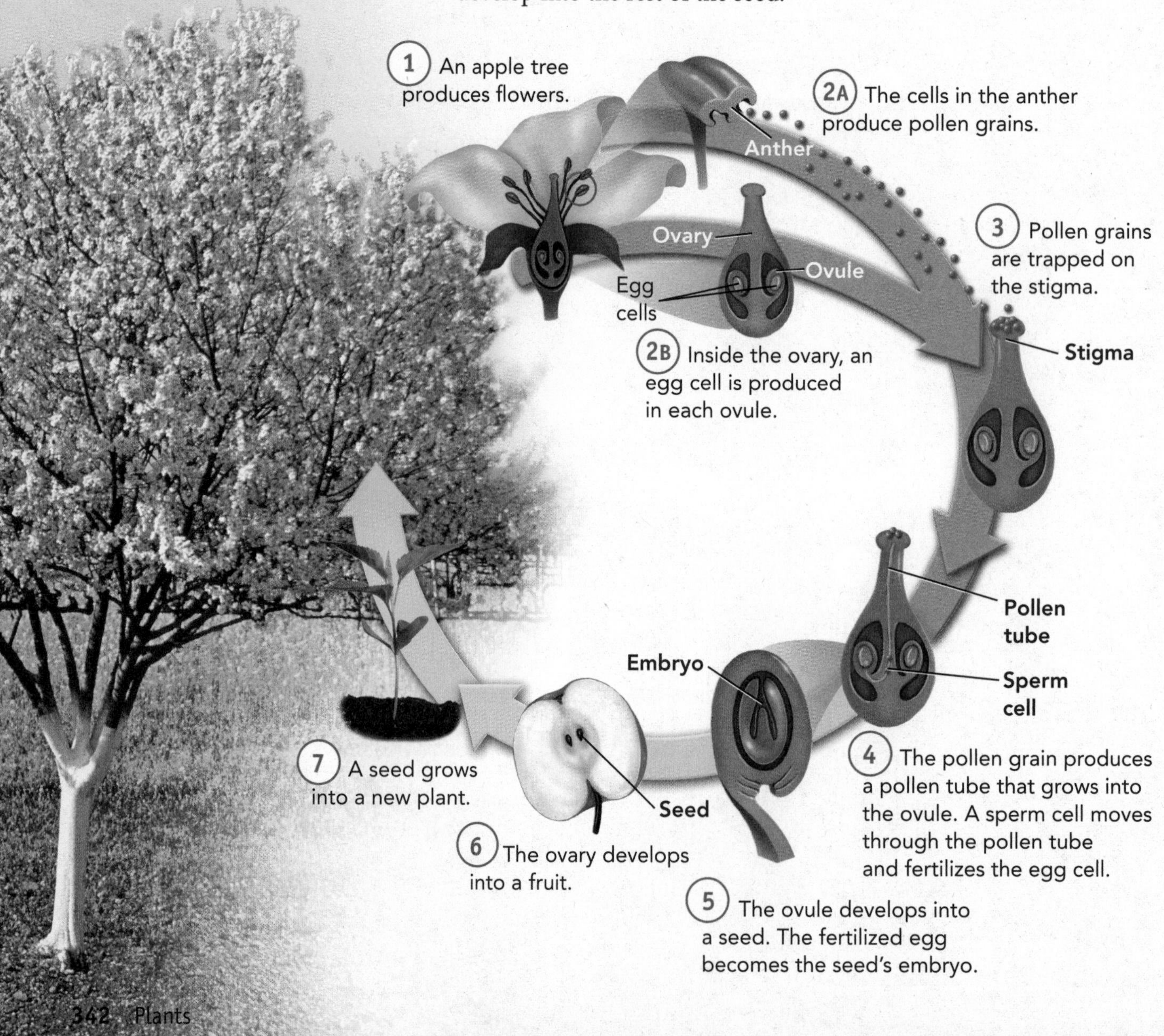

Fruit Development and Seed Dispersal As the seed develops, the ovary changes into a **fruit.** A fruit is the ripened ovary and other structures that enclose one or more seeds. Fruits include apples, cherries, tomatoes, squash, and many others. Fruits are the means by which angiosperm seeds are dispersed. Animals that eat fruits help to disperse their seeds by depositing them in new areas.

The *Arabidopsis* plant became the first plant to flower and produce seeds in the zero-gravity environment of outer space on a Soviet space station in 1982.

FIGURE 5

Flower to Fruit

Flowers eventually develop into fruit.

Sequence Write the numbers 1 through 4 in the blank circles to show the progression from flower to fruit.

Lab zone Do the Quick Lab *Where Are the Seeds?*

Assess Your Understanding

1a. Review (Fertilization/Asexual reproduction) occurs when a sperm cell unites with an egg cell.

b. Explain Why do plants like liverworts need to live in moist environments?

____

____

c. Relate Cause and Effect Underline the cause and circle the effect in the sentences below.

Pollination can occur when pollen on an insect is dropped onto the stigma.

Animals eating fruit is one way seeds are dispersed.

got it?

○ **I get it!** Now I know that all of the major plant groups reproduce ______________________

____

○ I need extra help with ______________________

Go to MY SCIENCE COACH *online for help with this subject.*

Plant Responses and Growth

What Are Three Stimuli That Produce Plant Responses?
LS.10a

How Do Plants Respond to Seasonal Changes?
LS.1h, LS.4b, LS.10a

MY PLANET DIARY

DISCOVERY

Flower Power

What makes a plant flower? Plants detect the amount of light each day. When there is just enough light, the plant sends a signal to the flower. But what is this signal? For almost 80 years, the answer remained a mystery. In 2008, scientists discovered the protein that was responsible. They linked the protein they thought controlled flowering to a fluorescent, or glowing, protein they obtained from a jellyfish. Then they watched the bright green protein travel with the flowering protein through the stem to make the plant bloom. Why does this experiment matter?

Global climate change is starting to hurt crops. Some places near the equator are becoming too warm to farm. Areas closer to Earth's poles may be needed to grow more crops as they warm. These areas, however, do not get as much sunlight. Scientists could use the flowering protein to encourage plants to flower without direct sunlight.

Communicate Discuss the question with a group of classmates. Then write your answer below.

In addition to getting the plants to flower with no light, what other challenges might scientists have to overcome when trying to get plants to succeed in a new area?

PLANET DIARY Go to **Planet Diary** to learn more about plant responses and growth.

Lab zone® Do the Inquiry Warm-Up *Can a Plant Respond to Touch?*

The green you see in these plant cells is from a fluorescent protein like the one used in the flowering experiment.

Vocabulary

- tropism • hormone • auxin • photoperiodism
- critical night length • short-day plant • long-day plant
- day-neutral plant • dormancy

Skills

- Reading: Relate Text and Visuals
- Inquiry: Draw Conclusions

What Are Three Stimuli That Produce Plant Responses?

Science Standards of Learning

LS.10a Investigate and understand phototropism and dormancy.

You may be one of those people who close their window shades at night because the morning light wakes you up. People respond to many stimuli each day. Did you know plants also respond to some of the same stimuli, including light?

Tropisms Animals usually respond to stimuli by moving. Unlike animals, plants usually respond by growing either toward or away from a stimulus. A plant's growth response toward or away from a stimulus is called a **tropism** (TROH piz um). If a plant grows toward the stimulus, it is said to show a positive tropism. If a plant grows away from a stimulus, it shows a negative tropism. **Touch, gravity, and light are three important stimuli that trigger growth responses, or tropisms, in plants.**

Touch

Some plants show a response to touch called thigmotropism. The prefix *thigmo-* comes from a Greek word that means "touch." The stems of many vines, such as morning glories, sweet peas, and grapes, show a positive thigmotropism. As the vines grow, they coil around any object they touch.

FIGURE 1

Plant Responses to Stimuli

The stimuli in space are not always the same as those on Earth.

Develop Hypotheses How might the roots of a plant grow in space without the influence of gravity?

____

____

____

____

____

Gravity

Plants can respond to gravity. This response is called gravitropism. Roots show positive gravitropism if they grow downward. Stems, on the other hand, show negative gravitropism. Stems grow upward against gravity.

Relate Text and Visuals Use what you have read to label the side of the plant with more auxin and the side with less auxin.

Light

All plants exhibit a response to light called phototropism. The leaves, stems, and flowers of plants grow toward light. This shows a positive phototropism. A plant receives more energy for photosynthesis by growing toward the light.

Plants are able to respond to stimuli because they produce hormones. A **hormone** produced by a plant is a chemical that affects how the plant grows and develops. One important plant hormone is named **auxin** (AWK sin). Auxin speeds up the rate at which a plant's cells grow and controls a plant's response to light. When light shines on one side of a plant's stem, auxin builds up in the shaded side of the stem. The cells on the shaded side begin to grow faster. The cells on the stem's shaded side are longer than those on its sunny side. The stem bends toward the light.

Lab zone® Do the Quick Lab *Watching Roots Grow.*

Assess Your Understanding

1a. Define What is a tropism?

____

____

____

____

____

b. Predict What do you think would happen if a plant did not create enough of the hormone that controlled flower formation?

____

____

____

got it?

O **I get it!** Now I know that plants respond to ______________________________

____

O I need extra help with ______________________________

Go to MY SCIENCE COACH *online for help with this subject.*

How Do Plants Respond to Seasonal Changes?

Science Standards of Learning

LS.1h Organize, graph, and interpret data, and use data to make predictions.

LS.4b Investigate and understand distinguishing characteristics of kingdoms of organisms.

LS.10a Investigate and understand phototropism and dormancy.

People have long observed that plants respond to the changing seasons. Some plants bloom in early spring, while others don't bloom until summer. The leaves on some trees change color in autumn and then fall off by winter.

Photoperiodism

What triggers a plant to flower? **The amount of darkness a plant receives determines the time of flowering in many plants.** A plant's response to seasonal changes in the length of night and day is called **photoperiodism.**

Plants respond differently to the length of nights. Some plants will only bloom when the nights last a certain length of time. This length, called the **critical night length,** is the number of hours of darkness that determines whether or not a plant will flower. For example, if a plant has a critical night length of 11 hours, it will flower only when nights are longer than 11 hours. You can read more on how different plants respond to night length in **Figure 2.**

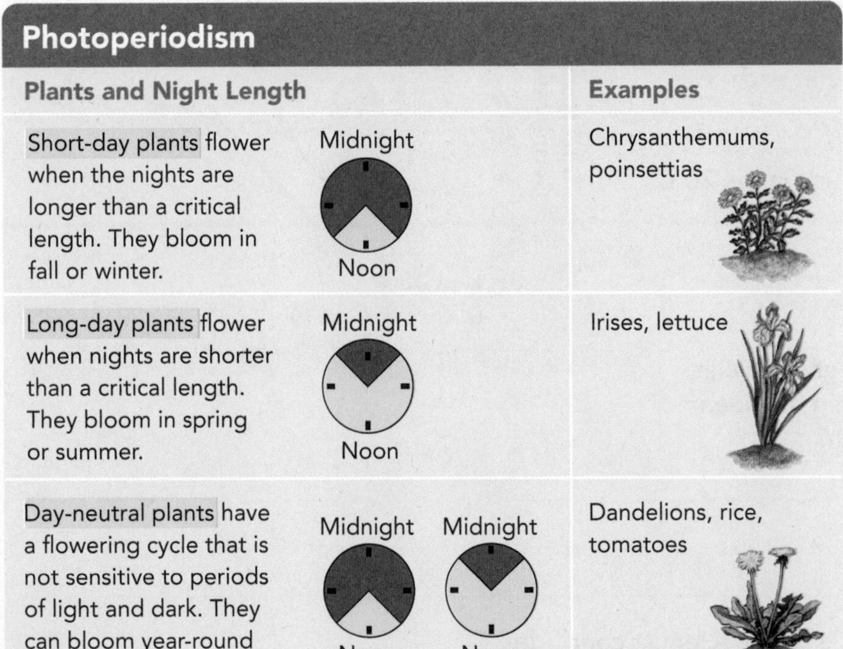

Photoperiodism

Plants and Night Length		Examples
Short-day plants flower when the nights are longer than a critical length. They bloom in fall or winter.	Midnight / Noon	Chrysanthemums, poinsettias
Long-day plants flower when nights are shorter than a critical length. They bloom in spring or summer.	Midnight / Noon	Irises, lettuce
Day-neutral plants have a flowering cycle that is not sensitive to periods of light and dark. They can bloom year-round depending on weather.	Midnight / Noon; Midnight / Noon	Dandelions, rice, tomatoes

FIGURE 2

Photoperiodism

Flowering plants can be grouped as short-day plants, long-day plants, and day-neutral plants.

Infer Suppose you are a farmer in a climate that supports plant growth all year-round but night length varies. Based on the categories in the chart, would you plant mostly one type of plant or a mixture of all three? Explain.

Winter Dormancy Some plants prepare differently than others for certain seasons. As winter draws near, many plants prepare to go into a state of **dormancy.** Dormancy is a period when an organism's growth or activity stops. **Dormancy helps plants survive freezing temperatures and the lack of liquid water.**

With many trees, the first visible change is that the leaves begin to turn color. Cooler weather and shorter days cause the leaves to stop making chlorophyll. As chlorophyll breaks down, yellow and orange pigments become visible. In addition, the plant begins to produce new red pigments. This causes the brilliant colors of autumn leaves. Over the next few weeks, sugar and water are transported out of the tree's leaves. When the leaves fall to the ground, the tree is ready for winter.

apply it!

One hundred radish seeds were planted in two identical trays of soil. One tray was kept at 10°C. The other tray was kept at 20°C. The trays received equal amounts of sun and water. The graph shows how many seeds germinated over time at each temperature.

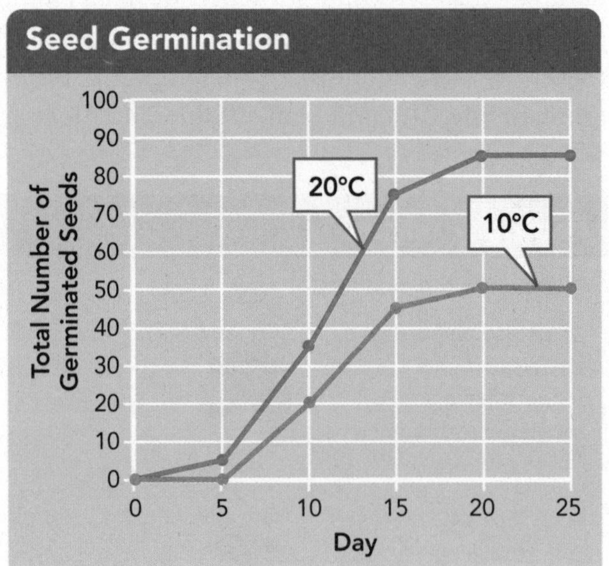

1 Read Graphs About how many seeds in the 20°C tray germinated on Day 13?

____

____

2 Draw Conclusions Based on the graph, what can you conclude about the relationship between the two temperatures and germination?

____

____

____

3 CHALLENGE After the experiment, a fellow scientist concludes that more seeds will *always* germinate at higher temperatures. Is the scientist right? Why?

____

____

____

____

Roving for Life in Space

How do you know a plant when you see it?

FIGURE 3

ART IN MOTION You are a scientist researching distant planets. You have sent a rover to collect samples from one of the planets and you get some exciting results. The rover has found three living things, and one of them is a plant! But, on the way back to Earth, the rover has a rough landing and the samples get mixed up. You run some tests in your lab to find which sample is the plant. The results are shown below.

Apply Concepts Circle the sample that is a plant. Then answer the question below.

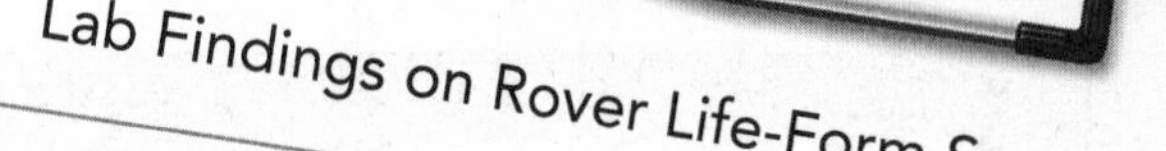

Lab Findings on Rover Life-Form Samples

	Sample 1	Sample 2	Sample 3
Reproduces sexually	Yes	Yes	No
Cells have cell walls	No	Yes	Yes
Contains vascular tissue	Yes	No	No
Multicellular	Yes	Yes	No
Autotroph	No	Yes	Yes
Responds to light	Yes	Yes	No

Choose one of the samples you did not circle. Why is this sample not a plant?

Do the Quick Lab *Seasonal Changes.*

Assess Your Understanding

2a. Review (Short-day/Long-day) plants flower when nights are shorter than a critical length.

b. Explain Why do the leaves of some trees change color in autumn?

c. ANSWER THE BIG Q How do you know a plant when you see it?

got it?

○ **I get it!** Now I know that plants respond to seasonal changes because

○ I need extra help with

Go to MY SCIENCE COACH *online for help with this subject.*

Plants in Everyday Life

 **How Are Plants Important to Everyday Life?**
LS.5c

MY PLANET DIARY

BLOG

Posted by: George

Location: Tacoma, Washington

I never really thought much about how important trees are until my dad and I planted a plum tree in our yard. I've watched it grow over the last couple of years. The first year we didn't get any plums. The next year, we had tons of plums and they were good! This made me think more about all that we get from plants —food to eat, wood to build houses, and cotton to make clothes!

Communicate **Discuss the question with a group of classmates. Then write your answer below.**

Describe a plant that is important to your everyday life.

____

____

____

____

____

____

PLANET DIARY Go to **Planet Diary** to learn more about plants in everyday life.

Do the Inquiry Warm-Up *Feeding the World.*

Vocabulary
- peat

Skills
- Reading: Identify the Main Idea
- Inquiry: Pose Questions

How Are Plants Important to Everyday Life?

Science Standards of Learning

LS.5c Investigate and understand photosynthesis as foundation of virtually all food webs.

What did you have for breakfast today? Cereal? Toast? Orange juice? Chances are you have already eaten something today that came from plants. Besides providing food, plants play many roles on Earth. **In addition to food, plants provide habitats. Plants can clean the water and protect the soil in an environment. Plants are also the base of many products important to human life, such as medicines, paper, and clothing.**

The Role of Plants in an Ecosystem

Plants play many roles in an ecosystem. You can see some of these roles in **Figure 1.** Recall that an ecosystem contains living things and the nonliving surroundings. People are included in ecosystems too!

An oak tree provides places for birds to nest, and acorns (seeds) for squirrels, deer, wild turkeys, and other species to eat. Insects eat the leaves, bark, wood, and fungi living in the tree.

People benefit from the tree as well. It can provide shade in summer and beautiful scenery during autumn. Oak wood is a valuable resource often used to make furniture.

The oak's roots hold onto the soil and prevent it from being washed or blown away. The roots also quickly absorb rainwater. Without the roots, the water could flow over the land. The moving water could pick up substances that cause pollution and deposit them into rivers or drinking water supplies.

FIGURE 1

The Roles of an Oak Tree

The roles of plants are often overlooked.

Identify List at least two other roles the oak tree serves for living or nonliving things.

____

____

How People Use Plants

People have found ways to directly use almost all plants. Green algae is often used in scientific research and as a thickening agent in some foods. Liverworts, club mosses, and other plants are used in parts of the world to treat conditions from fevers to itchy skin.

Many people use moss in agriculture and gardening. The moss that gardeners use contains sphagnum (SFAG num) moss. Sphagnum moss grows in a type of wetland called a bog. The still water in a bog is so acidic that decomposers cannot live in the water. When the plants die, they do not decay. Instead, the dead plants accumulate at the bottom of the bog. Over time, the mosses become compressed into layers and form a blackish-brown material called **peat.** In some parts of Europe and Asia, people use peat as a fuel to heat homes and to cook food.

Identify the Main Idea In the text under the heading How People Use Plants, underline at least three plant groups and circle one product made from each.

apply it!

You are at a grocery store buying cleaning products to clean your bathroom. You can choose a cleaner made from chemicals made in a lab or one made from plant-derived chemicals.

1 **Pose Questions** What questions should you ask before making your decision?

____

____

____

____

____

____

____

____

2 **CHALLENGE** What could be some disadvantages of the plant-based cleaner?

____

____

____

____

____

____

____

____

Peat drying after being extracted from a bog

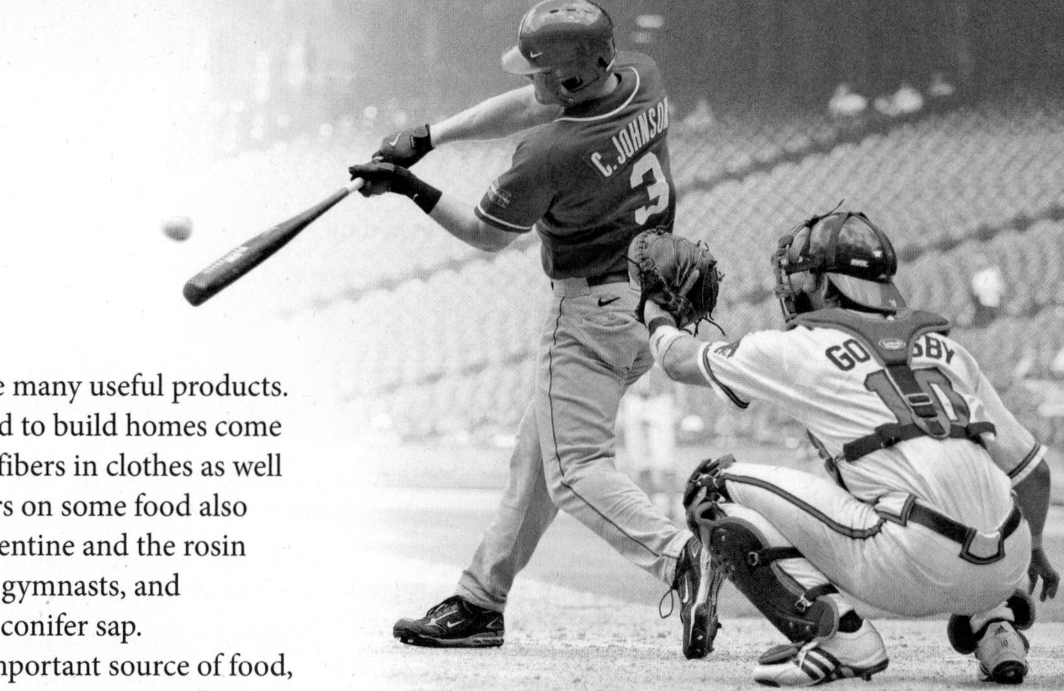

Gymnosperms provide many useful products. Paper and the lumber used to build homes come from conifers. The rayon fibers in clothes as well as the cellophane wrappers on some food also come from conifers. Turpentine and the rosin used by baseball pitchers, gymnasts, and musicians are made from conifer sap.

Angiosperms are an important source of food, clothing, and medicine. People eat a variety of vegetables, fruits, and cereals, all of which are angiosperms. The seeds of cotton plants are covered with cotton fibers. The stems of flax plants provide linen fibers. The sap of rubber trees is used to make rubber for tires and other products. Furniture is often made from the wood of maple, cherry, and oak trees. Some important medications come from angiosperms, too. For example, the heart medication digitalis comes from the leaves of the foxglove plant.

FIGURE 2

Plants in Your Life

You may not have realized how many things, like clothes and sports equipment, are made of plants!

Name **List at least five things in your everyday life that come from plants.**

______

______

______

______

Lab zone® Do the Quick Lab *Everyday Plants.*

Assess Your Understanding

1a. List Give two uses of moss.

______

b. Describe Why is conifer sap important?

______

______

______

______

c. Make Judgments Should governments spend more money on plant research than they currently do? Why?

______

______

______

______

______

got it?

○ **I get it!** Now I know that plants provide many useful things, such as ______

______

○ I need extra help with ______

Go to **MY SCIENCE COACH** *online for help with this subject.*

CHAPTER 10

Study Guide

Nearly all plants have cells surrounded by ________________, are ________________ that photosynthesize, and are made of many cells.

LESSON 1 What Is a Plant?

Nearly all plants are autotrophs and contain many cells surrounded by cell walls.

For plants to survive on land, they must have ways to obtain water and nutrients, retain water, support their bodies, transport materials and reproduce.

Vocabulary

- chlorophyll
- photosynthesis • tissue
- chloroplast • vacuole
- cuticle • vascular tissue

LESSON 2 Classifying Plants

Nonvascular plants are low-growing, have thin cell walls, and do not have roots.

Seedless vascular plants have vascular tissue and produce spores.

Seed plants have vascular tissue and seeds.

Vocabulary

- nonvascular plant • rhizoid • vascular plant
- phloem • xylem • frond • pollen • seed
- gymnosperm • angiosperm
- cotyledon • monocot • dicot

LESSON 3 Plant Structures

A plant's roots, stems, and leaves anchor the plant, absorb water and minerals, capture the sun's energy, and make food.

A seed contains a partially developed plant.

A typical flower contains sepals, petals, stamens, and pistils.

Vocabulary

- root cap • cambium • stoma • transpiration
- embryo • germination • flower • pollination
- sepal • petal • stamen • pistil • ovary

LESSON 4 Plant Reproduction

Plants have complex life cycles that include a sporophyte stage and a gametophyte stage.

All plants undergo sexual reproduction that involves fertilization.

Vocabulary

- sporophyte • gametophyte • annual • biennial
- perennial • fertilization • zygote • cone
- ovule • fruit

LESSON 5 Plant Responses and Growth

Plants show growth responses, or tropisms, toward touch, gravity, and light.

The amount of darkness a plant receives determines the time of flowering in many plants. Dormancy helps plants survive winter.

Vocabulary

- tropism • hormone • auxin • photoperiodism
- critical night length • short-day plant
- long-day plant • day-neutral plant • dormancy

LESSON 6 Plants in Everyday Life

In addition to food, plants provide habitats, clean water, and protect soil. Plants are also the base of many products, including medicine, paper, and clothing.

Vocabulary

- peat

Review and Assessment

LESSON 1 What Is a Plant?

1. In which cellular structure do plants store water and other substances?

   a. cuticle **b.** vacuole
   c. cell wall **d.** chloroplast

2. The pigment ________________ is found in chloroplasts.

3. **Make Generalizations** Complete the table below to describe plant adaptions for life on land.

Structure	Function
Roots	Help obtain water and nutrients
Cuticle	________________
Vascular tissue	________________

LESSON 2 Classifying Plants

4. Which of the following are seedless vascular plants?

   a. ferns **b.** liverworts
   c. gymnosperms **d.** angiosperms

5. Nonvascular plants have rootlike structures called ________________

6. **Compare and Contrast** How are gymnosperms and angiosperms alike and different?

LESSON 3 Plant Structures

7. A plant absorbs water and minerals through

   a. roots. **b.** stems.
   c. leaves. **d.** stomata.

8. Transpiration slows down when ________________ are closed.

9. **Relate Cause and Effect** When a strip of bark is removed all the way around the trunk of a tree, the tree dies. Explain why.

10. **Write About It** Plant structures do not look the same among all plants. For example, some leaves are short and others long. Explain why you think there is so much variation.

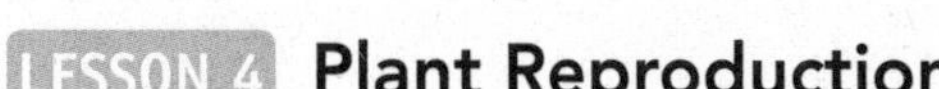

LESSON 4 Plant Reproduction

11. A zygote is the direct result of

    a. pollination.
    b. fertilization.
    c. biennial growth.
    d. the sporophyte stage.

12. ________________ complete their life cycles within one growing season.

13. **Sequence** Describe the major events in the plant life cycle. Use the terms *zygote, sperm, sporophyte, spores, gametophyte,* and *egg.*

CHAPTER 10

Review and Assessment

LESSON 5 Plant Responses and Growth

14. A plant's response to gravity is an example of a

a. dormancy. **b.** hormone.
c. tropism. **d.** critical night length.

15. The plant hormone ________________ affects the rate of cell growth.

16. Predict A particular short-day plant has a critical night length of 15 hours. Fill in the chart below to predict when this plant would flower.

Day Length	Night Length	Will It Flower?
9 h	15 h	____________
10 h	14 h	____________
7.5 h	16.5 h	____________

17. Develop Hypotheses Suppose climate change alters the environment of an oak tree from one with cold and snowy winters to one with warmer winters. Will the tree still go into a state of dormancy? Explain.

LESSON 6 Plants in Everyday Life

18. Which of the following is *not* a way that people use plants?

a. for food **b.** for clothing
c. for medicines **d.** for metal extracts

19. Over time, mosses may compact into ________________

20. Make Judgments Should the government put as much effort into protecting plants as they do animals? Why or why not?

APPLY THE BIG ?

How do you know a plant when you see it?

21. Plants are all around us. Describe a plant that you see often and then explain what makes it a plant.

Virginia SOL Test Prep

Read each question and choose the best answer.

1 The diagram above shows the parts of a flower. In which flower part does pollination take place?

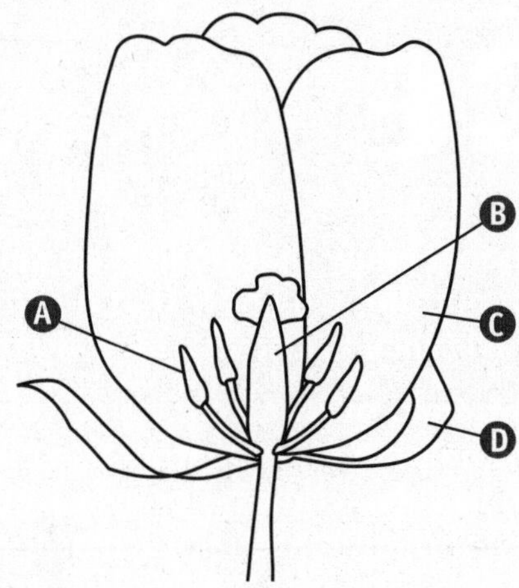

A part A
B part B
C part C
D part D

2 You examine plant cells under a microscope and notice many round, green structures within the cells. The structures are *most likely*—

F tissues
G vacuoles
H cell walls
J chloroplasts

3 Most gymnosperms produce ______, while most angiosperms produce ______.

A sperm, eggs
B pollen, cones
C cones, flowers
D flowers, fruits

4 What kind of tropism do roots display when they grow downward into the soil?

F gravitropism
G phototropism
H thigmotropism
J photoperiodism

5 The vegetables, fruits, and cereals that people eat all come from—

A peat
B angiosperms
C moss
D nonvascular plants

6 Based on the diagram, what can you conclude about Plant A and Plant B?

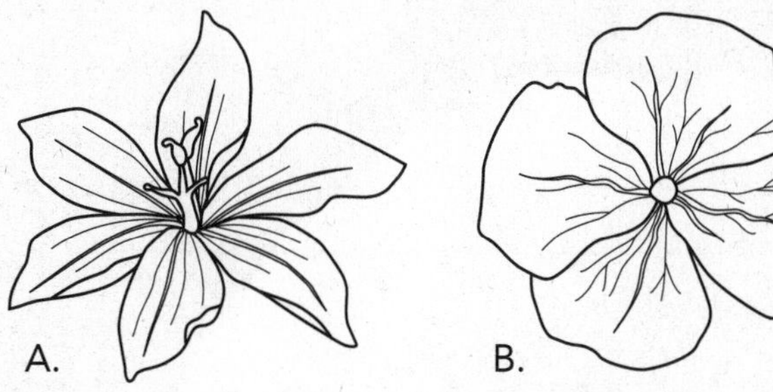

F Plant A is a monocot, and Plant B is a dicot.
G Plant A is a gymnosperm, and Plant B is a dicot.
H Plant A is an angiosperm, and Plant B is a gymnosperm.
J Plant A is a monocot, and Plant B is a gymnosperm.

SCIENCE MATTERS

Everyday Science

GRAINS OF EVIDENCE

You probably know that pollen can cause allergies, but did you know that it can also be used as evidence in criminal investigations?

A growing field of research, called forensic botany, is helping investigators use plant evidence to solve crimes. Forensic botany is the study of plant material, such as leaves, pollen, wood, or seeds, to investigate a crime. Because certain plants grow in specific areas and flower at specific times, plant material can help identify the time or place that a crime occurred.

Seeds or pollen found on a suspect's clothing can be used to link a suspect to a crime scene. Botanical evidence can also be found in a victim's stomach. Because certain plant parts cannot be digested, forensic botanists can even determine a victim's last meal!

Write About It Find out more about the life cycle of a plant described in this chapter. Draw a life cycle for the plant. Then describe how investigators could use knowledge of the plant's life cycle to solve a crime.

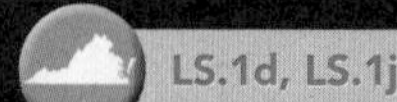

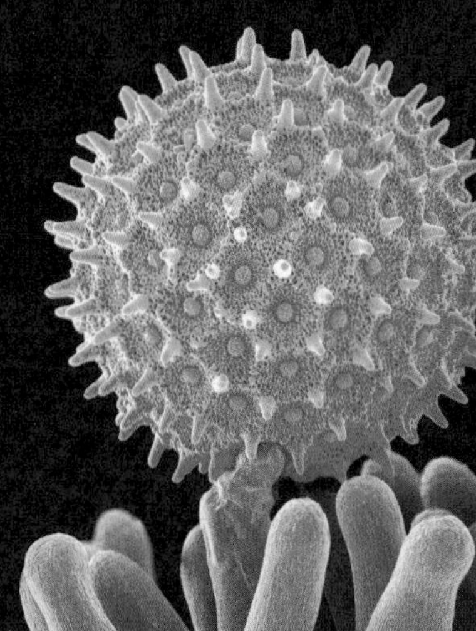

◀ Back in 1997 in New Zealand, pollen grains such as this one were used as the evidence to prove that a suspect was involved in a struggle at the crime scene.

THE Plant Doctor

Even as a young boy, George Washington Carver understood plants. Born into slavery in the 1860s, Carver spent his days studying plants. He observed that some plants needed a lot of sunlight and some needed very little. He experimented with mixtures of sand, soil, and clay to find out the kind of soil each plant needed. He knew so much about plants, neighbors called him the "plant doctor."

Carver received a master of science degree from Iowa State Agricultural College and began to teach and do research at Tuskegee Institute. Because Southern farmers grew only cotton, their soil was in poor condition and had started to erode. Carver taught farmers that crop rotation would enrich the soil. Many farmers found that the crops Carver suggested grew better in their soil, and that his methods made the soil healthier. Crop rotation is now a common farming technique.

Research It Dr. Carver taught farmers in the South to plant peanuts, sweet potatoes, and soybeans. The success of these crops often left farmers with more than they could use or sell. Research the many uses discovered by Dr. Carver for one of these crops and present them in a poster.

LS.1j, LS.11a, LS.11b, LS.11d, LS.11e

Dr. Carver inspecting plants in a research greenhouse ▶

HOW ARE THESE TWO LIVING THINGS DIFFERENT?

How do you know an animal when you see it?

These living things look alike and are both green. Each needs water and energy to grow. Yet one makes food, and the other has to find food.

Infer **What is different about these living things?**

UNTAMED SCIENCE Watch the **Untamed Science** video to learn more about animals.

Introduction to Animals

Science Standards of Learning

LS.1b, LS.1d, LS.1h, LS.1j, LS.3a, LS.3b, LS.4b, LS.4c, LS.7a, LS.7b, LS.10a, LS.10b

CHAPTER 11

Getting Started

Check Your Understanding

1. **Background** Read the paragraph below and then answer the question.

Mei's birthday present is a bird. She knows that to **survive**, an **organism** needs food, water, and oxygen. So at home she chooses a stable **environment** in a warm place, away from drafts. Here, she sets up a cage with dishes for food and paper for waste removal. Under Mei's care, her bird will have what it needs to live and grow.

To **survive** is to manage to stay alive, especially in difficult situations.

An **organism** is a living thing.

An **environment** is all the surrounding factors that affect the organism's life.

- What does an organism need to survive?

____

____

MY READING WEB If you had trouble completing the question above, visit **My Reading Web** and type in ***Introduction to Animals.***

Vocabulary Skill

Prefixes A prefix is a word part that is added to the beginning of a word to change its meaning. The table below lists prefixes that will help you learn terms used in this chapter.

Prefix	Meaning of Prefix	Example
endo-	inner	endoskeleton, *n.* internal skeleton
exo-	outer	exoskeleton, *n.* outer skeleton

2. **Quick Check Complete the following sentence with the correct terms from the table above.**

- The ____________________ of a crab, which is a tough outer shell, differs from the ____________________ of a cat, which is internal.

Chapter Preview

LESSON 1
- homeostasis • adaptation
- vertebrate • invertebrate
- **Relate Text and Visuals**
- Classify

LESSON 2
- tissue • organ • radial symmetry
- bilateral symmetry
- **Relate Cause and Effect**
- Make Models

LESSON 3
- cnidarian • mollusk
- arthropod • exoskeleton
- echinoderm • endoskeleton
- **Identify the Main Idea**
- Classify

LESSON 4
- chordate • notochord
- vertebra • ectotherm
- endotherm
- **Summarize**
- Draw Conclusions

LESSON 5
- fish • cartilage • amphibian
- reptile • bird • mammal
- mammary gland
- monotreme • marsupial
- placental mammal • placenta
- **Compare and Contrast**
- Interpret Data

LESSON 6
- pheromone • aggression
- territory • courtship behavior
- society • circadian rhythm
- hibernation • migration
- **Identify the Main Idea**
- Communicate

VOCAB FLASH CARDS For extra help with vocabulary, visit **Vocab Flash Cards** and type in ***Introduction to Animals.***

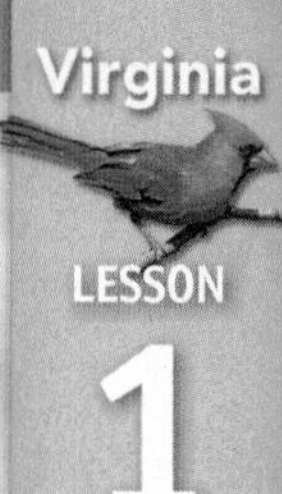

What Is an Animal?

What Are the Functions of Animals?
LS.4b

How Are Animals Classified?
LS.1b, LS.4b, LS.4c

my planet Diary

DISCOVERY

Animal Discoveries

What would a mammal never before seen look like? The answer lies in the mountains of Tanzania, Africa. There, scientists discovered a vertebrate, which is a mammal, in 2005. The animal, which has been named *Rhynochocyon udzungwensis,* is a species of giant elephant shrew. It weighs about 700 grams and measures about 30 centimeters in length, which is just a little longer than this book. This newly discovered mammal is larger than other elephant shrews, and it has its own distinctive color.

Other animals have also been discovered in the mountains of Tanzania. Unknown amphibians and reptiles have been discovered there as well. Each discovery reveals more of the diversity of the animals living on Earth.

Read the following question. Then write your answer below.

Do you think it is important to protect areas such as these mountains? Why?

PLANET DIARY Go to **Planet Diary** to learn more about animals.

Do the Inquiry Warm-Up *Is It an Animal?*

Science Standards of Learning

LS.4b Investigate and understand distinguishing characteristics of kingdoms of organisms.

What Are the Functions of Animals?

Like plants, animals live almost everywhere on Earth. Animals may have scales, feathers, shells, or fins. They may be brightly colored or completely see-through. Some animals do not have limbs. Others have too many limbs to count. You may wonder if animals have anything in common. Well, they do.

Vocabulary
- homeostasis
- adaptation
- vertebrate
- invertebrate

Skills
- Reading: Relate Text and Visuals
- Inquiry: Classify

Functions All animals are multicellular organisms that feed on other organisms and perform the same basic functions. The main functions of an animal are to obtain food and oxygen, keep internal conditions stable, move in some way, and reproduce. Keeping internal body conditions stable is called **homeostasis** (hoh mee oh stay sis).

Adaptations Structures and behaviors that allow animals to perform their functions are called **adaptations.** Teeth and limbs are adaptations that allow animals to obtain food and move. The pouch of a kangaroo is an adaptation for reproduction.

Relate Text and Visuals Match each animal to the function(s) it is performing.

Obtaining Food ______
Animals eat other organisms and raw materials for energy and for growth.

Reproducing ______
Animals make new individuals like themselves.

Moving ______
Animals move to perform other functions as well.

A

B

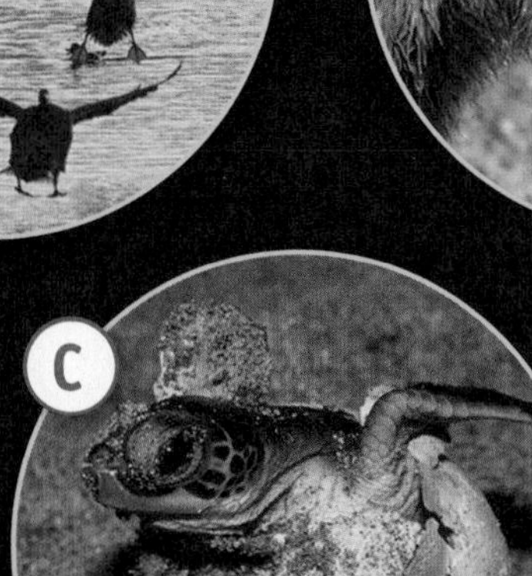

C

D

Do the Quick Lab *Get Moving.*

Assess Your Understanding

got it?

○ **I get it!** Now I know that the functions of animals are ______________________

○ I need extra help with ______________________

Go to **MY SCIENCE COACH** *online for help with this subject.*

LS.1b Develop classification system based on multiple attributes.

LS.4b Investigate and understand distinguishing characteristics of kingdoms of organisms.

LS.4c Investigate and understand distinguishing characteristics of major animal phyla and plant divisions.

How Are Animals Classified?

There are more than 1.6 million species of animals, and more are discovered each year. So far, biologists have classified animals into about 35 major groups. In **Figure 1,** you can see some of the major groups. Notice how the groups are arranged on branches. Animal groups on nearby branches are more closely related than groups on branches farther apart. For example, birds are more closely related to reptiles than they are to mammals.

Animals are classified according to how they are related to other animals. These relationships are determined by an animal's body structure, the way the animal develops, and its DNA. DNA is a chemical in cells that controls an organism's inherited characteristics.

All animals are either vertebrates or invertebrates. **Vertebrates** are animals with a backbone. **Invertebrates** are animals without a backbone.

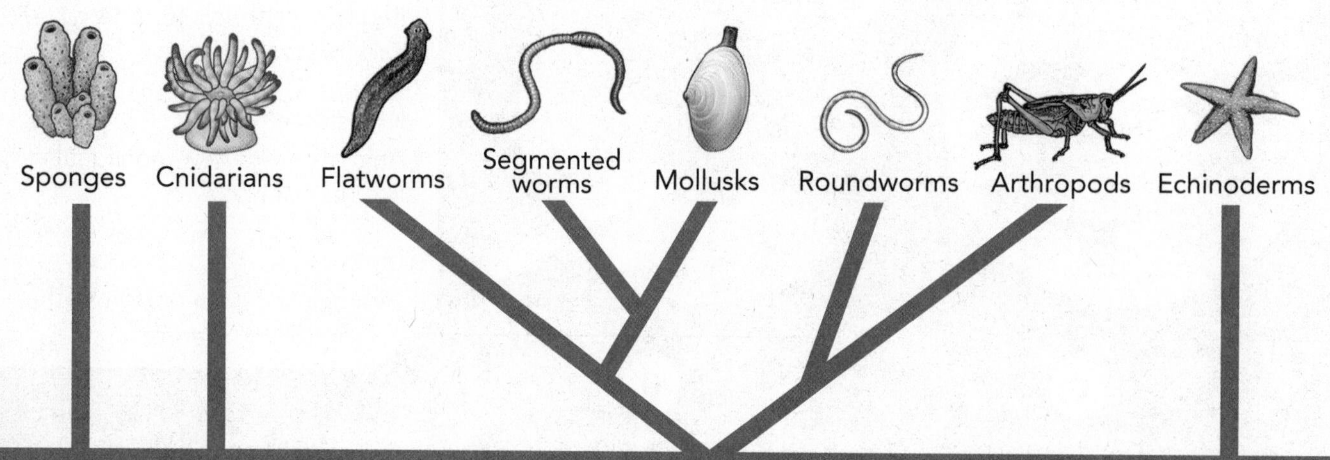

FIGURE 1

VIRTUAL LAB **Major Animal Groups**

Complete these tasks.

1. **Interpret Diagrams** Are flatworms more closely related to segmented worms or to roundworms? Circle your answer on the diagram.
2. CHALLENGE What do you think the bird branch coming off of the reptile branch indicates?

____

____

____

apply it!

Use the information in **Figure 1** to help you classify the animals at the right.

1 Classify Write the name of each animal's group in the box provided.

2 Identify Which animals are vertebrates? Which animals are invertebrates?

____

____

____

____

____

Fishes

Amphibians

Reptiles

Birds

Mammals

Vertebrates

Do the Quick Lab *Classifying Animals.*

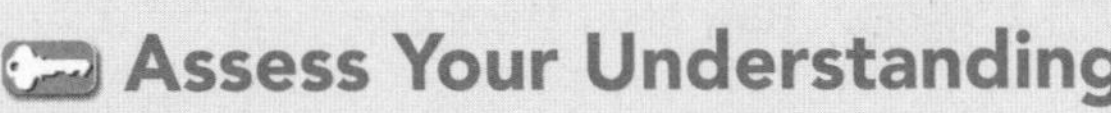

Assess Your Understanding

1a. Define What is a vertebrate?

____

____

b. Compare and Contrast How are vertebrates and invertebrates alike? How do they differ?

____

____

got it?

O **I get it!** Now I know that animals are classified based on ______________________________

____

O I need extra help with ______________________________

Go to **MY SCIENCE COACH** *online for help with this subject.*

Animal Body Plans

How Are Animal Bodies Organized?
LS.3a, LS.3b, LS.4b

How Is Symmetry Related to Body Structure?
LS.1b, LS.1d, LS.1j, LS.3b, LS.4b

my planet Diary

DISCOVERY

Spiny Sea Animals

What animal do you think of when you hear the word *spiny*? You might think of a porcupine, but sea urchins are spiny, too. These small, colorful creatures live in the ocean. Just by looking at them, you can't tell that studying sea urchins would lead to a major discovery about how animals reproduce.

In 1875, biologist Oskar Hertwig was studying a transparent egg of a sea urchin under a microscope. He saw a sperm, the male sex cell, enter the egg, the female sex cell, and fuse with the nucleus of the egg. He had discovered how sexual reproduction occurs.

Answer the question below.

How do you think a sea urchin's transparent egg was important to the discovery of how sexual reproduction occurs?

____

____

____

____

____

PLANET DIARY Go to **Planet Diary** to learn more about animal body plans.

Lab zone® Do the Inquiry Warm-Up *How Many Ways Can You Fold It?*.

LS.3a Investigate and understand cells, tissues, organs, and systems.

LS.3b Investigate and understand patterns of cellular organization and their relationship to life processes in living things.

LS.4b Investigate and understand distinguishing characteristics of kingdoms of organisms.

How Are Animal Bodies Organized?

Animals are diverse organisms. But the animals within each phylum have uniquely organized body structures. This organization is called a body plan. **The organization of an animal's cells into higher levels of structure, including tissues, organs, and organ systems, helps to describe an animal's body plan.**

Vocabulary
- tissue
- organ
- radial symmetry
- bilateral symmetry

Skills
- Reading: Relate Cause and Effect
- Inquiry: Make Models

Cells and Tissues

All animals are made up of many cells. Their cells are usually specialized and organized as tissues. A **tissue** is a group of similar cells that performs a specific function. Muscle tissue, nervous tissue, and connective tissue are all animal tissues. Bone and blood are examples of kinds of connective tissues.

Organs and Organ Systems

In most animals, tissues combine to form organs and organ systems. An **organ** is made up of different tissues. For example, the leg bone of a frog shown in **Figure 1** is an organ composed of bone tissue, nervous tissue, and blood. An organ performs more complex functions than the tissues that make it up could perform alone. Groups of organs make up organ systems. These systems perform the animal's broadest functions.

FIGURE 1

A Skeletal System's Organization

Different levels of organization are found in a frog's skeleton.

Describe **Tell what makes up each level of organization in this frog's skeletal system.**

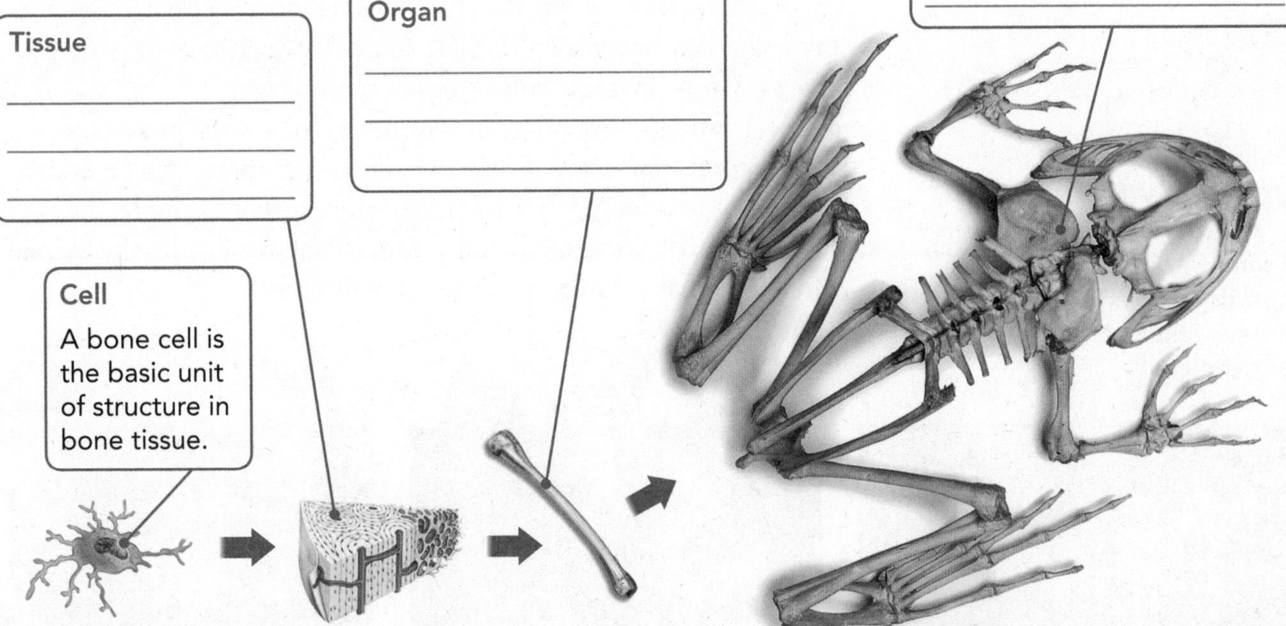

Lab zone® Do the Quick Lab *Organizing Animal Bodies.*

Assess Your Understanding

got it?

○ **I get it!** Now I know that animal bodies are organized into ________________

○ I need extra help with ________________

Go to my science COACH *online for help with this subject.*

Science Standards of Learning

LS.1b Develop classification system based on multiple attributes.

LS.1d Construct and use models and simulations to illustrate and explain phenomena.

LS.1j Use current applications to reinforce life science concepts.

LS.3b Investigate and understand patterns of cellular organization and their relationship to life processes in living things.

LS.4b Investigate and understand distinguishing characteristics of kingdoms of organisms.

How Is Symmetry Related to Body Structure?

Have you ever noticed a butterfly perched on a flower? You probably saw its colors and wing patterns. Did you also see that the pattern on the left side is a mirror image of the pattern on the right side? Many organisms and objects have this balanced display of body parts called symmetry.

A butterfly with bilateral symmetry

Types of Symmetry Animals have different types of symmetry, as you can see in **Figure 2.** Some animals have no symmetry, or are asymmetrical. For example, most sponges are asymmetrical. However, most animals have either radial symmetry or bilateral symmetry.

An animal has **radial symmetry** if many imaginary lines can be drawn through a central point to divide it into two mirror images. For example, from above, the shape of a jellyfish is circular. So any imaginary line drawn through its center divides it into mirror images. These lines are called lines of symmetry.

Most animals have bilateral symmetry. An animal or an object has **bilateral symmetry** if only one line of symmetry can be drawn to divide it into halves that are mirror images. For example, the dashed line you see drawn on the butterfly above divides the animal into halves that are mirror images of each other.

FIGURE 2

Types of Symmetry

 **Identify** Write the type of symmetry each animal has. Then draw lines of symmetry on each animal to support your choice.

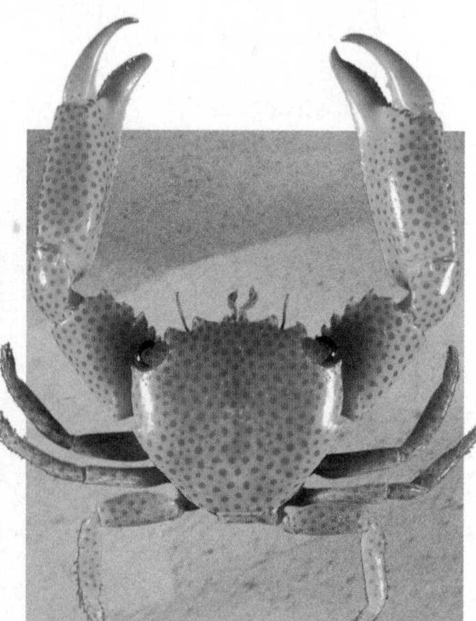

Symmetry and Body Structure The structures of animals are related to their symmetry. **The bodies of animals without symmetry are organized simply, with some specialized cells but no tissues. In contrast, animals with radial symmetry have complex body plans with tissues and usually with organ systems. Animals with bilateral symmetry have organ systems.**

Relate Cause and Effect In the second paragraph, underline an effect of having radial symmetry.

Radial Symmetry All animals with radial symmetry live in water. Some creep slowly along the ocean floor. Others stay in one spot as adults. A few can move quickly. Most animals with radial symmetry do not have front or back ends. Also, they do not have heads with specialized sense organs. This kind of symmetry allows them to take in information about their surroundings from all directions. This is an advantage for animals that usually move slowly.

apply it!

Many objects you see have symmetry, but some do not.

1. **Interpret Photos** Under each picture, write the type of symmetry shown by the object.
2. **Explain** Draw lines of symmetry on each object to support your choice.
3. **Make Models** Draw a common object not pictured here that has radial symmetry. Draw lines of symmetry to support your choice.

CHALLENGE Why is it an advantage for an animal to have its head be the first part of its body to enter a new area?

____

____

____

____

Bilateral Symmetry In general, animals with bilateral symmetry are larger and more complex than animals with radial symmetry. They have complex organ systems that help them function efficiently. Also, most animals with bilateral symmetry have streamlined bodies, which help them move quickly.

Most animals with bilateral symmetry have heads at their front ends. Having a head is important to an animal. Most of an animal's specialized sense organs, such as its eyes, are in its head, as you can see in **Figure 3.** In addition, a concentration of nervous tissue is found in an animal's head. Nervous tissue processes information for the animal and coordinates the animal's responses. In fact, an animal usually moves into a new area with its head first.

FIGURE 3

A Coral Reef

Many animals with bilateral and radial symmetry live in coral reefs.

Compare and Contrast In the Venn diagram, write how a sea star and a fish are alike and how they are different.

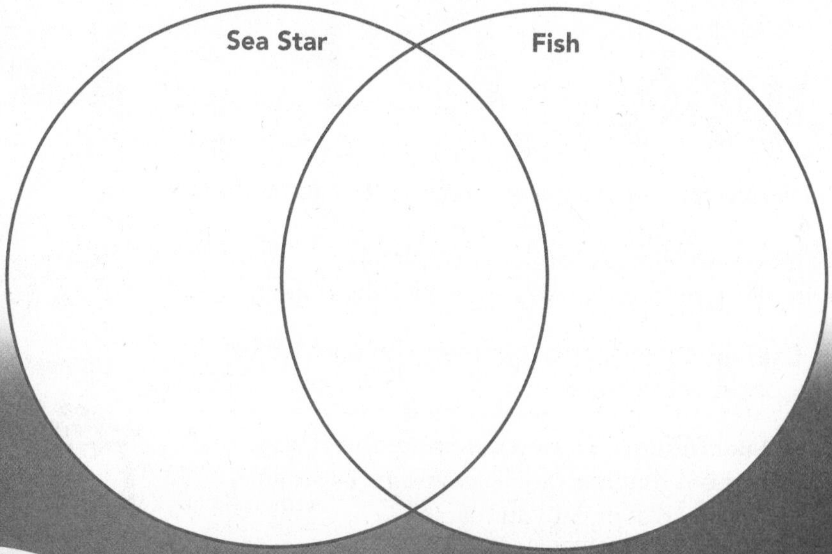

Sea Star

Fish

FIGURE 4

All animals have functions they perform. Most animals have some type of symmetry and an organization that includes organ systems.

Apply Concepts **Answer the questions in the boxes.**

2 What adaptations does this animal have for obtaining food?

1 What are the functions of this animal?

3 How is this animal organized and what type of symmetry does it have?

Lab zone® Do the Quick Lab *Front-End Advantages.*

Assess Your Understanding

1a. Infer Why do you think bilateral symmetry is an advantage for an animal?

b. ANSWER THE BIG Q How do you know an animal when you see it?

got it?

○ **I get it!** Now I know that symmetry relates to body structure because

○ I need extra help with

Go to MY SCIENCE COACH *online for help with this subject.*

Introduction to Invertebrates

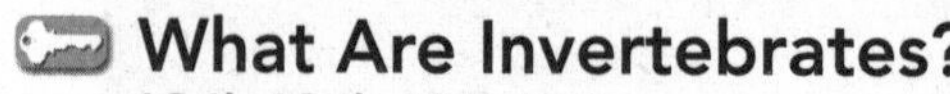

my planet Diary

Ready, Aim, Fire!

To *bombard* is to "attack with materials that explode." This action is exactly what the bombardier beetle does. This incredible insect sprays predators with an explosion of deadly chemicals from its own body!

Why don't the chemicals kill the beetle? The chemicals needed for the spray are stored in different places in the beetle's body. When the beetle defends itself, the chemicals are combined into a deadly mixture. The mixture is sprayed on a predator at a temperature of 100°C!

FUN FACTS

Communicate Discuss the following question with a partner. Then write your answer below.

What other animals do you know about that have unique forms of self defense? Describe their defenses.

___

___

___

PLANET DIARY Go to **Planet Diary** to learn more about invertebrates.

Do the Inquiry Warm-Up *How Do Natural and Synthetic Sponges Compare?*

Science Standards of Learning

LS.1b Develop classification system based on multiple attributes.

LS.1h Organize, graph, and interpret data, and use data to make predictions.

LS.1j Use current applications to reinforce life science concepts.

LS.4c Investigate and understand distinguishing characteristics of major animal phyla and plant divisions.

What Are Invertebrates?

At dusk near the edge of a meadow, a grasshopper leaps through the grass. Nearby, a hungry spider waits in its web. The grasshopper leaps into the web. It's caught! The spider bites the grasshopper to stun it and quickly wraps it in silk. The grasshopper will soon become a tasty meal for the spider.

Vocabulary
- cnidarian • mollusk • arthropod • exoskeleton
- echinoderm • endoskeleton

Skills
- Reading: Identify the Main Idea
- Inquiry: Classify

Invertebrate Characteristics A grasshopper and a spider are both invertebrates. **Animals that do not have backbones are invertebrates. The main invertebrate groups are sponges, cnidarians, flatworms, roundworms, segmented worms, mollusks, arthropods, and echinoderms.** About 96 percent of known animals are invertebrates. They live in every climate.

Sponges Sponges, such as the one shown in **Figure 1,** are asymmetrical invertebrates. They have some specialized cells but no tissues or organs. Unlike most animals you know, adult sponges stay in one place, like plants. But, like other animals, sponges take food into their bodies to get energy.

Cnidarians Jellyfishes and corals are examples of **cnidarians** (ny DEHR ee unz), invertebrates that have stinging cells and take food into a central body cavity. Cnidarians have radial symmetry. Although they lack organs, they do have some tissues.

FIGURE 1

INTERACTIVE ART **Sponges and Cnidarians**

Both sponges and cnidarians are animals that live in water.

Interpret Photos Based on symmetry, label these animals as sponges or cnidarians. Then write how sponges and cnidarians are alike and different.

Worms If you have ever worked in a garden, you have probably seen some worms. The three major phyla of worms are flatworms, roundworms, and segmented worms, which you can see in **Figure 2.** All worms have bilateral symmetry, with head and tail ends. They also have tissues, organs, and organ systems. Flatworms have flat, soft bodies. Some have eye spots on their heads that detect light. Roundworms look like smooth, thin tubes. They have two body openings: a mouth and an anus. Segmented worms have bodies made up of many linked sections called segments. They are the simplest animals with a brain. Their brains help them detect food and predators.

FIGURE 2

Worms

The three major phyla of worms are flatworms, roundworms, and segmented worms.

Classify In the boxes, write the phylum of each worm. Then write notes that describe each worm.

Phylum: ____________

Hookworm

Phylum: ____________

Earthworm

Planarian

Phylum: ____________

Mollusks Have you ever picked up seashells on the beach? Those seashells probably belonged to a mollusk. Invertebrates with soft, unsegmented bodies that are often protected by a hard shell are called **mollusks.** All mollusks have a thin layer of tissue called a mantle that covers their internal organs and an organ called a foot. Depending on the type of mollusk, the foot might be used for crawling, digging, or catching prey. **Figure 3** shows some mollusks.

The three major groups of mollusks are gastropods, bivalves, and cephalopods (SEF uh luh pahdz). Gastropods, such as snails, have a single shell or no shell, and a distinct head. Bivalves, such as clams, have two shells and a simple nervous system. Cephalopods may have an external or internal shell or no shell at all. They have good vision and large brains to help them remember what they've learned. A squid is a cephalopod with an internal shell.

Identify the Main Idea Underline the main idea in the second paragraph. Then circle the supporting details.

FIGURE 3

Mollusks

A snail, clam, and squid do not look alike, but they have the same basic structure.

Summarize Fill in each box in the chart for each organism. Then write a title for the chart.

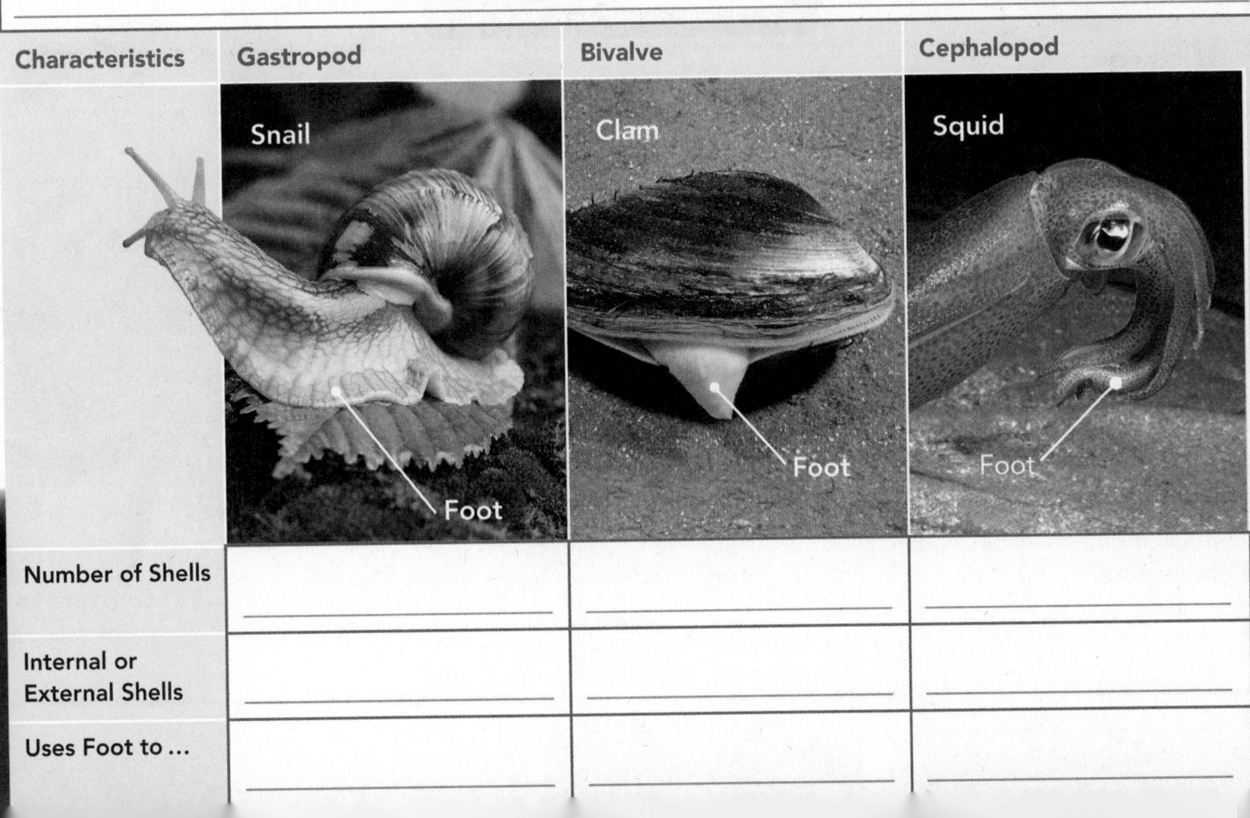

Characteristics	Gastropod	Bivalve	Cephalopod
Number of Shells			
Internal or External Shells			
Uses Foot to ...			

Smaller than a paper clip, honeybees are important insects. They collect nectar from flowers to make honey and pollinate some plants. Without the honey bee, an apple tree might not produce the apples you eat.

Arthropods At first you may not think that a crab and a spider have anything in common. But look at the spider and crab in **Figure 4.** Crabs and spiders are **arthropods,** or invertebrates that have hard outer coverings, segmented bodies, and pairs of jointed appendages. Legs, wings, and antennae are appendages. The outer covering is called an **exoskeleton,** or outer skeleton. At times, the exoskeleton is shed and replaced as the animal grows. One arthropod group, crustaceans, includes animals such as crabs. A second group, arachnids, includes animals such as spiders. A third group includes centipedes, millipedes, and insects, such as bees and ants.

do the math! Analyzing Data

This circle graph shows a distribution of animal groups.

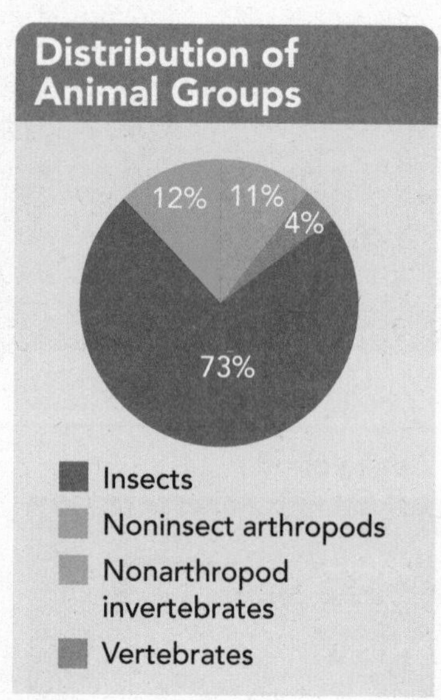

❶ **Read Graphs** What percentage of animals are not insects?

____

❷ CHALLENGE What percentage of animals are invertebrates that are not insects?

____

____

____

Arachnid

Insect

Crustacean

FIGURE 4

Arthropods

Members of the three arthropod groups have different characteristics.

Observe Tell how the number of pairs of legs of a spider and a bee differ.

____

____

____

____

____

Echinoderms An **echinoderm** is an invertebrate that has an internal skeleton and a system of fluid-filled tubes. An internal skeleton is called an **endoskeleton.** Echinoderms, shown in **Figure 5,** have radial symmetry. They use their system of tubes to move and obtain food and oxygen. Sea cucumbers, sea stars, sea urchins, and brittle stars are the major echinoderm groups.

Sea cucumber

Sea star

Sea urchins

Brittle stars

FIGURE 5

ART IN MOTION **Echinoderms**

Echinoderms are diverse animals, but all live in salt water.

Compare and Contrast In the chart, write a brief description of the shape and symmetry of each echinoderm.

	Sea Cucumber	Sea Star	Sea Urchin	Brittle Star
Shape				
Symmetry				

Lab zone® Do the Lab Investigation *Earthworm Responses.*

Assess Your Understanding

1a. Identify How are all cnidarians alike?

b. Explain If you saw a worm, how would you identify its phylum?

got it?

O **I get it!** Now I know that invertebrates

O I need extra help with

Go to MY SCIENCE COACH *online for help with this subject.*

Introduction to Vertebrates

What Are the Characteristics of Chordates and Vertebrates?
LS.4c

How Do Vertebrates Control Body Temperature?
LS.1b, LS.4c

my planet Diary

FUN FACTS

BRRRR! It's Freezing!

How can anything survive in Antarctica, the coldest and windiest place on Earth? Emperor penguins have many physical characteristics that help them live there. For example, they have a layer of fat that helps them stay warm. They also have short, stiff feathers that help to insulate and protect them from the freezing air.

However, the penguins' physical characteristics are not enough to stay warm in Antarctica during the winter. Emperor penguins cooperate to keep warm. They huddle together in groups and take turns standing on the outside of the huddle where it is the coldest. This way, every penguin gets a chance to stand in the middle of the huddle where it is the warmest. Now that's teamwork!

Read the following questions. Then write your answers below.

1. Why don't emperor penguins freeze to death in Antarctica?

____

2. What are other ways you know about that animals use to stay warm?

____

PLANET DIARY Go to **Planet Diary** to learn more about vertebrates.

Do the Inquiry Warm-Up *How Is an Umbrella Like a Skeleton?*

Vocabulary
- chordate
- notochord
- vertebra
- ectotherm
- endotherm

Skills
- Reading: Summarize
- Inquiry: Draw Conclusions

What Are the Characteristics of Chordates and Vertebrates?

The animals you are probably most familiar with are members of the phylum Chordata. Members of this phylum are called chordates (KAWR dayts). Most chordates, including all fishes, amphibians, reptiles, birds, and mammals, are vertebrates. A few chordates, such as sea squirts and lancelets, do not have backbones.

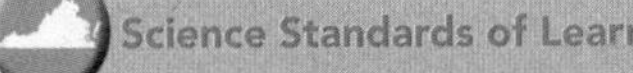

Science Standards of Learning

LS.4c Investigate and understand distinguishing characteristics of major animal phyla and plant divisions.

Chordate Characteristics

At some point in their lives, all chordates have three characteristics: a notochord, a nerve cord, and pouches in the throat area. Most chordates also have a backbone.

Notochord A **notochord** is a flexible rod that supports a chordate's back. The name *Chordata* comes from this structure's name.

Nerve Cord All chordates have a nerve cord that runs down their back. Your spinal cord is such a nerve cord. The nerve cord connects the brain to nerves in other parts of the body.

Throat Pouches At some point in their lives, chordates have pouches in their throat area. In fishes and lancelets, like the one shown in **Figure 1,** grooves between these pouches become gill slits. In most other vertebrates, the pouches disappear before birth.

FIGURE 1

Chordates

Lancelets show the three characteristics shared by all chordates at some point in their lives.

Relate Text and Visuals
Circle the labels of the three chordate characteristics. Then explain how a lancelet is different from a fish.

____

____

____

____

____

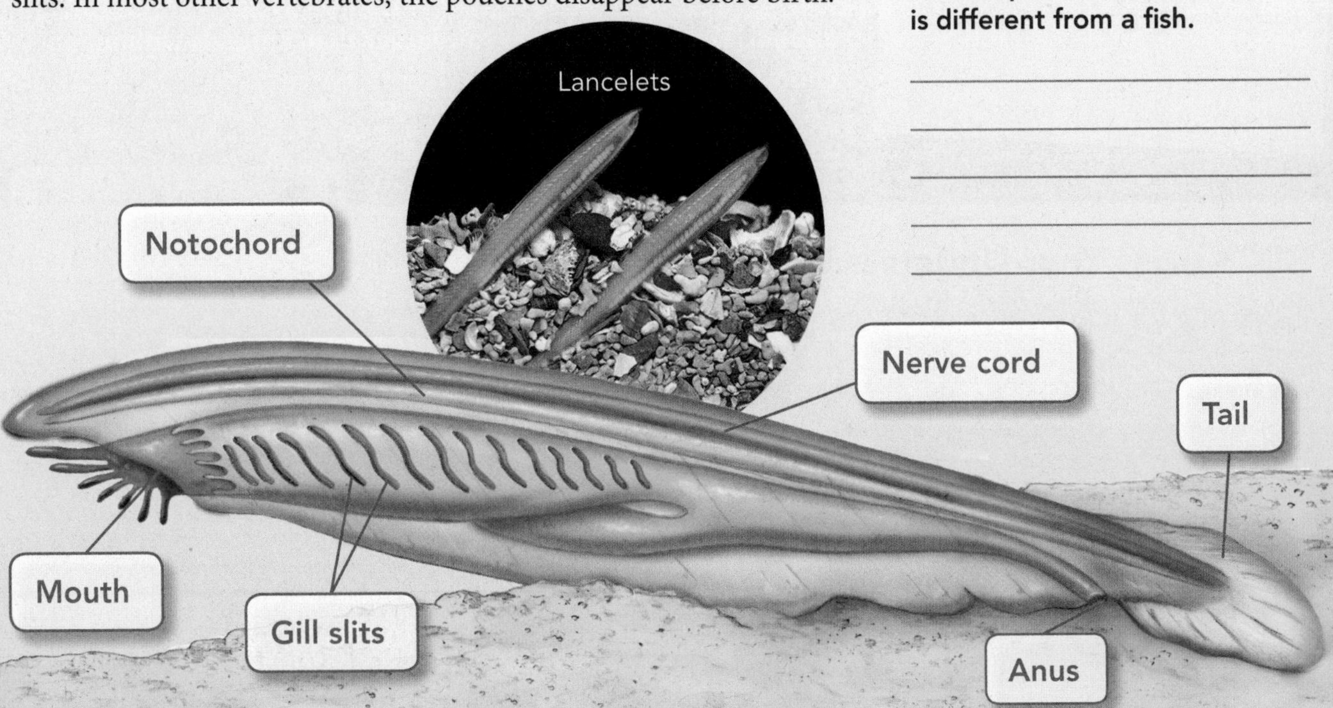

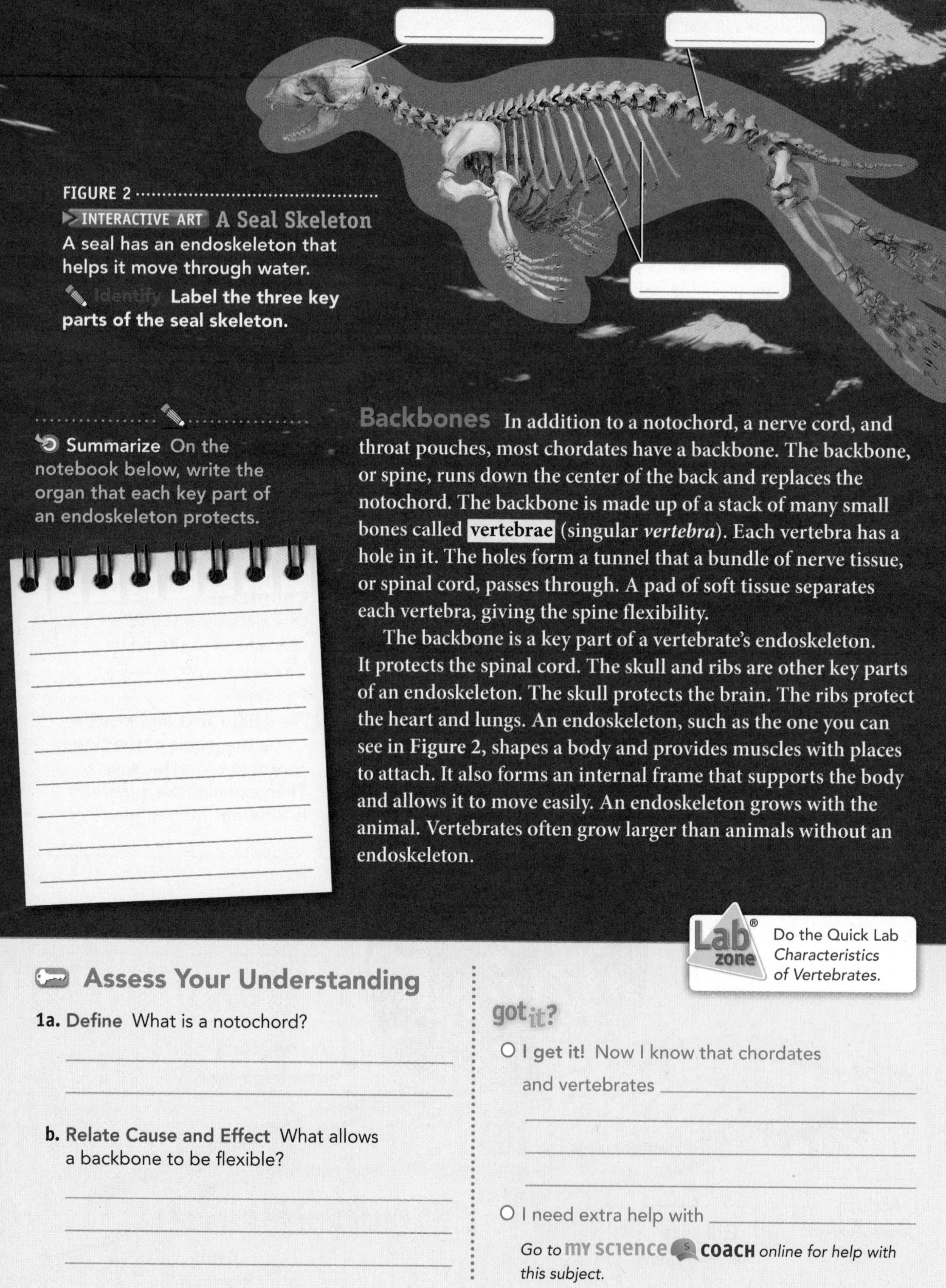

FIGURE 2

INTERACTIVE ART **A Seal Skeleton**

A seal has an endoskeleton that helps it move through water.

Identify **Label the three key parts of the seal skeleton.**

Summarize On the notebook below, write the organ that each key part of an endoskeleton protects.

Backbones In addition to a notochord, a nerve cord, and throat pouches, most chordates have a backbone. The backbone, or spine, runs down the center of the back and replaces the notochord. The backbone is made up of a stack of many small bones called **vertebrae** (singular *vertebra*). Each vertebra has a hole in it. The holes form a tunnel that a bundle of nerve tissue, or spinal cord, passes through. A pad of soft tissue separates each vertebra, giving the spine flexibility.

The backbone is a key part of a vertebrate's endoskeleton. It protects the spinal cord. The skull and ribs are other key parts of an endoskeleton. The skull protects the brain. The ribs protect the heart and lungs. An endoskeleton, such as the one you can see in **Figure 2**, shapes a body and provides muscles with places to attach. It also forms an internal frame that supports the body and allows it to move easily. An endoskeleton grows with the animal. Vertebrates often grow larger than animals without an endoskeleton.

Lab zone® Do the Quick Lab *Characteristics of Vertebrates.*

Assess Your Understanding

1a. Define What is a notochord?

b. Relate Cause and Effect What allows a backbone to be flexible?

got it?

○ **I get it!** Now I know that chordates and vertebrates

○ I need extra help with

Go to MY SCIENCE COACH *online for help with this subject.*

How Do Vertebrates Control Body Temperature?

The major groups of vertebrates differ in how they control body temperature. **Some vertebrates do not produce much internal heat. Therefore, their body temperatures change with the environment. Other vertebrates control their internal heat and maintain a constant body temperature.**

Amphibians, reptiles, and most fishes are ectotherms. An animal that produces little internal body heat is called an **ectotherm.** Its body temperature changes with temperature changes in its environment.

Birds and mammals are endotherms. An **endotherm** is an animal that controls the internal heat it produces and regulates its own temperature. An endotherm's body temperature is always fairly constant. Endotherms have adaptations such as sweat glands, fur, and feathers for maintaining body temperature.

Science Standards of Learning

LS.1b Develop classification system based on multiple attributes.

LS.4c Investigate and understand distinguishing characteristics of major animal phyla and plant divisions.

Vocabulary Prefixes The prefix *ecto-* means "outside." What do you think the prefix *endo-* means?

____

apply it!

Animals control body temperature in different ways.

1 **Draw Conclusions** Write whether you think each animal is an endotherm or ectotherm.

2 **CHALLENGE** Would it be more difficult for a penguin to live in a desert or a snake to live in a polar region? Explain.

____

Lab zone® Do the Quick Lab *Keeping Warm.*

Assess Your Understanding

got it?

O **I get it!** Now I know that vertebrates' body temperature ______________________

O I need extra help with ______________________

Go to **MY SCIENCE COACH** *online for help with this subject.*

Vertebrate Diversity

What Are the Major Groups of Vertebrates?
LS.1b, LS.4c

my planet Diary

FUN FACTS

Sending Messages

Have you ever felt like stomping your feet to show your frustration? People aren't the only ones who stomp their feet to express themselves. Researchers think that elephants communicate by stomping. For example, they think elephants stomp their feet to greet one another and send warnings.

What if an animal has no feet to stomp? It can sing! Many species of whales communicate with one another through song. They make different sounds to communicate different messages. Who knows what else researchers will discover about animal communication!

Communicate Discuss the following question with a partner. Then write your answers below.

What are three ways you communicate with others without using words?

PLANET DIARY Go to **Planet Diary** to learn more about vertebrate diversity.

Lab zone® Do the Inquiry Warm-Up *Exploring Vertebrates.*

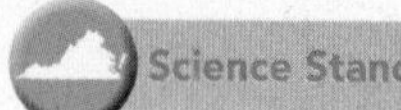

Science Standards of Learning

LS.1b Develop classification system based on multiple attributes.

LS.4c Investigate and understand distinguishing characteristics of major animal phyla and plant divisions.

What Are the Major Groups of Vertebrates?

Vertebrates, like all other animals, are diverse. They live in almost all types of environments on Earth and vary in shape, size, and color. **There are five major groups of vertebrates. They are fishes, amphibians, reptiles, birds, and mammals.** Members of each group share certain characteristics.

Vocabulary

- fish • cartilage • amphibian • reptile • bird
- mammal • mammary gland • monotreme • marsupial
- placental mammal • placenta

Skills

- Reading: Compare and Contrast
- Inquiry: Interpret Data

Fishes A **fish** is a vertebrate that lives in water and uses fins to move. Most fishes are ectotherms. They have scales and obtain oxygen through gills. They make up the largest group of vertebrates. Based on certain characteristics, fishes are organized into three major groups, which are shown in **Figure 1.**

Jawless fishes have no jaws or scales. They scrape, suck, and stab their food. Their skeletons are made of **cartilage,** a tissue more flexible than bone. Fish with jaws, scales, and skeletons made of cartilage are cartilaginous fishes (kahr tuh LAJ uh nuhs). Bony fishes have jaws, scales, and a pocket on each side of the head that holds the gills. Their skeletons are made of hard bone.

FIGURE 1

Types of Fishes

The three groups of fishes are jawless fishes, cartilaginous fishes, and bony fishes.

Summarize **Write on the notebook the characteristics of each group of fishes.**

Lamprey

Lamprey's mouth

Jawless fish

Gray reef shark

Cartilaginous fish

Bony fish

Goldfish

Gill pocket

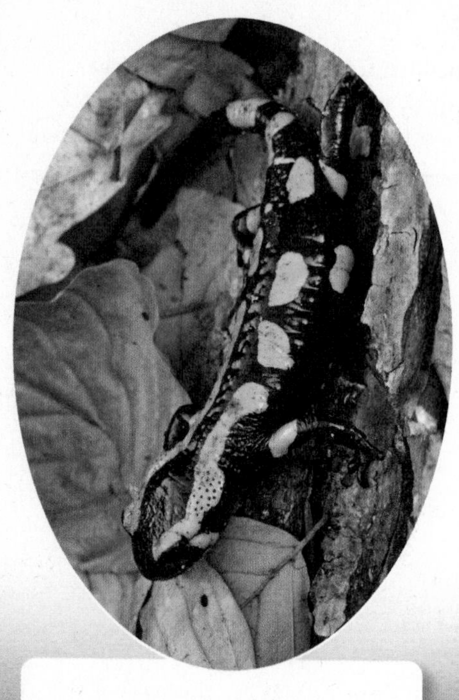

Amphibians You may know that some amphibians such as frogs can be noisy neighbors. Frogs, toads, and salamanders are examples of amphibians. An **amphibian** is a vertebrate that is ectothermic and spends its early life in water and its adult life on land. In fact, the word *amphibian* means "double life." Most amphibians spend their adult lives on land. But they return to water to lay eggs and reproduce. Look at the amphibians in **Figure 2.**

FIGURE 2

Amphibian Diversity

Adult salamanders have tails, but almost all adult frogs and toads do not.

Interpret Photos Label each type of amphibian. Explain the evidence in each picture that helped you decide.

do the math!

Vertebrate Diversity

The table shows the estimated number of species in each vertebrate group. Use the table to answer the questions.

1 Calculate About how many vertebrate species are there in all?

2 Interpret Data Which group has the greatest number of species? The least?

Estimated Number of Species of Vertebrates

Vertebrate Group	Number of Species
Fishes	30,700
Amphibians	6,347
Reptiles	8,734
Birds	9,990
Mammals	5,488

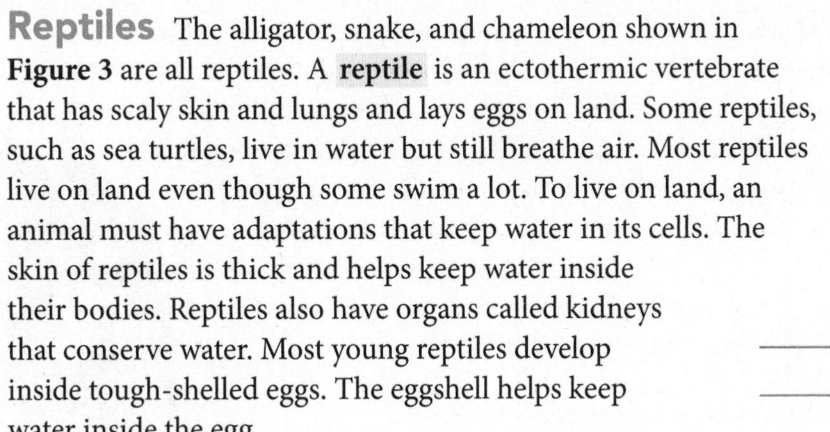

Reptiles The alligator, snake, and chameleon shown in **Figure 3** are all reptiles. A **reptile** is an ectothermic vertebrate that has scaly skin and lungs and lays eggs on land. Some reptiles, such as sea turtles, live in water but still breathe air. Most reptiles live on land even though some swim a lot. To live on land, an animal must have adaptations that keep water in its cells. The skin of reptiles is thick and helps keep water inside their bodies. Reptiles also have organs called kidneys that conserve water. Most young reptiles develop inside tough-shelled eggs. The eggshell helps keep water inside the egg.

Chameleon

FIGURE 3

Reptile Diversity

Reptiles are adapted to life on land.

 **Complete these tasks.**

1. **Draw Conclusions** In each box, describe how you know that the animal is a reptile.
2. CHALLENGE Explain how a shell keeps water inside an egg.

Snake

Alligator

This ibis wades through water with its tall, thin legs. It uses its long bill to find small prey.

Birds If you have ever watched birds at a feeder, you know how fascinating they are. A **bird** is an endothermic vertebrate that lays eggs and has feathers and a four-chambered heart. Birds are adapted for flight. They have wings and lightweight, nearly hollow bones. Shown in **Figure 4,** birds are the only modern animals with feathers.

FIGURE 4

Birds

Different adaptations allow birds to live in different environments.

Make Generalizations In each box, underline adaptations the bird has that help it survive. Then explain how you think feathers help birds survive.

____

This rainbow bee-eater uses its pointed bill to feed on bees and other insects, which it catches as it flies.

Sharp vision and keen hearing help owls like this tawny owl hunt at night. They use razor-sharp claws to grab prey.

Compare and Contrast In the Venn diagram, list how reptiles and birds are alike and different.

Birds | Reptiles

Mammals There are three main groups of mammals. **Mammals** are endothermic vertebrates that have skin covered with fur or hair, and a four-chambered heart. The young are fed with milk produced by organs, called **mammary glands,** in the mother's body.

The mammal groups differ in how their young develop. **Monotremes** lay eggs. **Marsupials** are born at an early stage of development, and they usually continue to develop in a pouch on the mother's body. A **placental mammal** develops inside its mother's body until its body systems can function independently. Materials are exchanged between the mother and the embryo through an organ called the **placenta.**

FIGURE 5

Mammals

The main groups of mammals are monotremes, marsupials, and placental mammals.

Review In each box, write a note about how the young of the group develops.

Placental Mammal

______

Marsupial

______

Monotreme

______

Lab zone® Do the Quick Lab *It's Plane to See.*

Assess Your Understanding

1a. Name Name the three groups of fishes.

______

b. Relate Cause and Effect Why can mammals live in colder environments than reptiles?

______

got it?

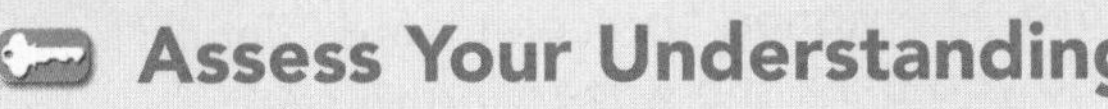

O **I get it!** Now I know that the major groups of vertebrates are ______

O I need extra help with ______

Go to MY SCIENCE COACH *online for help with this subject.*

Virginia

LESSON 6

Patterns of Behavior

UNLOCK THE BIG Q

What Are Three Ways That Animals Communicate?
LS.7a, LS.7b

What Are Examples of Competitive and Cooperative Behaviors?
LS.7a, LS.7b, LS.10b

What Is Cyclic Behavior?
LS.10a, LS.10b

MY PLANET DIARY

FUN FACTS

Do You Speak Gorilla?

Animals communicate in many ways, but they don't usually say things like, "My tooth hurts." That's more or less what Koko the gorilla said in 2004, when she needed to go to the dentist. Koko uses hand signals, based on American Sign Language, to communicate with humans.

Koko was born in 1971 at the San Francisco Zoo. When she was just one year old, she began to learn how to sign words, working with Dr. Francine Patterson. Through signs, Koko has shown emotion, creativity, and intelligence. Koko can make around 1,000 signs. She can also understand around 2,000 spoken words—but she herself can't speak. Gorillas can make noises, but they don't have the mouth structures necessary to form spoken words.

Read the text and then answer the questions below.

1. Once, Koko was trying to describe an object but did not know the word. She signed "bracelet" and "finger" together. What do you think she was trying to say?

____

2. If you could talk to Koko, what would you ask her?

____

____

____

Lab zone® Do the Inquiry Warm-Up *Communicating Without Words.*

PLANET DIARY Go to **Planet Diary** to learn more about patterns of behavior.

Vocabulary

- pheromone • aggression • territory
- courtship behavior • society • circadian rhythm
- hibernation • migration

Skills

- Reading: Identify the Main Idea
- Inquiry: Communicate

What Are Three Ways That Animals Communicate?

Science Standards of Learning

LS.7a Investigate and understand competition, cooperation, social hierarchy, and territorial imperative.

LS.7b Investigate and understand influence of behavior on a population.

Animal communication comes in many forms. Perhaps you've seen a cat hissing and arching its back. It is using sound and body posture to send a message that says, "Back off!" **Animals use sounds, scents, and body movements to communicate with one another.** An animal's ability to communicate helps it interact with other animals. Notice the gecko's body movements in **Figure 1.**

Animals communicate many kinds of messages using sound. Some animals use sound to attract mates. Female crickets, for example, are attracted to the sound of a male's chirping. Animals may also communicate warnings using sound. When a prairie dog sees a coyote or other predator approaching, it makes a yipping sound that warns other prairie dogs to hide in their burrows.

Animals also communicate with chemical scents. A chemical released by one animal that affects the behavior of another animal of the same species is called a **pheromone** (FEHR uh mohn). For example, perhaps you have seen a male house cat spraying a tree. The musky scent he leaves contains pheromones that advertise his presence to other cats in the neighborhood.

FIGURE 1

Body Language

This giant leaf-tailed gecko opens its mouth when it senses danger.

Infer What might the gecko be communicating with its body movement?

Do the Quick Lab *Modeling Animal Communication.*

Assess Your Understanding

got it?

- O **I get it!** Now I know that animals communicate using ______
- O I need extra help with ______

Go to my science coach *online for help with this subject.*

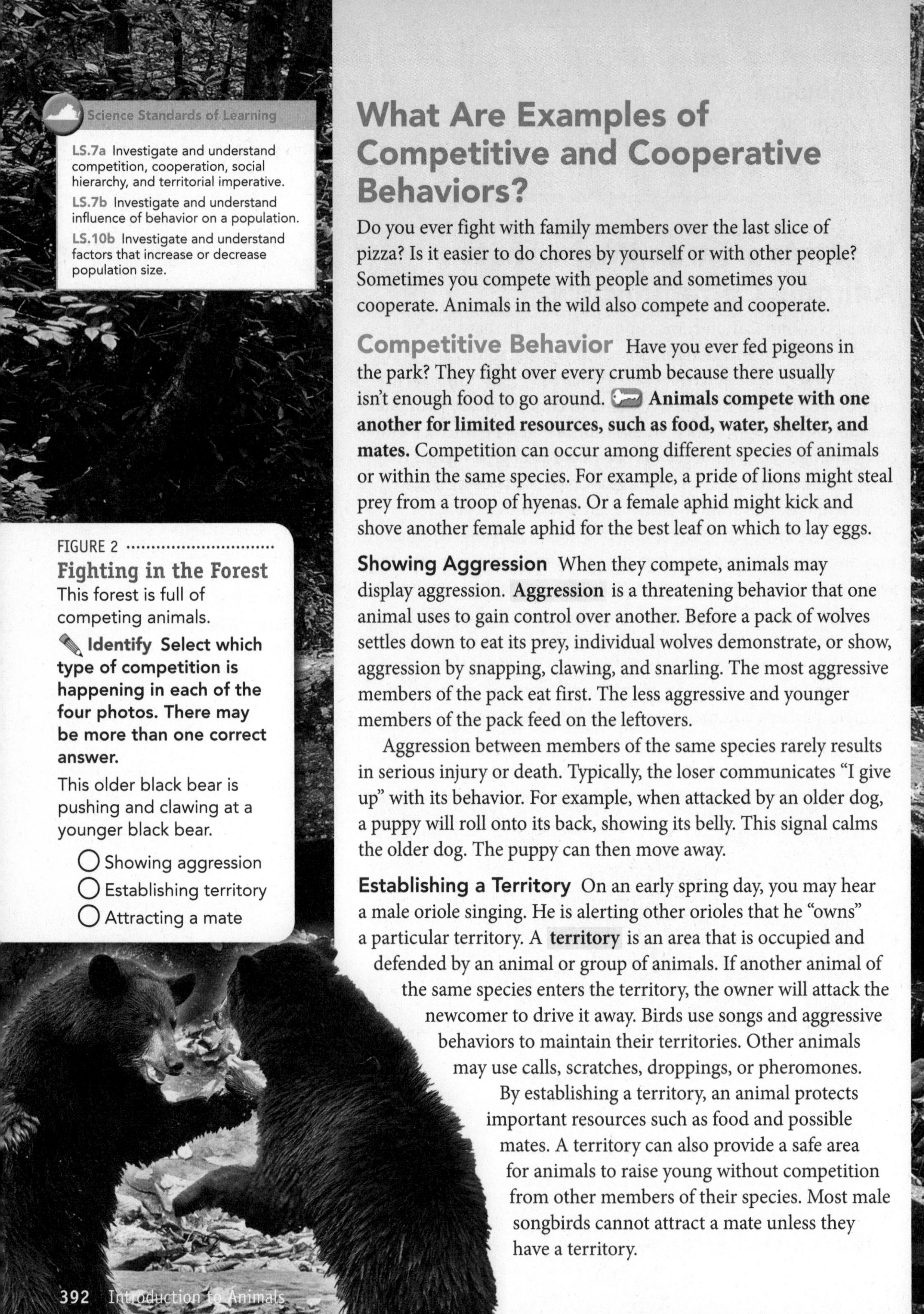

LS.7a Investigate and understand competition, cooperation, social hierarchy, and territorial imperative.
LS.7b Investigate and understand influence of behavior on a population.
LS.10b Investigate and understand factors that increase or decrease population size.

What Are Examples of Competitive and Cooperative Behaviors?

Do you ever fight with family members over the last slice of pizza? Is it easier to do chores by yourself or with other people? Sometimes you compete with people and sometimes you cooperate. Animals in the wild also compete and cooperate.

Competitive Behavior Have you ever fed pigeons in the park? They fight over every crumb because there usually isn't enough food to go around. **Animals compete with one another for limited resources, such as food, water, shelter, and mates.** Competition can occur among different species of animals or within the same species. For example, a pride of lions might steal prey from a troop of hyenas. Or a female aphid might kick and shove another female aphid for the best leaf on which to lay eggs.

Showing Aggression When they compete, animals may display aggression. **Aggression** is a threatening behavior that one animal uses to gain control over another. Before a pack of wolves settles down to eat its prey, individual wolves demonstrate, or show, aggression by snapping, clawing, and snarling. The most aggressive members of the pack eat first. The less aggressive and younger members of the pack feed on the leftovers.

Aggression between members of the same species rarely results in serious injury or death. Typically, the loser communicates "I give up" with its behavior. For example, when attacked by an older dog, a puppy will roll onto its back, showing its belly. This signal calms the older dog. The puppy can then move away.

Establishing a Territory On an early spring day, you may hear a male oriole singing. He is alerting other orioles that he "owns" a particular territory. A **territory** is an area that is occupied and defended by an animal or group of animals. If another animal of the same species enters the territory, the owner will attack the newcomer to drive it away. Birds use songs and aggressive behaviors to maintain their territories. Other animals may use calls, scratches, droppings, or pheromones.

By establishing a territory, an animal protects important resources such as food and possible mates. A territory can also provide a safe area for animals to raise young without competition from other members of their species. Most male songbirds cannot attract a mate unless they have a territory.

FIGURE 2

Fighting in the Forest

This forest is full of competing animals.

Identify Select which type of competition is happening in each of the four photos. There may be more than one correct answer.

This older black bear is pushing and clawing at a younger black bear.

- ○ Showing aggression
- ○ Establishing territory
- ○ Attracting a mate

A blue jay calls loudly from the top of a tree after he sees another blue jay.

- ◯ Showing aggression
- ◯ Establishing territory
- ◯ Attracting a mate

In the space below, explain why you chose your answer.

____

____

____

____

____

This male deer rubs his scent against several trees.

- ◯ Showing aggression
- ◯ Establishing territory
- ◯ Attracting a mate

A male frog inflates his throat to make a loud call. He advertises his location to females.

- ◯ Showing aggression
- ◯ Establishing territory
- ◯ Attracting a mate

Attracting a Mate A male and female salamander swim in the water, gracefully moving around one another. They are engaging in **courtship behavior,** activities that prepare males and females of the same species for mating. Courtship behavior ensures that the males and females of the same species recognize one another, so that mating and reproduction can take place. Courtship behavior is typically also competitive. For example, in some species, several males may perform courtship behaviors for a single female. She then chooses one of them to mate with.

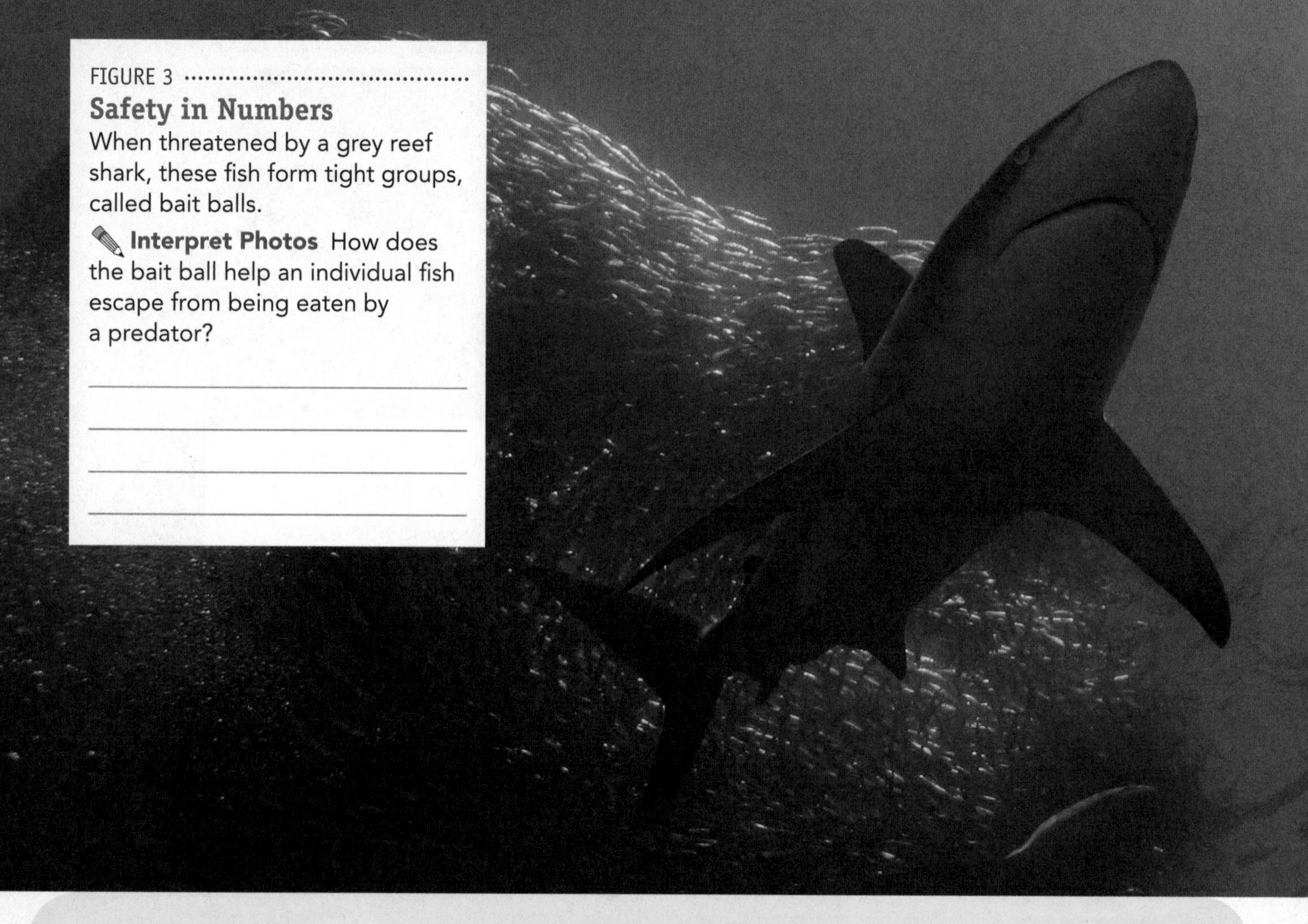

FIGURE 3

Safety in Numbers

When threatened by a grey reef shark, these fish form tight groups, called bait balls.

Interpret Photos How does the bait ball help an individual fish escape from being eaten by a predator?

____

____

____

____

Identify the Main Idea

Living in the wild is hard work! Some animals cooperate in order to survive. In your own words, write three important reasons why animals show cooperative behaviors.

____

____

____

____

____

____

____

____

Cooperative Behavior

Not all animal behaviors are competitive. **Animals living in groups cooperate to survive.** Although many animals live alone and only rarely meet one of their own kind, other animals live in groups. Some fishes form schools, and some insects live in large groups. Hoofed mammals, such as bison and wild horses, often form herds. Living in a group helps some animals stay alive. For example, group members may protect one another or work together to find food.

How can group members help one another? If an elephant gets stuck in a mudhole, for example, other members of its herd will dig it out. When animals such as lions hunt in a group, they can often kill larger prey than a single hunter can.

Safety in Groups

Living in groups often protects animals against predators. Fish that swim in schools, such as the ones in **Figure 3,** are often safer than fish that swim alone. It is harder for predators to see and select an individual fish in a large group.

Animals in a group sometimes cooperate to fight off a predator. For example, North American musk oxen form a defensive circle against a wolf or other predator. Their calves are sheltered in the middle of the circle. The adult musk oxen stand with their horns lowered, ready to charge. The predator often gives up rather than face a whole herd of angry musk oxen.

FIGURE 4

The Hive Is Alive!

A hive may have tens of thousands of worker bees.

Explain **Why do you think a honeybee society has more worker bees than any other type?**

Queen bee

Worker bees

apply it!

Communicate Discuss with your classmates one way that you have cooperated with your friends at school. Then describe how the cooperative behavior helped you.

Animal Societies Some animals, including termites, honeybees, ants, and naked mole rats, live in groups called societies. A **society** is a group of closely related animals of the same species that work together in a highly organized way. In a society, there is a division of labor—different individuals perform different tasks. A honeybee society, for example, has only one egg-laying queen. But there are thousands of worker bees that build, defend, and maintain the hive. Some workers feed larvae. Some bring back nectar and pollen from flowers as food for the hive. Other worker bees guard the entrance to the hive. **Figure 4** shows a honeybee society.

Lab® zone Do the Lab Investigation *One for All.*

Assess Your Understanding

1a. List What are two cooperative behaviors?

b. Explain How are aggression and establishing a territory related?

c. Apply Concepts Male red-winged blackbirds display red patches on their shoulders to defend their territory. What would happen if these red patches were dyed black?

got it?

O **I get it!** Now I know that examples of competitive and cooperative behavior are

O I need extra help with

Go to MY SCIENCE COACH *online for help with this subject.*

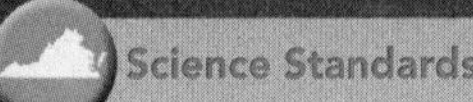

Science Standards of Learning

LS.10a Investigate and understand hibernation and dormancy.

LS.10b Investigate and understand factors that increase or decrease population size.

What Is Cyclic Behavior?

Some animal behaviors, called cyclic behaviors, occur in regular, predictable patterns. **Cyclic behaviors usually change over the course of a day or a season.**

Daily Cycles Behavior cycles that occur over a period of approximately one day are called **circadian rhythms** (sur KAY dee un). For example, blowflies search for food during the day and rest at night. In contrast, field mice are active during the night and rest by day. Animals that are active during the day can take advantage of sunlight, which makes food easy to see. On the other hand, animals that are active at night do not encounter predators that are active during the day.

Hibernation Other behavior cycles are related to seasons. For example, some animals, such as woodchucks and chipmunks, are active during warm seasons but hibernate during the cold winter. **Hibernation** is a state of greatly reduced body activity that occurs during the winter when food is scarce. During hibernation, all of an animal's body processes, such as breathing and heartbeat, slow down. This slowdown reduces the animal's need for food. In fact, hibernating animals do not eat. Their bodies use stored fat to meet their reduced nutrition needs.

Migration While many animals live their lives in one area, others migrate. **Migration** is the regular, seasonal journey of an animal from one place to another and back again. Some animals migrate short distances. Dall's sheep, for example, spend summers near the tops of mountains and move lower down for the winters. Other animals migrate thousands of kilometers. Arctic terns fly more than 17,000 kilometers between the North and South poles.

Animals usually migrate to an area that provides a lot of food or a good environment for reproduction. Most migrations are related to the changing seasons and take place twice a year, in the spring and in the fall. American redstarts, for example, are insect-eating birds that spend the summer in North America. There, they mate and raise young. In the fall, insects become scarce, so the redstarts migrate south to areas where they can find plenty of food.

Scientists have discovered that migrating animals find their way using sight, taste, and other senses, including some that humans do not have. Some birds and sea turtles, for example, have a magnetic sense that acts something like a compass needle. Migrating birds also seem to navigate by using the positions of the sun, moon, and stars. Salmon use scent and taste to locate the streams where they were born, and return there to mate.

did you know?

Every November on Christmas Island, located in the Indian Ocean, about 120 million red crabs migrate from their forest home to breeding grounds on the coast. Sometimes, the crabs must pass through towns to get to the ocean. The people who live on this small island find crabs in the roads, schools, and even their homes!

FIGURE 5

On the Move

The migration route of monarch butterflies is sometimes as long as 3,600 kilometers. In the fall, monarchs fly south from Canada and the United States and spend the winter in the mountains of Mexico.

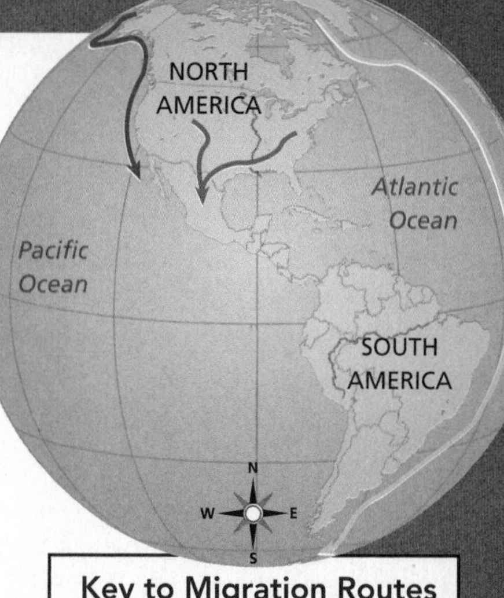

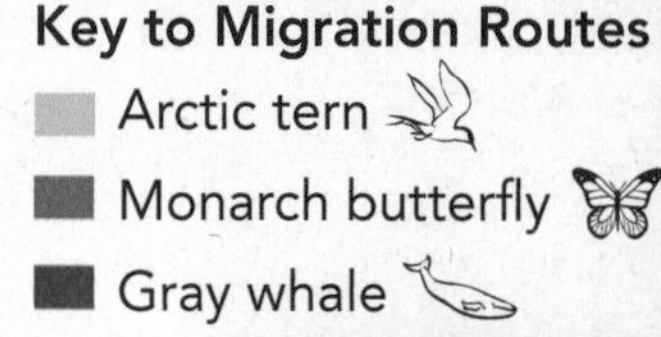

Use the map to answer the following questions.

1. **Interpret Maps** Circle the animal that has a migration route that passes more than one continent. Then, write the name of the animal on the line below.

A.  B.  C.

____

2. CHALLENGE Why do you think gray whales travel to warm, southern waters to give birth to their calves?

____

____

____

____

____

▲ This gray whale and her calf will travel for two to three months to return to their feeding grounds in the north.

Birds of a Feather...

FIGURE 6

REAL-WORLD INQUIRY Black-browed albatrosses live in colonies that can number close to 500,000 birds. Albatrosses behave in ways that enable them to reproduce and successfully raise their chicks.

Interpret Photos Read the descriptions of black-browed albatross reproduction and behavior. Then, answer the questions on the lines provided.

2

Reproduction

This parent albatross is sitting on its egg. Which type of fertilization resulted in this egg?

____

Why would external fertilization be difficult for albatrosses?

____

____

____

1

Courtship Behavior

Albatross courtship behavior involves calling and dancing. Why is it so important that these two albatrosses perform courtship behavior?

____

____

____

____

____

____

____

3 Colony Life

How is this chick able to recognize and take food from its parent?

____

____

____

____

In the photo below, you can see a colony of albatrosses. What type of cooperative behavior are they showing? How does this behavior help them survive?

____

____

____

____

____

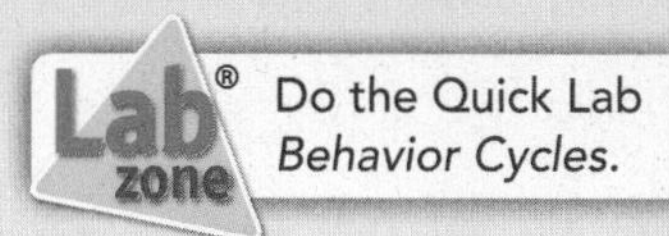

Do the Quick Lab *Behavior Cycles.*

Assess Your Understanding

2a. Review The regular, seasonal journey of an animal from one place to another and back again is called (migration/hibernation).

b. Compare and Contrast How are circadian rhythms and hibernation alike and different?

____

____

____

____

____

c. CHALLENGE Why may building a road through a forest interfere with migration?

____

____

____

d. Predict How does an animal's behavior help it survive and reproduce? Predict how an animal's ability to survive and reproduce also affects the population of its species.

____

____

____

____

____

____

____

____

got it?

○ **I get it!** Now I know that cyclic behaviors ________________

____

____

○ I need extra help with ________________

Go to MY SCIENCE COACH *online for help with this subject.*

CHAPTER 11

Study Guide

I would know an animal by its ______________, ______________________________, and ________________.

LESSON 1 What Is an Animal?

The main functions of an animal are to obtain food and oxygen, keep internal conditions stable, move in some way, and reproduce.

Animals are classified according to how they are related to other animals. These relationships are determined by an animal's body structure, the way the animal develops, and its DNA.

Vocabulary

- homeostasis
- adaptation
- vertebrate
- invertebrate

LESSON 2 Animal Body Plans

The organization of an animal's cells into higher levels of structure helps to describe an animal's body plan.

Animals without symmetry have no tissues. Animals with radial symmetry have tissues and usually have organ systems. Animals with bilateral symmetry have organ systems.

Vocabulary

- tissue
- organ
- radial symmetry
- bilateral symmetry

LESSON 3 Introduction to Invertebrates

Animals that do not have backbones are invertebrates.

Vocabulary

- cnidarian
- mollusk
- arthropod
- exoskeleton
- echinoderm
- endoskeleton

LESSON 4 Introduction to Vertebrates

At some point in their lives, all chordates have three characteristics: a notochord, a nerve cord, and pouches in the throat area.

The body temperatures of some vertebrates change with the environment. Other vertebrates maintain a constant body temperature.

Vocabulary

- chordate
- notochord
- vertebra
- ectotherm
- endotherm

LESSON 5 Vertebrate Diversity

There are five major groups of vertebrates. They are fishes, amphibians, reptiles, birds, and mammals.

Vocabulary

- fish
- cartilage
- amphibian
- reptile
- bird
- mammal
- mammary gland
- monotreme
- marsupial
- placental mammal
- placenta

LESSON 6 Patterns of Behavior

Animals use sounds, scents, and body movements to communicate with one another.

Animals compete and cooperate with one another for limited resources.

Cyclic behaviors usually change over the course of a day or a season.

Vocabulary

- pheromone
- aggression
- territory
- courtship behavior
- society
- circadian rhythm
- hibernation
- migration

Review and Assessment

LESSON 1 What Is an Animal?

1. The process that the body uses to maintain a stable internal environment is called
   a. adaptation. b. endothermic.
   c. homeostasis. d. sweating.

2. The presence of a ________________ determines whether an animal is a vertebrate or an invertebrate.

3. **Identify the Main Idea** What are the five main functions of animals?

4. **Draw Conclusions** Suppose a book titled *Earth's Animals* is about vertebrates. Is its title a good one? Explain your answer.

5. **Apply Concepts** Some insects and birds can fly. Despite this similarity, why are insects and birds classified as different groups?

6. **Write About It** Choose an animal that you know well and describe a day in its life. Include the functions it carries out and the adaptations it uses to survive in its environment.

LESSON 2 Animal Body Plans

7. What is the highest level of organization an animal can have?
   a. cells b. organ systems
   c. organs d. tissues

8. An animal with many lines of symmetry has ________________ symmetry.

9. **Compare and Contrast** Describe how the symmetry of a sea star, a sponge, and a fish differ.

LESSON 3 Introduction to Invertebrates

10. Mollusks with two shells are called
    a. cephalopods. b. sea stars.
    c. bivalves. d. gastropods.

11. An ________________ has a system of fluid-filled tubes for obtaining food and oxygen.

12. **Make Generalizations** Suppose you see an animal. You wonder if it is an arthropod. What characteristics would you look for?

13. **Write About It** Explain whether a snail or a sponge has a higher level of organization and how this organization helps the invertebrate.

CHAPTER 11

Review and Assessment

LESSON 4 Introduction to Vertebrates

14. All vertebrates are

    a. chordates. b. invertebrates.
    c. fishes. d. reptiles.

15. A ____________________ is replaced by a backbone in many vertebrates.

16. **Infer** Would an ectotherm or an endotherm be more active on a cold night? Explain.

17. **Write About It** Your friend has both a hamster and a lizard as pets. She wants to buy a heat lamp for each of them to keep them warm. Tell her whether each pet needs a heat lamp to stay warm. Include the two ways animals maintain their body temperatures in your answer.

LESSON 5 Vertebrate Diversity

18. A reptile

    a. is an endotherm. b. lives only in water.
    c. has gills. d. has scaly skin.

19. __________ are the only animals with feathers.

20. **Summarize** What is the main difference between the three mammal groups?

21. **Classify** Into which group of fishes would you classify a fish with jaws and a skeleton made of cartilage?

LESSON 6 Patterns of Behavior

22. Some cats mark their territory by spraying a chemical scent known as a

    a. courtship behavior.
    b. circadian rhythm.
    c. cooperative behavior.
    d. pheromone.

23. Animals use ____________________ to find a mate.

24. **Make Generalizations** How do migration and hibernation help animals to survive?

APPLY THE BIG ?

How do you know an animal when you see it?

25. Look at the squid below. Describe how you know it is an animal. Include details about its functions and its adaptations to survive.

Virginia SOL Test Prep

Read each question and choose the best answer.

1 A lancelet is shown below. Which of its characteristics belong to a chordate?

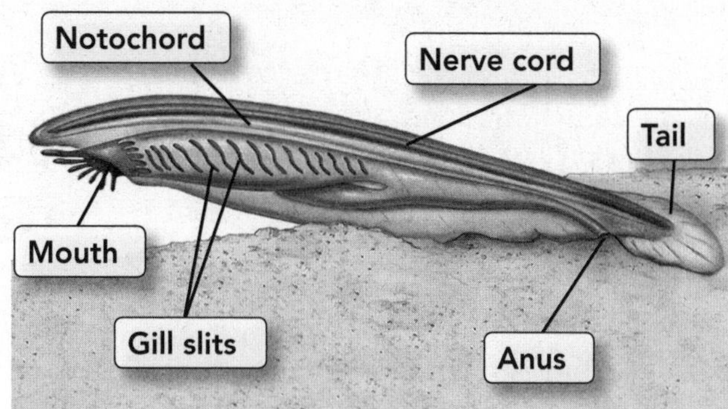

A the mouth, gill slits, and nerve cord
B the gill slits, notochord, and nerve cord
C the notochord, nerve cord, and tail
D the gill slits, notochord, and mouth

2 Which characteristics do birds and mammals have in common?

F Both are endothermic vertebrates.
G Both have fur or hair.
H Both have a three-chambered heart.
J Both are vertebrates that produce milk.

3 Which of the following best describes the function of the placenta?

A delivers oxygen to the body's cells
B stores food inside the body before swallowing and digesting it
C directs and coordinates a mammal's complex movements
D passes materials between a mother and her offspring before it is born

4 What kind of evidence is used to determine the relationships between animals?

F evidence from the way an animal develops
G evidence from an animal's DNA
H evidence from an animal's body structure
J all of the above

5 Which describes an ectothermic animal?

A an animal that has a thick coat of fur
B an animal that sweats when the environment is too hot
C an animal that depends on the sun to raise its body temperature
D an animal that maintains its body temperature when walking through snow

6 An example of a competitive behavior is—

F bees living together in a hive
G a school of fish escaping a predator
H a bear defending its territory
J wolves hunting prey as a group

7 How might a thick layer of fat help a seal?

A It is an endotherm, so a thick layer of fat helps lower its body temperature.
B It is an endotherm, so a thick layer of fat helps keep it warm in the cold water.
C It is an ectotherm, so a thick layer of fat keeps it warm on a cold night.
D It is an ectotherm, so a thick layer of fat helps raise its body temperature.

SCIENCE MATTERS

Kids Doing Science

JUNIOR ZOOKEEPERS

What is a lemur's favorite snack? Are baboons grumpy when they wake up in the morning? What, exactly, goes on behind the scenes at a zoo? If you want to know the answers to these questions, find out about Junior Zookeeper programs.

Many zoos throughout the country have volunteer programs for teenagers. Junior Zookeepers' tasks can include caring for zoo animals and assisting in zoo research. At some zoos, volunteers even help design and run educational programs. These volunteers serve as guides to help the public learn more from the zoo exhibits.

Some jobs are a little messy. You might have to help clean up the elephant cages! But the rewards can be just as big—taking care of animals can be a life-changing experience.

Design It Find out more about how zoo habitats are designed. How do zookeepers simulate an animal's habitat? How do they design exhibits that educate the public? Then choose an animal and design a model zoo exhibit that simulates its habitat and educates the public about the animal.

A Slimy Defense

If there were a contest for the most disgusting animal in the sea, the hagfish would probably win. This eel-like creature is almost blind, and it feeds by burrowing into the flesh of dead animals on the ocean floor. If a hagfish is attacked, it releases large amounts of thick slime, which can suffocate any predator foolish enough to attack! This thick gooey slime contains threads that are almost as strong as spider silk. Studies of hagfish slime may one day help scientists make materials that are stronger than the fabric we now use in bulletproof vests!

Write About It Find examples of how biological research has inspired the development of technology. Then make a poster that describes three examples. Explain how the technology affected society.

LS.1j

Hot Science

SUPERCOOLING FROGS

When you think of animals in Alaska, you probably think of caribou, arctic foxes, polar bears, and lynx. But what about frogs? Alaska is also home to a species of frog that freezes completely during the winter. When the temperatures warm again, the frog will thaw and be completely fine!

The wood frog has several adaptations that allow it to freeze. Much of the water from the frog's cells moves into its body cavity before the water freezes. This prevents the ice from damaging tissues. High levels of glucose protect the frog's cells from freezing. Finally, the wood frog may even ingest bacteria that allow it to control the rate at which freezing occurs!

Research It Find out about other animals that have adapted to live in extreme conditions. Then create an illustrated guide that shows how three of these animals survive in extreme environments.

LS.9c

Why Do Clownfish Play With Poison?

How do living things affect one another?

Clownfish live among the poisonous and stinging tentacles of sea anemones to avoid being eaten by larger fish. Amazingly, the clownfish do not get stung! This is because a fluid called mucus protects the skin of the fish. **Develop Hypotheses How might a sea anemone benefit from having clownfish around?**

UNTAMED SCIENCE Watch the **Untamed Science** video to learn more about interactions between organisms.

Populations and Communities

CHAPTER 12

Science Standards of Learning

LS.1a, LS.1b, LS.1d, LS.1e, LS.1f, LS.1g, LS.1h, LS.1i, LS.1j, LS.4d, LS.5c, LS.6b, LS.6c, LS.8b, LS.8c, LS.8d, LS.8e, LS.10b, LS.10c, LS.13a

CHAPTER

12 Getting Started

Check Your Understanding

1. **Background** Read the paragraph below and then answer the question.

Raquel planted a garden in a sunny area near her home. First, she loosened the **soil,** so the plant roots could easily grow. If days passed with no **precipitation,** she watered the plants. That was all she had to do—the rest of what the plants needed came from the **atmosphere!**

Soil is made up of rock fragments, water, air, and decaying plant and animal matter.

Rain, hail, sleet, and snow are all types of **precipitation.**

Earth's **atmosphere** contains oxygen, carbon dioxide, nitrogen, and other gases.

- How do soil, precipitation, and the atmosphere help a plant grow?

____

____

____

MY READING WEB If you had trouble completing the question above, visit **My Reading Web** and type in ***Populations and Communities.***

Vocabulary Skill

Latin Word Origins Some key terms in this chapter contain word parts with Latin origins. The table below lists two of the Latin words that key terms come from.

Latin Word	Meaning of Latin Word	Example
aptare	to fit	adaptation, *n.* a characteristic that allows an organism to live successfully in its environment
migrare	to move	immigration, *n.* movement into a population

2. **Quick Check The terms *immigration* and *emigration* both come from the Latin word *migrare*. Circle the meaning of *migrare* in the table above.**

Chapter Preview

LESSON 1

- organism • habitat
- biotic factor • abiotic factor
- species • population
- community • ecosystem
- ecology

Compare and Contrast
Draw Conclusions

LESSON 2

- birth rate • death rate
- immigration • emigration
- population density
- limiting factor
- carrying capacity

Relate Cause and Effect
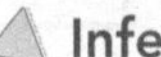
Infer

LESSON 3

- natural selection • adaptation
- niche • competition • predation
- predator • prey • symbiosis
- mutualism • commensalism
- parasitism • parasite • host

Relate Text and Visuals
Classify

LESSON 4

- succession • primary succession
- pioneer species
- secondary succession

Compare and Contrast

Observe

VOCAB FLASH CARDS For extra help with vocabulary, visit **Vocab Flash Cards** and type in ***Populations and Communities.***

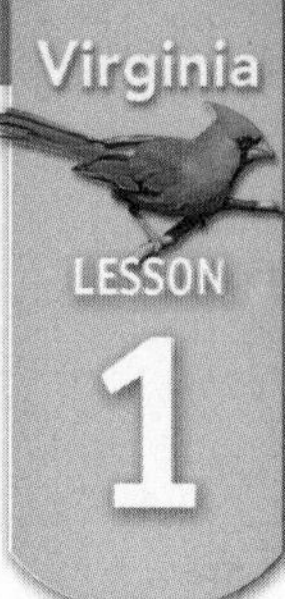

Living Things and the Environment

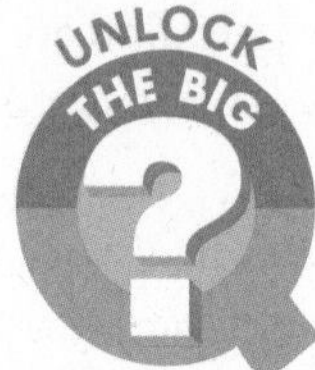

- What Does an Organism Get From Its Environment?
  LS.6b, LS.6c
- What Are the Two Parts of an Organism's Habitat?
  LS.1d, LS.1f, LS.1i, LS.1j, LS.5c, LS.6b, LS.6c
- How Is an Ecosystem Organized?
  LS.1d, LS.4d, LS.6b, LS.6c

my planet Diary

DISCOVERY

Love Song

The gray, golden brown, and Goodman's mouse lemurs are some of the world's smallest primates. These three lemurs look similar. Looking so similar makes it difficult for the lemurs to find members of their own kind or species during mating season. However, it seems that the lemurs can identify their own species by song. Scientists recorded the mating calls of the three species of lemurs. They discovered that the lemurs reacted more to the calls from their own species. This allows the lemurs to pick the right mate, even at night.

Communicate Answer these questions. Discuss your answers with a partner.

1. If you were looking for your sneakers among several pairs that looked just like yours, what characteristics would make it easier for you to find them?

   ____

   ____

2. What do you think would happen if a lemur mated with a different kind of lemur?

   ____

   ____

> PLANET DIARY Go to **Planet Diary** to learn more about habitats.

Golden brown mouse lemur

Goodman's mouse lemur

Gray mouse lemur

Lab zone® Do the Inquiry Warm-Up *What's in the Scene?*

Vocabulary
- organism • habitat • biotic factor • abiotic factor
- species • population • community • ecosystem
- ecology

Skills
- Reading: Compare and Contrast
- Inquiry: Draw Conclusions

What Does an Organism Get From Its Environment?

Science Standards of Learning

LS.6b Investigate and understand interactions resulting in a flow of energy and matter throughout an ecosystem.

LS.6c Investigate and understand complex relationships within terrestrial, freshwater, and marine ecosystems.

If you were to visit Alaska, you might see a bald eagle fly by. A bald eagle is one type of **organism,** or living thing. Different types of organisms live in different types of surroundings, or environments. **An organism gets food, water, shelter, and other things it needs to live, grow, and reproduce from its environment.** An environment that provides the things a specific organism needs to live, grow, and reproduce is called its **habitat.**

In a forest habitat, mushrooms grow in the damp soil and woodpeckers build nests in tree trunks. Organisms live in different habitats because they have different requirements for survival and reproduction. Some organisms live on a prairie, with its flat terrain, tall grasses, and low rainfall amounts. A prairie dog, like the one shown in **Figure 1,** obtains the food and shelter it needs from a prairie habitat. It could not survive on this rocky ocean shore. Likewise, the prairie would not meet the needs of a sea star.

FIGURE 1

What's Wrong With This Picture?
Most people would never expect to see a prairie dog at the beach.

List Give three reasons why this prairie dog would not survive in this habitat.

___

___

___

___

Do the Quick Lab *Organisms and Their Habitats.*

Assess Your Understanding

got it?

- O **I get it!** Now I know that an organism's environment provides ___
- O I need extra help with ___

Go to MY SCIENCE COACH *online for help with this subject.*

Science Standards of Learning

LS.1d Construct and use models and simulations to illustrate and explain phenomena.

LS.1f Identify dependent variables, independent variables, and constants.

LS.1i Identify, interpret, and evaluate patterns in data.

LS.1j Use current applications to reinforce life science concepts.

LS.5c Investigate and understand photosynthesis as foundation of virtually all food webs.

LS.6b Investigate and understand interactions resulting in a flow of energy throughout an ecosystem.

LS.6c Investigate and understand complex relationships within terrestrial ecosystems.

Compare and Contrast In the paragraphs at the right, circle how biotic and abiotic factors are similar and underline how they are different.

What Are the Two Parts of an Organism's Habitat?

To meet its needs, a prairie dog must interact with more than just the other prairie dogs around it. **An organism interacts with both the living and nonliving parts of its habitat.**

Biotic Factors What living things can you see in the prairie dog's habitat shown in **Figure 2**? The parts of a habitat that are living, or once living, and interact with an organism are called **biotic factors** (by AHT ik). The plants that provide seeds and berries are biotic factors. The ferrets and eagles that hunt the prairie dog are also biotic factors. Worms and bacteria are biotic factors that live in the soil underneath the prairie grass. Prairie dog scat, owl pellets, and decomposing plant matter are also biotic factors.

Abiotic Factors Not all of the factors that organisms interact with are living. **Abiotic factors** (ay by AHT ik) are the nonliving parts of an organism's habitat. These factors, as shown in **Figure 2,** include sunlight, soil, temperature, oxygen, and water.

FIGURE 2

Factors in a Prairie Habitat

A prairie dog interacts with many biotic and abiotic factors in the prairie habitat.

Relate Text and Visuals **Add another biotic factor to the picture. For each abiotic factor, draw a line from the text box to an example in the picture.**

Sunlight Because sunlight is needed for plants to make their own food, it is an important abiotic factor for most living things.

Soil Soil consists of varying amounts of rock fragments, nutrients, air, water, and the decaying remains of living things. The soil in an area influences the kinds of plants and animals that can live and grow there.

Temperature The temperatures that are typical in an area determine the types of organisms that can live there.

Oxygen Most living things require oxygen to carry out their life processes. Organisms on land obtain oxygen from air. Aquatic organisms obtain oxygen that is dissolved in the water around them.

Water All living things require water to carry out their life processes. Plants and algae need water along with sunlight and carbon dioxide to make their own food. Other living things depend on plants and algae for food.

apply it!

Salt is an abiotic factor found in some environments. To see how the amount of salt affects the hatching of brine shrimp eggs, varying amounts of salt were added to four different 500-mL beakers.

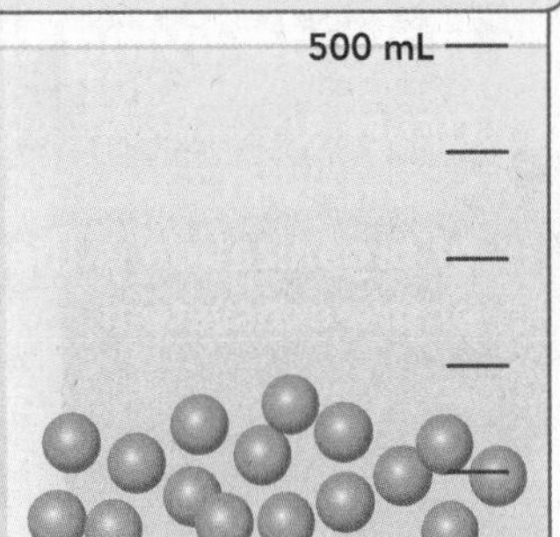

Beaker A
500 mL spring water

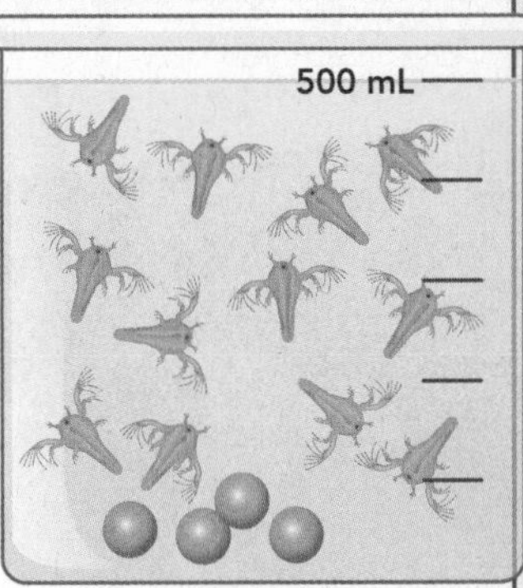

Beaker B
500 mL spring water
+ 2.5 g salt

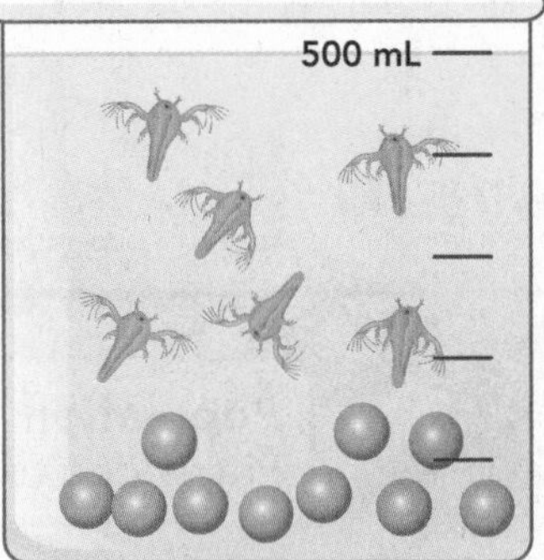

Beaker C
500 mL spring water
+ 7.5 g salt

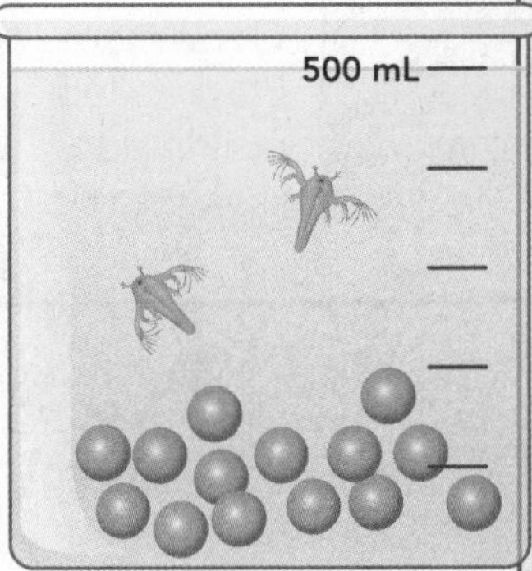

Beaker D
500 mL spring water
+ 15 g salt

1 **Observe** In which beaker(s) did the eggs, shown as purple circles, hatch? ________

2 **Infer** The manipulated variable was

____

3 **Infer** The responding variable was ________

____

4 CHALLENGE Beaker ______ was the control.

5 **Draw Conclusions** What can you conclude about the amount of salt in the shrimps' natural habitat?

____

____

____

Do the Lab Investigation *World in a Bottle.*

Assess Your Understanding

1a. Interpret Diagrams List two biotic and two abiotic factors in **Figure 2.**

____

b. Draw Conclusions Name two abiotic factors in your habitat and explain how your life would be different without them.

____

got it?

O **I get it!** Now I know that the two parts of an organism's habitat are ________________

O I need extra help with ________________

Go to **MY SCIENCE COACH** *online for help with this subject.*

EXPLORE THE BIG ?

Ecological Organization

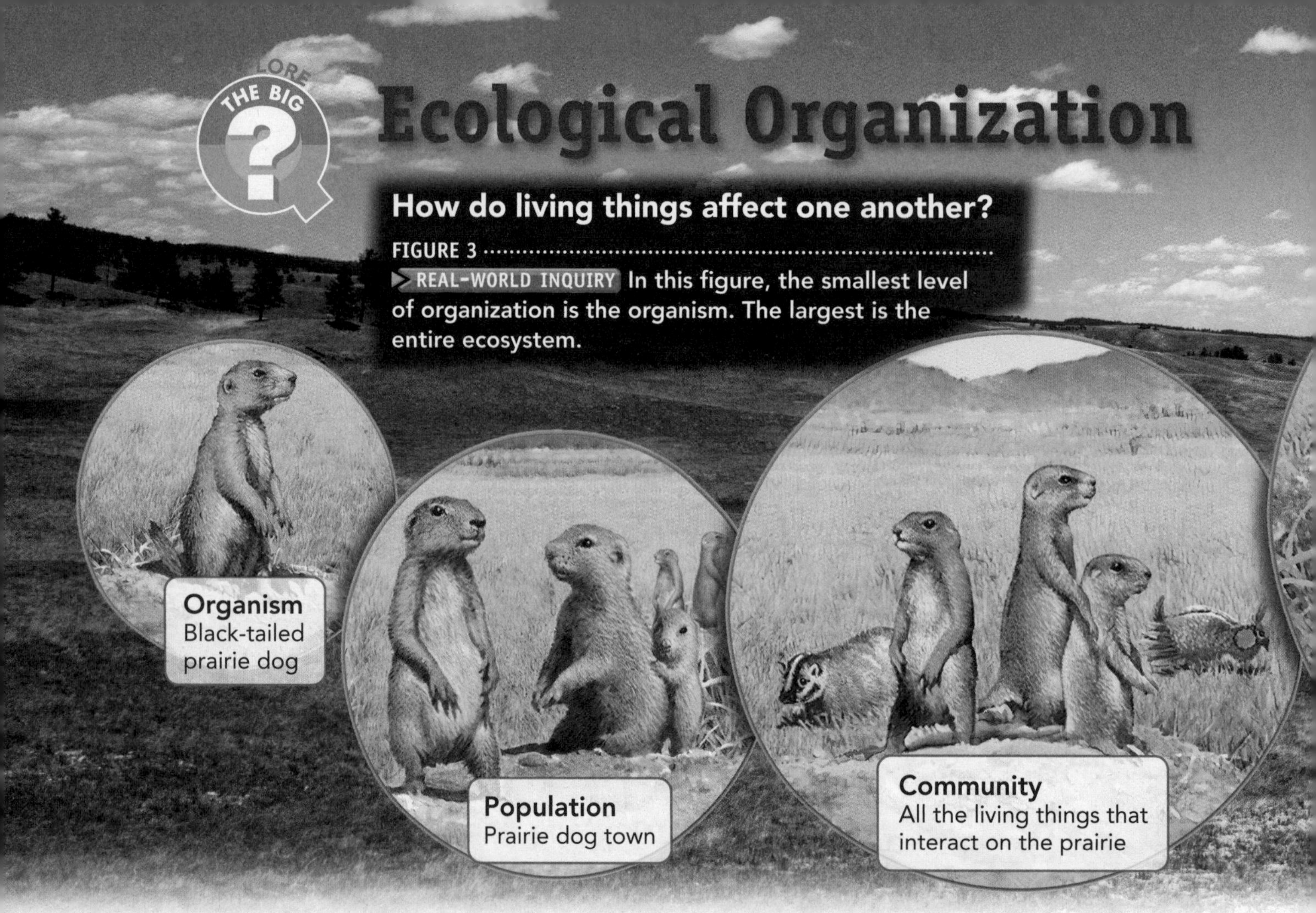

How do living things affect one another?

FIGURE 3

REAL-WORLD INQUIRY In this figure, the smallest level of organization is the organism. The largest is the entire ecosystem.

Organism
Black-tailed prairie dog

Population
Prairie dog town

Community
All the living things that interact on the prairie

LS.1d Construct and use models and simulations to illustrate and explain phenomena.

LS.4d Investigate and understand characteristics that define a species.

LS.6b Investigate and understand interactions resulting in a flow of energy and matter throughout an ecosystem.

LS.6c Investigate and understand complex relationships within terrestrial, freshwater, and marine ecosystems.

How Is an Ecosystem Organized?

Most organisms do not live all alone in their habitat. Instead, organisms live together in populations and communities that interact with abiotic factors in their ecosystems.

Organisms Black-tailed prairie dogs that live in prairie dog towns on the Nebraska plains are all members of one species. A **species** (SPEE sheez) is a group of organisms that can mate with each other and produce offspring that can also mate and reproduce.

Populations All the members of one species living in a particular area are referred to as a **population.** The prairie dogs in the Nebraska town are one example of a population.

Communities A particular area contains more than one species of organism. The prairie, for instance, includes prairie dogs, hawks, snakes, and grasses. All the different populations that live together in an area make up a **community.**

Ecosystems The community of organisms that live in a particular area, along with their nonliving environment, make up an **ecosystem.** A prairie is just one of the many different ecosystems found on Earth. Other ecosystems are deserts, oceans, ponds, and forests.

Figure 3 shows the levels of organization in a prairie ecosystem. **The smallest level of organization is a single organism, which belongs to a population that includes other members of its species. The population belongs to a community of different species. The community and abiotic factors together form an ecosystem.**

Because the populations in an ecosystem interact with one another, any change affects all the different populations that live there. The study of how organisms interact with each other and with their environment is called **ecology.**

Lab zone® Do the Quick-Lab *Organizing an Ecosystem.*

Assess Your Understanding

2a. Classify All of the different kinds of organisms in a forest are a (community/ population).

b. ANSWER THE BIG ? How do living things affect one another?

______

______

______

got it?

○ **I get it!** Now I know that ecosystems are organized into ______

______

______

○ I need extra help with ______

Go to MY SCIENCE COACH *online for help with this subject.*

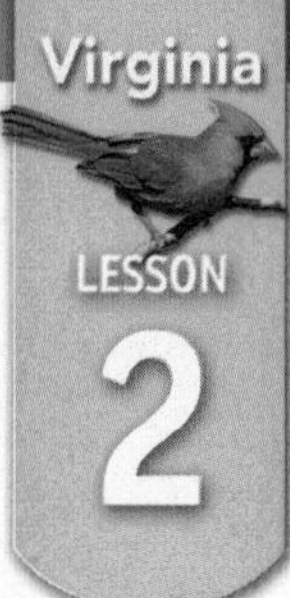

Virginia

LESSON 2

Populations

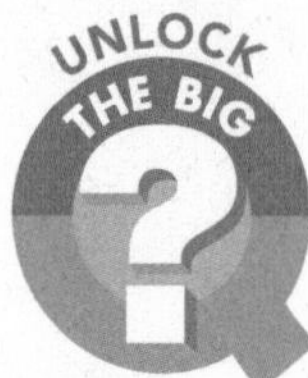

How Do Populations Change in Size?
LS.1h, LS.1i, LS.10b, LS.10c

What Factors Limit Population Growth?
LS.10b, LS.10c

my planet Diary

TECHNOLOGY

Prairie Dog Picker-Upper

Did you know that vacuum cleaners do more than just clean carpets? Across the Great Plains, farmers are using specially designed vacuum cleaners to help them remove black-tailed prairie dogs from the farm land. Prairie dogs can eat crops, cause soil erosion, and endanger cattle and farm machinery. The prairie dog vacuum uses a 4-in. plastic hose to suck prairie dogs out of the ground at 483 km/h! The prairie dogs end up in a padded tank, usually unharmed. They are then relocated or donated to the U.S. Fish and Wildlife Service to be fed to endangered eagles, hawks, and black-footed ferrets.

Prairie dogs

Communicate Discuss these questions with a group of classmates. Write your answers below.

1. If all of the prairie dogs were removed, how do you think the prairie ecosystem would be affected?

2. Should prairie dogs be used as food for endangered species? Explain.

PLANET DIARY Go to **Planet Diary** to learn more about populations.

Do the Inquiry Warm-Up *Populations.*

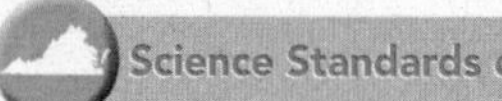

Science Standards of Learning

LS.1h Organize, graph, and use data to make predictions.

LS.1i Identify, interpret, and evaluate patterns in data.

LS.10b Investigate and understand factors that increase or decrease population size.

LS.10c Investigate and understand that populations are dynamic through catastrophic disturbances.

How Do Populations Change in Size?

Ecologists are scientists who study biotic and abiotic factors of an ecosystem and the interactions between them. Some ecologists study populations and monitor the sizes of populations over time. **Populations can change in size when new members join the population or when members leave the population.**

Vocabulary
- birth rate
- death rate
- immigration
- emigration
- population density
- limiting factor
- carrying capacity

Skills
- Reading: Relate Cause and Effect
- Inquiry: Infer

Births and Deaths The most common way in which new individuals join a population is by being born into it. If more individuals are born into a population than die in any period of time, a population can grow. So when the **birth rate,** the number of births per 1,000 individuals for a given time period, is greater than its **death rate,** the number of deaths per 1,000 individuals for a given time period, the population may increase. The main way that individuals leave a population is by dying. If the birth rate is the same as the death rate, then the population may stay the same. In situations where the death rate is higher than the birth rate, then the population may decrease.

do the math!

Data Table

Year	Births	Deaths
1	32	8
2	28	13
3	47	21
4	33	16

Depending on the size and age of the female, an American Alligator can lay between 10 and 50 eggs per year.

1. **Graph** Using the data table and colored pencils, create a double bar graph showing alligator births and deaths for four years.
2. Label the *x*-axis and *y*-axis.
3. Write a title for the graph.
4. Fill in the graph using the colors shown.
5. **Develop Hypotheses** What factors might explain the number of births and deaths in Year 3?

____

____

____

____

____

____

____

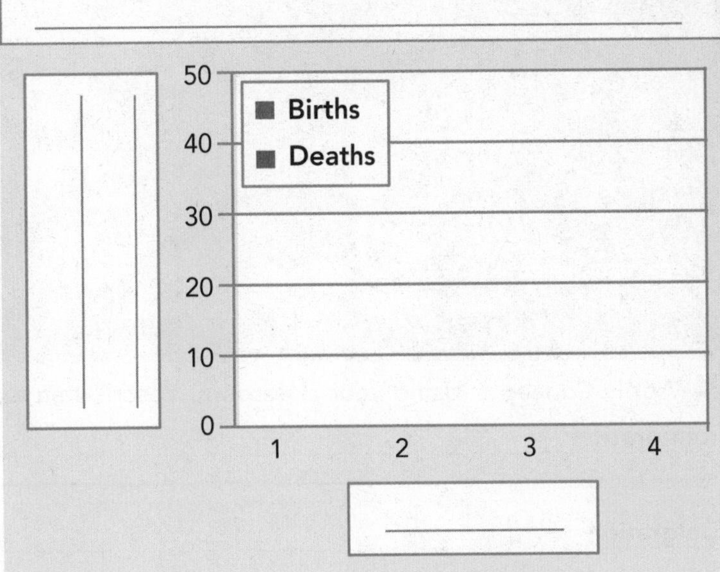

The Population Statement When the birth rate in a population is greater than the death rate, the population will generally increase. This can be written as a mathematical statement using the "is greater than" sign:

If birth rate > death rate, population size increases.

However, if the death rate in a population is greater than the birth rate, the population size will generally decrease. This can also be written as a mathematical statement:

If death rate > birth rate, population size decreases.

Vocabulary Latin Word Origins
Both the terms *immigration* ("moving into a population") and *emigration* ("moving out of a population") come from the Latin word *migrare* ("to move"). What do you think the prefixes *im–* and *e–* mean?

______

______

______

______

Immigration and Emigration

The size of a population also can change when individuals move into or out of the population. **Immigration** (im ih GRAY shun) means moving into a population. **Emigration** (em ih GRAY shun) means leaving a population. For instance, if food is scarce, some members of an antelope herd may wander off in search of better grassland. If they become permanently separated from the original herd, they will no longer be part of that population.

FIGURE 1

Immigration

In 1898, white-tailed deer were almost extinct in Iowa due to over-hunting. The deer population was reestablished as animals from Minnesota, Wisconsin, and Missouri immigrated into Iowa.

Apply Concepts **Using your classroom, describe an example of each of the following.**

Immigration: ______

______

Emigration: ______

______

Graphing Changes in Population Changes in a population's size can be displayed on a line graph. Figure 2 shows a graph of the changes in a rabbit population. The vertical axis identifies the number of rabbits in the population, while the horizontal axis shows time. The graph represents the size of the rabbit population over a ten-year period.

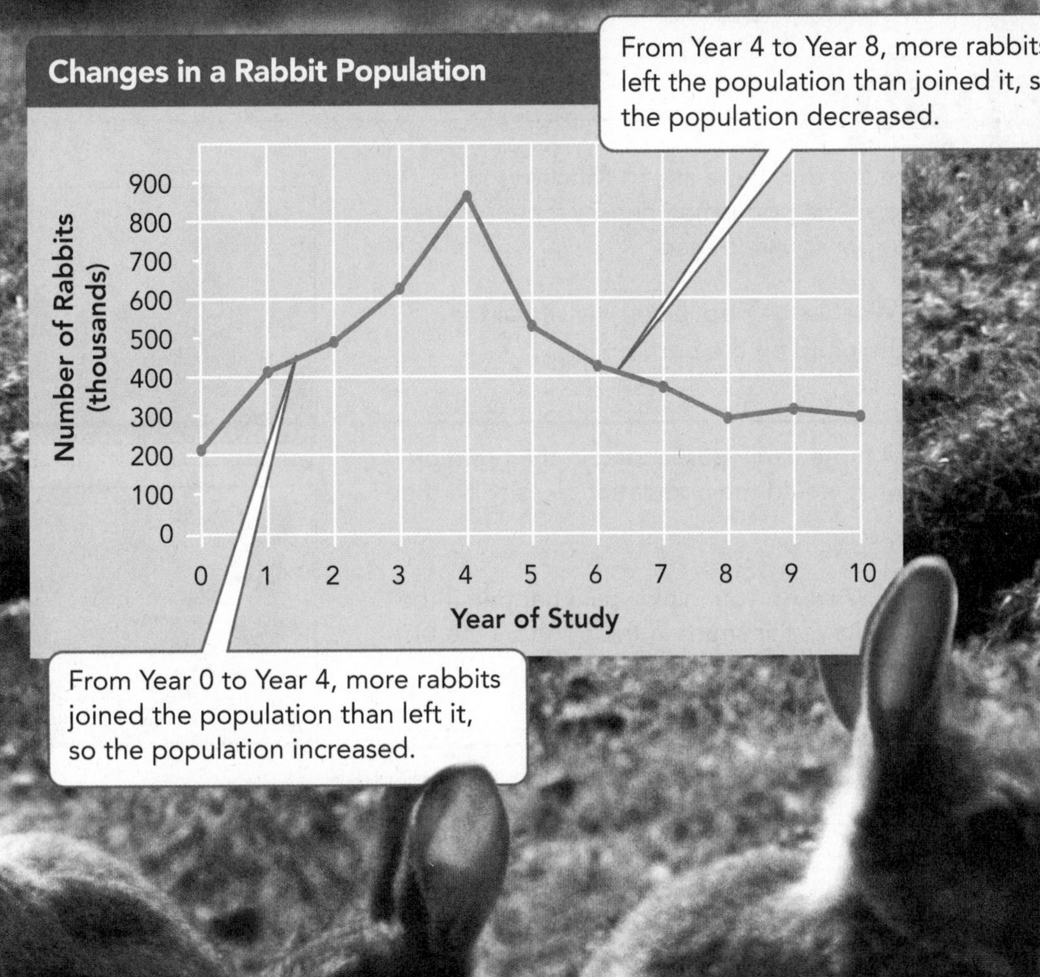

FIGURE 2

INTERACTIVE ART **Changes in a Rabbit Population**

This graph shows how the size of a rabbit population changed over ten years.

1. **Interpret Data** In Year ______, the rabbit population reached its highest point.
2. **Read Graphs** What was the size of the rabbit population in that year? ________________

3. CHALLENGE How do you think the rabbit population affected the fox population over the same ten-year period? Explain your reasoning.

Population Density Sometimes an ecologist needs to know more than just the total size of a population. In many situations, it is helpful to know the **population density**—the number of individuals in an area of a specific size. Population density can be written as an equation:

$$\text{Population density} = \frac{\text{Number of individuals}}{\text{Unit area}}$$

For example, suppose you counted 20 butterflies in a garden measuring 10 square meters. The population density would be 20 butterflies per 10 square meters, or 2 butterflies per square meter.

apply it!

In the pond on the top, there are 10 flamingos in 8 square meters. The population density is 1.25 flamingos per square meter.

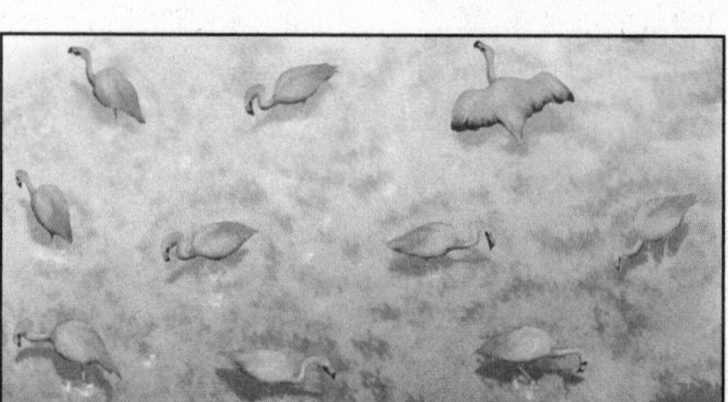

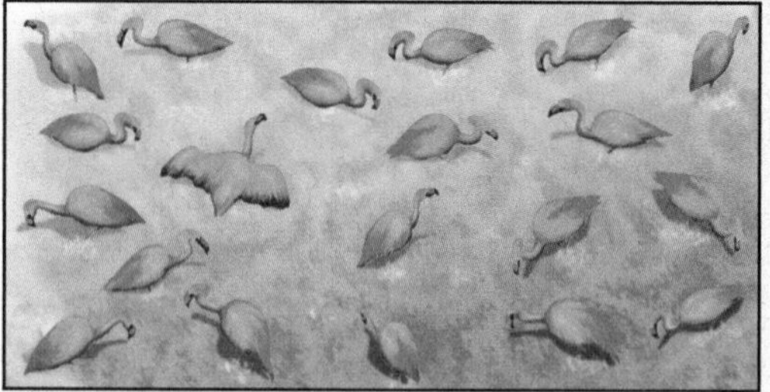

1 Calculate What is the population density of the flamingos in the pond on the bottom?

____

2 Infer If 14 more flamingos landed in the pond on the bottom, what would the population density be then?

____

3 CHALLENGE What do you think would happen if the population density of flamingos in the pond on the bottom became too great?

____

____

____

Lab zone Do the Quick Lab *Growing and Shrinking.*

Assess Your Understanding

1a. Review Two ways to join a population are _______ and _______.

Two ways to leave a population are _______ and _______.

b. Calculate Suppose a population of 8 wolves has produced 20 young in a year. If 7 wolves have died, how many wolves are in the population now? (Assume no wolves have moved into or out of the population for other reasons.)

____

got it?

O **I get it!** Now I know that population size changes due to _______________

____

O I need extra help with _______________

Go to **MY SCIENCE COACH** *online for help with this subject.*

What Factors Limit Population Growth?

When the living conditions in an area are good, a population will generally grow. But eventually some environmental factor will cause the population to stop growing. A **limiting factor** is an environmental factor that causes a population to stop growing or decrease in size. **Some limiting factors for populations are weather conditions, space, food, and water.**

Science Standards of Learning

LS.10b Investigate and understand factors that increase or decrease population size.

LS.10c Investigate and understand that ecosystems, communities, populations, organisms are dynamic through climate changes and catastrophic disturbances.

Climate

Changes in climate conditions, such as temperature and the amount of rainfall, can place severe limits on the growth of a population. A cold spring season can kill the young of many species of organisms, including birds and mammals. Rare and destructive events like floods, hurricanes, and tornadoes, as shown in **Figure 3,** can also disturb entire communities of organisms. Catastrophic events like these can have long-lasting negative effects on population sizes of many different species.

Relate Cause and Effect As you read about the four factors that can limit populations, fill in the graphic organizer below.

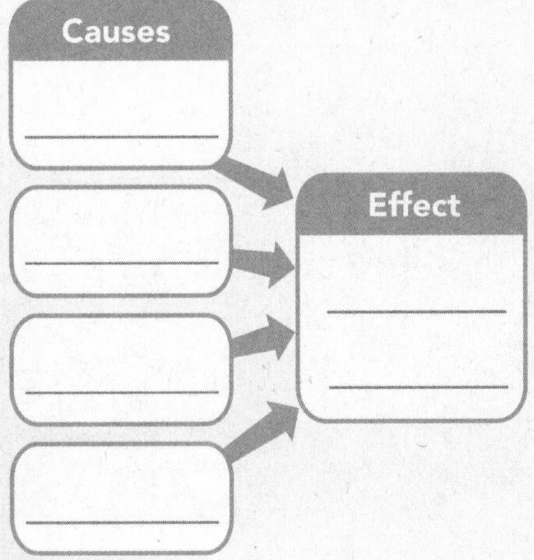

FIGURE 3

Weather as a Limiting Factor

A tornado or flood can destroy nests and burrows.

Identify Name two types of natural disasters that you think can also limit population growth.

____

____

Tornado funnel touching ground

Some plants, like the black walnut tree, release chemicals into the environment that discourage other plants from growing too close. This process is called allelopathy (uh luh LOP uh thee).

Space Space is another limiting factor for populations. Gannets are seabirds that are usually seen flying over the ocean. They come to land only to nest on rocky shores. But the nesting shores get very crowded. If a pair does not find room to nest, they will not be able to add any offspring to the gannet population. So nesting space on the shore is a limiting factor for gannets. If there were more nesting space, more gannets would be able to nest. The population could increase.

Figure 4 shows how space is also a limiting factor for plants. The amount of space in which a plant grows determines whether the plant can obtain the sunlight, water, and soil nutrients it needs. For example, many pine seedlings sprout each year in forests. But as the seedlings grow, the roots of those that are too close together run out of space. Branches from other trees may block the sunlight the seedlings need. Some of the seedlings then die, limiting the size of the pine population.

Food and Water Organisms require food and water to survive. When food and water are in limited supply, they can be limiting factors. Suppose a giraffe must eat 10 kilograms of leaves each day to survive. The trees in an area can provide 100 kilograms of leaves a day while remaining healthy. Five giraffes could live easily in this area, because they would need just 50 kilograms of food a day. But 15 giraffes could not all survive—there would not be enough food. No matter how much shelter, water, and other resources there were, the population would not grow much larger than 10 giraffes. The largest population that an area can support is called its **carrying capacity.** The carrying capacity of this giraffe habitat would be 10 giraffes. The size of a population can vary, but usually stays near its carrying capacity because of the limiting factors in its habitat.

FIGURE 4

Space as a Limiting Factor

If no more tulip plants can grow in this field, the field has reached its carrying capacity for tulips.

List Name three things a plant needs to survive.

apply it!

Giant pandas live in the mountains of south central China. Most (99 percent) of the pandas' diet is made up of the bamboo plant. Bamboo is not nutrient rich. Pandas spend 55 percent of their day eating between 9 and 38 kilograms of bamboo. Getting enough bamboo to eat can be a challenge. Farming and the timber industry have destroyed the pandas' habitat and bamboo forests. In addition, when a bamboo plant flowers, the plant dies and does not regrow for several years. It is difficult for scientists to know exactly how many giant pandas exist in the wild. The best estimate is that there are about 1,600 of them. Due to the small population size, this species is classified as endangered.

Communicate Write a letter to the editor that describes how food and space may be limiting factors for the giant panda species. Add a headline to your letter.

____

____

____

____

____

____

____

Lab zone® Do the Quick Lab *Elbow Room.*

Assess Your Understanding

2a. Summarize When the climate changes or there is not enough ________ or ________ or ________, a population can (begin/stop) growing in size.

b. Relate Cause and Effect Choose a limiting factor and describe the factor's effect on population growth.

____

____

____

got it?

O I get it! Now I know that populations can be limited when ____

____

O I need extra help with ____

Go to MY SCIENCE COACH *online for help with this subject.*

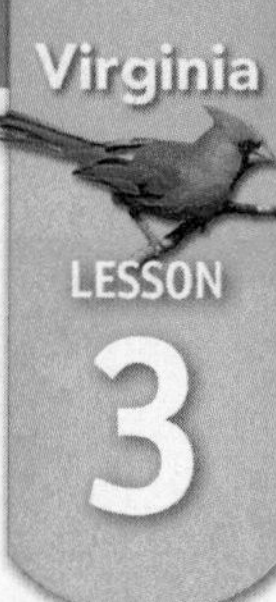

Interactions Among Living Things

- How Do Adaptations Help an Organism Survive? LS.8e, LS.13a
- What Are Competition and Predation? LS.1h, LS.1i, LS.1j, LS.8b, LS.8c, LS.8e, LS.13a
- What Are the Three Types of Symbiosis? LS.1b, LS.8c, LS.8d

my planet Diary

FUN FACT

Predator Power

What predator can close its jaws the fastest? You might think it is a lion or a shark, but you would be wrong. It is the trap-jaw ant that has the fastest strike in the animal kingdom. The trap-jaw ant closes its mouth around its prey in 0.13 milliseconds at speeds of 35 to 64 meters per second! The force created when its jaw snaps shut also helps the ant escape danger by either jumping up to 8.3 centimeters high or 39.6 centimeters sideways.

A trap-jaw ant stalks its prey.

Communicate Answer the questions below. Discuss your answers with a partner.

1. How does the trap-jaw ant's adaptation help it avoid becoming the prey of another organism?

2. What are some adaptations that other predators have to capture prey?

PLANET DIARY Go to **Planet Diary** to learn more about predators.

Do the Inquiry Warm-Up *Can You Hide a Butterfly?*

LS.8e Investigate and understand niches.

LS.13a Investigate and understand relationships of mutation, adaptation, natural selection, and extinction.

How Do Adaptations Help an Organism Survive?

As day breaks, a sound comes from a nest tucked in the branch of a saguaro cactus. Two young red-tailed hawks are preparing to fly. Farther down the stem, a tiny elf owl peeks out of its nest in a small hole. A rattlesnake slithers around the base of the saguaro, looking for breakfast. Spying a shrew, the snake strikes it with needle-like fangs. The shrew dies instantly.

Vocabulary
- natural selection • adaptation • niche • competition
- predation • predator • prey • symbiosis • mutualism
- commensalism • parasitism • parasite • host

Skills
- Reading: Relate Text and Visuals
- Inquiry: Classify

Figure 1 shows some organisms that live in, on, and around the saguaro cactus. Each organism has unique characteristics. These characteristics affect the individual's ability to survive and reproduce in its environment.

Natural Selection A characteristic that makes an individual better suited to a specific environment may eventually become common in that species through a process called **natural selection.** Natural selection works like this: Individuals whose unique characteristics are well-suited for an environment tend to survive and produce more offspring. Offspring that inherit these characteristics also live to reproduce. In this way, natural selection results in **adaptations,** the behaviors and physical characteristics that allow organisms to live successfully in their environments. For example, the arctic hare has fur that turns from gray to white in the winter which helps camouflage the hare against the snow.

Individuals with characteristics poorly suited to a particular environment are less likely to survive and reproduce. Over time, poorly suited characteristics may disappear from the species. If a species cannot adapt to changes in its environment, the entire species can disappear from Earth and become extinct.

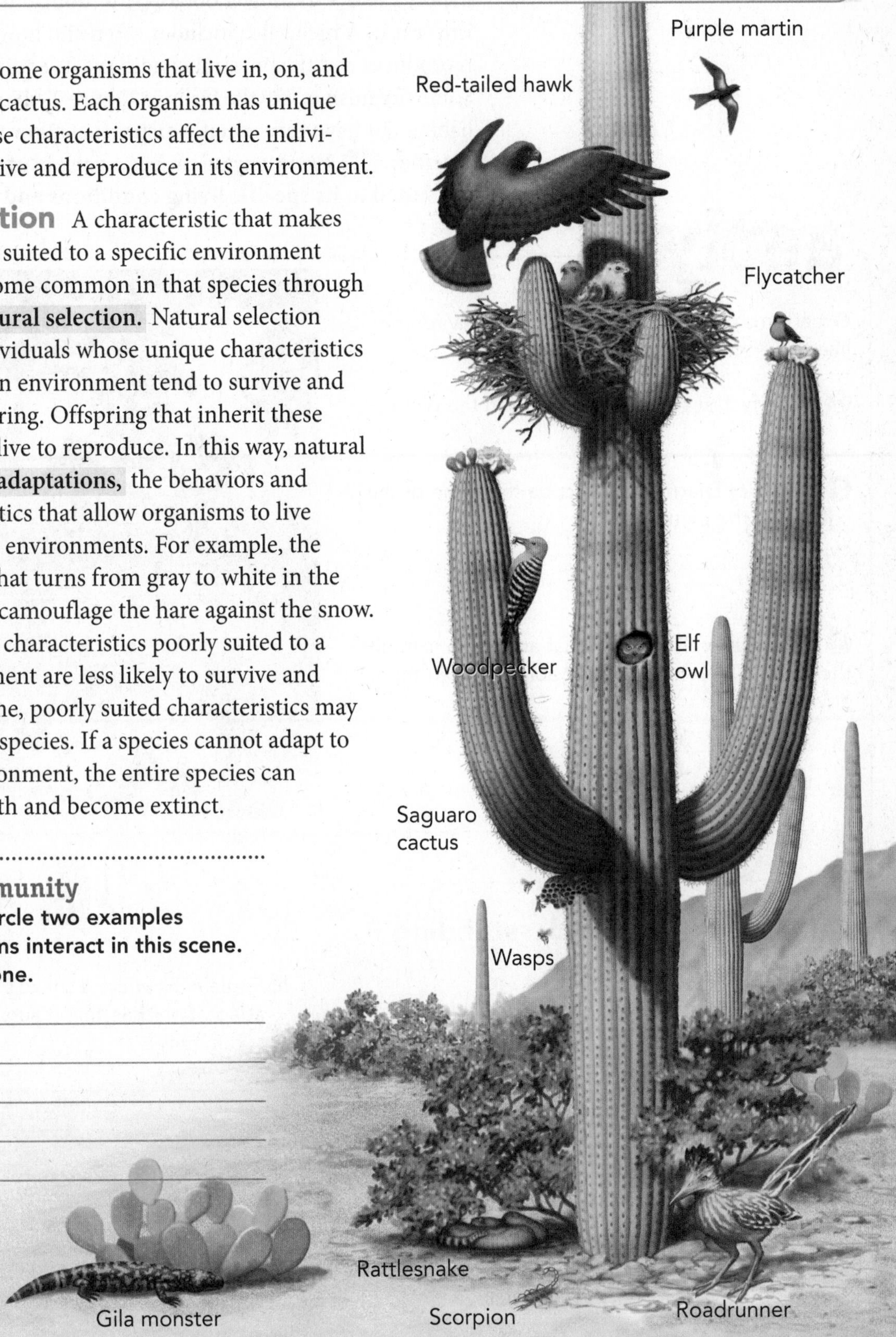

FIGURE 1

Saguaro Community

Describe Circle two examples of how organisms interact in this scene. Describe each one.

____

____

____

____

____

Niche The organisms in the saguaro community have adaptations that result in specific roles. The role of an organism in its habitat is called its **niche.** A niche includes what type of food the organism eats, how it obtains this food, and what other organisms eat it. A niche also includes when and how the organism reproduces and the physical conditions it requires to survive. Some organisms, like the birds in **Figure 2,** share the same habitat but have very specific niches that allow them to live together. **Every organism has a variety of adaptations that are suited to its specific living conditions and help it survive.**

apply it!

Organisms occupy many niches in an environment like the one in this picture.

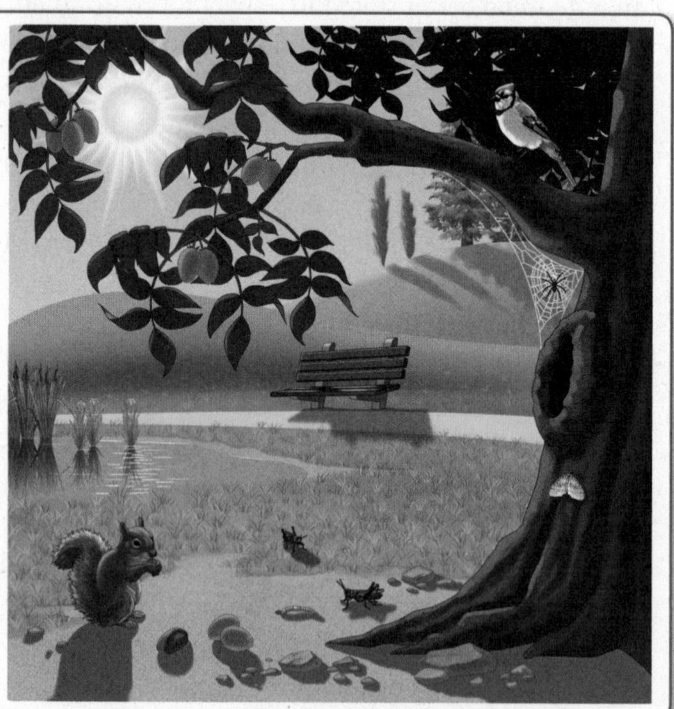

1 **Identify** List two abiotic factors in the picture.

____

2 **Interpret Diagrams** Describe the niche of the squirrel in the picture.

____

____

3 **Make Generalizations** What adaptations might the squirrel have that make it able to live in this environment?

____

____

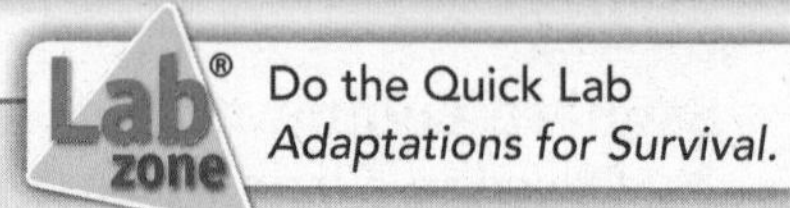

Do the Quick Lab *Adaptations for Survival.*

Assess Your Understanding

1a. Define Adaptations are the _______________ and _______________ characteristics that allow organisms to live successfully in their environments.

b. Explain How are a snake's sharp fangs an adaptation that help it survive in the saguaro community?

____

____

got it?

O **I get it!** Now I know that adaptations are _______________

____

O I need extra help with _______________

Go to MY SCIENCE COACH *online for help with this subject.*

What Are Competition and Predation?

Science Standards of Learning

LS.1h Organize, graph, and interpret data, and use data to make predictions.

LS.1i Identify, interpret, and evaluate patterns in data.

LS.1j Use current applications to reinforce life science concepts.

LS.8b Investigate and understand the relationship between predators and prey.

LS.8c Investigate and understand competition and cooperation.

LS.8e Investigate and understand niches.

LS.13a Investigate and understand relationships of mutation, adaptation, natural selection, and extinction.

During a typical day in the saguaro community, a range of interactions takes place among organisms. **Two major types of interactions among organisms are competition and predation.**

Competition Different species can share the same habitat and food requirements. For example, the flycatcher and the elf owl both live on the saguaro and eat insects. However, these two species do not occupy exactly the same niche. The flycatcher is active during the day, while the owl is active mostly at night. If two species occupy the same niche, one of the species might eventually die off. The reason for this is **competition.** The struggle between organisms to survive as they attempt to use the same limited resources is called competition. For example, weeds in a garden compete with vegetable crops for soil nutrients, water, and sunlight.

In any ecosystem, there are limited amounts of food, water, and shelter. Organisms that share the same habitat often have adaptations that enable them to reduce competition. For example, the three species of warblers in **Figure 2** specialize in feeding only in a certain part of the spruce tree.

Cape May Warbler
This species feeds at the tips of branches near the top of the tree.

Bay-Breasted Warbler
This species feeds in the middle part of the tree.

Yellow-Rumped Warbler
This species feeds in the lower part of the tree and at the bases of the middle branches.

FIGURE 2

Niche and Competition

Each of these warbler species occupies a very specific location in its habitat. By feeding on insects in different areas of the tree, the birds avoid competing for food and are able to live together.

1. **Predict** What could happen if these warbler species fed in the same location on the tree?

2. **List** For what resources do the tree and the grass compete?

FIGURE 3

Predation

This tiger shark and this albatross are involved in a predator-prey interaction.

Interpret Photos Label the predator and the prey in the photo.

Predation In **Figure 3,** a tiger shark bursts through the water to seize an albatross in its powerful jaws. An interaction in which one organism kills another for food or nutrients is called **predation.** The organism that does the killing is the **predator.** The organism that is killed is the **prey.** Even though they do not kill their prey, organisms like cows and giraffes are also considered predators because they eat plants.

Predation can have a major effect on a prey population size. Recall that when the death rate exceeds the birth rate in a population, the population size can decrease. So, if there are too many predators in an area, the result is often a decrease in the size of the prey population. But a decrease in the number of prey results in less food for their predators. Without adequate food, the predator population can decline. Generally, populations of predators and their prey rise and fall in related cycles.

FIGURE 4

Predator Adaptations

A jellyfish's tentacles contain a poisonous substance that paralyzes tiny water animals. The sundew is a plant that is covered with sticky bulbs on stalks. When a fly lands on a bulb, it remains snared in the sticky goo while the plant digests it.

Make Models Imagine an ideal predator to prey upon a porcupine. Draw or describe your predator below and label its adaptations.

Predator Adaptations Predators, such as those in **Figure 4**, have adaptations that help them catch and kill their prey. A cheetah can run very fast for a short time, enabling it to catch its prey. Some predators, such as owls and bats, have adaptations that enable them to hunt at night when their prey, small mammals and insects, are active.

Prey Adaptations How do organisms avoid being killed by effective predators? The smelly spray of a skunk and the sharp quills of a porcupine help keep predators at a distance. As you can see in **Figure 5,** organisms have many kinds of adaptations that help them avoid becoming prey.

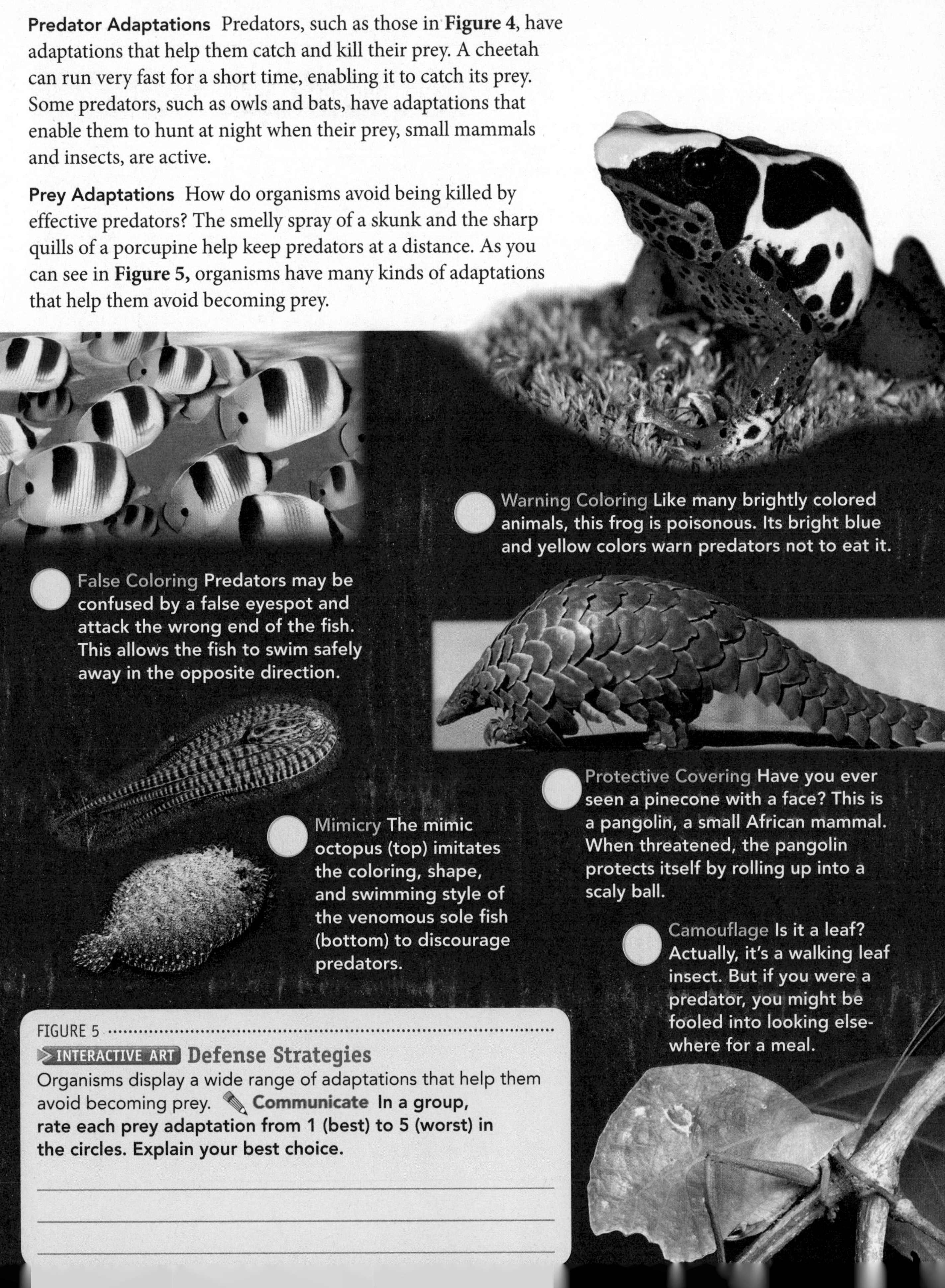

Warning Coloring Like many brightly colored animals, this frog is poisonous. Its bright blue and yellow colors warn predators not to eat it.

False Coloring Predators may be confused by a false eyespot and attack the wrong end of the fish. This allows the fish to swim safely away in the opposite direction.

Protective Covering Have you ever seen a pinecone with a face? This is a pangolin, a small African mammal. When threatened, the pangolin protects itself by rolling up into a scaly ball.

Mimicry The mimic octopus (top) imitates the coloring, shape, and swimming style of the venomous sole fish (bottom) to discourage predators.

Camouflage Is it a leaf? Actually, it's a walking leaf insect. But if you were a predator, you might be fooled into looking elsewhere for a meal.

FIGURE 5

INTERACTIVE ART **Defense Strategies**

Organisms display a wide range of adaptations that help them avoid becoming prey. **Communicate In a group, rate each prey adaptation from 1 (best) to 5 (worst) in the circles. Explain your best choice.**

____

____

____

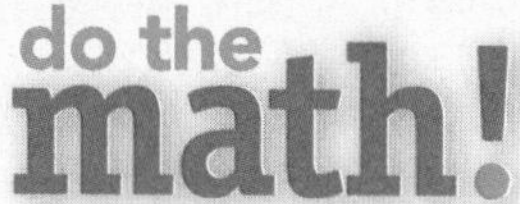

Predator-Prey Interactions

On Isle Royale, an island in Lake Superior, the populations of wolves (the predator) and moose (the prey) rise and fall in cycles. Use the graph to answer the questions.

Wolf and Moose Populations on Isle Royale

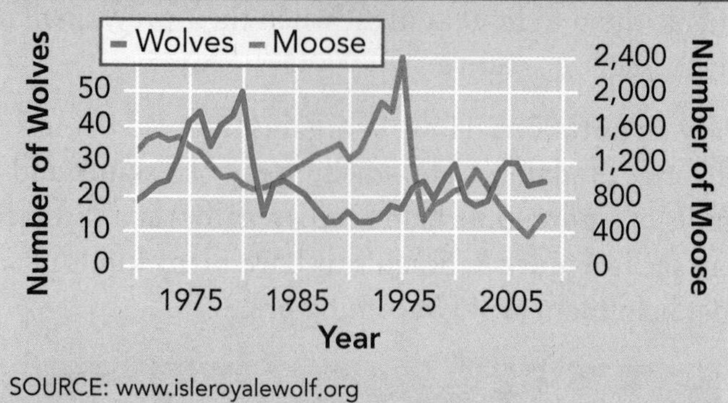

SOURCE: www.isleroyalewolf.org

1 **Read Graphs** What variable is plotted on the horizontal axis? What two variables are plotted on the vertical axis?

2 **Interpret Data** How did the moose population change between 2002 and 2007? What happened to the wolf population from 2003 through 2006?

3 **Draw Conclusions** How might the change in moose population have led to the change in the wolf population?

4 **Explain** What adaptations does a wolf have that make it a successful predator?

5 **Predict** How might disease in the wolf population one year affect the moose population the next year?

Lab zone® Do the Quick Lab *Competition and Predation.*

Assess Your Understanding

2a. Review Two main ways in which organisms interact are ______ and ______.

b. Describe Give an example of competition. Explain your answer.

c. Apply Concepts Owls often prey on mice. What adaptations do you think the mice have that help them avoid becoming prey?

got it?

O **I get it!** Now I know that competition and predation ______

O I need extra help with ______

Go to MY SCIENCE COACH *online for help with this subject.*

What Are the Three Types of Symbiosis?

Science Standards of Learning

LS.1b Develop a classification system based on multiple attributes.

LS.8c Investigate and understand competition and cooperation.

LS.8d Investigate and understand symbiotic relationships.

In addition to competition and predation, symbiosis is a third type of interaction among organisms. **Symbiosis** (sim bee OH sis) is any relationship in which two species live closely together and at least one of the species benefits. **The three main types of symbiotic relationships are mutualism, commensalism, and parasitism.**

Mutualism In some relationships, two species may depend on one another. This is true for some species of acacia trees and stinging ants in South America. The stinging ants nest only in the acacia tree, whose thorns discourage the ants' predators. The tree also provides the ants' only food. The ants, in turn, attack other animals that approach the tree and clear competing plants away from the base of the tree. This relationship is an example of **mutualism** (MYOO choo uh liz um). A relationship in which both species benefit is called mutualism. Other examples of mutualism can be seen in **Figure 6.**

FIGURE 6

Mutualism

An oxpecker rides and snacks aboard an impala. The oxpecker eat ticks living on the impala's ears. This interaction is an example of mutualism because both organisms benefit.

1. **Infer** How does the oxpecker benefit?

2. **Infer** How does the impala benefit?

3. **CHALLENGE** Explain how the relationship between the hummingbird and the flower is an example of mutualism.

Commensalism Have you ever seen a bird build a nest in a tree? The bird gets a place to live while the tree is unharmed. This relationship is an example of commensalism. **Commensalism** (kuh MEN suh liz um) is a relationship in which one species benefits and the other species is neither helped nor harmed. In nature, commensalism is not very common because two species are usually either helped or harmed a little by any interaction.

Relate Text and Visuals List the names of the parasites and the hosts in **Figure 7**.

Parasites	Hosts

Parasitism Many family pets get treated with medication to prevent tick and flea bites. Without treatment, pets can suffer from severe health problems as a result of these bites. A relationship that involves one organism living with, on, or inside another organism and harming it is called **parasitism** (PA ruh sit iz um). The organism that benefits is called a **parasite.** The organism it lives on or in is called a **host.** The parasite is usually smaller than the host. In a parasitic relationship, the parasite benefits while the host is harmed. Unlike a predator, a parasite does not usually kill the organism it feeds on. If the host dies, the parasite could lose its source of food or shelter.

Some parasites, like fleas and ticks, have adaptations that enable them to attach to their host and feed on its blood. Other examples of parasitism are shown in **Figure 7.**

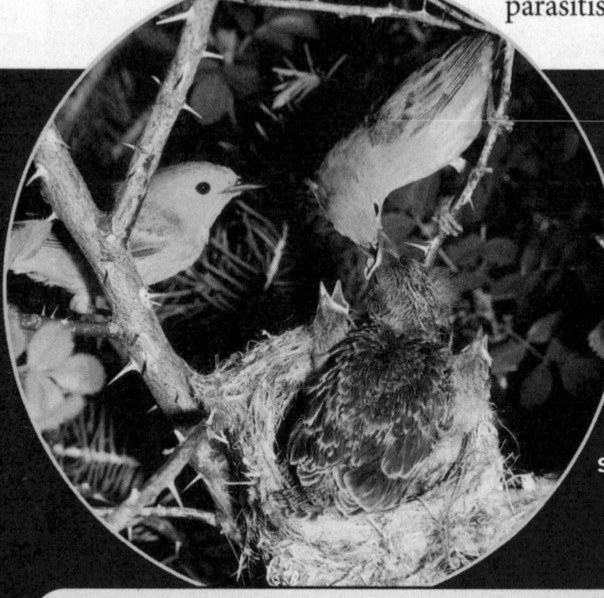

A parasitic cowbird laid its eggs in a yellow warbler's nest. The cowbird chick is outcompeting the warbler chicks for space and food.

Fish lice feed on the blood and other internal fluids of fish.

Dwarf mistletoe is a small parasitic flowering plant that grows into the bark of trees to obtain water and nutrients.

FIGURE 7

Parasitism

There are many examples of parasitic relationships. Besides fleas, ticks, and tapeworms, some plants and birds are parasites. **Explain Why doesn't a parasite usually kill its host?**

Classify Each photograph on the right represents a different type of symbiosis. Classify each interaction as mutualism, commensalism, or parasitism. Explain your answers.

Interaction 1: A remora fish attaches itself to the underside of a shark without harming the shark, and eats leftover bits of food from the shark's meals.

Interaction 2: A vampire bat drinks the blood of horses.

Interaction 3: A bee pollinates a flower.

1 Interaction 1

____

____

2 Interaction 2

____

____

3 Interaction 3

____

____

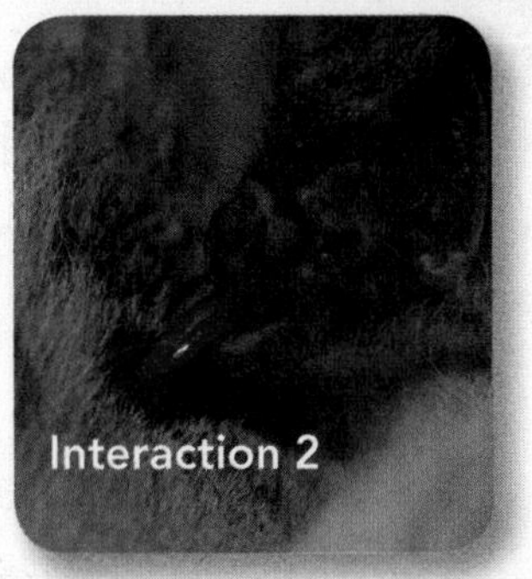

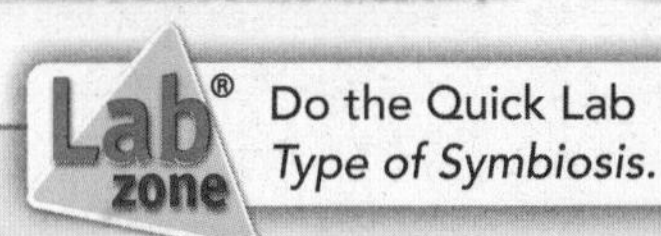

Do the Quick Lab *Type of Symbiosis.*

Assess Your Understanding

3a. Identify The three types of symbiosis are _______________, _______________, and _______________.

b. Classify Microscopic mites live at the base of human eyelashes, where they feed on tiny bits of dead skin. What type of symbiosis could this be? Explain your answer.

____

____

____

c. Compare and Contrast Name each type of symbiosis and explain how the two species are affected.

____

____

____

____

____

____

____

got it?

O **I get it!** Now I know that the three types of symbiosis differ in _______________

____

O I need extra help with _______________

Go to MY SCIENCE COACH *online for help with this subject.*

Virginia

LESSON 4

Changes in Communities

How Do Primary and Secondary Succession Differ?

LS.1d, LS.10b, LS.10c

my planet Diary

Fighting Fire With Fire

Wildfires are often reported in the national news. The images associated with these reports show how damaging these fires can be to property and to some ecosystems. What you may not know is that fire can actually help fight wildfires! Controlled burns, or prescribed burns, are fires that are purposely and carefully set by professional foresters. Prescribed burns are used to remove materials such as dead, dry branches and leaves that can fuel wildfires. A wildfire that occurs in an area that has previously been burned would cause less damage and be easier for firefighters to control.

This forester is carefully igniting a controlled burn.

MISCONCEPTION

Communicate Discuss these questions with a classmate. Write your answers below.

1. Why should only professional foresters set prescribed fires?

____

2. What do you think could be some other benefits to using prescribed burns in an ecosystem?

____

PLANET DIARY Go to **Planet Diary** to learn more about succession.

Do the Inquiry Warm-Up *How Communities Change.*

Science Standards of Learning

LS.1d Construct and use models and simulations to illustrate and explain phenomena.

LS.10b Investigate and understand factors that increase or decrease population size.

LS.10c Investigate and understand that ecosystems and organisms are dynamic through catastrophic disturbances.

How Do Primary and Secondary Succession Differ?

Fires, floods, volcanoes, hurricanes, and other natural disasters can change communities very quickly. But even without disasters, communities change. The series of predictable changes that occur in a community over time is called **succession.**

Vocabulary
- succession
- primary succession
- pioneer species
- secondary succession

Skills
- Reading: Compare and Contrast
- Inquiry: Observe

Primary Succession When a new island is formed by the eruption of an undersea volcano or an area of rock is uncovered by a melting sheet of ice, no living things are present. Over time, living things will inhabit these areas. **Primary succession** is the series of changes that occurs in an area where no soil or organisms exist.

Figure 1 shows how an area might change following a volcanic eruption. Just like the pioneers that first settled new frontiers, the first species to populate an area are called **pioneer species.** They are often carried to the area by wind or water. Typical pioneer species are mosses and lichens. Lichens are fungi and algae growing in a symbiotic relationship. As pioneer species grow, they help break up the rocks. When the organisms die, they provide nutrients that enrich the thin layer of soil that is forming on the rocks.

As plant seeds land in the new soil, they begin to grow. The specific plants that grow depend on the climate of the area. For example, in a cool, northern area, early seedlings might include alder and cottonwood trees. Eventually, succession may lead to a community of organisms that does not change unless the ecosystem is disturbed. Reaching this mature community can take centuries.

FIGURE 1

ART IN MOTION Primary Succession

Primary succession occurs in an area where no soil and no organisms exist.

Sequence In the circles, number the stage of primary succession to show the correct order of events.

Soil Creation
As pioneer species grow and die, soil forms. Some plants grow in this new soil.

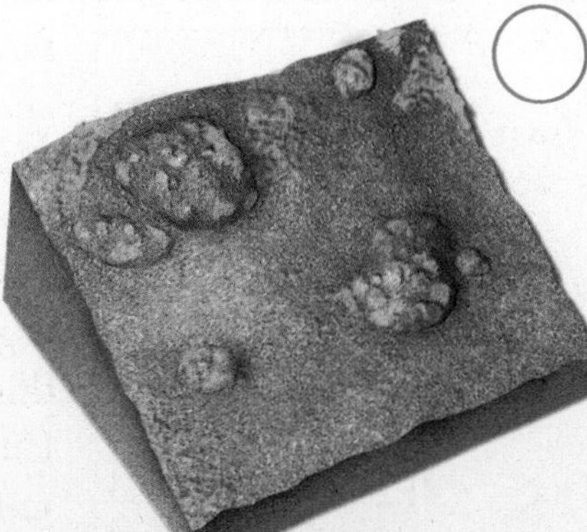

Pioneer Species
The first species to grow are pioneer species such as mosses and lichens.

Volcanic Eruption
Shortly after a volcanic eruption, there is no soil, only ash and rock.

Fertile Soil and Maturing Plants
As more plants die, they decompose and make the soil more fertile. New plants grow and existing plants mature in the fertile soil.

FIGURE 2

ART IN MOTION **Secondary Succession**

Secondary succession occurs following a disturbance to an ecosystem, such as clearing a forest for farmland.

Describe **Write a brief title that describes what happens at each of the four stages of secondary succession.**

Increasing time

Title: ______________________

Grasses and wildflowers have taken over this abandoned field.

Title: ______________________

After a few years, pine seedlings and other trees replace some of the grasses and wildflowers.

apply it!

Compare and Contrast Based on your reading, complete the table below.

Factors in Succession	Primary Succession	Secondary Succession
Possible Cause	Volcanic eruption	
Type of Area		
Existing Ecosystem?		

Secondary Succession In October 2007, huge wildfires raged across Southern California. The changes following the California fires are an example of secondary succession. **Secondary succession** is the series of changes that occurs in an area where the ecosystem has been disturbed, but where soil and organisms still exist. Natural disturbances that have this effect include fires, hurricanes, and tornadoes. Human activities, such as farming, logging, or mining, may also disturb an ecosystem and cause secondary succession to begin.

Unlike primary succession, secondary succession occurs in a place where an ecosystem currently exists. Secondary succession usually occurs more rapidly than primary succession because soil already exists and seeds from some plants remain in the soil. You can follow the process of succession in an abandoned field in **Figure 2.** After a century, a forest develops. This forest community may remain for a long time.

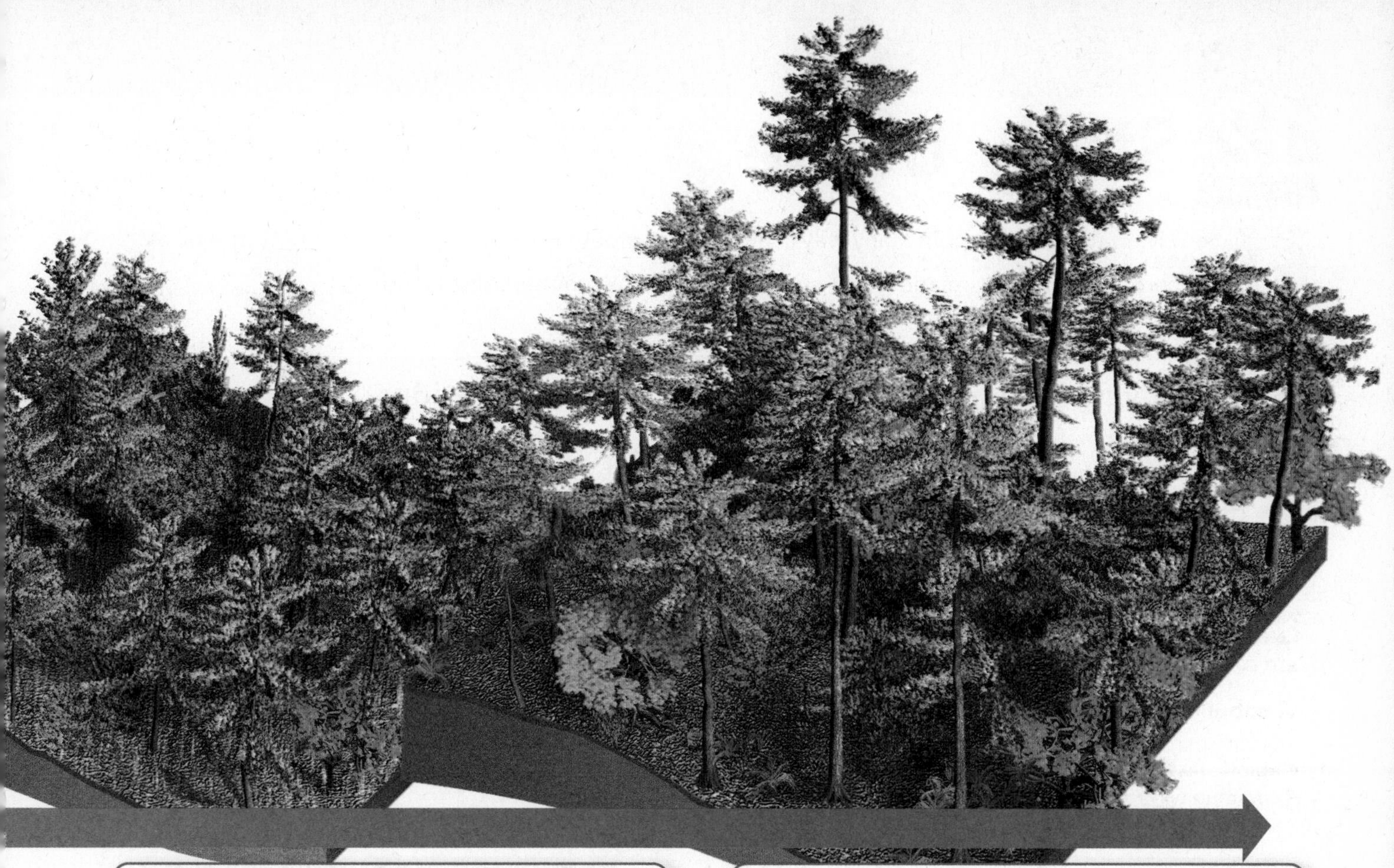

Title: ______________________

As tree growth continues, the trees begin to crowd out the grasses and wildflowers.

Title: ______________________

Eventually, a forest of mostly oak, hickory, and some pine dominates the landscape.

Lab zone® Do the Quick Lab *Primary or Secondary.*

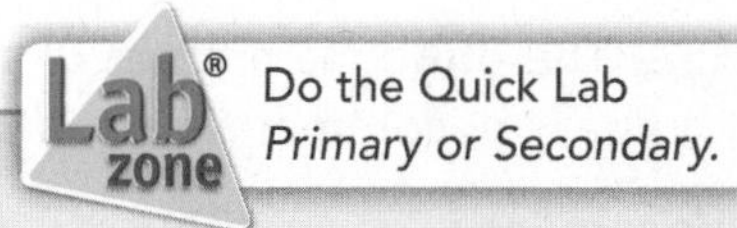

Assess Your Understanding

1a. Define Pioneer species are the ____________ species to populate an area.

b. Observe Is grass poking through a sidewalk crack primary or secondary succession? Why?

____

____

____

c. CHALLENGE Why are the changes during succession predictable?

____

____

____

____

got it?

O **I get it!** Now I know that primary and secondary succession differ in ______________________________

____

O I need extra help with ______________________________

Go to **MY SCIENCE COACH** *online for help with this subject.*

CHAPTER 12

Study Guide

Living things interact in many ways, including competition and ______________, as well as through symbiotic relationships such as mutualism, commensalism, and ________________.

LESSON 1 Living Things and the Environment

An organism gets the things it needs to live, grow, and reproduce from its environment.

Biotic and abiotic factors make up a habitat.

The levels of organization in an ecosystem are organism, population, and community.

Vocabulary

- organism • habitat • biotic factor
- abiotic factor • species • population
- community • ecosystem • ecology

LESSON 2 Populations

Populations can change in size when new members join the population or when members leave the population.

Some limiting factors for populations are weather conditions, space, food, and water.

Vocabulary

- birth rate • death rate • immigration
- emigration • population density
- limiting factor • carrying capacity

LESSON 3 Interactions Among Living Things

Every organism has a variety of adaptations that are suited to its specific living conditions to help it survive.

Two major types of interactions among organisms are competition and predation.

The three main types of symbiotic relationships are mutualism, commensalism, and parasitism.

Vocabulary

- natural selection • adaptation • niche • competition
- predation • predator • prey • symbiosis • mutualism
- commensalism • parasitism • parasite • host

LESSON 4 Changes in Communities

Unlike primary succession, secondary succession occurs in a place where an ecosystem currently exists.

Vocabulary

- succession
- primary succession
- pioneer species
- secondary succession

Review and Assessment

LESSON 1 Living Things and the Environment

1. A prairie dog, a hawk, and a snake are all members of the same
   - a. niche.
   - b. community.
   - c. species.
   - d. population.

2. Grass is an example of a(n) ________________ in a habitat.

3. **Sequence** Put these levels in order from the smallest to the largest: population, organism, ecosystem, community.

____

____

4. **Apply Concepts** Name two biotic and two abiotic factors you might find in a forest ecosystem.

____

____

5. **Draw Conclusions** In 1815, Mount Tambora, a volcano in Indonesia, erupted. So much volcanic ash and dust filled the atmosphere that 1816 is referred to as the "Year Without a Summer." How might a volcanic eruption affect the abiotic factors in an organism's habitat?

____

____

____

____

____

6. **Write About It** Write at least one paragraph describing your habitat. Describe how you get the food, water, and shelter you need from your habitat. How does this habitat meet your needs in ways that another would not?

LESSON 2 Populations

7. All of the following are limiting factors for populations except
   - a. space.
   - b. food.
   - c. time.
   - d. weather.

8. ________________ occurs when individuals leave a population.

Use the data table to answer the questions below. Ecologists monitoring a deer population collect data during a 30-year study.

Year	0	5	10	15	20	25	30
Population (thousands)	15	30	65	100	40	25	10

9. **Graph** Use the data to make a line graph.

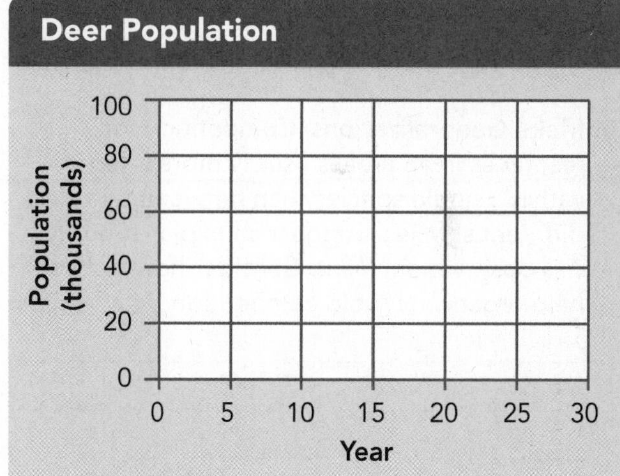

10. **Interpret Data** In which year was the deer population the highest? The lowest?

____

11. **Develop Hypotheses** In Year 16 of the study, this region experienced a severe winter. How might this have affected the deer population?

____

____

____

____

CHAPTER

12 Review and Assessment

LESSON 3 Interactions Among Living Things

12. In which type of interaction do both species benefit?

a. predation
b. mutualism
c. commensalism
d. parasitism

13. A parasite lives on or inside its ___________.

14. **Relate Cause and Effect** Name two prey adaptations. How does each adaptation protect the organism?

15. **Make Generalizations** Competition for resources in an area is usually more intense within a single species than between two different species. Suggest an explanation for this observation. (*Hint:* Consider how niches help organisms avoid competition.)

16. **Write About It** Some scientists think that the relationship between clownfish and sea anemones is an example of commensalism. Other scientists think that the relationship is mutualism. If this relationship is actually mutualism, how might both the clownfish and sea anemone benefit?

LESSON 4 Changes in Communities

17. The series of predictable changes that occur in a community over time is called

a. natural selection
b. ecology
c. commensalism
d. succession

18. ___________________________ are the first species to populate an area.

19. **Classify** Lichens and mosses have just begun to grow on the rocky area shown below. What type of succession is occurring? Explain.

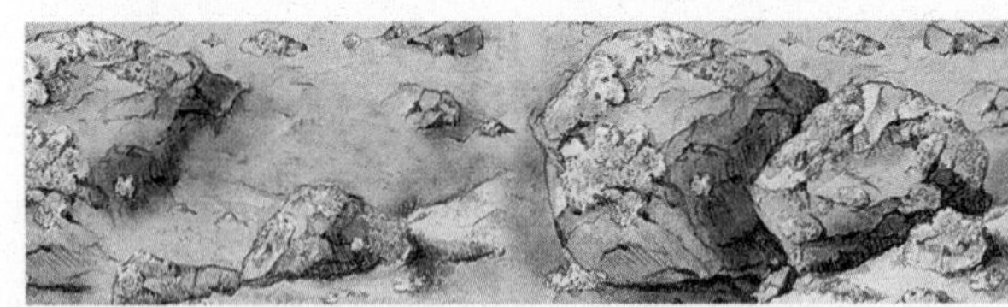

APPLY THE BIG ? How do living things affect one another?

20. Humans interact with their environment on a daily basis. These interactions can have both positive and negative effects. Using at least four vocabulary terms from this chapter, describe a human interaction and the effect it has on the environment.

Virginia SOL Test Prep

Read each question and choose the best answer.

1 Symbiotic relationships include mutualism, commensalism, and parasitism. Which of the images below shows mutualism?

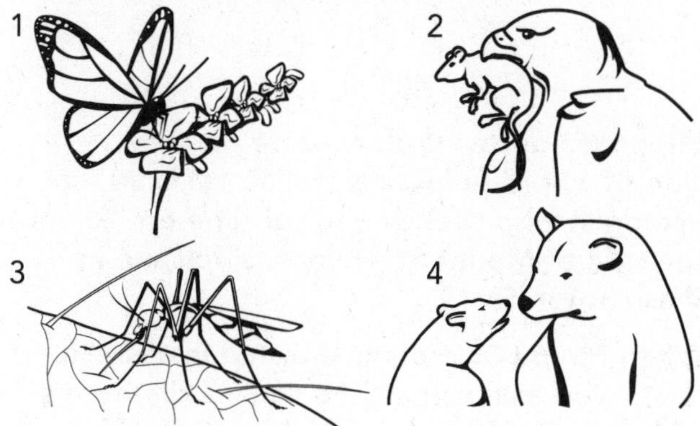

A Image 1

B Image 2

C Image 3

D Image 4

2 In general, which of the following is a true statement about population size?

F If birth rate < death rate, population size increases.

G If death rate < birth rate, population size decreases.

H If birth rate > death rate, population size increases.

J If death rate > birth rate, population size increases.

3 Ecosystems have different levels of organization. A group of similar organisms makes up a ________________, which, along with other types of organisms, makes up a(n) ________________.

A species, population

B habitat, ecosystem

C population, community

D population, habitat

4 Three different bird species all live in the same trees in an area, but competition between the birds rarely occurs. Which of the following is a likely explanation for this lack of competition?

F The three species occupy different niches.

G The three species eat the same food.

H The three species have a limited supply of food.

J The three species live in the same part of the trees.

5 Which of the following is a typical pioneer species?

A grass

B lichen

C pine trees

D soil

6 An organism interacts with both the biotic and abiotic factors in its habitat. Which is an abiotic factor shown in the drawing below?

F plants

G insects

H fish

J sunlight

7 The series of changes that occurs in an area where no soil or organisms exist is called—

A commensalism

B secondary succession

C carrying capacity

D primary succession

SCIENCE MATTERS

Careers

SUCCESSION ECOLOGIST

These lupine plants are growing out of the volcanic ash on Mount St. Helens, 20 years after its last eruption.

Suppose your workplace were on the side of a volcano! Roger del Moral is an ecologist who spends a lot of time on the side of Mount St. Helens, a volcano in Washington State.

When Mount St. Helens erupted in 1980, it destroyed as much as 518 square kilometers of forest. Del Moral and his team study how plant communities form in the aftermath of volcanic eruptions. They visit the volcano regularly to identify plants and estimate the remaining populations of plants to describe how the plant communities are recovering. This work enables researchers to develop more effective ways to help areas recover from human-caused environmental changes.

Del Moral loves his work and says, "My work on Mount St. Helens allows me to follow my passion, train students, and contribute to a better understanding of how the world works."

If you are interested in ecology, try volunteering or interning at a local park or field museum. National parks also have Junior Naturalist programs designed to give you experience in the field.

Compare It Find a park in your neighborhood or town and describe the kinds of plants you find. Make a table in which you list each kind of plant, describe it, describe where it grew, and draw conclusions about the reasons why it might have grown there.

LS.1a, LS.1b, LS.1i, LS.1j, LS.8e, LS.10b, LS.10c

Binocular Boot Camp

▼ Populations of common and rare birds can be estimated based on input from students like you!

Kids Doing Science

Scientists need all the help they can get estimating large populations! Binocular Boot Camp, a program for kids in Sonoma Valley, California, trains kids to identify the songs, calls, and flight patterns of birds. Participants form teams and identify and count as many birds as they can in one afternoon. The information they gather gets entered into a huge database of bird observations.

You don't have to go to Binocular Boot Camp to help, though. For four days in February, schools, clubs, and individuals in the United States and Canada take part in the Great Backyard Bird Count (GBBC). All you need to do is count birds for 15 minutes, then fill out a form to help scientists learn how climate change, habitat change, and other factors affect bird populations.

Research It Find out more about the GBBC. Design a poster or use presentation software to create a presentation to convince your school to participate.

LS.1j

Bird Radio

Think Like a Scientist

How accurate are estimates of bird populations? Scientists at North Carolina State University wondered whether background noise affects scientists' ability to count bird populations. They used Bird Radio to find out.

Bird Radio won't be on the top 40—unless birds get a vote. It plays bird songs to simulate a wild bird population. Researchers adjusted background noise and the number of different bird songs. They learned that this affected people's ability to estimate the number of "birds" singing on Bird Radio. Even slight increases in background noise reduced the accuracy of population counts by up to 40 percent! Scientists are using these data to develop better ways to estimate bird populations.

Test It Create a log sheet for population estimates. The next time you are in a room with other people, close your eyes and try to estimate the number of people in the room. Then count them. Was your estimate close? What factors affected it? Try this experiment in five different settings and record what happens each time.

LS.1a, LS.1e, LS.1f, LS.1g, LS.1i, LS.1j

WHERE DOES FOOD COME FROM?

How do energy and matter move through ecosystems?

Flying around hunting for food, this barn owl spots a mouse for dinner. But what did the mouse eat? Perhaps it nibbled on seeds or a caterpillar. Then you might ask, where did the seeds and caterpillar get their food?

Develop Hypotheses **Where do living things get their food?**

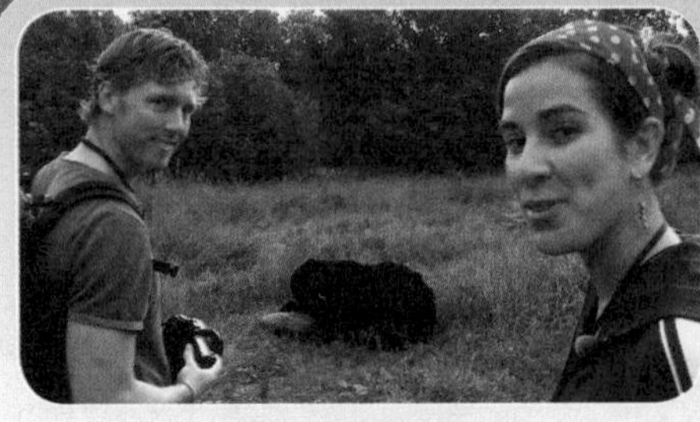

UNTAMED SCIENCE Watch the **Untamed Science** video to learn more about ecosystems and biomes.

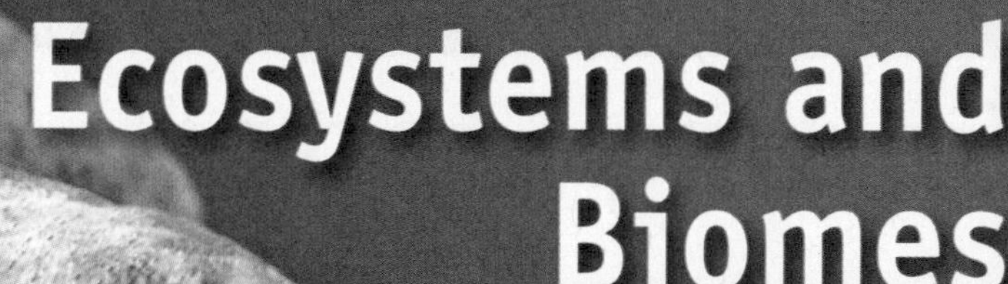

Ecosystems and Biomes

Science Standards of Learning

LS.1a, LS.1c, LS.1d, LS.1f, LS.1h, LS.1i, LS.1j, LS.5a, LS.5b, LS.5c, LS.6a, LS.6b, LS.6c, LS.6d, LS.7a, LS.8a, LS.8b, LS.9a, LS.9b, LS.9c, LS.10b, LS.10c, LS.11b, LS.11c, LS.11d, LS.11e

CHAPTER

13 Getting Started

Check Your Understanding

1. **Background** Read the paragraph below and then answer the question.

> One morning, Han walks to the park and sits by the pond. He has just studied **ecosystems** in class, and now, looking at the pond, he realizes he sees things in a new way. He notices a turtle sunning itself on a rock, and knows that the sun and rock are **abiotic factors,** while the turtle, and other living things, are **biotic factors.**

The community of organisms that live in a particular area, along with their nonliving environment, make up an **ecosystem.**

Abiotic factors are the nonliving parts of an organism's habitat.

Biotic factors are the living parts of an organism's habitat.

- Name one more biotic factor and one more abiotic factor that Han might see at the pond.

____

____

MY READING WEB If you had trouble answering the question above, visit **My Reading Web** and type in ***Ecosystems and Biomes.***

Vocabulary Skill

Prefixes Some words can be divided into parts. A root is the part of the word that carries the basic meaning. A prefix is a word part that is placed in front of the root to change the word's meaning. The prefixes below will help you understand some vocabulary in this chapter.

Prefix	Meaning	Example
bio-	life	biogeography, *n.* the study of where organisms live
inter-	between	intertidal, *adj.* ocean zone between the highest high-tide line and the lowest low-tide line

2. **Quick Check Circle the prefix in each boldface word below.**
   - There was an **intermission** between the acts of the play.
   - The **biosphere** is the area where life exists.

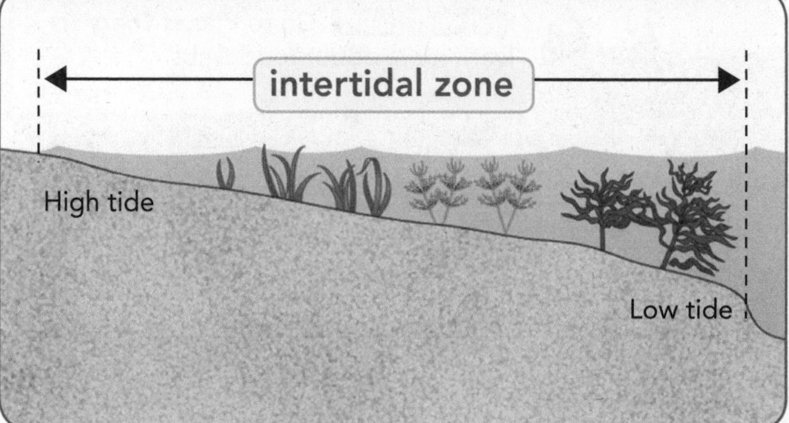

Chapter Preview

LESSON 1

- producer • consumer
- herbivore • carnivore • omnivore
- scavenger • decomposer
- food chain • food web
- energy pyramid

Relate Text and Visuals
Classify

LESSON 2

- evaporation • condensation
- precipitation • nitrogen fixation

Sequence
Infer

LESSON 3

- biome • climate • desert
- rain forest • emergent layer
- canopy • understory • grassland
- savanna • deciduous tree
- boreal forest • coniferous tree
- tundra • permafrost

Compare and Contrast
Draw Conclusions

LESSON 4

- estuary
- intertidal zone
- neritic zone

Outline
Communicate

LESSON 5

- biogeography
- continental drift • dispersal
- exotic species

Relate Cause and Effect
Predict

 VOCAB FLASH CARDS For extra help with vocabulary, visit **Vocab Flash Cards** and type in ***Ecosystems and Biomes.***

Energy Flow in Ecosystems

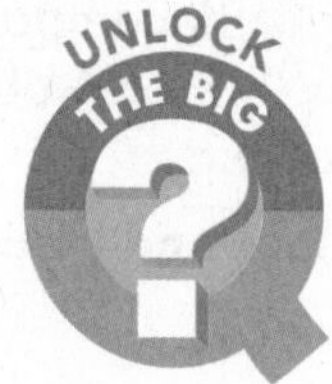

What Are the Energy Roles in an Ecosystem?
LS.5a, LS.5b, LS.5c, LS.6b, LS.8a

How Does Energy Move Through an Ecosystem?
LS.1d, LS.1j, LS.6b, LS.6c, LS.6d, LS.8b

my planet Diary

DISCOVERY

I'll Have the Fish

Scientists have noticed something fishy going on with the wolves in British Columbia, Canada. During autumn, the wolves ignore their typical food of deer and moose and feast on salmon instead. Salmon are very nutritious and lack the big horns and hoofs that can injure or kill wolves. Plus, there are plenty of fish in a small area, making them easier to find and catch.

Many animals, including the wolves, depend upon the salmon's annual mating trip upstream. Losing this important food source to overfishing would hurt the populations of bears, wolves, birds, and many other animals.

Communicate **Discuss these questions with a classmate. Write your answers below.**

1. What are two reasons the wolves may eat fish in autumn instead of deer or moose?

____

____

2. What effect could overfishing salmon have on an ecosystem?

____

____

____

____

____

PLANET DIARY Go to **Planet Diary** to learn more about food webs.

Do the Inquiry Warm-Up *Where Did Your Dinner Come From?*

Vocabulary

- producer • consumer • herbivore • carnivore
- omnivore • scavenger • decomposer • food chain
- food web • energy pyramid

Skills

- Reading: Relate Text and Visuals
- Inquiry: Classify

What Are the Energy Roles in an Ecosystem?

Do you play an instrument in your school band? If so, you know that each instrument has a role in a piece of music. Similar to instruments in a band, each organism has a role in the movement of energy through its ecosystem.

An organism's energy role is determined by how it obtains food and how it interacts with other organisms. **Each of the organisms in an ecosystem fills the energy role of producer, consumer, or decomposer.**

Producers Energy enters most ecosystems as sunlight. Some organisms, like the plants and algae shown in **Figure 1,** and some types of bacteria, capture the energy of sunlight and store it as food energy. These organisms use the sun's energy to turn water and carbon dioxide into food molecules in a process called photosynthesis.

An organism that can make its own food is a **producer.** Producers are the source of all the food in an ecosystem. In a few ecosystems, producers obtain energy from a source other than sunlight. One such ecosystem is found in rocks deep beneath the ground. Certain bacteria in this ecosystem produce their own food using the energy in hydrogen sulfide, a gas that is present in their environment.

Science Standards of Learning

LS.5a Investigate and understand energy transfer between sunlight and chlorophyll.

LS.5b Investigate and understand transformation of water and carbon dioxide into sugar and oxygen in photosynthesis.

LS.5c Investigate and understand photosynthesis as foundation of virtually all food webs.

LS.6b Investigate and understand interactions resulting in a flow of energy and matter throughout an ecosystem.

LS.8a Investigate and understand the relationships among producers, consumers, and decomposers in food webs.

FIGURE 1

Producers

Producers are organisms that can make their own food.

Identify Complete the shopping list below to identify the producers that are part of your diet.

- ○ wheat
- ○ corn
- ○ banana
- ○
- ○
- ○
- ○
- ○
- ○

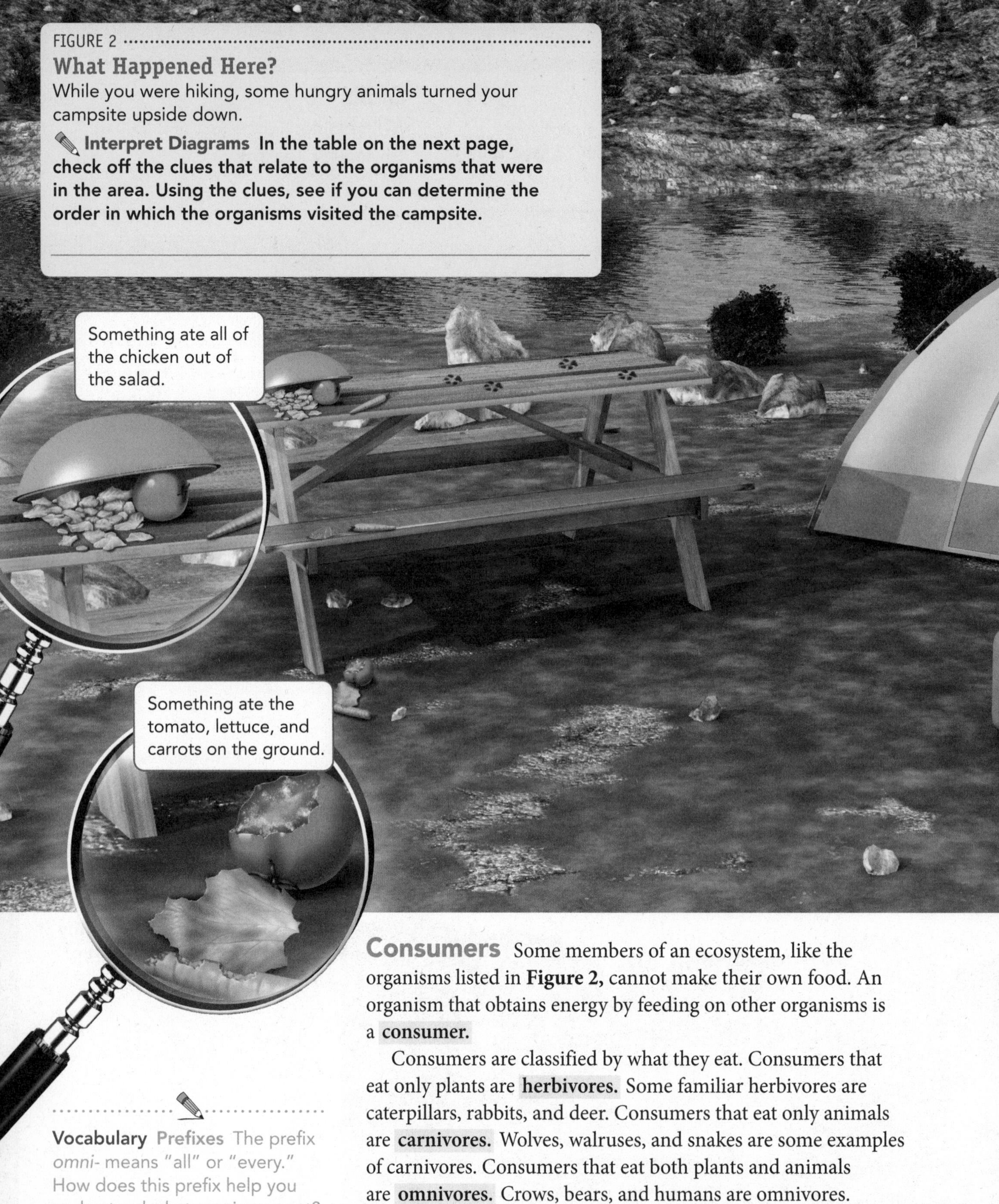

FIGURE 2

What Happened Here?

While you were hiking, some hungry animals turned your campsite upside down.

Interpret Diagrams In the table on the next page, check off the clues that relate to the organisms that were in the area. Using the clues, see if you can determine the order in which the organisms visited the campsite.

Consumers Some members of an ecosystem, like the organisms listed in **Figure 2,** cannot make their own food. An organism that obtains energy by feeding on other organisms is a **consumer.**

Consumers are classified by what they eat. Consumers that eat only plants are **herbivores.** Some familiar herbivores are caterpillars, rabbits, and deer. Consumers that eat only animals are **carnivores.** Wolves, walruses, and snakes are some examples of carnivores. Consumers that eat both plants and animals are **omnivores.** Crows, bears, and humans are omnivores.

Some carnivores are scavengers. A **scavenger** is a carnivore that feeds on the bodies of dead organisms. Scavengers include catfish and vultures.

Vocabulary Prefixes The prefix *omni-* means "all" or "every." How does this prefix help you understand what omnivores eat?

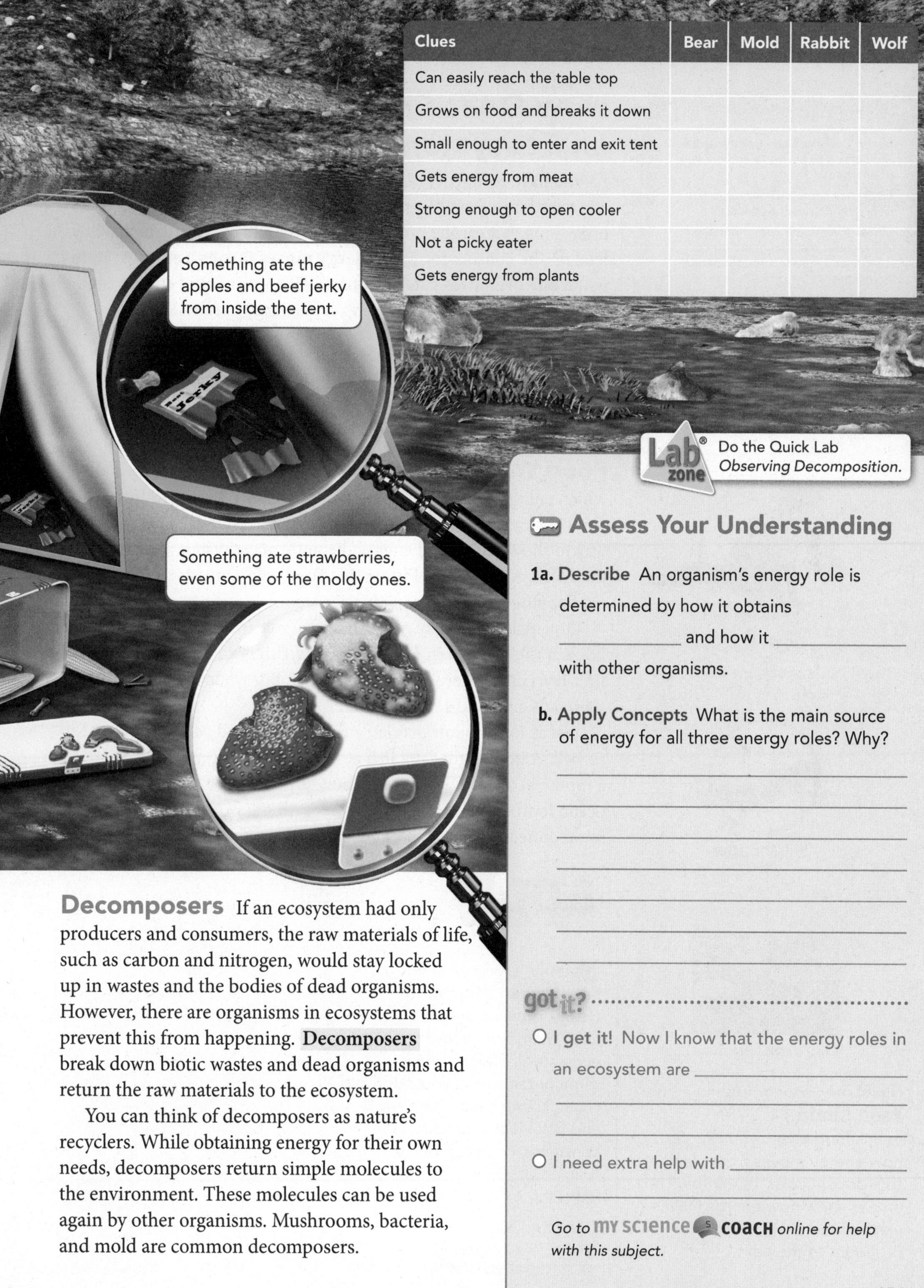

Clues	Bear	Mold	Rabbit	Wolf
Can easily reach the table top				
Grows on food and breaks it down				
Small enough to enter and exit tent				
Gets energy from meat				
Strong enough to open cooler				
Not a picky eater				
Gets energy from plants				

Decomposers If an ecosystem had only producers and consumers, the raw materials of life, such as carbon and nitrogen, would stay locked up in wastes and the bodies of dead organisms. However, there are organisms in ecosystems that prevent this from happening. **Decomposers** break down biotic wastes and dead organisms and return the raw materials to the ecosystem.

You can think of decomposers as nature's recyclers. While obtaining energy for their own needs, decomposers return simple molecules to the environment. These molecules can be used again by other organisms. Mushrooms, bacteria, and mold are common decomposers.

Lab® zone Do the Quick Lab *Observing Decomposition.*

Assess Your Understanding

1a. Describe An organism's energy role is determined by how it obtains _______________ and how it _______________ with other organisms.

b. Apply Concepts What is the main source of energy for all three energy roles? Why?

____

____

____

____

____

____

____

got it? ....

O **I get it!** Now I know that the energy roles in an ecosystem are ____

____

____

O I need extra help with ____

____

Go to **MY SCIENCE COACH** *online for help with this subject.*

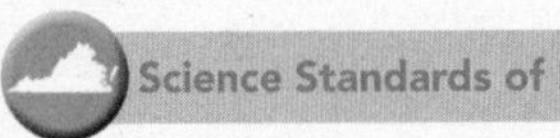

Science Standards of Learning

LS.1d Construct and use models and simulations to illustrate and explain phenomena.

LS.1j Use current applications to reinforce life science concepts.

LS.6b Investigate and understand interactions resulting in a flow of energy and matter throughout an ecosystem.

LS.6c Investigate and understand complex relationships within terrestrial, freshwater, and marine ecosystems.

LS.6d Investigate and understand energy flow in food webs and energy pyramids.

LS.8b Investigate and understand the relationship between predators and prey.

How Does Energy Move Through an Ecosystem?

As you have read, energy enters most ecosystems as sunlight and is converted into food by producers. This energy is transferred to the organisms that eat the producers, and then to other organisms that feed on the consumers. **Energy moves through an ecosystem when one organism eats another.** This movement of energy can be shown as food chains, food webs, and energy pyramids.

Food Chains One way to show how energy moves in an ecosystem is with a food chain. A **food chain** is a series of events in which one organism eats another and obtains energy. You can follow one example of a food chain in **Figure 3.**

Food Webs A food chain shows only one possible path along which energy can move through an ecosystem. Most producers and consumers are part of many food chains. A more realistic way to show the flow of energy through an ecosystem is with a food web. As shown in **Figure 4,** a **food web** consists of many overlapping food chains in an ecosystem.

Organisms may play more than one role in an ecosystem. Look at the crayfish in **Figure 4.** A crayfish is an omnivore that is a first-level consumer when it eats plants. But when a crayfish eats a snail, it is a second-level consumer.

Just as food chains overlap and connect, food webs interconnect as well. A gull might eat a fish at the ocean, but it might also eat a mouse at a landfill. The gull, then, is part of two food webs—an ocean food web and a land food web. All the world's food webs interconnect in what can be thought of as a global food web.

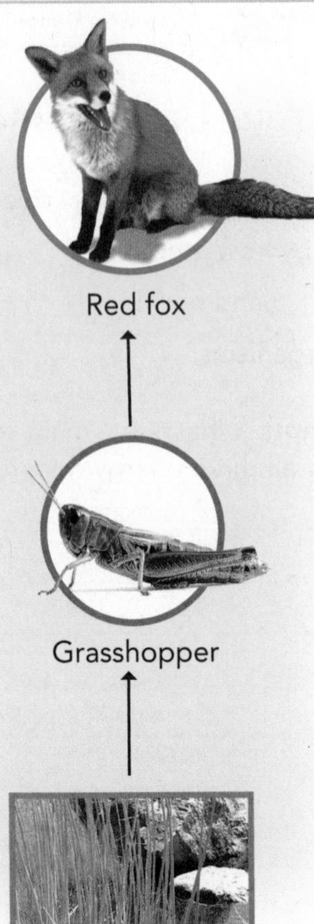

FIGURE 3

Food Chain

In this food chain, you can see how energy moves from plants, to a grasshopper, to the fox. The arrows show how energy moves up the food chain, from one organism to the next.

apply it!

Classify Using what you have learned about food chains, draw or describe a food chain from your local ecosystem. Show at least three organisms in your food chain. Name each organism and label it as a producer, consumer, or decomposer.

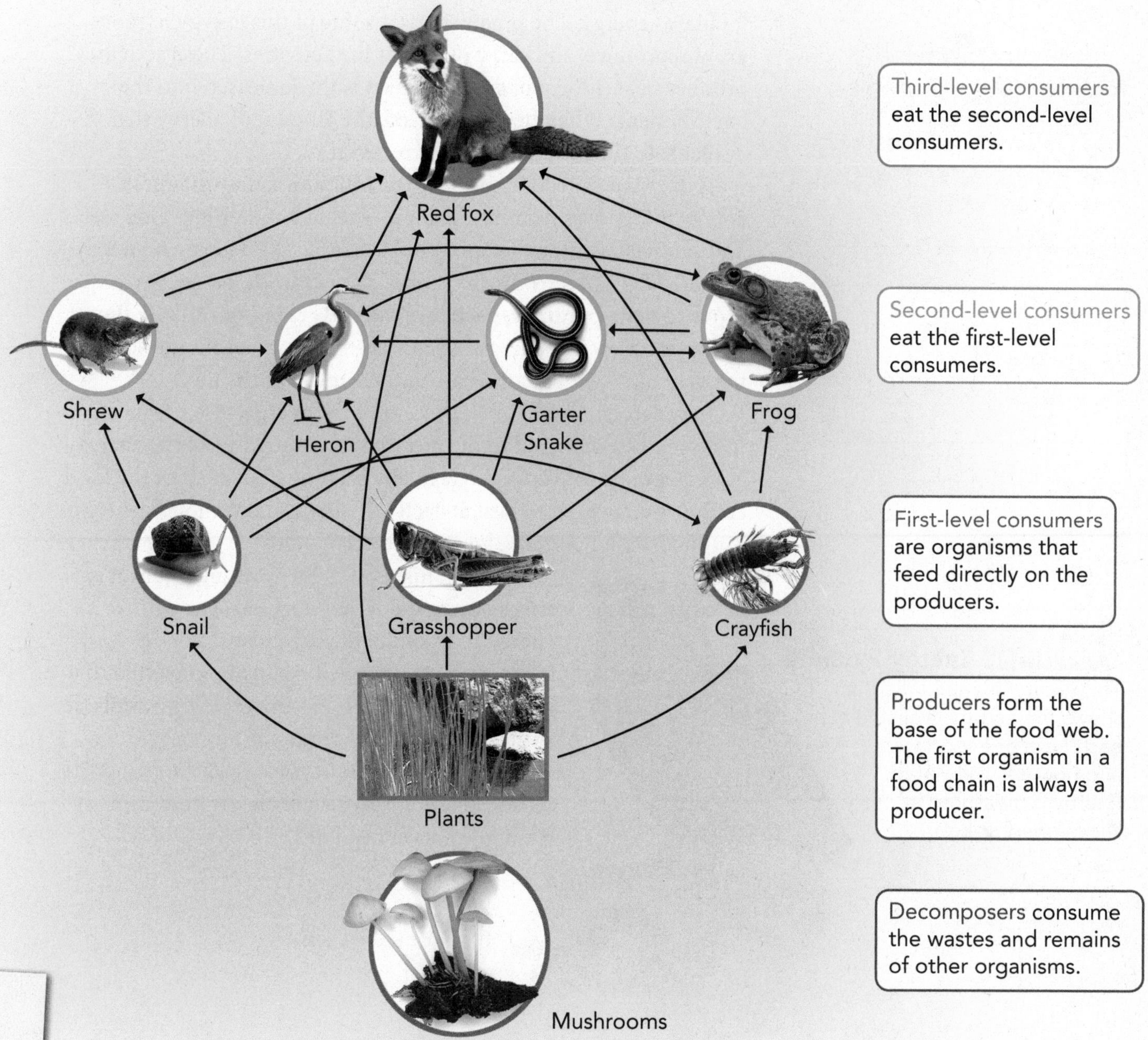

Red fox

Shrew

Heron

Garter Snake

Frog

Snail

Grasshopper

Crayfish

Plants

Mushrooms

Third-level consumers eat the second-level consumers.

Second-level consumers eat the first-level consumers.

First-level consumers are organisms that feed directly on the producers.

Producers form the base of the food web. The first organism in a food chain is always a producer.

Decomposers consume the wastes and remains of other organisms.

FIGURE 4

Food Web

A food web consists of many interconnected food chains.

Complete the tasks.

1. **Interpret Diagrams** Pick two organisms from the food web. Draw arrows connecting them to the decomposers.

2. **Relate Text and Visuals** How can the fox be both a second-level and third-level consumer?

Relate Text and Visuals Look at the energy pyramid. Why is a pyramid the best shape to show how energy moves through an ecosystem?

Energy Pyramids

When an organism in an ecosystem eats, it obtains energy. The organism uses some of this energy to move, grow, reproduce, and carry out other life activities. These activities produce heat, a form of energy, which is then released into the environment. When heat is released, the amount of energy that is available to the next consumer is reduced.

A diagram called an **energy pyramid** shows the amount of energy that moves from one feeding level to another in a food web. You can see an energy pyramid in **Figure 5.** **The most energy is available at the producer level of the pyramid. As energy moves up the pyramid, each level has less energy available than the level below.** An energy pyramid gets its name from the shape of the diagram—wider at the base and narrower at the top.

In general, only about 10 percent of the energy at one level of a food web is transferred to the next higher level. Most of the energy at each level is converted to heat. Since about 90 percent of the food energy is converted to heat at each step, there is not enough energy to support many feeding levels in an ecosystem.

The organisms at higher feeding levels of an energy pyramid do not necessarily require less energy to live than the organisms at lower levels. Because so much energy is converted to heat at each level, the amount of energy available at the producer level limits the number of consumers that the ecosystem is able to support. As a result, there are usually fewer organisms at the highest level in a food web.

FIGURE 5

VIRTUAL LAB Energy Pyramid

This energy pyramid diagram shows the energy available at each level of a food web and how it is calculated. Energy is measured in kilocalories, or kcal.

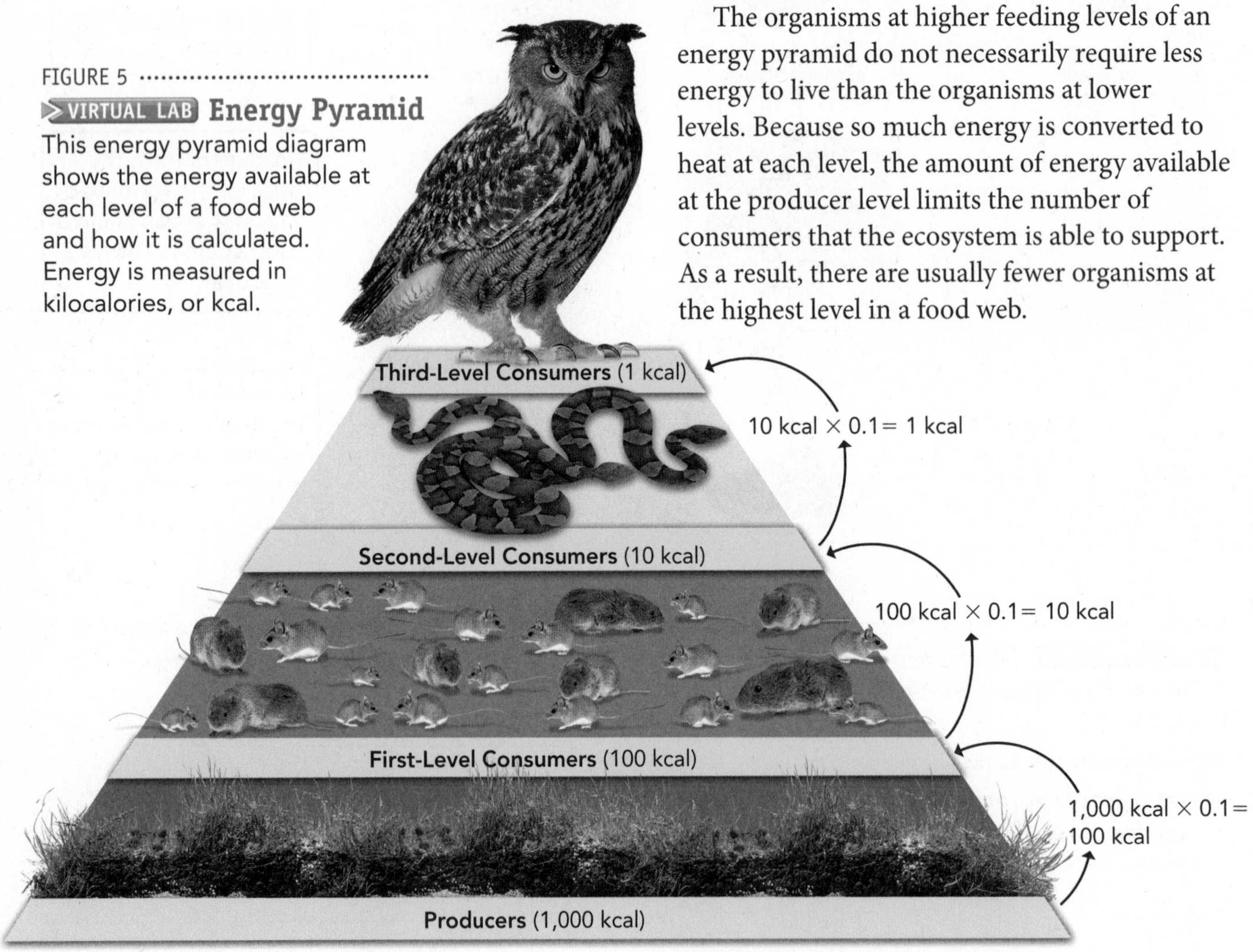

do the math!

Energy Pyramids

Suppose that the producers at the base of an energy pyramid contain 330,000 kilocalories.

Calculate Using **Figure 5** as a guide, label how much energy would be available at each level of the pyramid based on the questions below.

Third-Level Consumers

Second-Level Consumers

First-Level Consumers

330,000 kcal

Producers

1. If mice ate all of the plants, how much energy would be available to them as first-level consumers?
2. If all of the mice were eaten by snakes, how much energy would the snakes receive?
3. If all of the snakes were eaten by the owl, how much energy would the owl receive?
4. CHALLENGE About how much energy would the owl use for its life processes or lose as heat? ______
5. CHALLENGE How much energy would be stored in the owl's body? ______

Lab zone® Do the Lab Investigation *Ecosystem Food Chains.*

Assess Your Understanding

2a. Define A food (web/chain) is a series of events in which one organism eats another and obtains energy. A food (web/chain) consists of many overlapping food (webs/chains).

b. Compare and Contrast Why is a food web a more realistic way of portraying an ecosystem than a food chain?

______

c. Relate Cause and Effect Why are there usually fewer organisms at the top of an energy pyramid?

______

got it? ....

O **I get it!** Now I know that energy moves through an ecosystem when ______

O I need extra help with ______

Go to **MY SCIENCE COACH** *online for help with this subject.*

Cycles of Matter

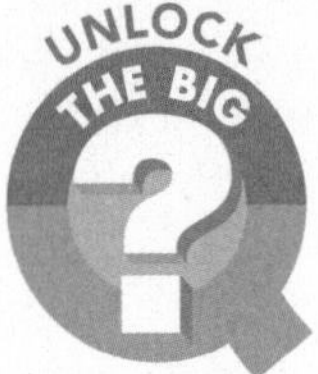

What Processes Are Involved in the Water Cycle?
LS.6a, LS.6b

How Are the Carbon and Oxygen Cycles Related?
LS.5b, LS.5c, LS.6a, LS.6b, LS.6c, LS.6d

How Does Nitrogen Cycle Through Ecosystems?
LS.1d, LS.6a, LS.6b, LS.6c, LS.6d

my planet Diary

DISASTER

Canaries and Coal

Have you ever stopped to listen to a bird sing? If you were a coal miner in the early 1900s, your life may have depended on it! Sometimes miners stumbled upon pockets of carbon monoxide, a toxic, odorless gas that makes it difficult for the body to get enough oxygen. Without fresh air circulating in the mineshafts, the miners would fall asleep and eventually die. To prevent this disaster from happening, canaries were used to monitor the air quality. A singing canary indicated that all was well. If the canary stopped singing and died, the miners knew that they needed to quickly leave the mine.

Answer the question below.

Do you think it was ethical, or fair, to use canaries this way? Explain.

____

____

____

____

PLANET DIARY Go to **Planet Diary** to learn more about cycles of matter.

Do the Inquiry Warm-Up *Are You Part of a Cycle?*

Science Standards of Learning

LS.6a Investigate and understand carbon, water, and nitrogen cycles.

LS.6b Investigate and understand interactions resulting in a flow of energy and matter throughout an ecosystem.

What Processes Are Involved in the Water Cycle?

Recycling is important for ecosystems because matter is limited. To understand how matter cycles through an ecosystem, you need to know a few terms that describe the structure of matter. Matter is made up of tiny particles called atoms. Two or more atoms that are joined and act as a unit make up a molecule. For example, a water molecule consists of two hydrogen atoms and one oxygen atom.

Water is essential for life. The water cycle is the continuous process by which water moves from Earth's surface to the atmosphere and back. **The processes of evaporation, condensation, and precipitation make up the water cycle.**

Vocabulary
- evaporation
- condensation
- precipitation
- nitrogen fixation

Skills
- Reading: Sequence
- Inquiry: Infer

FIGURE 1

INTERACTIVE ART **Water Cycle**

In the water cycle, water moves continuously from Earth's surface to the atmosphere and back.

Identify As you read, label the three processes of the water cycle in the diagram.

Evaporation

How does water from the ground get into the air? The process by which molecules of liquid water absorb energy and change to a gas is called **evaporation.** The energy for evaporation comes from the heat of the sun. In the water cycle, liquid water evaporates from oceans, lakes, and other sources and forms water vapor, a gas, in the atmosphere. Smaller amounts of water also evaporate from living things. Plants release water vapor from their leaves. You release liquid water in your wastes and water vapor when you exhale.

Condensation As water vapor rises higher in the atmosphere, it cools down. The cooled vapor then turns back into tiny drops of liquid water. The process by which a gas changes to a liquid is called **condensation.** The water droplets collect around dust particles and form clouds.

Precipitation As more water vapor condenses, the drops of water in the clouds grow larger. Eventually the heavy drops fall to Earth as **precipitation**—rain, snow, sleet, or hail. Precipitation may fall into oceans, lakes, or rivers. The precipitation that falls on land may soak into the soil and become groundwater, or run off the land, flowing back into a river or ocean.

Do the Quick Lab *Following Water.*

Assess Your Understanding

got it?

- O **I get it!** Now I know that the processes of the water cycle are ________________
- O I need extra help with ________________

Go to **my science COACH** *online for help with this subject.*

Science Standards of Learning

LS.5b Investigate and understand transformation of water and carbon dioxide into sugar and oxygen in photosynthesis.

LS.5c Investigate and understand photosynthesis as foundation of virtually all food webs.

LS.6a Investigate and understand carbon, water, and nitrogen cycles.

LS.6b Investigate and understand the interactions resulting in a flow of energy and matter throughout an ecosystem.

LS.6c Investigate and understand complex relationships within terrestrial ecosystems.

LS.6d Investigate and understand energy flow in food webs.

How Are the Carbon and Oxygen Cycles Related?

Carbon and oxygen are also necessary for life. Carbon is an essential building block in the bodies of living things. For example, carbon is a major component of bones and the proteins that build muscles. And most organisms use oxygen for their life processes. **In ecosystems, the processes by which carbon and oxygen are recycled are linked. Producers, consumers, and decomposers all play roles in recycling carbon and oxygen.**

The Carbon Cycle Most producers take in carbon dioxide gas from the air during food-making or photosynthesis. They use carbon from the carbon dioxide to make food—carbon-containing molecules such as sugars and starches. As consumers eat producers, they take in the carbon-containing molecules. Both producers and consumers then break down the food to obtain energy. As the food is broken down, producers and consumers release carbon dioxide and water into the environment. When producers and consumers die, decomposers break down their remains and return carbon molecules to the soil. Some decomposers also release carbon dioxide into the air.

The Oxygen Cycle Look at **Figure 2.** Like carbon, oxygen cycles through ecosystems. Producers release oxygen as a result of photosynthesis. Most organisms take in oxygen from the air or water and use it to carry out their life processes.

Human Impact Human activities also affect the levels of carbon and oxygen in the atmosphere. When humans burn oil and other plant-based fuels, carbon dioxide is released into the atmosphere. Carbon dioxide levels can also rise when humans clear forests for lumber, fuel, and farmland. Increasing levels of carbon dioxide are a major factor in global warming. As you know, producers take in carbon dioxide during photosynthesis. When trees are removed from the ecosystem, there are fewer producers to absorb carbon dioxide. There is an even greater effect if trees are burned down to clear a forest. When trees are burned down, additional carbon dioxide is released during the burning process.

apply it!

Producers, consumers, and decomposers all play a role in recycling carbon and oxygen.

Infer On the lines below, describe how you think a cow eating grass is part of both the carbon and oxygen cycles.

____

____

____

____

____

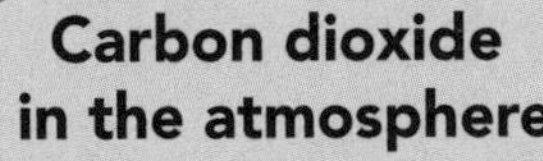

FIGURE 2

Carbon and Oxygen Cycles

Producers, consumers, and decomposers all play a role in recycling carbon and oxygen.

Describe When humans burn fuel or cut down trees, they (increase/decrease) **levels of carbon dioxide in the atmosphere.**

Do the Quick Lab *Carbon and Oxygen Blues.*

Assess Your Understanding

1a. Identify Carbon and oxygen are both ________________ in an ecosystem.

b. Develop Hypotheses How might the death of all the producers in a community affect the carbon and oxygen cycles?

____

got it?

○ **I get it!** Now I know that the carbon and oxygen cycles are related by ________________

○ I need extra help with ________________

Go to **MY SCIENCE COACH** *online for help with this subject.*

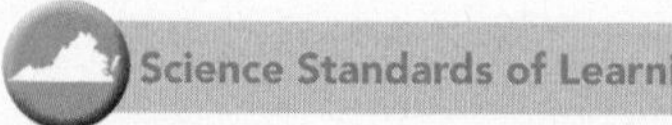

Science Standards of Learning

LS.1d Construct and use models and simulations to illustrate and explain phenomena.

LS.6a Investigate and understand carbon, water, and nitrogen cycles.

LS.6b Investigate and understand interactions resulting in a flow of energy and matter throughout an ecosystem.

LS.6c Investigate and understand complex relationships within terrestrial, freshwater, and marine ecosystems.

LS.6d Investigate and understand energy flow in food webs and energy pyramids.

How Does Nitrogen Cycle Through Ecosystems?

Like carbon, nitrogen is one of the necessary building blocks that make up living things. For example, in addition to carbon, nitrogen is also an important component of proteins. **In the nitrogen cycle, nitrogen moves from the air into the soil, into living things, and back into the air or soil.** Since the air around you is about 78 percent nitrogen gas, you might think that it would be easy for living things to obtain nitrogen. However, most organisms cannot use nitrogen gas. Nitrogen gas is called "free" nitrogen because it is not combined with other kinds of atoms.

Nitrogen Fixation Most organisms can use nitrogen only after it has been "fixed," or combined with other elements to form nitrogen-containing compounds. The process of changing free nitrogen into a usable form of nitrogen, as shown in **Figure 4,** is called **nitrogen fixation.** Most nitrogen fixation is performed by certain kinds of bacteria. These bacteria live in bumps called nodules (NAHJ oolz) on the roots of legumes. These plants include clover, beans, peas, alfalfa, peanuts, and some trees.

The relationship between the bacteria and the legumes is an example of mutualism. Both the bacteria and the plants benefit from this relationship: The bacteria feed on the plants' sugars, and the plants are supplied with nitrogen in a usable form.

Return of Nitrogen to the Environment

Once nitrogen is fixed, producers can use it to build proteins and other complex compounds. Nitrogen can cycle from the soil to producers and then to consumers many times. At some point, however, bacteria break down the nitrogen compounds completely. These bacteria then release free nitrogen back into the air, causing the cycle to continue.

FIGURE 3

Growth in Nitrogen-Poor Soil

Pitcher plants can grow in nitrogen-poor soil because they obtain nitrogen by trapping insects in their tube-shaped leaves. The plants then digest the insects and use their nitrogen compounds.

Circle the correct word in each sentence.

1. **Identify** If nitrogen in the soil isn't (fixed/free), then most organisms cannot use it.
2. CHALLENGE The relationship between the pitcher plant and the insects is an example of (competition/predation/symbiosis).

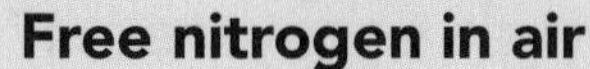

Free nitrogen in air

Soil bacteria release some free nitrogen into the air.

Consumers eat nitrogen compounds in plants.

Decomposers return simple nitrogen compounds to the soil.

Plants use simple nitrogen compounds to make proteins and other complex compounds.

Bacteria in root nodules fix free nitrogen into simple compounds.

Fixed nitrogen in soil

FIGURE 4

Nitrogen Cycle

In the nitrogen cycle, free nitrogen from the air is fixed into compounds. Consumers can then use these nitrogen compounds to carry out their life processes.

Observe Nitrogen compounds become available to organisms (in the soil/in the plants/in the air).

Sequence In the frames below, draw a comic strip or describe a situation that shows the order of events in the nitrogen cycle.

1

2

3

4

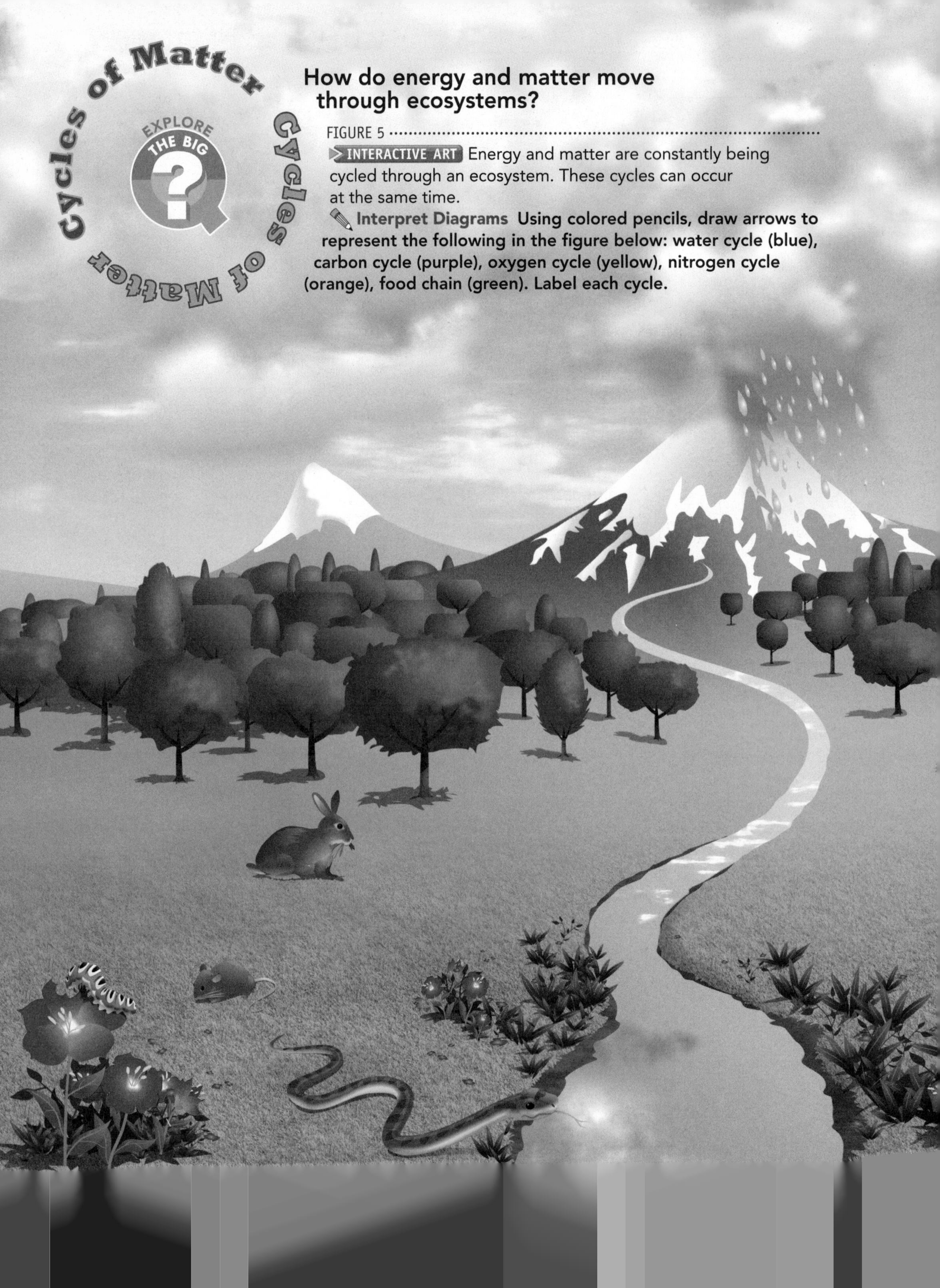

How do energy and matter move through ecosystems?

FIGURE 5

INTERACTIVE ART Energy and matter are constantly being cycled through an ecosystem. These cycles can occur at the same time.

Interpret Diagrams **Using colored pencils, draw arrows to represent the following in the figure below: water cycle (blue), carbon cycle (purple), oxygen cycle (yellow), nitrogen cycle (orange), food chain (green). Label each cycle.**

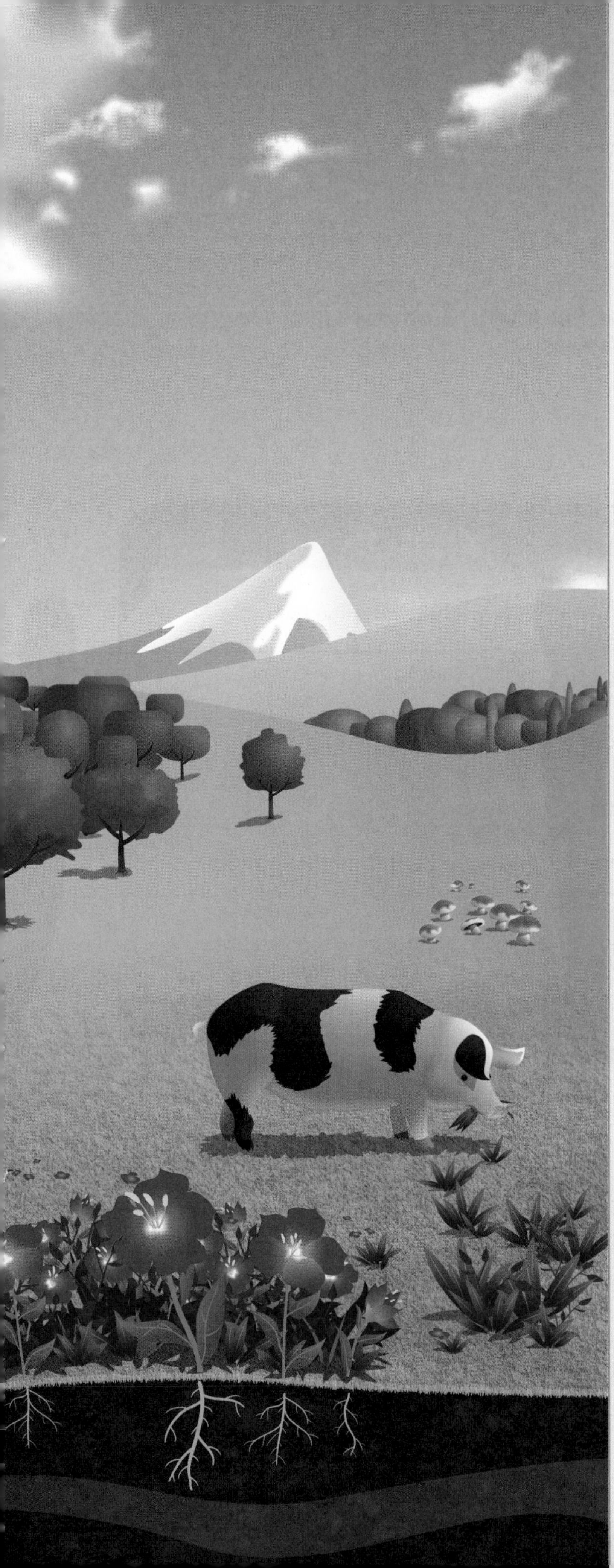

Lab zone® Do the Quick Lab *Playing Nitrogen Cycle Roles.*

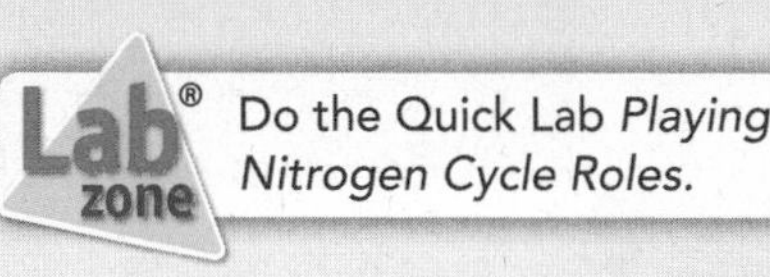

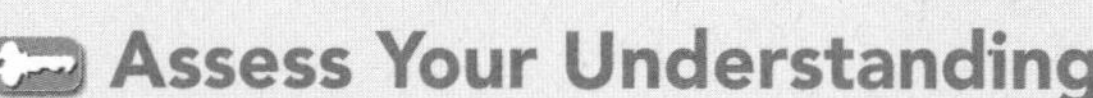

Assess Your Understanding

2a. Describe (Fixed/Free) nitrogen is not combined with other kinds of atoms.

b. Predict What might happen in a community if farmers did not plant legume crops?

c. ANSWER THE BIG Q How do energy and matter move through ecosystems?

got it?

O I get it! Now I know that the nitrogen cycle

O I need extra help with

Go to MY SCIENCE COACH *online for help with this subject.*

Biomes

What Are the Six Major Biomes?
LS.1f, LS.6c, LS.9a, LS.9b, LS.9c

my planet Diary

That's Super Cool!

Misconception: It is always fatal when body temperatures drop below freezing.

Fact: In the tundra, arctic ground squirrels hibernate up to eight months a year. During this time, a squirrel's body temperature drops below freezing! This is called supercooling and gives the squirrel the lowest body temperature of any mammal. Without waking, a squirrel will shiver for several hours every couple of weeks to increase its body temperature.

MISCONCEPTION

Answer the question below.

What do you think are the advantages of supercooling?

____

____

____

____

____

____

PLANET DIARY Go to **Planet Diary** to learn more about biomes.

Lab zone® Do the Inquiry Warm-Up *How Much Rain Is That?*

Science Standards of Learning

LS.1f Identify dependent variables, independent variables, and constants.

LS.6c Investigate and understand complex relationships within terrestrial, freshwater, and marine ecosystems.

LS.9a Investigate and understand differences between ecosystems and biomes.

LS.9b Investigate and understand characteristics of land, marine, and freshwater ecosystems.

LS.9c Investigate and understand adaptations that enable organisms to survive within a specific ecosystem.

What Are the Six Major Biomes?

Imagine that you are taking part in an around-the-world scientific expedition. On this expedition you will collect data on the typical climate and organisms of each of Earth's biomes. A **biome** is a group of ecosystems with similar climates and organisms.

The six major biomes are desert, rain forest, grassland, deciduous forest, boreal forest, and tundra. It is mostly the **climate**—the average annual temperature and amount of precipitation—in an area that determines its biome. Climate limits the species of plants that can grow in an area. In turn, the species of plants determine the kinds of animals that live there.

Vocabulary

- biome • climate • desert • rain forest
- emergent layer • canopy • understory • grassland
- savanna • deciduous tree • boreal forest
- coniferous tree • tundra • permafrost

Skills

- Reading: Compare and Contrast
- Inquiry: Draw Conclusions

Desert Biomes The first stop on your expedition is a desert. You step off the bus into the searing heat. A **desert** is an area that receives less than 25 centimeters of rain per year. Some of the driest deserts may not receive any precipitation in a year! Deserts often undergo large shifts in temperature during the course of a day. A scorching hot desert like the Namib Desert in Africa cools rapidly each night when the sun goes down. Other deserts, such as the Gobi in central Asia, have a yearly average temperature that is below freezing.

Organisms that live in the desert, like the fennec in **Figure 1**, must be adapted to little or no rain and to extreme temperatures. For example, the stem of a saguaro cactus has folds that are similar to the pleats in an accordion. The stem expands to store water when it is raining. Gila monsters can spend weeks at a time in their cool underground burrows. Many other desert animals are most active at night when the temperatures are cooler.

FIGURE 1

Desert

Organisms must be adapted to live in the desert.

Complete these tasks.

1. CHALLENGE How do you think the fennec's ears and fur are adaptations to the desert's extreme temperatures?

2. **List** Write five things you'll need to be well adapted to desert conditions. Pack carefully!

Supply List

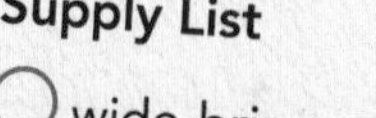

Equator

Desert Biomes

Desert

Compare and Contrast As you read about temperate and tropical rain forests, fill in the Venn diagram.

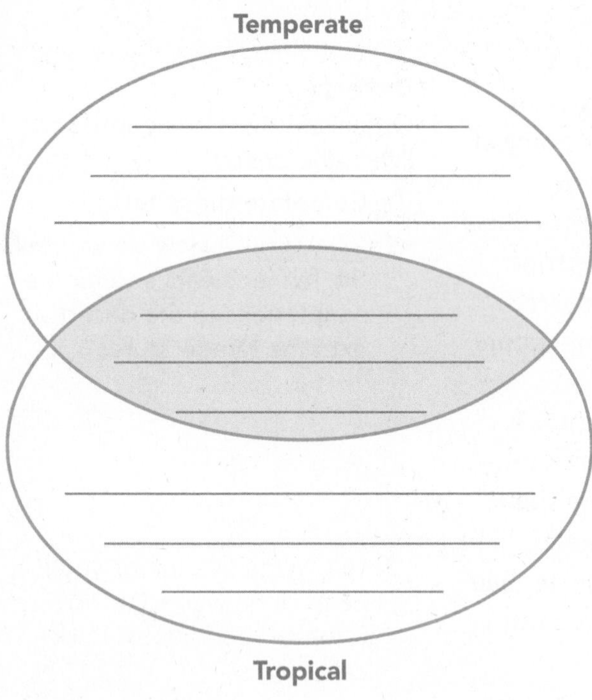

Rain-Forest Biomes

The second stop on your expedition is a rain forest. **Rain forests** are forests in which large amounts of rain fall year-round. This biome is living up to its name—it's pouring! After a short shower, the sun reappears. However, very little sunlight reaches the ground.

Plants are everywhere in the rain forest. Some plants, like the vines hanging from tree limbs, even grow on other plants! And animals are flying, creeping, and slithering all around you.

Temperate Rain Forests

You may think that a rain forest is a warm, humid "jungle" in the tropics. But there is another type of rain forest. The Pacific Northwest of the United States receives more than 300 centimeters of rain a year. Huge trees grow there, including redwoods, cedars, and firs. Many ecologists refer to this ecosystem as a temperate rain forest. The term *temperate* means "having moderate temperatures."

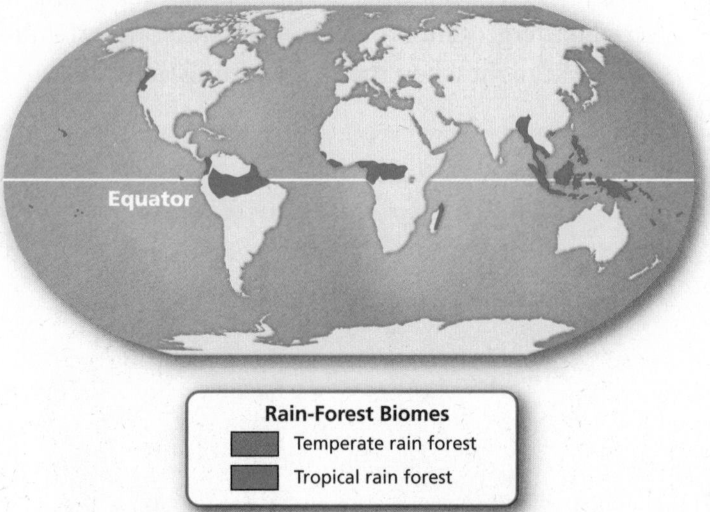

Equator

Rain-Forest Biomes
- Temperate rain forest
- Tropical rain forest

FIGURE 2

Temperate Rain Forests

The sugar pine is the tallest kind of pine tree, reaching heights of 53 to 61 meters. It also produces the largest pine cones. A sugar pine cone can reach a length of 30 to 56 centimeters. The sugar pine cone shown here is actual size!

Identify What conditions do you think allow a tree to grow so tall?

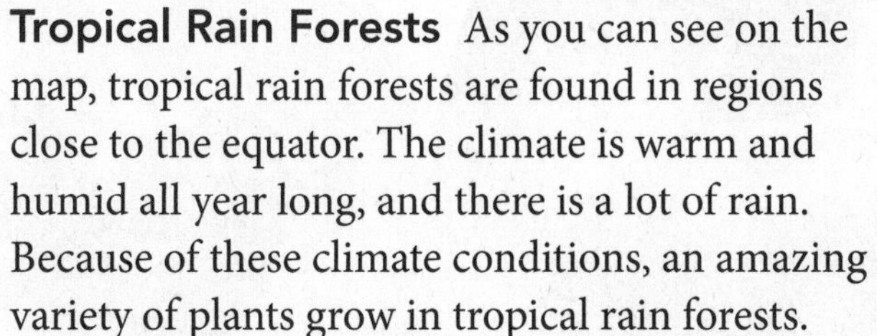

Tropical Rain Forests As you can see on the map, tropical rain forests are found in regions close to the equator. The climate is warm and humid all year long, and there is a lot of rain. Because of these climate conditions, an amazing variety of plants grow in tropical rain forests.

Trees in the rain forest form several distinct layers. The **emergent layer** is the tallest layer of the rainforest and receives the most sunlight. It can reach up to 70 meters. Underneath, trees up to 50 meters tall form a leafy roof called the **canopy.** Below the canopy, a layer of shorter trees and vines, around 15 meters high, form an **understory.** Understory plants grow well in the shade formed by the canopy. The forest floor is nearly dark, so only a few plants live there. Look at the tree layers in **Figure 3.**

The abundant plant life in tropical rain forests provides habitats for many species of animals. Ecologists estimate that millions of species of insects live in tropical rain forests. These insects serve as a source of food for many reptiles, birds, and mammals. Many of these animals, in turn, are food sources for other animals. Although tropical rain forests cover only a small part of the planet, they probably contain more species of plants and animals than all the other biomes combined.

FIGURE 3

Tropical Rain Forests

On the edge of this tropical rain forest, an amazing variety of organisms can be found in the different layers.

Relate Text and Visuals Based on your reading, label the four distinct layers of the tropical rain forest in the boxes above.

Rhea, South America A

Cassowary, Australia B

Ostrich, Africa C

FIGURE 4

Grasslands

The rhea, cassowary, and ostrich are grassland birds that live on different continents.

Interpret Maps On the world map, identify the continents in which these three birds are located. List three characteristics that these grassland birds all share.

____

____

____

____

____

Grassland Biomes The third stop on the expedition is a grassy plain called a prairie. Temperatures are more comfortable here than they were in the desert. The breeze carries the scent of soil warmed by the sun. This rich soil supports grasses as tall as you. Startled by your approach, sparrows dart into hiding places among the waving grass stems.

Although the prairie receives more rain than a desert, you may notice only a few scattered areas of trees and shrubs. Ecologists classify prairies, which are generally found in the middle latitudes, as grasslands. A **grassland** is an area that is populated mostly by grasses and other nonwoody plants. Most grasslands receive 25 to 75 centimeters of rain each year. Fires and droughts are common in this biome. Grasslands that are located closer to the equator than prairies are known as savannas. A **savanna** receives as much as 120 centimeters of rain each year. Scattered shrubs and small trees grow on savannas, along with grass.

Grasslands are home to many of the largest animals on Earth—herbivores such as elephants, bison, antelopes, zebras, giraffes, kangaroos, and rhinoceroses. Grazing by these large herbivores maintains the grasslands. Their grazing keeps young trees and bushes from sprouting and competing with the grass for water and sunlight. You can see some grassland birds in **Figure 4.**

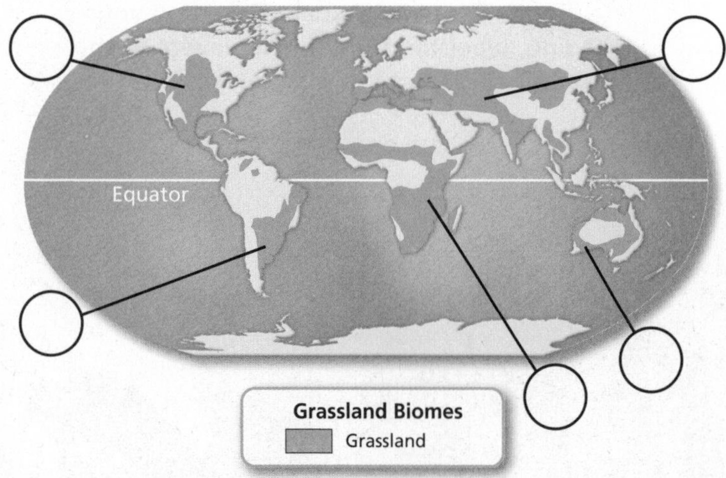

Deciduous Forest Biomes Your trip to the fourth biome takes you to another forest. It is now late summer. Cool mornings here give way to warm days. Several members of the expedition are busy recording the numerous plant species. Others are looking through binoculars, trying to identify the songbirds.

You are now visiting a deciduous forest biome. Many of the trees in this forest are **deciduous trees** (dee SIJ oo us), trees that shed their leaves and grow new ones each year. Oaks and maples are examples of deciduous trees. Deciduous forests receive at least 50 cm of rain per year, enough to support the growth of trees and other plants. Temperatures can vary greatly during the year. The growing season usually lasts five to six months.

The variety of plants in a deciduous forest creates many different habitats. Many species of birds live in different parts of the forest, eating the insects and fruits in their specific areas. Mammals such as chipmunks and skunks live in deciduous forests. In a North American deciduous forest you might also see wood thrushes and white-tailed deer.

If you were to return to this biome in the winter, you would not see much wildlife. Many of the bird species migrate, or fly great distances, to warmer areas. Some of the mammals hibernate, or enter a state of greatly reduced body activity similar to sleep. Look at **Figure 5.** During the winter months, animals that hibernate get energy from fat stored in their bodies.

did you know?

How far would you be willing to migrate? The bobolink has one of the longest songbird migration routes. The birds travel south from southern Canada and the northern United States to northern Argentina. This migration route is approximately 20,000 kilometers round trip!

FIGURE 5

Deciduous Forest

Most of the trees in a deciduous forest have leaves that change color and drop to the forest floor each autumn. In the leaves, this dormouse hibernates through the winter.

Infer Is hibernation an adaptation to life in a deciduous forest? Explain your answer.

____

____

____

____

____

FIGURE 6

Boreal Forest

✎ This lynx and snowshoe hare are adapted to life in the boreal forest.

1. **Infer** Choose the best answer. The feet of each animal are an adaptation to its
   - ○ food.
   - ○ climate.
   - ○ predators.
   - ○ all of the above
2. **Explain** Defend your answer.

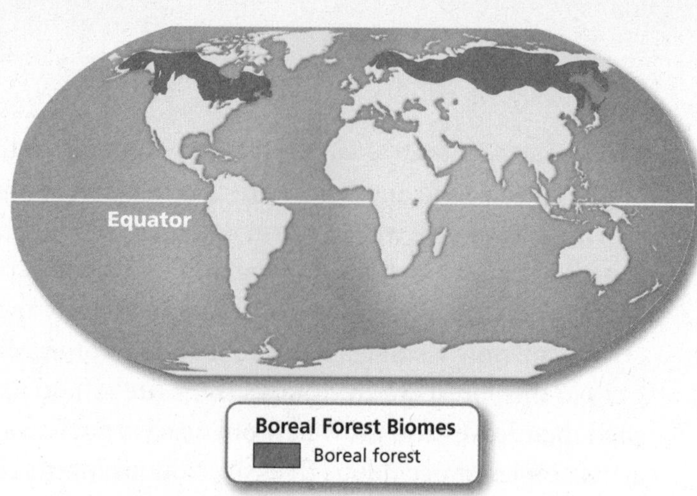

Boreal Forest Biomes Now the expedition heads north to a colder biome, the boreal forest. The term *boreal* means "northern," and **boreal forests** are dense forests found in upper regions of the Northern Hemisphere. The expedition leaders claim they can identify a boreal forest by its smell. When you arrive, you catch a whiff of the spruce and fir trees that blanket the hillsides. Feeling the chilly early fall air, you pull a jacket and hat out of your bag.

Boreal Forest Plants Most of the trees in the boreal forest are **coniferous trees** (koh NIF ur us), trees that produce their seeds in cones and have leaves shaped like needles. The boreal forest is sometimes referred to by its Russian name, the *taiga* (TY guh). Winters in these forests are very cold. The snow can reach heights well over your head! Even so, the summers are rainy and warm enough to melt all the snow.

Tree species in the boreal forest are well adapted to the cold climate. Since water is frozen for much of the year, trees must have adaptations that prevent water loss. Coniferous trees, such as firs and hemlocks, all have thick, waxy needles that prevent water from evaporating.

Boreal Forest Animals Many of the animals of the boreal forest eat the seeds produced by the coniferous trees. These animals include red squirrels, insects, and birds such as finches. Some herbivores, such as moose and beavers, eat tree bark and new shoots. The variety of herbivores in the boreal forest supports many predators, including lynx, otters, and great horned owls. **Figure 6** shows an herbivore and its predator.

Tundra Biomes As you arrive at your last stop, the driving wind gives you an immediate feel for this biome. The **tundra** is extremely cold and dry. Expecting deep snow, many are surprised to learn that the tundra may receive no more precipitation than a desert.

Most of the soil in the tundra is frozen all year. This frozen soil is called **permafrost.** During the short summer, the top layer of soil thaws, but the underlying soil remains frozen. Because rainwater cannot soak into the permafrost, shallow ponds and marshy areas appear in the summer.

Tundra Plants Mosses, grasses, and dwarf forms of a few trees can be found in the tundra. Most of the plant growth takes place during the long days of the short summer season. North of the Arctic Circle, the sun does not set during midsummer.

Tundra Animals In summer, the insects are abundant. Insect-eating birds take advantage of the plentiful food by eating as much as they can. But when winter approaches, these birds migrate south. Mammals of the tundra include caribou, foxes, and wolves. The mammals that remain on the tundra during the winter grow thick fur coats. What can these animals find to eat on the tundra in winter? The caribou scrape snow away to find lichens. Wolves follow the caribou and look for weak members of the herd to prey upon.

FIGURE 7

Tundra

Although the ground is frozen for most of the year, mosses, grasses, and dwarf willow trees grow here.

Communicate Discuss with a partner why there are no tall trees on the tundra. Describe two factors that you think may influence tree growth.

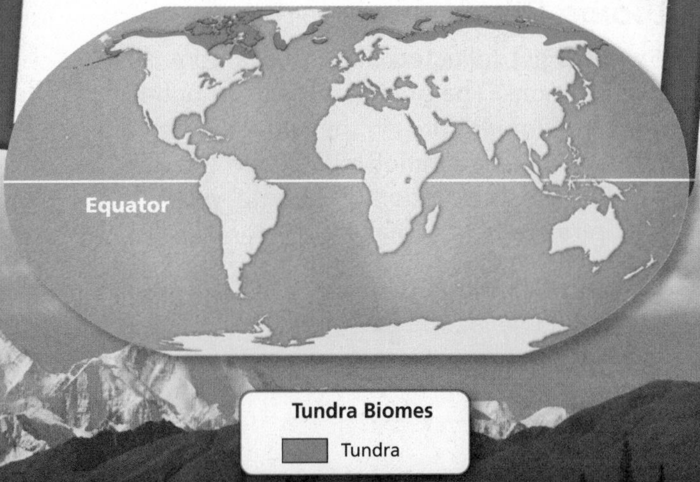

Equator

Tundra Biomes

Tundra

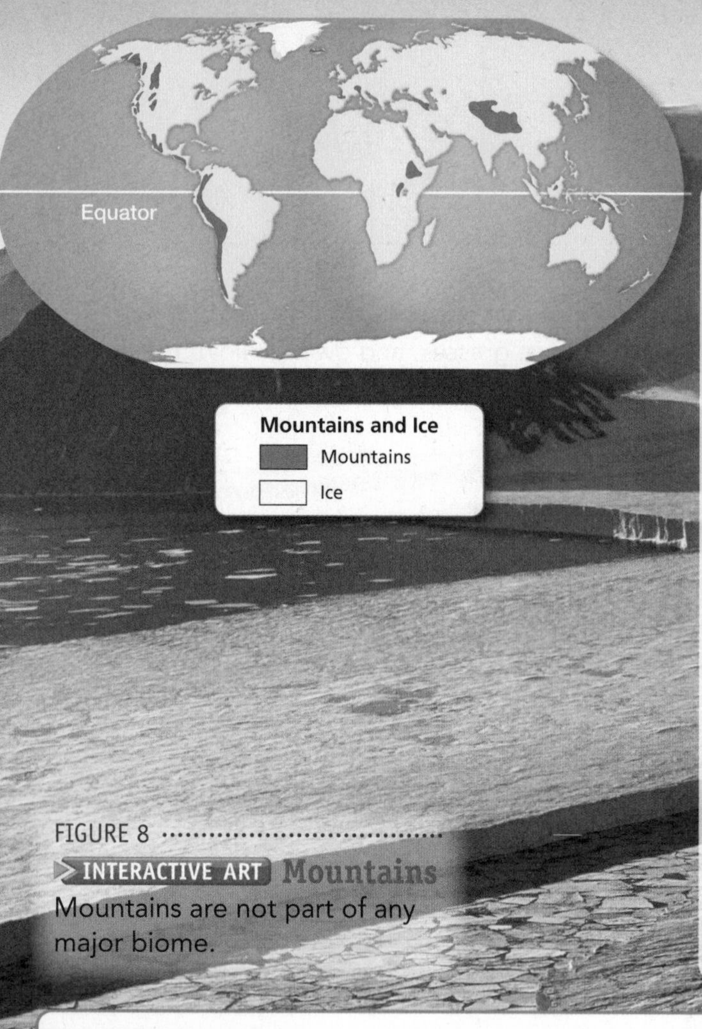

FIGURE 8
INTERACTIVE ART Mountains
Mountains are not part of any major biome.

Mountains and Ice Some land areas are not classified as biomes. Recall that biomes are defined by abiotic factors such as climate and soil, and by biotic factors such as plant and animal life. Because the organisms that live in these areas vary, mountain ranges and land covered with thick ice sheets are not considered biomes.

The climate of a mountain changes from its base to its summit. If you were to hike all the way up a tall mountain, you would pass through a series of biomes. At the base, you might find grasslands. As you climbed, you might pass through deciduous forest and then boreal forest. As you neared the top, your surroundings would resemble the cold, dry tundra.

Other places are covered year-round with thick ice sheets. Most of Greenland and Antarctica fall into this category. Organisms that are adapted to life on ice include leopard seals and polar bears.

do the math!

Biome Climates

An ecologist collected climate data from two locations. The graph shows the monthly average temperatures in the two locations. The total yearly precipitation in Location A is 250 centimeters. In Location B, the total yearly precipitation is 14 centimeters.

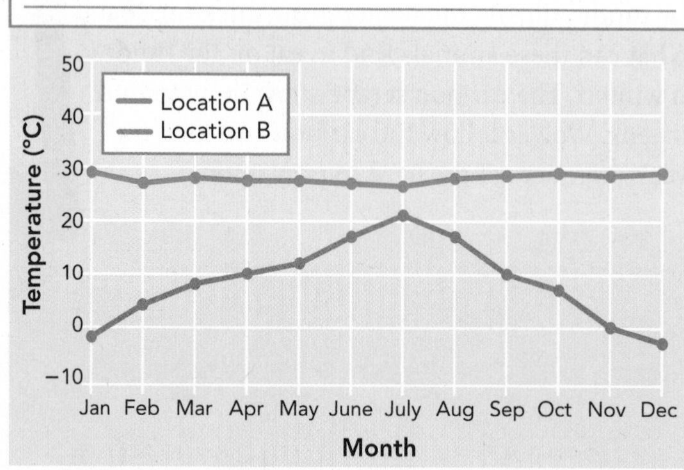

1. **Read Graphs** Provide a title for the graph. What variable is plotted on the horizontal axis? On the vertical axis?

2. **Interpret Data** Study the graph. How would you describe the temperature over the course of a year in Location A? In Location B?

3. **Draw Conclusions** Given the precipitation and temperature data for these locations, in which biome would you expect each to be located?

apply it!

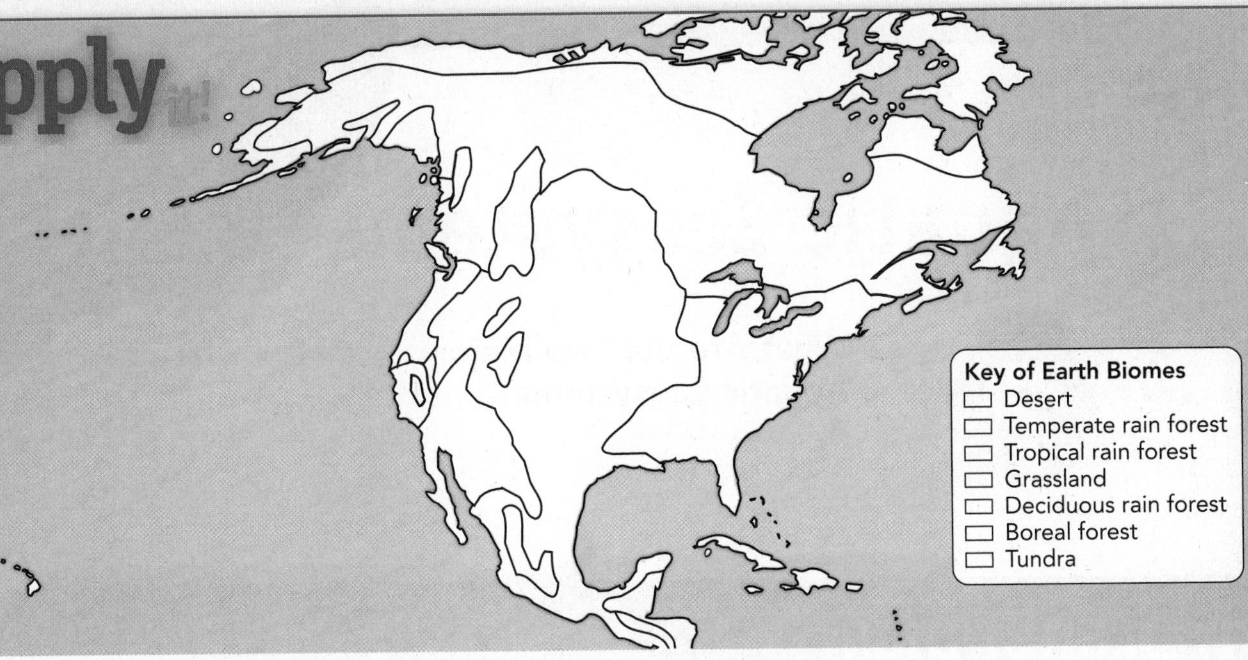

Key of Earth Biomes
- Desert
- Temperate rain forest
- Tropical rain forest
- Grassland
- Deciduous rain forest
- Boreal forest
- Tundra

❶ **Interpret Maps** Using the colors shown in the biome maps throughout this lesson, color in the key above. Use the key to color in the areas on the map of North America.

❷ **Draw Conclusions** Where are most of the boreal forests located? Why are there no boreal forests in the Southern Hemisphere?

____

____

____

____

____

____

❸ **Describe** Mark the area in which you live with an X on the map. What is the climate like where you live? How do you think your climate affects which organisms live there?

____

____

____

____

____

____

____

____

Lab zone® Do the Quick Lab *Inferring Forest Climates.*

Assess Your Understanding

1a. Review ____________________ and ____________________ are the two main factors that determine an area's biome.

b. Infer What biome might you be in if you were standing on a bitterly cold, dry plain with only a few, short trees scattered around?

____

got it?

○ **I get it!** Now I know that the six major biomes are ____________________

____

○ I need extra help with ____________________

Go to MY SCIENCE COACH *online for help with this subject.*

Aquatic Ecosystems

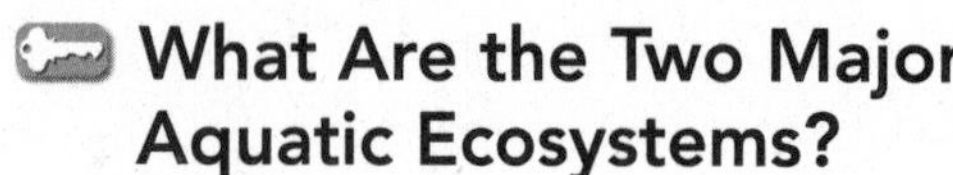

What Are the Two Major Aquatic Ecosystems?

LS.6c, LS.9b, LS.9c

MY PLANET DIARY

TECHNOLOGY

Underwater *Alvin*

Meet *Alvin*, an HOV (Human-Occupied Vehicle). Equipped with propulsion jets, cameras, and robotic arms, *Alvin* helps scientists gather data and discover ecosystems that exist deep in the ocean. Built in 1964, *Alvin* was one of the world's first deep-ocean submersibles and has made more than 4,500 dives. *Alvin* is credited with finding a lost hydrogen bomb, exploring the first known hydrothermal vents, and surveying the wreck of the *Titanic*.

Calculate **Suppose that on each of the 4,500 dives *Alvin* has made, a new pilot and two new scientists were on board. How many scientists have seen the deep ocean through *Alvin's* windows? How many people, in total, traveled in *Alvin*?**

____

____

PLANET DIARY Go to **Planet Diary** to learn more about aquatic ecosystems.

Do the Inquiry Warm-Up *Where Does It Live?*

Science Standards of Learning

LS.6c Investigate and understand complex relationships within terrestrial, freshwater, and marine ecosystems.

LS.9b Investigate and understand characteristics of land, marine, and freshwater ecosystems.

LS.9c Investigate and understand adaptations that enable organisms to survive within a specific ecosystem.

What Are the Two Major Aquatic Ecosystems?

Since almost three quarters of Earth's surface is covered with water, many living things make their homes in and near water. **There are two types of aquatic, or water-based, ecosystems: freshwater ecosystems and marine (or saltwater) ecosystems.** All aquatic ecosystems are affected by the same abiotic, or nonliving, factors: sunlight, temperature, oxygen, and salt content. Sunlight is an important factor in aquatic ecosystems because it is necessary for photosynthesis in the water just as it is on land. Half of all oxygen produced on Earth comes from floating algae called phytoplankton. Because water absorbs sunlight, there is only enough light for photosynthesis to occur near the surface or in shallow water.

Vocabulary
- estuary
- intertidal zone
- neritic zone

Skills
- Reading: Outline
- Inquiry: Communicate

Freshwater Ecosystems

No worldwide expedition would be complete without exploring Earth's waters. Even though most of Earth's surface is covered with water, only 3 percent of the volume is fresh water. Freshwater ecosystems include streams, rivers, ponds, and lakes. On this part of your expedition, you'll find that freshwater biomes provide habitats for a variety of organisms.

Streams and Rivers At the source of a mountain stream, the water flows slowly. Plants take root on the bottom, providing food for insects and homes for frogs. These consumers then provide food for larger consumers. Stream currents increase as streams come together to make larger streams, often called rivers. Animals here are adapted to strong currents. For example, trout have streamlined bodies to swim in the rushing water. As the current speeds up, it can become cloudy with sediment. Few plants or algae grow in this fast-moving water. Consumers such as snails feed on leaves and seeds that fall into the stream. At lower elevations, streams are warmer and often contain less oxygen, affecting the organisms that can live in them.

Ponds and Lakes Ponds and lakes are bodies of still, or standing, fresh water. Lakes are generally larger and deeper than ponds. Ponds are often shallow enough that sunlight can reach the bottom, allowing plants to grow there. In large ponds and most lakes, however, algae floating at the surface are the major producers. Many animals are adapted for life in still water. Dragonflies, snails, and frogs live along the shores of ponds. In the open water, sunfish feed on insects and algae close to the surface. Scavengers such as catfish live near the bottoms of ponds. Bacteria and other decomposers also feed on the remains of other organisms.

Outline As you read, make an outline on a separate sheet of paper that includes the different types of aquatic ecosystems. Use the red headings for the main ideas and the black headings for the supporting details.

FIGURE 1

Freshwater Ecosystems

Water lilies live in ponds and lakes.

Answer the questions.

1. **Identify** What are two abiotic factors that can affect water lilies?

2. CHALLENGE What adaptations do fish have that allow them to live in water?

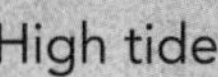
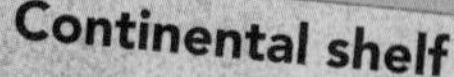

Marine Ecosystems The expedition now heads to the coast to explore some marine biomes. On your way, you'll pass through an estuary. An **estuary** (ES choo ehr ee), is found where the fresh water of a river meets the salt water of an ocean. Algae and plants provide food and shelter for animals, including crabs and fish. Many animals use the calm waters of estuaries for breeding grounds. Last, you explore the different ocean zones as described in **Figure 2.**

Ocean Zones

Zone	Location	Inhabitants
Intertidal zone	Located on the shore between the highest high-tide line and the lowest low-tide line	Organisms must be able to survive pounding waves and the sudden changes in water levels and temperature that occur with high and low tides. For example, barnacles and sea stars cling to the rocks while clams and crabs burrow in the sand.
Neritic zone	Region of shallow water found below the low-tide line and extending over the continental shelf	Sunlight passes through shallow water, allowing photosynthesis to occur. Many living things, such as algae and schools of fish, live here. Coral reefs can also be found here in warmer waters.
Surface zone, open ocean	Located beyond the neritic zone and extending from the water's surface to about 200 meters deep	Sunlight penetrates this zone, allowing photosynthesis to occur in floating phytoplankton and other algae. Tuna, swordfish, and some whales depend on the algae for food.
Deep zone, open ocean	Located beneath the surface zone to the ocean floor	Little, if any, sunlight passes through. Animals feed on the remains of organisms that sink down. Organisms, like the giant squid and anglerfish, are adapted to life in the dark.

FIGURE 2

Marine Ecosystems

The ocean is home to a number of different ecosystems.

Classify Using the clues, determine at which depth each organism belongs. In the circles in the ocean, write the letter for each organism in the correct zone.

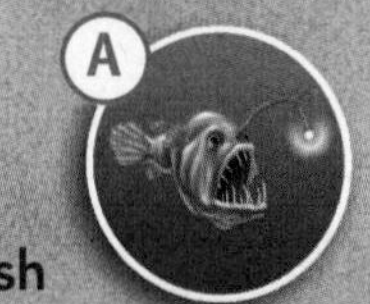

Anglerfish
Females have a lighted lure to help them attract prey in the dark.

Tripod Fish
This fish has three elongated fins to help it stand.

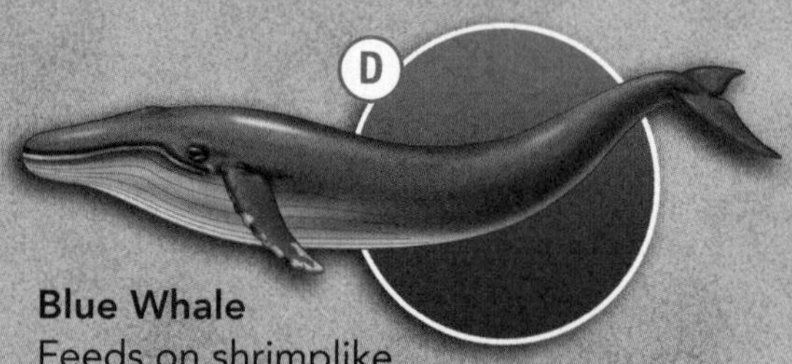

Yellowfin Tuna
Found in open waters and has been known to eat squid

Blue Whale
Feeds on shrimplike creatures at depths of more than 100 meters during the day

Swordfish
Often seen jumping out of the water to stun smaller fish

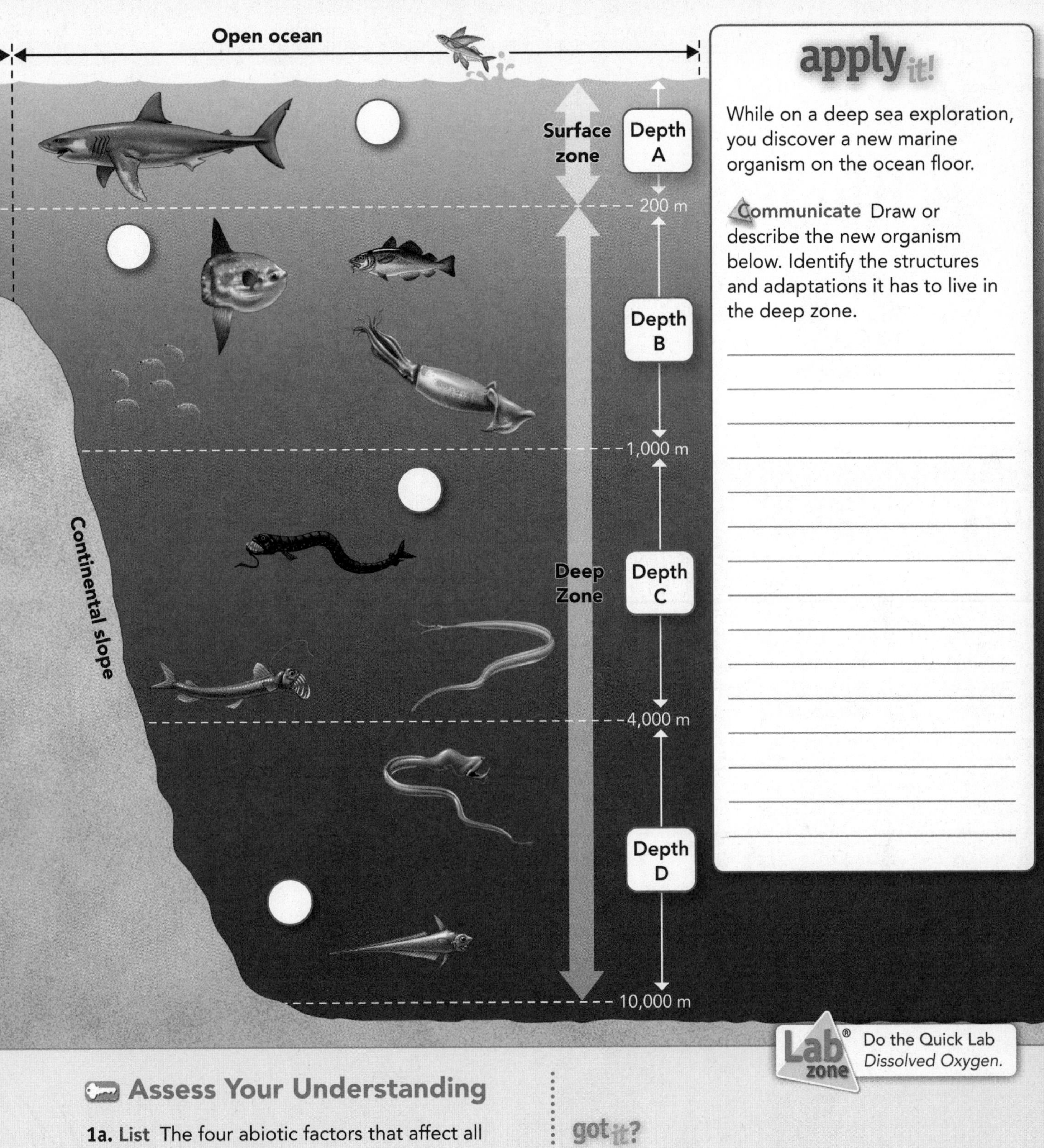

apply it!

While on a deep sea exploration, you discover a new marine organism on the ocean floor.

Communicate Draw or describe the new organism below. Identify the structures and adaptations it has to live in the deep zone.

Lab zone® Do the Quick Lab *Dissolved Oxygen.*

Assess Your Understanding

1a. List The four abiotic factors that affect all aquatic ecosystems are

b. Make Generalizations Why is sunlight important to all aquatic ecosystems?

got it?

○ **I get it!** Now I know that the two major types of aquatic ecosystems are

○ I need extra help with

Go to **MY SCIENCE COACH** *online for help with this subject.*

Biogeography

LS.7a, LS.10b, LS.11c

my planet Diary

FUN FACT

Australia's Animals

When you think of Australia, what animal comes to mind? Most likely, you think of a kangaroo or a koala. Did you know that these animals are marsupials, mammals that carry their young in a pouch? You might be surprised to learn that most marsupials exist only in Australia. Now, can you name any monotremes, or mammals that lay eggs? The only monotremes that exist are platypuses and echidnas, both native to Australia. Lots of unique animals are native to Australia because it is completely surrounded by water.

Communicate Answer the following questions with a classmate.

1. What are two types of mammals that are common in Australia?

____

2. Would you ever expect a platypus to move from Australia to the United States? Explain.

____
____
____
____

PLANET DIARY Go to **Planet Diary** to learn more about biogeography.

Lab zone® Do the Inquiry Warm-Up *How Can You Move a Seed?*

Vocabulary
- biogeography
- continental drift
- dispersal
- exotic species

Skills
- Reading: Relate Cause and Effect
- Inquiry: Predict

What Factors Affect Species Dispersal?

LS.7a Investigate and understand competition, cooperation, social hierarchy, territorial imperative.
LS.10b Investigate and understand factors that increase or decrease population size.
LS.11c Investigate and understand changes in species competition.

Do you think all of the people who live in your hometown were born there? Some of them may have come from different cities, states, or countries. Just as humans do, different plants and animals live in different parts of the world. The study of where organisms live and how they got there is called **biogeography.** Biogeographers also study factors that have led to the worldwide distribution of species that exist today.

The movement of the Earth's continents is one factor that has affected how species are distributed. The continents are parts of huge blocks of solid rock, called plates, that make up Earth's surface. These plates have been moving very slowly for millions of years. As the plates move, the continents move with them in a process called **continental drift. Figure 1** shows how the continents have moved over time. Notice that about 225 million years ago, all of the continents were part of one huge landmass, called Pangaea.

Continental drift has had a great impact on species distribution. For example, Australia drifted away from the other landmasses millions of years ago. Organisms from other parts of the world could not reach the isolated island, and unique Australian species developed in this isolation.

Continental drift, wind, water, and living things are all means of distributing species. Other factors, such as physical barriers, competition, and climate, can limit species dispersal.

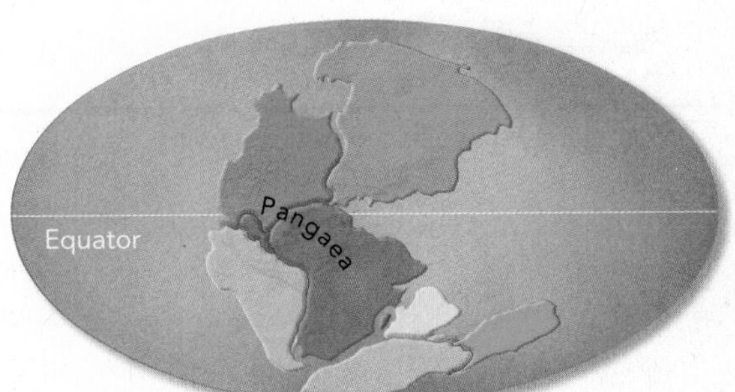

225 Million Years Ago

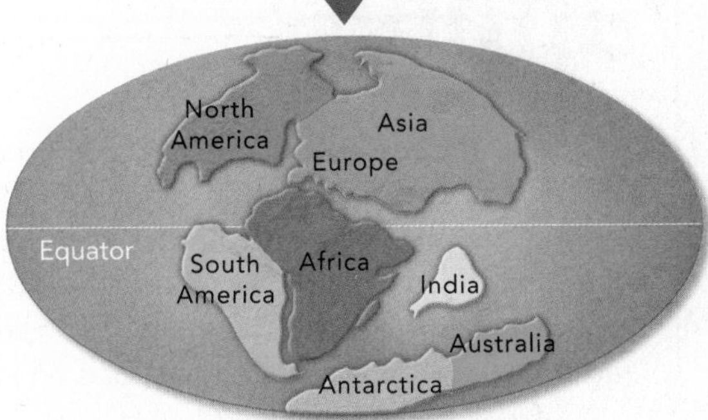

115 Million Years Ago

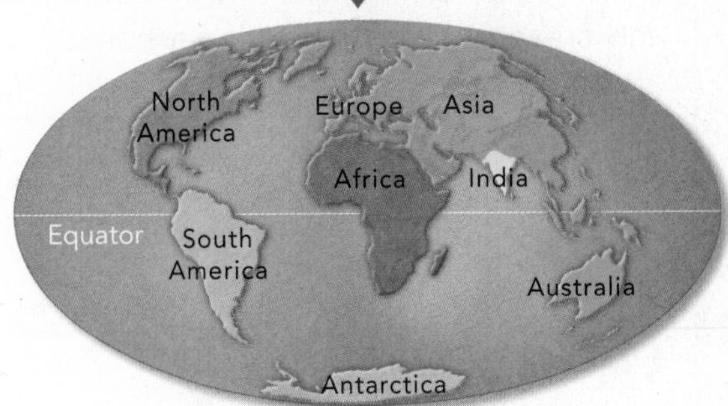

Earth Today

FIGURE 1

INTERACTIVE ART **Continental Drift**

The movement of landmasses is one factor affecting the distribution of organisms.

Observe How has Australia's location changed over time?

____

____

____

Means of Dispersal

The movement of organisms from one place to another is called **dispersal.** Dispersal can be caused by gravity, wind, water, or living things, such as the blue jay in **Figure 2.**

Wind and Water

Many animals move into new areas on their own. But plants and small organisms need help in moving from place to place. Wind can disperse seeds, fungi spores, tiny spiders, and other small, light organisms. Birds use the wind to fly to new locations. Similarly, water transports objects that float, such as coconuts and leaves. Small animals, such as insects or snails, may get a ride to a new home on top of these floating rafts. Water also transports organisms like fish and marine mammals.

FIGURE 2

INTERACTIVE ART **Means of Dispersal**

Seeds can be dispersed by the wind or by organisms like this blue jay.

Other Living Things

Organisms can also be dispersed by other living things. If your dog or cat has ever come home covered with sticky plant burs, you have seen an example of dispersal. Humans have sped up the dispersal of organisms, both intentionally and unintentionally, as they travel around the world. An **exotic species** is an organism that is carried into a new location by people. Exotic species have contributed to the decline or elimination of native species.

apply it!

In 1780, a Japanese ship ran aground on one of Alaska's uninhabited Aleutian Islands. Rats from the ship swam to the island. Since then, the rats on this island, now called Rat Island, have preyed upon and destroyed seabird populations and the overall ecosystem. "Rat spills" from ships are one of the leading causes of seabird extinctions on islands worldwide.

1 **Communicate** With a partner, identify ways in which sailors can control rats on board their ships and prevent them from going ashore.

____

____

____

____

____

____

2 **Predict** Do you think the role of humans in the dispersal of species will increase or decrease in the next 50 years? Defend your answer.

____

____

____

____

____

____

Limits to Dispersal With all these means of dispersal, you might expect to find the same species in many places around the world. Of course, that's not so. Three factors that limit distribution of a species are physical barriers, competition, and climate.

Physical Barriers Water and mountains form barriers that are hard to cross. These features can limit the movement of organisms. For example, once Australia became separated from the other continents, organisms could not easily move to or from Australia.

Competition When an organism enters a new area, it must compete for resources with the species that already live there. To survive, the organism must find a unique niche, or role. Existing species may outcompete the new species. In this case, competition is a barrier to dispersal. Sometimes, in certain situations, new species outcompete and displace the existing species.

Climate The typical weather pattern in an area over a long period of time is the area's climate. Climate differences can limit dispersal. For example, the climate changes greatly as you climb a tall mountain. The warm, dry mountain base, the cooler and wetter areas higher up, and the cold, windy top all support different species. Those species that thrive at the base may not survive at the top.

Relate Cause and Effect In the paragraphs at the left, circle the factors that can limit dispersal. Then underline the effects of these limits.

FIGURE 3

Limits to Dispersal

Physical barriers, like the Grand Canyon and the Colorado River, can make it difficult for species to move around.

Lab zone® Do the Quick Lab *Relating Continental Drift to Dispersal.*

Assess Your Understanding

1a. Explain What role do humans play in the dispersal of species?

____

b. CHALLENGE Suppose that a new species of insect were introduced to your area. Explain how competition might limit its dispersal.

____

got it?

○ **I get it!** Now I know that species dispersal is affected by ________________

○ I need extra help with ________________

Go to MY SCIENCE COACH *online for help with this subject.*

CHAPTER

13 Study Guide

Producers, ____________________, and ____________________ help to cycle energy through ecosystems.

LESSON 1 Energy Flow in Ecosystems

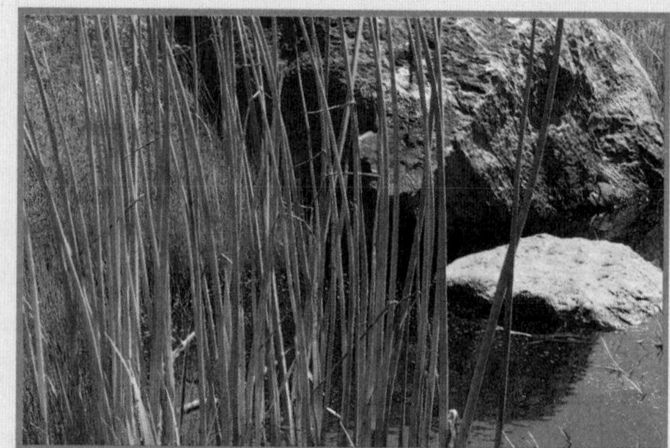

Each of the organisms in an ecosystem fills the energy role of producer, consumer, or decomposer.

Energy moves through an ecosystem when one organism eats another.

The most energy is available at the producer level of the pyramid. As energy moves up the pyramid, each level has less energy available than the level below.

Vocabulary

- producer • consumer • herbivore • carnivore • omnivore
- scavenger • decomposer • food chain • food web • energy pyramid

LESSON 2 Cycles of Matter

The processes of evaporation, condensation, and precipitation make up the water cycle.

The processes by which carbon and oxygen are recycled are linked. Producers, consumers, and decomposers play roles in recycling both.

Nitrogen moves from the air into the soil, into living things, and back into the air or soil.

Vocabulary

- evaporation • condensation
- precipitation • nitrogen fixation

LESSON 3 Biomes

The six major biomes are desert, rain forest, grassland, deciduous forest, boreal forest, and tundra.

Vocabulary

- biome • climate • desert • rain forest
- emergent layer • canopy • understory
- grassland • savanna • deciduous tree
- boreal forest • coniferous tree • tundra
- permafrost

LESSON 4 Aquatic Ecosystems

There are two types of aquatic, or water-based, ecosystems: freshwater ecosystems and marine (or saltwater) ecosystems.

Vocabulary

- estuary
- intertidal zone
- neritic zone

LESSON 5 Biogeography

Continental drift, wind, water, and living things are all means of distributing species. Other factors, such as physical barriers, competition, and climate, can limit species dispersal.

Vocabulary

- biogeography • continental drift
- dispersal • exotic species

Review and Assessment

LESSON 1 Energy Flow in Ecosystems

1. A diagram that shows how much energy is available at each feeding level in an ecosystem is a(n)
   a. food web. **b.** food chain.
   c. water cycle. **d.** energy pyramid.

2. A(n) ________________ is a consumer that eats only plants.

3. **Interpret Diagrams** Which organisms in the illustration are producers? Consumers?

4. **Compare and Contrast** How are food chains and food webs different?

5. **Write About It** Think about your own food web. Name the producers and consumers that make up your diet.

LESSON 2 Cycles of Matter

6. When drops of water in a cloud become heavy enough, they fall to Earth as
   a. permafrost. **b.** evaporation.
   c. precipitation. **d.** condensation.

7. Evaporation, condensation, and precipitation are the three main processes in the ________________

8. **Infer** Which process is responsible for the droplets visible on the glass below? Explain.

9. **Classify** Which group of organisms is the source of oxygen in the oxygen cycle? Explain.

10. **Make Generalizations** Describe the roles of producers and consumers in the carbon cycle.

11. **Draw Conclusions** What would happen if all the nitrogen-fixing bacteria disappeared?

CHAPTER 13

Review and Assessment

LESSON 3 Biomes

12. Little precipitation and extreme temperatures are main characteristics of which biome?

    a. desert b. grassland
    c. boreal forest d. deciduous forest

13. A ________________ is a group of ecosystems with similar climates and organisms.

14. **Compare and Contrast** How are the tundra and desert similar? How are they different?

LESSON 4 Aquatic Ecosystems

15. In which ocean zone would you find barnacles, sea stars, and other organisms tightly attached to rocks?

    a. neritic zone b. intertidal zone
    c. estuary ecosystem d. freshwater ecosystem

16. Coral reefs are found in the shallow, sunny waters of the ________________

17. **Compare and Contrast** How are a pond and lake similar? How do they differ?

LESSON 5 Biogeography

18. What is a likely method of dispersal for seeds that are contained within a small berry?

    a. wind b. water
    c. an animal d. continental drift

19. The study of where organisms live and how they got there is called

    ____

20. **Predict** When might seed dispersal not be beneficial?

APPLY THE BIG ? How do energy and matter cycle through ecosystems?

21. Many acres of the Amazon rain forest have been destroyed to create farmland. Describe how the amount of energy in the food web for this area might be affected. How might the carbon and oxygen cycle also be affected?

Virginia SOL Test Prep

Read each question and choose the best answer.

1 At which level of this energy pyramid is the *least* energy available?

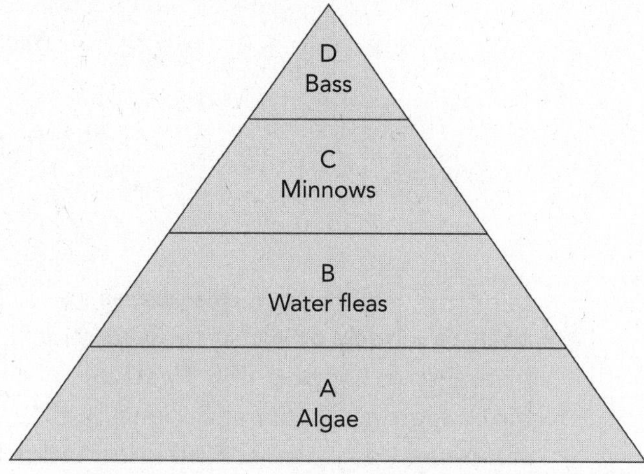

A Level A
B Level B
C Level C
D Level D

2 You are in an area in Virginia where the fresh water of the Chesapeake Bay meets the Atlantic Ocean. Which of the following terms describes where you are?

F tundra
G estuary
H neritic zone
J intertidal zone

3 Which pair of terms could apply to the same organism?

A carnivore and producer
B consumer and carnivore
C scavenger and herbivore
D producer and omnivore

4 Many Canadian forests contain coniferous trees, such as fir and spruce. The winter is long and cold. Which term describes this biome?

F tundra
G grassland
H boreal forest
J deciduous forest

5 Organisms can be dispersed in all of the following ways *except* by—

A wind
B water
C temperature
D other organisms

6 Bacteria in root nodules fixes free nitrogen from—

F decomposers
G other bacteria
H plant proteins
J the air

7 Which organisms break down biotic wastes and return raw materials back to the ecosystem?

A decomposers
B producers
C consumers
D **scavengers**

SCIENCE MATTERS

Everyday Science

A Lake Can't Last forever

Much like living things, lakes change over time and even have life spans. Scientists call this change "lake succession". One way this occurs is through eutrophication.

Eutrophication refers to the addition of nutrients to bodies of water. It occurs naturally, but human activity can speed up the process. Nutrients—especially phosphorus and nitrogen—are necessary for algae and plants to grow in lakes. However, too many nutrients, such as those from fertilizers and sewage, can lead to excessive algae growth or "blooms."

These blooms often kill plant and animal life by upsetting the oxygen and carbon dioxide cycles. Decomposers, such as bacteria, feed off the algae, using up dissolved oxygen in the water in the process. This limits the amount and kinds of aquatic life that can live there.

Over many years, a lake becomes shallower when it fills with dying plant and animal matter. Material also builds up from outside the lake. The lake becomes a marsh that, over time, turns into dry land.

Research It With your classmates, analyze a body of water to determine its ability to support life. To study biotic factors, obtain and identify samples of organisms. Find information about how to count the kinds and numbers of invertebrates to judge pollution levels. Then look at abiotic factors. Use thermometers, probeware, and water chemistry kits to determine temperature, dissolved oxygen, and pH levels. Research information about how these factors affect the survival of organisms. Compile findings in a table and graph data. Pass records on to future classes to interpret and predict changes over time.

LS.1a, LS.1c, LS.1h, LS.1i, LS.1j, LS.10b, LS.10c, LS.11b, LS.11c, LS.11d, LS.11e

Trees: Environmental Factories

Some of the most important members of your community don't volunteer. They consume huge amounts of water and they make a mess. Despite these drawbacks, these long-standing community members do their share. Who are these individuals? They're trees!

Keeping it clean: Trees remove pollutants from the air. Some researchers have calculated the value of the environmental cleaning services that trees provide. One study valued the air-cleaning service that trees in the Chicago area provide at more than $9 million every year.

Keeping it cool: Trees provide shade and lower air temperature by the process of transpiration. Pollutants, like ozone and smog, form more easily when air temperatures are high, so by keeping the air cool, trees also keep it clean.

Acting locally and globally: Trees help fight global environmental problems such as climate change. Trees remove carbon dioxide from the air and store the carbon as they grow. Experts estimate that urban trees in the United States remove more than 700 million tons of carbon from the air every year.

Helping the local economy: Trees are also good for business. One study found that shoppers spend more money in urban areas where trees are planted than they do in similar areas that don't have trees!

Research It Examine a topographical map of the area where you live. Compare it to an aerial photograph from a library or local archive. Identify areas with a lot of trees, and areas that you think could benefit from more trees. Create a proposal to plant trees in one of the areas you identified. What kinds of trees will you plant? What do those trees need in order to grow well?

Schools, clubs, and civic groups all over the United States volunteer to plant trees in their communities. ▶

WHAT MIGHT HAPPEN IF BATS DISAPPEARED?

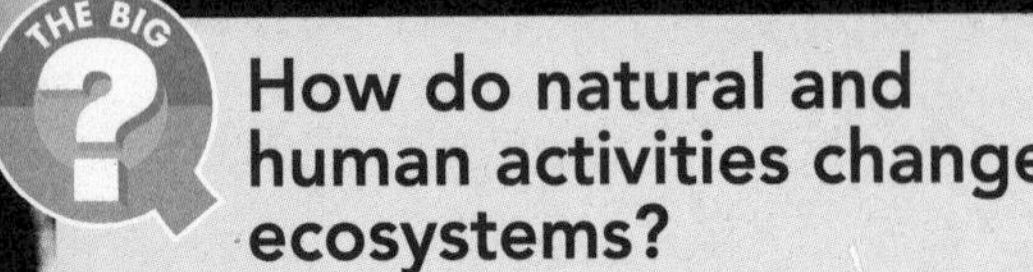

How do natural and human activities change ecosystems?

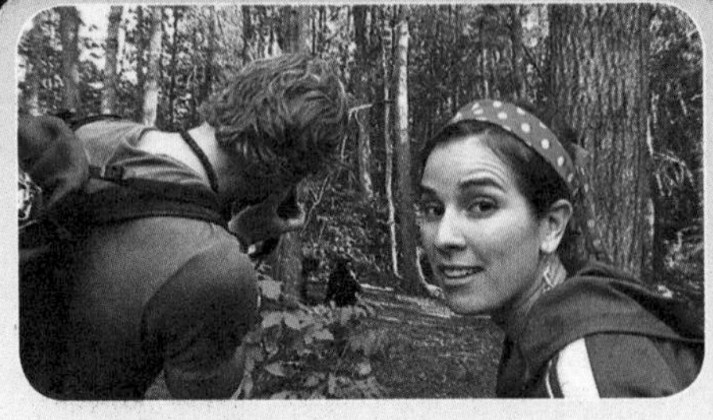

UNTAMED SCIENCE Watch the **Untamed Science** video to learn more about ecosystems.

Have you ever looked up on a warm evening to see fluttering bats searching for insects? A bat may consume nearly 50% of its body weight in insects in one night. Unfortunately, many cave-dwelling bats are dying because of a fungal condition called white-nose syndrome. Researchers are studying causes of the fungus to find ways to save these valuable creatures.

Develop Hypotheses **Predict how the loss of bats could affect ecosystems.**

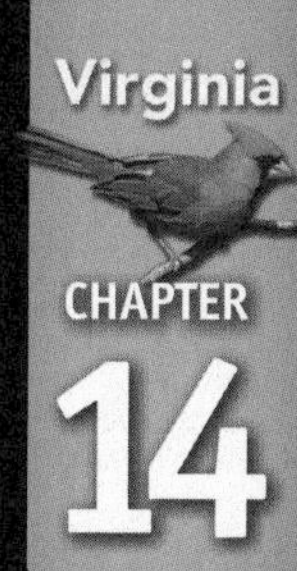

Ecosystems and Human Activity

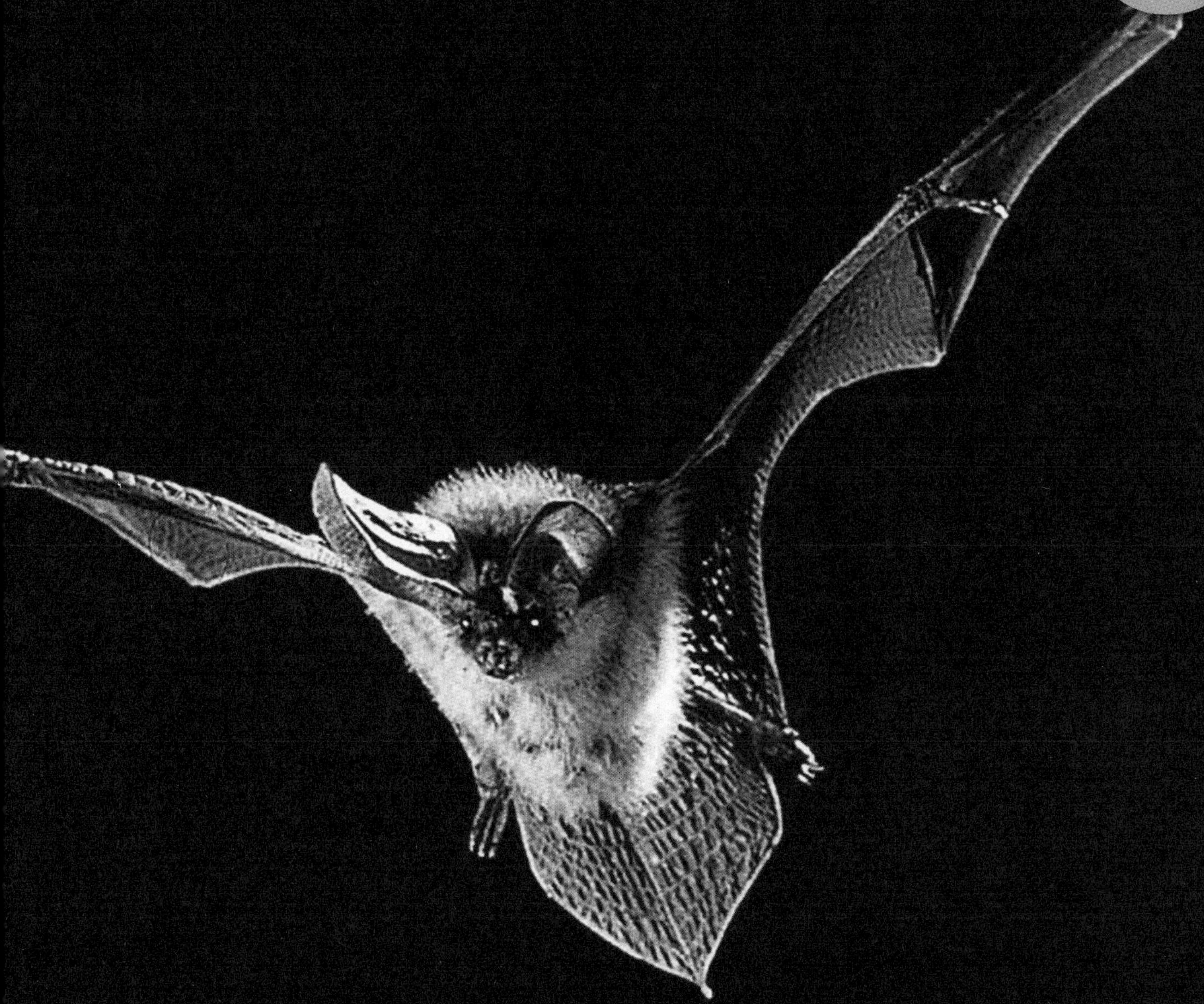

Science Standards of Learning

LS.1d, LS.1h, LS.1i, LS.1j, LS.10b, LS.10c, LS.11a, LS.11b, LS.11c, LS.11d, LS.11e, LS.13a, LS.13b, LS.13c

CHAPTER

14 Getting Started

Check Your Understanding

1. **Background** Read the paragraph below and then answer the question.

Ed is observing his **ecology** project for the tenth day in a row. He holds the bottle up to see the **habitat** inside. The snails, fish, and plants inside the bottle all look healthy. He can even see some baby snails. It is a whole **ecosystem** in a bottle!

Ecology is the study of how organisms interact with each other and their environment.

A **habitat** is an environment that provides the things a specific organism needs to live, grow, and reproduce.

An **ecosystem** is the community of organisms that live in a particular area, along with their nonliving environment.

- How are the terms *ecosystem* and *ecology* related?

____

____

MY READING WEB If you had trouble completing the question above, visit **My Reading Web** and type in ***Ecosystems and Human Activity.***

Vocabulary Skill

Identify Related Word Forms You can increase your vocabulary by learning related forms of a word. For example, if you know the verb *produce* means "to make," you can figure out that the meaning of the noun *product* is "something that is made." The table below shows two vocabulary words in this chapter and their related word forms.

Verb	Noun	Adjective
pollute to contaminate Earth's land, water, or air	**pollution** the contamination of Earth's land, water, or air	**pollutive** contaminating Earth's land, water, or air
conserve to manage resource use wisely	**conservation** the practice of managing resource use wisely	**conservational** managing resource use wisely

2. **Quick Check Complete the sentence with the correct form of the word from the table above.**

- Air ____________________ is a problem in many of the world's major cities.

Chapter Preview

LESSON 1

- point source
- nonpoint source
- biodegradable

Identify the Main Idea
Classify

LESSON 2

- natural resource
- soil conservation
- crop rotation
- contour plowing
- conservation plowing

Summarize
Observe

LESSON 3

- biodiversity • keystone species
- gene • extinction
- endangered species
- threatened species
- habitat destruction
- habitat fragmentation
- poaching • captive breeding

Compare and Contrast
Infer

VOCAB FLASH CARDS For more help with vocabulary, visit **Vocab Flash Cards** and type in ***Ecosystems and Human Activity.***

Protecting Land and Soil

What Are Some Sources of Land Pollution?
LS.1i, LS.10b, LS.11a, LS.11b, LS.11d, LS.11e

How Can Land Pollution Be Reduced?
LS.11e

my planet Diary

FUN FACT

Life Beneath Your Feet

The soil beneath your feet may not look very interesting, but it's packed with life! Many microscopic organisms live in soil and affect the lives of other organisms. Some bacteria, like the *Pseudomonas* shown above, can protect plants from disease. Hundreds of thousands of soil mites can live in a single square meter of soil. And tiny worms called nematodes eat plants, bacteria, fungi, and even other nematodes!

Bacterium

Use what you have read and your experiences to answer the questions below.

1. What are some examples of organisms that live in soil?

2. Describe soil you have seen or touched. What did it feel like? How did it smell? What creatures did you see in it?

PLANET DIARY Go to **Planet Diary** to learn more about soil.

Nematode

Mite

Lab zone® Do the Inquiry Warm-Up *What Can You Do to Protect Land and Soil Near Your School?*

Vocabulary
- point source
- nonpoint source
- biodegradable

Skills
- Reading: Identify the Main Idea
- Inquiry: Classify

What Are Some Sources of Land Pollution?

Science Standards of Learning

LS.1i Identify, interpret, and evaluate patterns in data.
LS.10b Investigate and understand factors that increase or decrease population size.
LS.11a Investigate and understand food production and harvest.
LS.11b Investigate and understand changes in habitat size, quality, or structure.
LS.11d Investigate and understand population disturbances and factors that threaten or enhance species survival.
LS.11e Investigate and understand environmental issues.

The Fourth of July parade is over. People have gone home. But the trash isn't gone. Paper, plastic bags, apple cores, and gum wrappers litter the street. Trash is a form of land pollution, or the contamination of Earth's land. **Most land pollution results from human activities. Producing trash and dumping wastes from agriculture, industry, homes, mining, and other human activities are some sources of land pollution.**

Types of Land Pollution Earth's land is an important resource. Think about the crops and animals that provide food, such as the food shown in **Figure 1.** Crops and animals need space to live. You need land, too. Your home is probably on land. Your family car is parked on land when you go shopping. The buildings you shop in are built on land. However, the amount of usable land is limited. People must protect it.

Two types of land pollution are solid waste and chemical contamination. Trash left after a parade is solid waste. Animal wastes are also solid wastes. The chemicals found in pesticides and herbicides that farmers put on their crops to kill insects and weeds are examples of chemical contamination. These chemicals can enter the soil and contaminate or pollute it.

FIGURE 1

Land Use and Pollution

People use animals and crops to make many products.

Apply Concepts In the boxes, describe how land was used to produce this hamburger. Give examples of the land pollution that may have resulted from producing this hamburger.

Land Use	Land Pollution

Sources of Land Pollution

Natural events such as volcano eruptions can cause land pollution. But human activities are the major source of land pollution. These activities include agriculture, mining, energy production, and manufacturing. In addition, people produce sewage and garbage from everyday living.

Wastes produced during human activities have either a point source or a nonpoint source. A **point source** is a specific source of pollution that can be easily identified. For example, the crowds watching a parade are a point source of trash. A **nonpoint source** may be widespread or come from somewhere unknown. Chemicals in soil have nonpoint sources of pollution if their origin is unknown. Learn more about how human activities can cause land pollution in **Figure 2.**

Identify the Main Idea Underline the main idea of the second paragraph.

FIGURE 2

Human Pollution Sources

Many human activities contribute to land pollution.

Read about the kinds of activities that cause pollution and complete these tasks.

1. **Classify** Write an example of pollution for each kind of activity. Then classify the example as having a point or nonpoint source.
2. **Compare and Contrast** How are the natural and human-caused patterns of land pollution different?

______

______

______

Agricultural Wastes

Animal wastes and the chemicals in fertilizers, pesticides, and herbicides can pollute soil. Once in the soil, the chemicals may be absorbed by plant roots. People and animals may then eat the plants and ingest these chemicals.

______

______

Plane spraying chemicals over a field

Sewage Wastes

The water and wastes that people wash down drains are called sewage. Sewage includes solid wastes that contain harmful microorganisms. In city sewer systems, the microorganisms are killed in waste-treatment plants. However, many homes in rural areas process sewage in underground tanks. Harmful microorganisms can enter soil and the water supply if a tank leaks or fails.

______

______

Sewage treatment plant

Coal-burning plant

Mining and Manufacturing Wastes

Wastes from mines may pile up. Factories produce metals and chemical wastes when products are made. If these wastes enter the soil, they can harm animals that eat the plants growing there. Polluted soil may prevent some crops from growing.

Alaskan pipeline

Energy Production

Oil and coal are major sources of energy. Pipelines and underground storage tanks can leak oil into the soil. When power plants burn coal, coal ashes are formed. Coal ashes contain toxic chemicals much like the ashes produced naturally by erupting volcanoes.

Garbage

Garbage is anything people discard. Some garbage, such as paper and food waste, is **biodegradable.** It breaks down by natural processes and forms harmless substances. Other garbage, such as plastic items and metal cans, is not biodegradable. It decomposes slowly.

do the math!

The garbage items listed in the table are often put in landfills.

Garbage	Decomposition Time
Plastic milk jug	1 million years
Disposable diaper	550 years
Aluminum can	200–500 years
Food can	90 years
Leather shoe	45 years
Wool sock	1 year
Paper bag	1 month
Banana peel	3–4 weeks

1 **Calculate** How many more months does it take for a food can to decompose than a paper bag?

2 **Interpret Data** What makes up most of the volume of a typical landfill?

3 CHALLENGE What do biodegradable items have in common?

FIGURE 3

Pathway of DDT Pollution

Fish, brown pelicans, and water plants made up a DDT pollution pathway in a Gulf coast ecosystem before DDT was banned. Brown pelicans now thrive due to the ban on DDT in 1972.

Interpret Diagrams Draw arrows in the diagram to show the pathway of DDT pollution through the ecosystem.

Land Pollution in an Ecosystem Chemical pollutants on land or in soil usually spread through an ecosystem. For example, the brown pelican was once common along the coast of the Gulf of Mexico. Although these large birds had few natural enemies, their population decreased dramatically during the 1940s. By the 1960s, they had almost disappeared from the region.

The brown pelicans disappeared because the shells of their eggs were so thin that they broke before the young hatched. High levels of DDT in the bodies of the brown pelicans were causing their eggshells to get thinner. Scientists discovered how pelicans got DDT into their bodies. First, plants growing near the water's edge absorbed DDT from the soil. Fish ate the plants. Then the brown pelicans ate the fish. Use **Figure 3** to show the pathway of DDT through the ecosystem.

Lab zone® Do the Quick Lab *Which Type of Pollution Is Worst?*

Assess Your Understanding

1a. Name What is a natural source of land pollution?

____

b. Infer Would the DDT in a pond in the 1960s likely have had a point or a nonpoint source?

____

got it?

○ **I get it!** Now I know that some sources of land pollution include ______________________________

____

○ I need extra help with ______________________________

Go to MY SCIENCE COACH *online for help with this subject.*

How Can Land Pollution Be Reduced?

LS.11e Investigate and understand environmental issues.

People need to produce less trash to reduce the amount of land pollution. **Reducing, reusing, and recycling can reduce the amounts of trash and land pollution.**

You can do many things to reduce the amount of trash you produce. For example, you can avoid buying products that are overly packaged. You can compost kitchen scraps and yard waste instead of throwing them in the trash can. You can use fewer paper products by using washable dishes, metal utensils, and glass cups instead of disposable ones.

Reusing items also cuts down on waste. It avoids or delays throwing an item in the trash. Save and reuse grocery bags. Donate unwanted clothing to charity.

Recycling turns waste items into valuable resources. In addition, making new items from recycled items saves energy and raw materials. Recycled plastic bottles can become T-shirts, combs, and picnic tables. Aluminum cans can be cleaned and used over and over. Look at **Figure 4.**

FIGURE 4

> INTERACTIVE ART **Reduce, Reuse, Recycle**

You can help to reduce land pollution.

Describe Write how you could reduce, reuse, and recycle to keep these bottles from polluting the land.

______

______

______

______

______

______

Lab zone Do the Quick Lab *What Can You Do to Reduce Land Pollution?*

Assess Your Understanding

got it?

O **I get it!** Now I know that three ways to produce less trash are ______

______

O I need extra help with ______

Go to **my science COACH** *online for help with this subject.*

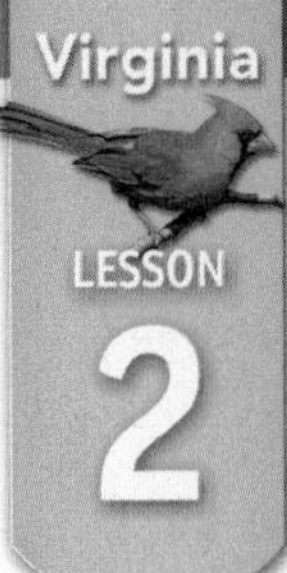

Virginia

LESSON 2

Soil Conservation

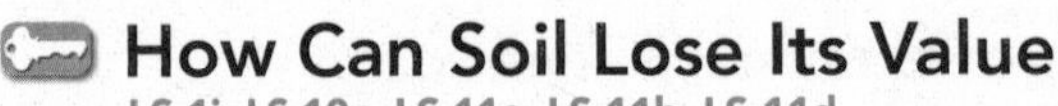

How Can Soil Lose Its Value?
LS.1j, LS.10c, LS.11a, LS.11b, LS.11d

How Can Soil Be Conserved?
LS.11a, LS.11e

my planet Diary

DISASTER

The Dust Bowl

In the 1800s, farmers began to settle the Great Plains of the central United States. Some were used to thin, rocky soil. They were excited to find prairies full of thick, rich soil covered with grasses. Farmers quickly plowed up most of the available land. By 1930, almost all of the Great Plains had been turned into farms or ranches.

But as they plowed, farmers dug up plants that held the soil together. Then a long drought in the 1930s caused the soil to dry out. The soil in parts of the Great Plains, including Texas, Oklahoma, Kansas, and Colorado, turned to dust. Without plants to hold the soil in place, it blew away. Wind caused huge dust storms and clouds of black dirt. Farms throughout the central United States were destroyed. The area most affected by this became known as the Dust Bowl.

Look at the photograph and review the information about the Dust Bowl. Then answer the questions below.

1. What happened during the Dust Bowl?

2. Why do you think the Dust Bowl is considered a disaster?

PLANET DIARY Go to **Planet Diary** to learn more about how soil can be damaged.

Do the Inquiry Warm-Up *How Can You Keep Soil From Washing Away?*

Vocabulary
- natural resource
- soil conservation
- crop rotation
- contour plowing
- conservation plowing

Skills
 Reading: Summarize
Inquiry: Observe

How Can Soil Lose Its Value?

Today, much of the area affected by the Dust Bowl is once again covered with farms. But the Dust Bowl was a reminder of how important soil is for humans.

The Value of Soil A **natural resource** is anything in the environment that humans use. Soil is one of Earth's most valuable natural resources because everything that lives on land, including humans, depends directly or indirectly on soil. Plants depend directly on the soil to live and grow. Humans and animals depend on plants—or on other animals that depend on plants—for food.

Fertile soil is valuable because there is a limited supply of it. Less than one eighth of the land on Earth has soils that are well suited for farming. Soil is also in limited supply because it takes a long time to form. It can take hundreds of years for just a few centimeters of soil to form.

Science Standards of Learning

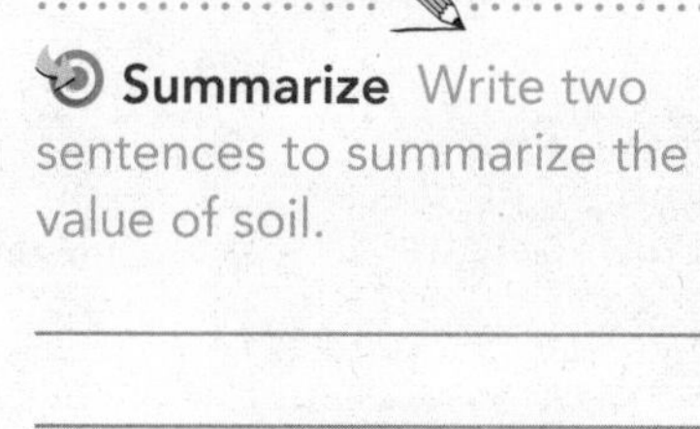

LS.1j Use current applications to reinforce life science concepts.
LS.10c Investigate and understand that ecosystems change through catastrophic disturbances.
LS.11a Investigate and understand food production and harvest.
LS.11b Investigate and understand changes in habitat size, quality, or structure.
LS.11d Investigate and understand population disturbances and factors that threaten or enhance species survival.

Summarize Write two sentences to summarize the value of soil.

FIGURE 1
Prairie Grasses
Prairie soils like those found on the Great Plains are still among the most fertile in the world.

Make Generalizations Based on the illustration below, how do you think prairie grasses protect soil?

apply it!

The two photos show samples of different soils.

1 **Observe** List two visible differences between the two soil samples.

2 CHALLENGE Which sample would you predict is more fertile? (Sample A/Sample B)

A

B

Soil Damage and Loss Human actions and changes in the environment can affect soil. **The value of soil is reduced when soil loses its fertility or when topsoil is lost due to erosion.**

Loss of Fertility Soil can be damaged when it loses its fertility. This can happen through loss of moisture and nutrients. This type of soil damage occurred in large parts of the southern United States in the late 1800s, where cotton was the only crop. Cotton used up many nutrients in the soil, and those nutrients were not replaced.

Loss of Topsoil Whenever soil is exposed, water and wind can quickly erode it. Plant cover can protect soil from erosion in several ways. Plants break the force of falling rain, and plant roots hold the soil together.

Wind erosion is most likely to occur in areas where farming methods are not suited to dry conditions. For example, wind erosion contributed to the Dust Bowl on the Great Plains. Farmers plowed up the prairie grasses that held the soil together. Without roots to hold it, the soil blew away more easily.

Lab® zone Do the Lab Investigation *Investigating Soils and Drainage.*

Assess Your Understanding

1a. Explain Why is soil valuable?

b. Relate Cause and Effect How does wind erosion affect the value of soil?

got it?

O **I get it!** Now I know that soil can lose value when

O I need extra help with

Go to **MY SCIENCE COACH** *online for help with this subject.*

How Can Soil Be Conserved?

Science Standards of Learning

LS.11a Investigate and understand food production and harvest.

LS.11e Investigate and understand environmental issues.

Today, many farmers use methods of soil conservation. **Soil conservation** is the management of soil to limit its destruction. **Soil can be conserved through practices such as contour plowing, conservation plowing, and crop rotation.**

Changes in Crops

Some crops, such as corn and cotton, take up large amounts of nutrients from the soil. Others, such as peanuts, alfalfa, and beans, help restore soil fertility. These plants, called legumes, have small lumps on their roots that contain nitrogen-fixing bacteria. These bacteria make the important nutrient nitrogen available in a form that plants can use.

In **crop rotation,** a farmer plants different crops in a field each year. One year, the farmer plants a crop such as corn or cotton. The next year, the farmer plants crops that use fewer soil nutrients, such as oats, barley, or rye. The year after that the farmer sows legumes to restore the nutrient supply.

Changes in Plowing

In **contour plowing,** farmers plow their fields along the curves of a slope instead of in straight rows. This method helps slow the runoff of excess rainfall and prevents it from washing the soil away. In **conservation plowing,** dead weeds and stalks of the previous year's crop are plowed into the ground to help return soil nutrients, retain moisture, and hold soil in place.

FIGURE 2

> REAL-WORLD INQUIRY

Farming Methods

Peanuts (above) are useful for crop rotation. The bacteria on their roots make nitrogen available. Contour plowing (left) is one way to conserve soil.

Make Judgments **Which method would you recommend to a farmer who wanted to maintain soil fertility?**

____

____

____

____

Do the Quick Lab *Soil Conservation.*

Assess Your Understanding

got it?

○ **I get it!** Now I know that soil can be conserved by _______________

____

○ I need extra help with _______________

Go to MY SCIENCE COACH *online for help with this subject.*

Biodiversity

What Is Biodiversity's Value?
LS.10b, LS.11a, LS.11c

What Factors Affect Biodiversity?
LS.10c, LS.11b, LS.11d

How Do Humans Affect Biodiversity?
LS.1d, LS.10b, LS.10c, LS.11b, LS.11c, LS.11d, LS.11e

my planet Diary

BLOG

Posted by: Max

Location: Hagerstown, Maryland

I went to summer camp to learn about wildlife and how to protect it. One of the activities that I liked the most was making "bat boxes." These are wooden homes for brown bats, which often need places to nest. Making these houses is important, because without brown bats, there would be too many mosquitoes. I hope the bats like their new homes as much as I loved making them.

Communicate Discuss the question with a group of classmates. Then write your answers below.

How do you think helping the bats in an area helps other species nearby?

PLANET DIARY Go to **Planet Diary** to learn more about biodiversity.

Do the Inquiry Warm-Up *How Much Variety Is There?*

LS.10b Investigate and understand factors that increase or decrease population size.

LS.11a Investigate and understand food production and harvest.

LS.11c Investigate and understand changes in species competition.

What Is Biodiversity's Value?

No one knows exactly how many species live on Earth. As you can see in **Figure 1,** scientists have identified more than 1.6 million species so far. The number of different species in an area is called the area's **biodiversity.** It is difficult to estimate the total biodiversity on Earth because many areas have not been thoroughly studied.

Vocabulary

- biodiversity • keystone species • gene • extinction
- endangered species • threatened species
- habitat destruction • habitat fragmentation
- poaching • captive breeding

Skills

- Reading: Compare and Contrast
- Inquiry: Infer

There are many reasons why preserving biodiversity is important. One reason to preserve biodiversity is that wild organisms and ecosystems are a source of beauty and recreation. **In addition, biodiversity has both economic value and ecological value within an ecosystem.**

Economic Value Many plants, animals, and other organisms are economically valuable for humans. These organisms provide people with food and supply raw materials for clothing, medicine, and other products. No one knows how many other useful species have not yet been identified. Ecosystems are economically valuable, too. Many companies now run wildlife tours to rain forests, savannas, mountains, and other places. This ecosystem tourism, or ecotourism, is an important source of jobs and money for such nations as Brazil, Costa Rica, and Kenya.

Ecological Value All the species in an ecosystem are connected to one another. Species may depend on each other for food and shelter. A change that affects one species can affect all the others.

Some species play a particularly important role in their ecosystems. A **keystone species** is a species that influences the survival of many other species in an ecosystem. Sea otters, as shown in **Figure 2,** are one example of a keystone species.

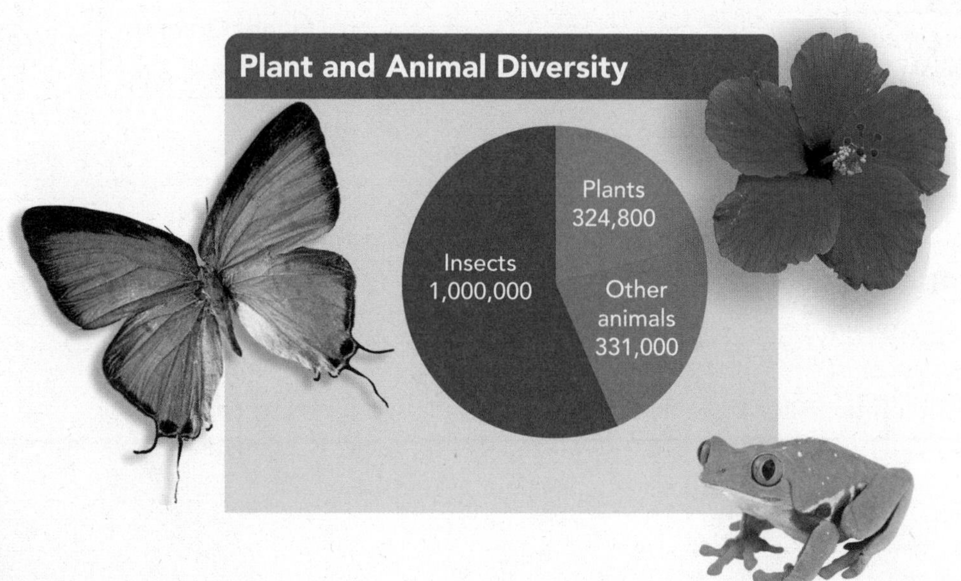

FIGURE 1

Species Diversity

There are many more species of insects than plant or other animal species on Earth!

Calculate What percentage of species shown on the pie graph do insects represent? Round your answer to the nearest tenth.

FIGURE 2

Keystone Otters

Sea otters are a keystone species in the kelp forest ecosystem.

Describe Read the comic. In the empty panel, draw or explain what happened to the kelp forest when the otters returned. Write a caption for your panel.

The sea otter is a keystone species in a kelp forest ecosystem.

In the 1800s, many otters were killed for their fur.

Under new laws that banned the hunting of sea otters, the sea otter population grew again.

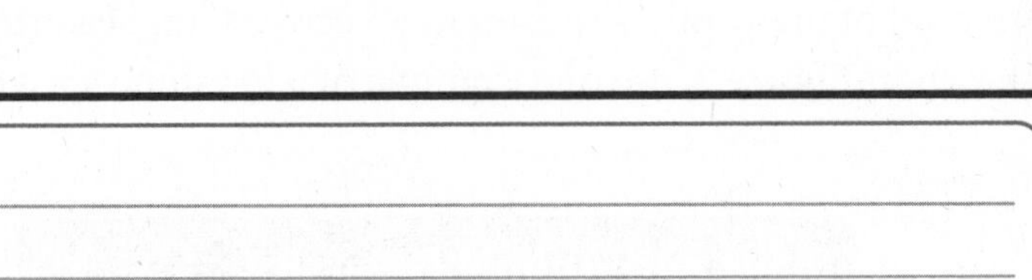

Lab zone® Do the Quick Lab *Modeling Keystone Species.*

Assess Your Understanding

got it?

O **I get it!** Now I know that biodiversity has

O I need extra help with

Go to MY SCIENCE COACH *online for help with this subject.*

What Factors Affect Biodiversity?

Biodiversity varies from place to place on Earth. **Factors that affect biodiversity in an ecosystem include climate, area, niche diversity, genetic diversity, and extinction.**

Climate The tropical rain forests of Latin America, southeast Asia, and central Africa are the most diverse ecosystems in the world. The reason for the great biodiversity in the tropics is not fully understood. Many scientists hypothesize that it has to do with climate. For example, tropical rain forests have fairly constant temperatures and large amounts of rainfall throughout the year. Many plants grow year-round. This continuous growing season means that food is always available for other organisms.

Area See **Figure 3.** Within an ecosystem, a large area will usually contain more species than a small area. For example, you would usually find more species in a 100-square-meter area than in a 10-square-meter area.

FIGURE 3

Park Size

A park manager has received three park plans. The dark green area represents the park.

Complete each task.

1. **Identify** Circle the plan the manager should choose to support the most biodiversity.
2. **Calculate** Suppose that 15 square meters of the park could support seven species of large mammals. About how many species could the park you circled support?

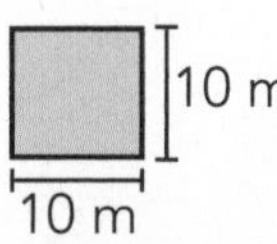

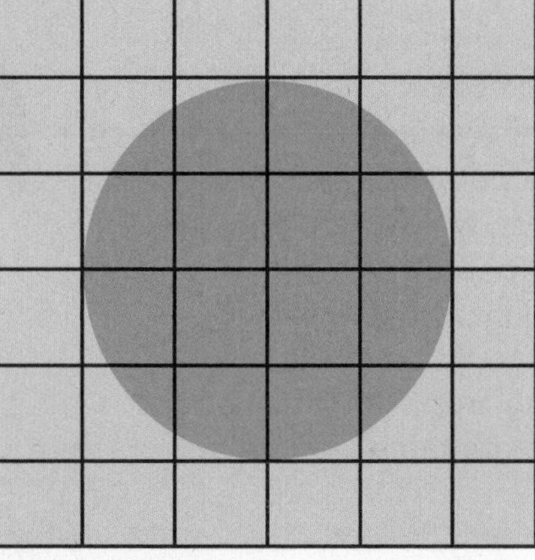

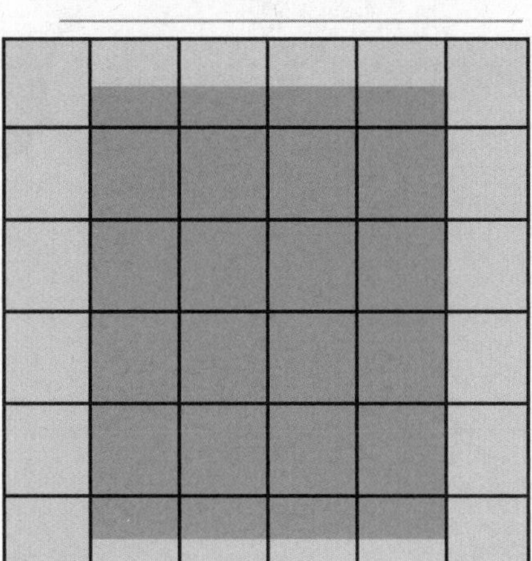

Science Standards of Learning

LS.10c Investigate and understand that ecosystems change through climate changes.

LS.11b Investigate and understand changes in habitat size, quality, or structure.

LS.11d Investigate and understand population disturbances and factors that threaten or enhance species survival.

Rain forests cover only about seven percent of the Earth's land surface. But they contain more than half of the world's species, including the chimpanzee!

Niche Diversity Coral reefs are the second most diverse ecosystems in the world. Found only in shallow, warm waters, coral reefs are often called the rain forests of the sea. A coral reef supports many different niches. Recall that a niche is the role of an organism in its habitat, or how it makes its living. A coral reef enables a greater number of species to live in it than a more uniform habitat, such as a flat sandbar, does.

Genetic Diversity Diversity is very important within a species. The greatest genetic diversity exists among species of unicellular organisms. Organisms in a healthy population have diverse traits such as color and size. **Genes** are located within cells and carry the hereditary information that determines an organism's traits. Organisms inherit genes from their parents.

The organisms in one species share many genes. But each organism also has some genes that differ from those of other individuals. Both the shared genes and the genes that differ among individuals make up the total gene pool of that species. Species that lack a diverse gene pool are less able to adapt to and survive changes in the environment.

apply it!

New potato plants are created from pieces of the parent plant. So a potato crop has the same genetic makeup as the parent plant. In 1845, Ireland was struck by a potato famine. A rot-causing fungus destroyed potato crops, which were an important part of the Irish diet. Many people died of starvation, and many more left the country to find food.

1 **Apply Concepts** How did a potato crop without a variety of different genes lead to the Irish potato famine of 1845?

2 CHALLENGE What could farmers do to prevent another potato famine?

Extinction of Species The disappearance of all members of a species from Earth is called **extinction.** Extinction is a natural process that occurs when organisms do not adapt to changes in their environment. In the last few centuries, the number of species becoming extinct has increased dramatically. Once a population drops below a certain level, the species may not recover. People have directly caused the extinction of many species through habitat destruction, hunting, or other actions.

Species in danger of becoming extinct in the near future are called **endangered species.** Species that could become endangered in the near future are called **threatened species.** Endangered and threatened species are found on every continent and in every ocean.

Green sea turtle ▲

Blackburn's sphinx moth ▲

FIGURE 4

Endangered Species

Large animals, like the green sea turtle, are the most publicized endangered species. Did you know insects and plants can also be endangered? Infer **Why do you think some endangered species get more attention than others?**

______

______

______

______

______

Hawaiian alula ▲

Do the Quick Lab *Grocery Gene Pool.*

Assess Your Understanding

1a. Review A (smaller/larger) area will contain more species than a (smaller/larger) area.

b. Explain How is biodiversity related to niches?

______

______

______

c. Compare and Contrast What is the difference between an endangered species and a threatened species?

______

______

______

got it?

O **I get it!** Now I know that the factors that affect biodiversity include ______

______

O I need extra help with ______

Go to MY SCIENCE COACH *online for help with this subject.*

Science Standards of Learning

LS.1d Construct and use models and simulations to illustrate and explain phenomena.

LS.10b Investigate and understand factors that increase or decrease population size.

LS.11b Investigate and understand changes in habitat size, quality, or structure.

LS.11d Investigate and understand population disturbances and factors that threaten or enhance species survival.

LS.11e Investigate and understand environmental issues.

How Do Humans Affect Biodiversity?

Humans interact with their surroundings every day. The many choices people make impact the environment and affect species. **Biodiversity can be negatively or positively affected by the actions of humans.**

Damaging Biodiversity A natural event, such as a hurricane, can damage an ecosystem, wiping out populations or even entire species. Human activities can also threaten biodiversity and cause extinction. These activities include habitat destruction, poaching, pollution, and the introduction of exotic species.

FIGURE 5

Habitat Fragmentation

Breaking habitats into pieces can have negative effects on the species that live there.

Interpret Diagrams In the first diagram below, a road divides a habitat in two. On the second diagram, redraw the road so it divides the habitat's resources equally.

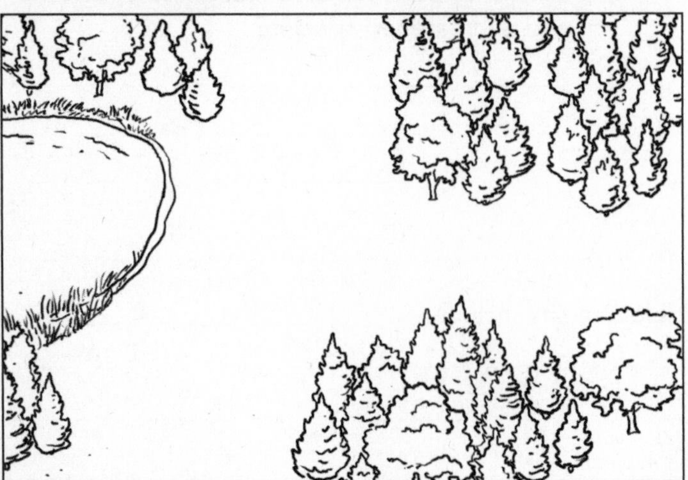

Habitat Destruction The major cause of extinction is **habitat destruction,** the loss of a natural habitat. Clearing forests or filling in wetlands changes those ecosystems. Breaking larger habitats into smaller, isolated pieces, or fragments, is called **habitat fragmentation.** See **Figure 5.** Some species may not survive such changes to their habitats.

Poaching The illegal killing or removal of wildlife from their habitats is called **poaching.** Some endangered species are valuable to poachers. Animals can be sold as pets or used to make jewelry, coats, belts, or shoes. Plants can be sold as houseplants or used to make medicines.

Pollution Some species are endangered because of pollution. Pollution may reach animals through the water they drink, the air they breathe, or the food they eat. Pollutants may kill or weaken organisms or cause birth defects.

Exotic Species Introducing exotic species into an ecosystem can threaten biodiversity. Exotic species can outcompete and damage native species. The gypsy moth was introduced into the United States in 1869 to increase silk production. Gypsy moth larvae have eaten the leaves off of millions of acres of trees in the northeastern United States.

Suppose people start to overfish this area. How might this change the ecosystem? Explain.

Suppose a tsunami, a huge ocean wave, were to hit this ecosystem, destroying much of the reef. Do you think the ecosystem would come back after the tsunami? Explain.

Lab zone® Do the Quick Lab *Humans and Biodiversity.*

Assess Your Understanding

2a. Define What is poaching?

b. ANSWER THE BIG ? How do natural and human activities change ecosystems?

got it?

O **I get it!** Now I know that humans affect biodiversity

O I need extra help with

Go to MY SCIENCE COACH *online for help with this subject.*

CHAPTER 14

Study Guide

A species that cannot adapt to natural or human activities can become __________.

LESSON 1 Protecting Land and Soil

Most land pollution results from human activities. Producing trash and dumping wastes from agriculture, industry, homes, mining, and other human activities are some sources of land pollution.

Reducing, reusing, and recycling can reduce the amounts of trash and land pollution.

Vocabulary

- point source
- nonpoint source
- biodegradable

LESSON 2 Soil Conservation

The value of soil is reduced when soil loses its fertility and when topsoil is lost due to erosion.

Soil can be conserved through practices such as contour plowing, conservation plowing, and crop rotation.

Vocabulary

- natural resource
- soil conservation
- crop rotation
- contour plowing
- conservation plowing

LESSON 3 Biodiversity

Biodiversity has both economic value and ecological value within an ecosystem.

Factors that affect biodiversity include climate, area, niche diversity, genetic diversity, and extinction.

Biodiversity can be negatively or positively affected by the actions of humans.

Vocabulary

- biodiversity
- keystone species
- gene
- extinction
- endangered species
- threatened species
- habitat destruction
- habitat fragmentation
- poaching
- captive breeding

Review and Assessment

LESSON 1 Protecting Land and Soil

1. Which causes most land pollution?
   - **a.** agricultural wastes
   - **b.** energy production
   - **c.** human activities
   - **d.** garbage items

2. ______________________ items break down by natural processes.

3. **Describe** How could you reuse three items that you usually throw away?

4. **Relate Cause and Effect** The population of the United States is increasing, but the amount of trash going to landfills is decreasing. What could cause this difference?

5. **Classify** Give an example of a point source and a nonpoint source contribution to pollution.

6. **Write About It** Volcano ash and coal ash from a coal-burning power plant both contain toxic chemicals. Identify a possible pathway of these chemicals into an ecosystem.

LESSON 2 Soil Conservation

7. Which technique returns nutrients to soil?
   - **a.** chemical weathering
   - **b.** contour plowing
   - **c.** crop rotation
   - **d.** wind erosion

8. What role do grasses play in conserving the soil of the prairies?
   - **a.** holding the soil in place
   - **b.** increasing wind erosion
   - **c.** decreasing the amount of fertile soil
   - **d.** making nitrogen available to plants

9. **Draw Conclusions** Why is soil important to people and to other living things?

10. **Relate Cause and Effect** How did human activities contribute to the Dust Bowl?

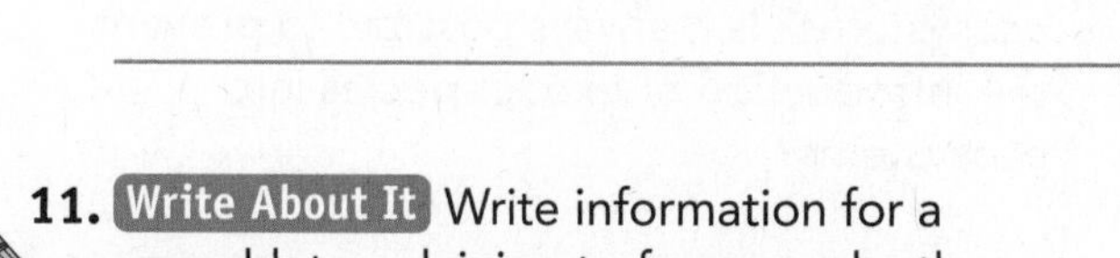

11. **Write About It** Write information for a pamphlet explaining to farmers why they should use conservation plowing and contour plowing. Explain how these methods would help conserve soil.

CHAPTER 14

Review and Assessment

LESSON 3 Biodiversity

12. The most effective way to preserve biodiversity is through
    - a. captive breeding.
    - b. habitat destruction.
    - c. habitat preservation.
    - d. habitat fragmentation.

13. ______________________ occurs when all members of a species disappear from Earth.

14. **Predict** How could the extinction of a species today affect your life in 20 years?

15. List three ways that humans depend on plant and animal resources to survive.

16. **Write About It** When people transport agricultural products such as plants to other countries, exotic insects living on or in the products may be shipped accidentally. What steps might people take to prevent these exotic insects from harming the native ecosystems? Is it always possible to prevent the introduction of exotic species into ecosystems?

How do natural and human activities change ecosystems?

17. People regularly set controlled fires in some ecosystems to prevent the growth of invasive plants. What impact do the fires have on these ecosystems? On the atmosphere?

Virginia SOL Test Prep

Read each question and choose the best answer.

1 According to the circle graph, by what percentage would recycling have to increase in order to become the most used method of waste disposal?

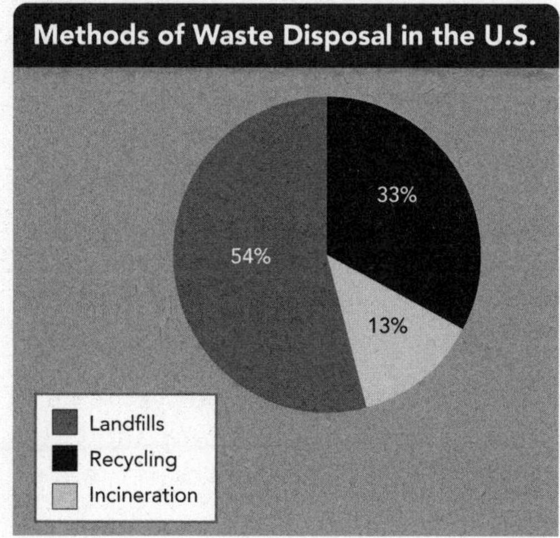

A 13% B 18%
C 21% D 22%

2 Fertile soil is an important resource because—

F no new soil can be produced.
G everything that lives on land depends on soil.
H there is an unlimited supply of fertile soil.
J plants cannot grow in fertile soil.

3 Which is a nonpoint source of pollution?

A chemicals on a field
B an oil leak from an unknown source
C a sewage treatment plant
D a pipe dumping wastewater

4 Which of the following terms describes a species that is in danger of becoming extinct in the near future?

F captive species
G keystone species
H threatened species
J endangered species

5 A farmer wants to reduce the amount of runoff in his fields. Which of the following methods would be most helpful?

A contour plowing
B conservation plowing
C crop rotation
D topsoil erosion

6 Which of the following is a way that humans can have a positive effect on biodiversity?

F poaching
G captive breeding
H introducing exotic species
J destroying habitats

7 An example of niche diversity is a—

A tundra
B steppe
C coral reef
D desert

Congratulations, It's an Island!

▲ Island of Surtsey today. People are not allowed to live on the island, but scientists who have permission to research there have built a research station.

On November 15, 1963, a fiery eruption shot out from the icy sea, off the south coast of Iceland, spewing gigantic clouds of ash.

A new island, Surtsey, formed. A volcanic eruption began 130 meters under the sea and forced volcanic ash to the surface. Eventually, the layers of lava and ash formed a volcanic cone that rose above sea level—the birth of Surtsey.

Eruptions continued for nearly four years as steady flows of lava moved outward and cooled in the sea. By the end, Surtsey had an area of 2.7 square kilometers.

It takes a long time for a new island to cool down! At the very base of the island, water flows through layers of loose rocks. When it makes contact with the extremely hot magma chamber deep under the sea, the water evaporates. Steam travels through the layers of porous rock at the base of the island, heating the island up.

To protect Surtsey's environment, the government of Iceland allows only a handful of scientists to visit the delicate new environment. Surtsey is a natural laboratory that gives scientists valuable information on how plant and animal populations begin on a volcanic island.

Research It **The arrival of living things on Surtsey is an example of primary succession. Research the organisms that live on Surtsey, or in another area of newly formed lava rock. Make a storyboard showing primary succession on Surtsey or on the area you have researched. Organize and include available data on your storyboard. Use the data to make predictions about how Surtsey or the area you have chosen may change over time.**

 LS.1d, LS.1h, LS.10c

Teen Finds Fossils

In early 2007, sixteen-year-old Sierra Sarti-Sweeney went for a walk at Boca Ciega Millenium Park in Seminole, Florida. She wanted to take some nature pictures. She did not expect to stumble on a mammoth!

During her walk, Sierra noticed bones in a stream bed. With her older brother, Sean, she brought the bones to local scientists. The bone Sierra found was the tooth of a prehistoric Columbian mammoth. Archaeologists say that the tooth and other fossils Sierra found could be as much as 100,000 years old!

Since Sierra's find, digging at the site has uncovered even more bones, including those from prehistoric camels, 2-meter turtles, and saber-toothed cats. According to scientists, the findings suggest that this part of Florida was once like the African savanna region.

For Sierra, the experience was exciting. She even had a call from a late-night television host. Finding the tooth confirmed Sierra's desire to be a zoologist and to keep looking at the world around her.

Design It Plan an exhibit of Sierra's findings. Make a brochure for the exhibit and develop a presentation of the fossils found at Boca Ciega Millenium Park. In the brochure, compare the fossils in Sierra's findings to current day species showing how animals have changed over time.

Kids Doing Science

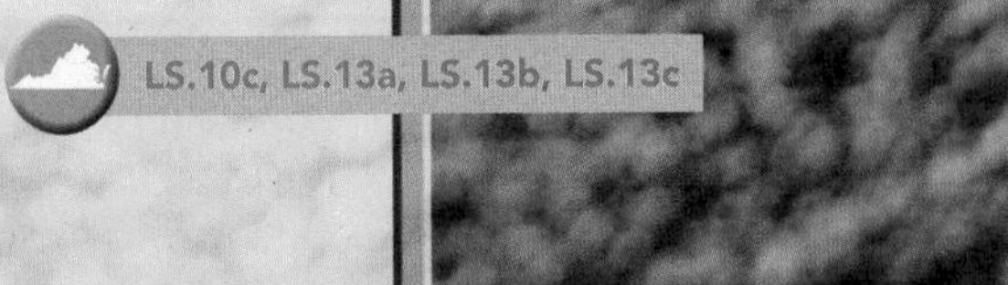

LS.10c, LS.13a, LS.13b, LS.13c

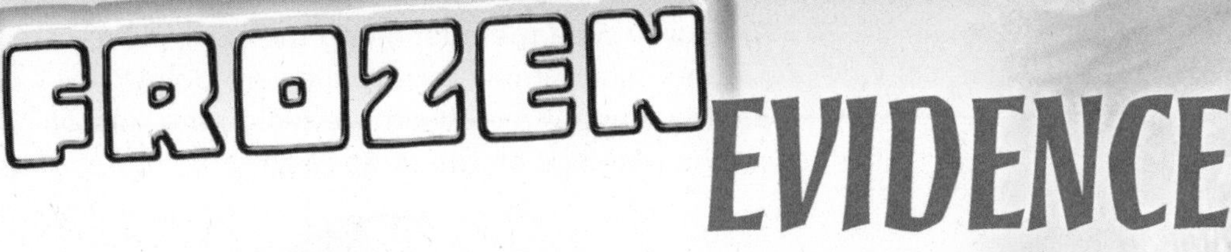

FROZEN EVIDENCE

Hot Science

In the giant ice cap at the South Pole, a continuous record of snow exists reaching back more than 800,000 years. Scientists have drilled 3.2 kilometers down into the ice. From the cores they pull up, scientists learn about the temperature and the different gases in the air when each layer was formed.

These cores show that temperatures go up and down in cycles. Long ice ages (about 90,000 years) follow short warm periods (about 10,000 years). The climate record also shows that temperatures and amounts of carbon dioxide change together. If carbon dioxide levels rise, temperatures also rise.

Research It Find at least three sources that explain the ice cores project. Write an essay critiquing the explanations provided. Note any bias, misinformation, or missing information.

LS.1j

Researchers extract samples from the ice at the South Pole. ▲

APPENDIX A

Using a Laboratory Balance

The laboratory balance is an important tool in scientific investigations. Different kinds of balances are used in the laboratory to determine the masses and weights of objects. You can use a triple-beam balance to determine the masses of materials that you study or experiment with in the laboratory. An electronic balance, unlike a triple-beam balance, is used to measure the weights of materials.

The triple-beam balance that you may use in your science class is probably similar to the balance illustrated in this Appendix. **To use the balance properly, you should learn the name, location, and function of each part of the balance you are using. What kind of balance do you have in your science class?**

The Triple-Beam Balance

The triple-beam balance is a single-pan balance with three beams calibrated in grams. The back, or 100-gram, beam is divided into ten units of 10 grams each. The middle, or 500-gram, beam is divided into five units of 100 grams each. The front, or 10-gram, beam is divided into ten units of 1 gram each. Each of the units on the front beam is further divided into units of 0.1 gram. What is the largest mass you could find with a triple-beam balance?

The following procedure can be used to find the mass of an object with a triple-beam balance:

1. Place the object on the pan.
2. Move the rider on the middle beam notch by notch until the horizontal pointer on the right drops below zero. Move the rider back one notch.
3. Move the rider on the back beam notch by notch until the pointer again drops below zero. Move the rider back one notch.
4. Slowly slide the rider along the front beam until the pointer stops at the zero point.
5. The mass of the object is equal to the sum of the readings on the three beams.

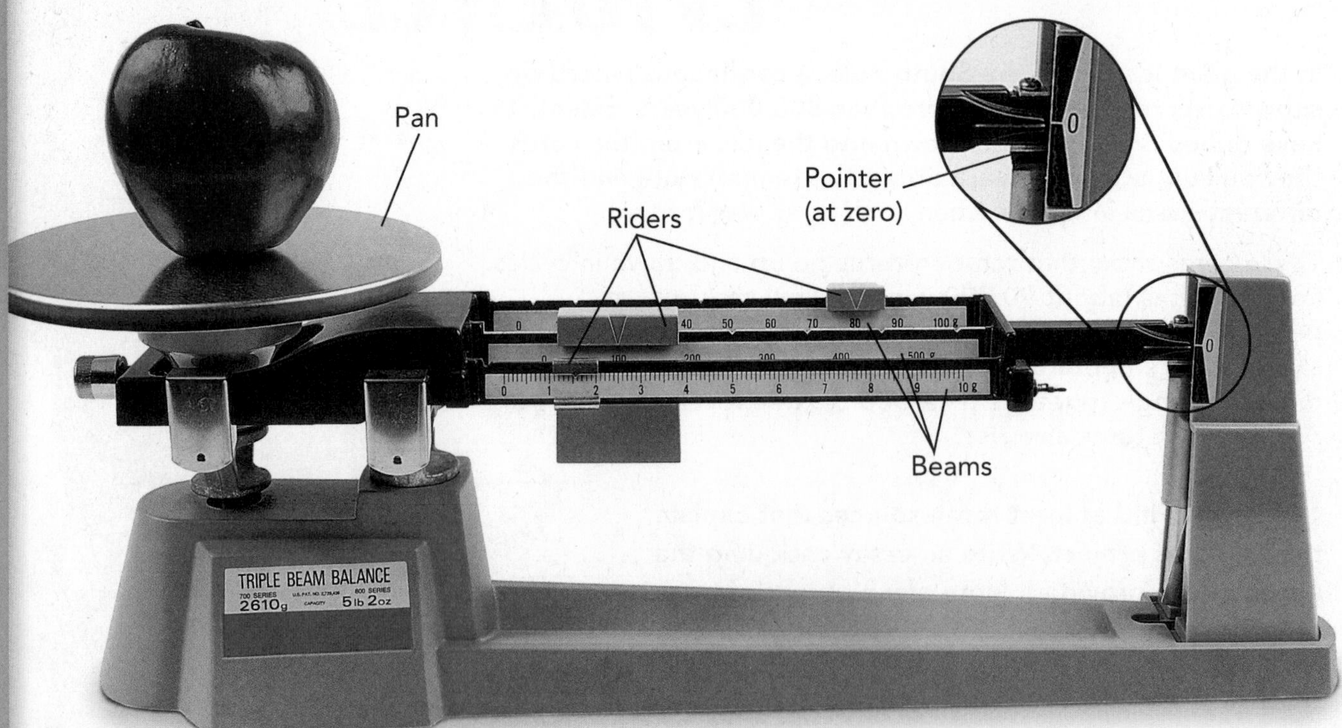

APPENDIX B

Probeware in the Science Classroom

Probeware is scientific equipment that uses sensors, or probes, to make data collection faster and easier. There are different probes to measure everything from pH and dissolved oxygen of water to temperature and the pressure of air. The probes collect data and can be connected to hand-held devices, laptops, or desktop computers that record and display the data.

These probes are connected to a hand-held device that records the data.

These students are using probeware to test the water quality of a stream.

Probeware is a powerful scientific tool because probes record data continuously, giving you more data to work with than you could record yourself. Because the technology is portable, you also can measure and record data out in the field. Rather than bringing water samples back from a lake, for example, you can test the pH and dissolved oxygen of the water right there. All the information is stored on the device.

The other major benefit of probeware is that it can display the data it collects and records in a variety of graphical forms. With the press of a button, software can present the data as any kind of table or graph that you choose, letting you spend more time analyzing your results instead of creating tables and graphs yourself.

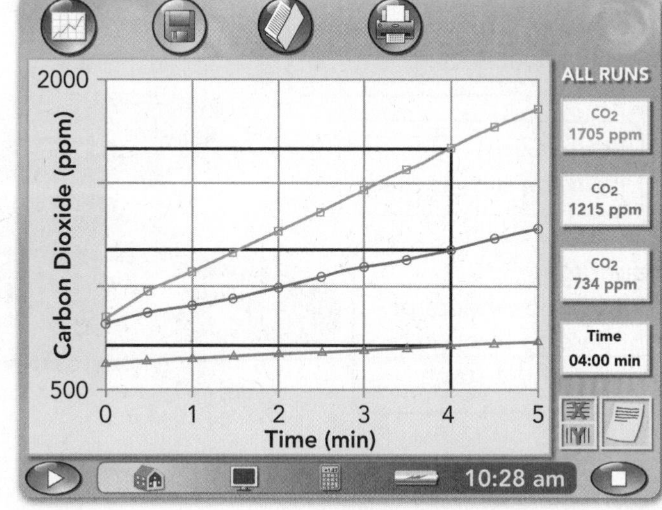

Probeware was used to generate this line graph for an experiment involving respiration and CO_2 levels. It displays the results of three runs of the experiment on the same graph.

APPENDIX C

Using a Microscope

The microscope is an essential tool in the study of life science. It allows you to see things that are too small to be seen with the unaided eye.

You will probably use a compound microscope like the one you see here. The compound microscope has more than one lens that magnifies the object you view.

Typically, a compound microscope has one lens in the eyepiece, the part you look through. The eyepiece lens usually magnifies 10×. Any object you view through this lens would appear 10 times larger than it is.

A compound microscope may contain one or two other lenses called objective lenses. If there are two, they are called the low-power and high-power objective lenses. The low-power objective lens usually magnifies 10×. The high-power objective lens usually magnifies 40×.

To calculate the total magnification with which you are viewing an object, multiply the magnification of the eyepiece lens by the magnification of the objective lens you are using. For example, the eyepiece's magnification of 10× multiplied by the low-power objective's magnification of 10× equals a total magnification of 100×.

Use the photo of the compound microscope to become familiar with the parts of the microscope and their functions.

The Parts of a Microscope

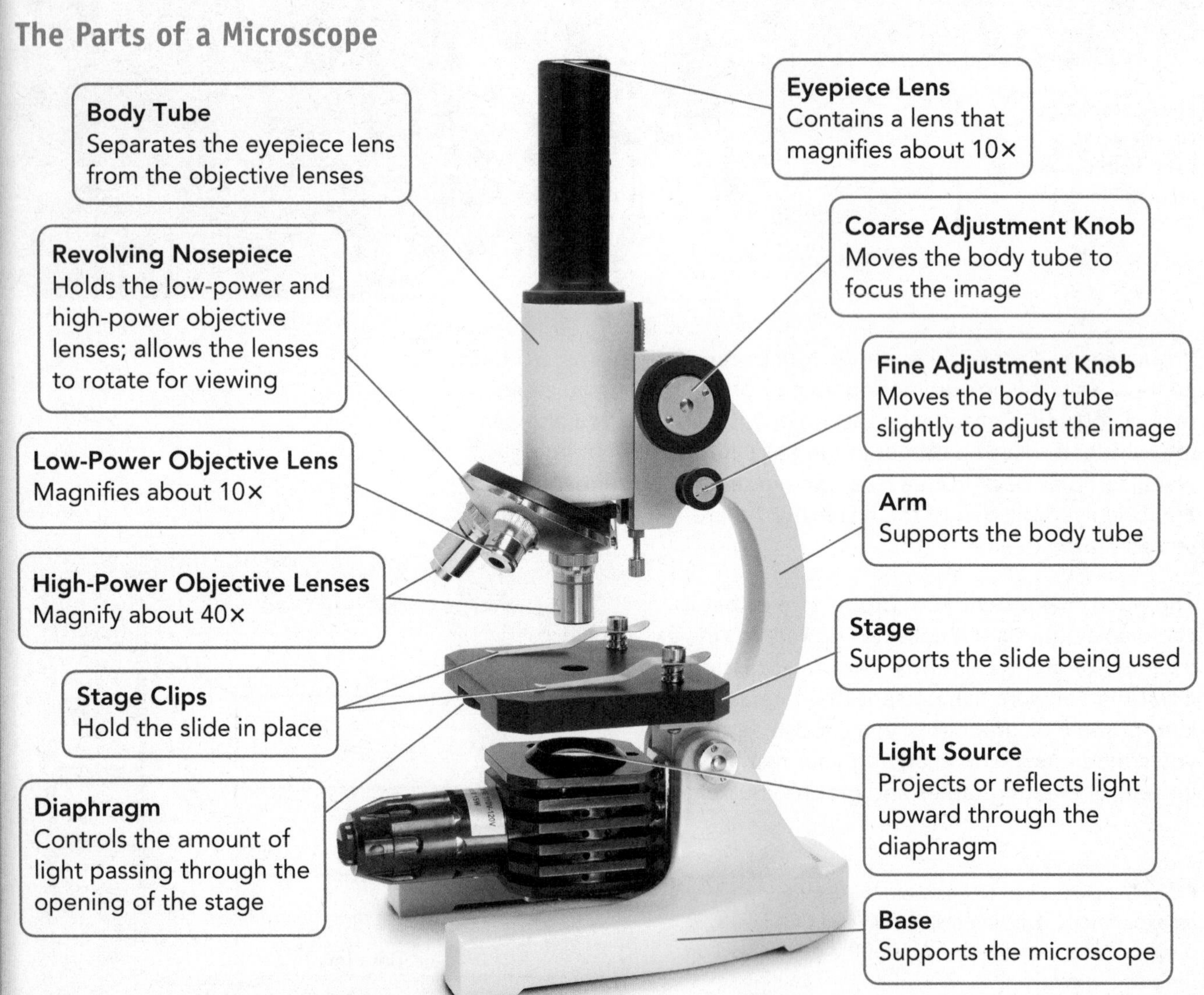

Using the Microscope

Use the following procedures when you are working with a microscope.

1. To carry the microscope, grasp the microscope's arm with one hand. Place your other hand under the base.
2. Place the microscope on a table with the arm toward you.
3. Turn the coarse adjustment knob to raise the body tube.
4. Revolve the nosepiece until the low-power objective lens clicks into place.
5. Adjust the diaphragm. While looking through the eyepiece, also adjust the mirror until you see a bright white circle of light. **CAUTION:** *Never use direct sunlight as a light source.*
6. Place a slide on the stage. Center the specimen over the opening on the stage. Use the stage clips to hold the slide in place. **CAUTION:** *Glass slides are fragile.*
7. Look at the stage from the side. Carefully turn the coarse adjustment knob to lower the body tube until the low-power objective almost touches the slide.
8. Looking through the eyepiece, very slowly turn the coarse adjustment knob until the specimen comes into focus.
9. To switch to the high-power objective lens, look at the microscope from the side. Carefully revolve the nosepiece until the high-power objective lens clicks into place. Make sure the lens does not hit the slide.
10. Looking through the eyepiece, turn the fine adjustment knob until the specimen comes into focus.

Making a Wet-Mount Slide

Use the following procedures to make a wet-mount slide of a specimen.

1. Obtain a clean microscope slide and a coverslip. **CAUTION:** *Glass slides and coverslips are fragile.*
2. Place the specimen on the center of the slide. The specimen must be thin enough for light to pass through it.
3. Using a plastic dropper, place a drop of water on the specimen.
4. Gently place one edge of the coverslip against the slide so that it touches the edge of the water drop at a 45° angle. Slowly lower the coverslip over the specimen. If you see air bubbles trapped beneath the coverslip, tap the coverslip gently with the eraser end of a pencil.
5. Remove any excess water at the edge of the coverslip with a paper towel.

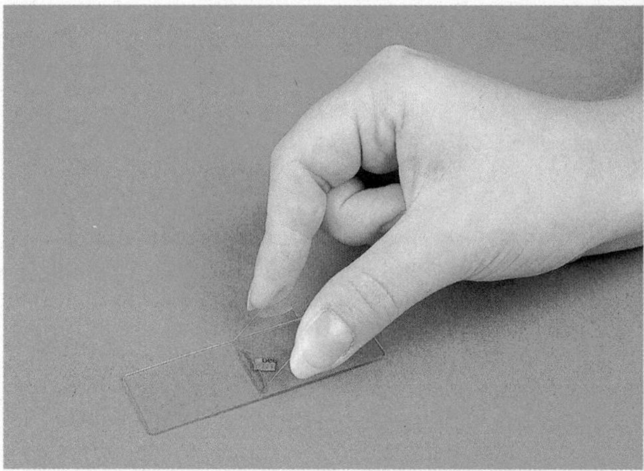

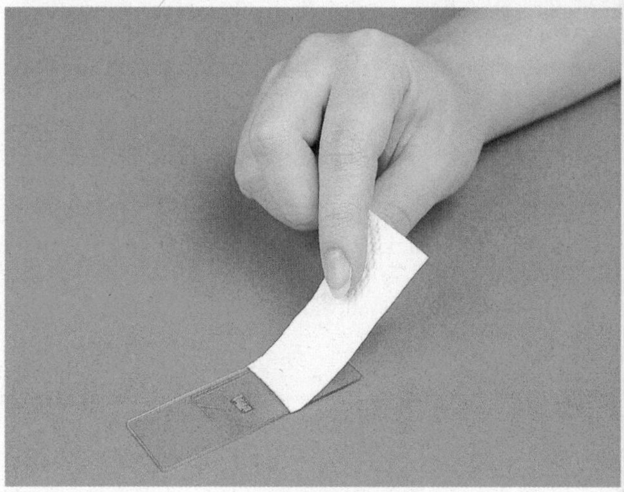

GLOSSARY

A

abiotic factor A nonliving part of an organism's habitat. (412)
factor abiótico La parte sin vida del hábitat de un organismo.

accuracy How close a measurement is to the true or accepted value. (50)
exactitud Cuán cerca está una medida del valor verdadero o aceptado.

active transport The movement of materials across a cell membrane using cellular energy. (148)
transporte activo Proceso que usa la energía celular para mover materiales a través de la membrana celular.

adaptation An inherited behavior or physical characteristic that helps an organism survive and reproduce in its environment. (285)
adaptación Comportamiento o característica física hereditaria que le permite a un organismo sobrevivir y reproducirse en su ambiente.

aggression A threatening behavior that one animal uses to gain control over another animal. (392)
agresión Comportamiento amenazador que un animal usa para controlar a otro.

alleles The different forms of a gene. (193)
alelos Diferentes formas de un gen.

amphibian A vertebrate whose body temperature is determined by the temperature of its environment, and that lives its early life in water and its adult life on land. (386)
anfibio Animal vertebrado cuya temperatura corporal depende de la temperatura de su entorno, y que vive la primera etapa de su vida en el agua y su vida adulta en la tierra.

angiosperm A flowering plant that produces seeds enclosed in a protective fruit. (324)
angiosperma Planta con flores que produce semillas encerradas en una fruta protectora.

annual A flowering plant that completes its life cycle in one growing season. (337)
anual Planta con flores que completa su ciclo de vida en una sola temporada de crecimiento.

anomalous data Data that do not fit with the rest of a data set. (54)
datos anómalos Información que no encaja con los otros datos de un conjunto de datos.

arthropod An invertebrate that has an external skeleton, a segmented body, and jointed appendages. (378)
artrópodo Invertebrado que tiene un esqueleto externo, un cuerpo segmentado y apéndices articulados.

asexual reproduction A reproductive process that involves only one parent and produces offspring that are genetically identical to the parent. (87)
reproducción asexual Proceso reproductivo que consiste de un solo reproductor y que produce individuos que son genéticamente idénticos al reproductor.

autotroph An organism that is able to capture energy from sunlight or chemicals and use it to produce its own food. (91)
autótrofo Organismo capaz de capturar y usar la energía solar o de sustancias químicas para producir su propio alimento.

auxin A plant hormone that speeds up the rate at which a plant's cells grow and controls a plant's response to light. (346)
auxina Hormona vegetal que acelera la velocidad del crecimiento de las células de una planta y que controla la respuesta de la planta a la luz.

B

biennial A flowering plant that completes its life cycle in two years. (337)
bienal Planta con flores que completa su ciclo de vida en dos años.

bilateral symmetry A body plan in which a single imaginary line divides the body into left and right sides that are mirror images of each other. (370)
simetría bilateral Esquema del cuerpo en el que una línea imaginaria divide el cuerpo en dos partes, izquierda y derecha, que son el reflejo la una de la otra.

binomial nomenclature The classification system in which each organism is given a unique, two-part scientific name indicating its genus and species. (96)
nomenclatura binaria Sistema de clasificación en el que cada organismo tiene un nombre científico específico de dos partes que indica el género y la especie.

biodegradable Capable of being broken down by bacteria and other decomposers. (495)
biodegradable Sustancia que las bacterias y otros descomponedores pueden descomponer.

biodiversity The total number of different species on Earth, including those on land, in the water, and in the air. (502)
biodiversidad Número total de especies diferentes que habitan la Tierra, incluyendo especies terrestres, marinas y del aire.

biogeography The study of where organisms live and how they got there. (479)
biogeografía Estudio del hábitat de los organismos y de cómo han llegado a ese hábitat.

biome A group of ecosystems with similar climates and organisms. (464)
bioma Grupo de ecosistemas con organismos y climas parecidos.

biotic factor A living or once living part of an organism's habitat. (412)
factor biótico Parte viva, o que alguna vez tuvo vida, del hábitat de un organismo.

bird A vertebrate whose body temperature is regulated by its internal heat, lays eggs, and has feathers and a four-chambered heart. (388)
ave Vertebrado cuya temperatura corporal es regulada por su calor interno, que produce huevos y que tiene plumas y un corazón de cuatro cavidades.

birth rate The number of births per 1,000 individuals for a certain time period. (417)
tasa de natalidad Número de nacimientos por 1,000 individuos durante un período de tiempo determinado.

boreal forest Dense forest of evergreens located in the upper regions of the Northern Hemisphere. (470)
bosque boreal Bosque denso donde abundan las plantas coníferas y que se encuentra en las regiones más al norte del hemisferio norte.

branching tree diagram A diagram that shows probable evolutionary relationships among organisms and the order in which specific characteristics may have evolved. (107)
árbol ramificado Diagrama que muestra las relaciones evolucionarias probables entre los organismos y el orden en que ciertas características específicas podrían haber evolucionado.

C

cambium A layer of cells in a plant that produces new phloem and xylem cells. (328)
cámbium Una capa de células de una planta que produce nuevas células de floema y xilema.

cancer A disease in which some body cells grow and divide uncontrollably, damaging the parts of the body around them. (237)
cáncer Enfermedad en la que algunas células del cuerpo crecen y se dividen sin control, y causan daño a las partes del cuerpo que las rodean.

canopy A leafy roof formed by tall trees in a rain forest. (467)
dosel Techo de hojas que forman los árboles en la selva tropical.

captive breeding The mating of animals in zoos or wildlife preserves. (509)
reproducción en cautiverio Apareamiento de animales en zoológicos y reservas naturales.

carbohydrate An energy-rich organic compound, such as a sugar or a starch, that is made of the elements carbon, hydrogen, and oxygen. (140)
carbohidrato Compuesto orgánico rico en energía, como un azúcar o almidón, formado por los elementos carbono, hidrógeno y oxígeno.

carnivore A consumer that obtains energy by eating only animals. (450)
carnívoro Consumidor que adquiere su energía al alimentarse de animales solamente.

carrier A person who has one recessive allele and one dominant allele for a trait. (255)
portador Persona que tiene un alelo recesivo y un alelo dominante para un rasgo.

carrying capacity The largest population that a particular environment can support. (422)
capacidad de carga Población mayor que un ambiente en particular puede mantener.

cartilage A connective tissue that is more flexible than bone and that protects the ends of bones and keeps them from rubbing together. (385)
cartílago Tejido conector más flexible que el hueso, que protege los extremos de los huesos y evita que se rocen.

GLOSSARY

cell The basic unit of structure and function in living things. (86)
célula Unidad básica de la estructura y función de todos los seres vivos.

cell cycle The series of events in which a cell grows, prepares for division, and divides to form two daughter cells. (174)
ciclo celular Serie de sucesos en los que una célula crece, se prepara para dividirse y se divide para formar dos células hijas.

cell membrane A thin, flexible barrier that surrounds a cell and controls which substances pass into and out of a cell. (129)
membrana celular Barrera delgada y flexible alrededor de la célula, que controla lo que entra y sale de la célula.

cell theory A widely accepted explanation of the relationship between cells and living things. (122)
teoría celular Explicación ampliamente aceptada sobre la relación entre las células y los seres vivos.

cell wall A rigid supporting layer that surrounds the cells of plants and some other organisms. (129)
pared celular Capa fuerte de apoyo alrededor de las células de las plantas y algunos otros organismos.

cellular respiration The process in which oxygen and glucose undergo a complex series of chemical reactions inside cells, releasing energy. (167)
respiración celular Proceso en el cual el oxígeno y la glucosa pasan por una serie compleja de reacciones químicas dentro de las células y así liberan energía.

chemotherapy The use of drugs to treat diseases such as cancer. (239)
quimioterapia Uso de medicamentos para tratar enfermedades como el cáncer.

chlorophyll A green photosynthetic pigment found in the chloroplasts of plants, algae, and some bacteria. (163)
clorofila Pigmento verde fotosintético de los cloroplastos de las plantas, algas y algunas bacterias.

chloroplast An organelle in the cells of plants and some other organisms that captures energy from sunlight and changes it to an energy form that cells can use in making food. (135)
cloroplasto Orgánulo de las células vegetales y otros organismos que absorbe energía de la luz solar y la convierte en una forma de energía que las células pueden usar para producir alimentos.

chordate An animal that has a notochord, a nerve cord, and throat pouches at some point in its life. (381)
cordado Animal que tiene un notocordio, un cordón nervioso y bolsas en la garganta en determinada etapa de su vida.

chromosome A threadlike structure within a cell's nucleus that contains DNA that is passed from one generation to the next. (174)
cromosoma Estructura filamentosa en el núcleo celular que contiene el ADN que se transmite de una generación a la siguiente.

circadian rhythm A behavioral cycle that occurs over a period of about one day. (396)
ritmo circadiano Ciclo de comportamiento que ocurre durante el transcurso de aproximadamente un día.

classification The process of grouping things based on their similarities. (95)
clasificación Proceso de agrupar cosas según sus semejanzas.

classifying The process of grouping together items that are alike in some way. (8)
clasificar Proceso de agrupar objetos con algún tipo de semejanza.

climate The average annual conditions of temperature, precipitation, winds, and clouds in an area. (464)
clima Condiciones promedio anuales de temperatura, precipitación, viento y nubosidad de un área.

clone An organism that is genetically identical to the organism from which it was produced. (265)
clon Organismo genéticamente idéntico al organismo del que proviene.

cnidarian A radially symmetrical invertebrate that uses stinging cells to capture food and defend itself. (375)
cnidario Invertebrado de simetría radiada que usa células urticantes para obtener alimentos y defenderse.

codominance A situation in which both alleles for a gene are expressed equally. (203)
codominancia Situación en la que ambos alelos de un gen se manifiestan de igual manera.

commensalism A type of symbiosis between two species in which one species benefits and the other species is neither helped nor harmed. (432)
comensalismo Tipo de relación simbiótica entre dos especies en la cual una especie se beneficia y la otra especie ni se beneficia ni sufre daño.

community All the different populations that live together in a particular area. (414)
comunidad Todas las poblaciones distintas que habitan en un área específica.

competition The struggle between organisms to survive as they attempt to use the same limited resources in the same place at the same time. (427)
competencia Lucha por la supervivencia entre organismos que se alimentan de los mismos recursos limitados en el mismo lugar y al mismo tiempo.

compound A substance made of two or more elements chemically combined in a specific ratio, or proportion. (139)
compuesto Sustancia formada por dos o más elementos combinados químicamente en una razón o proporción específica.

condensation The change in state from a gas to a liquid. (457)
condensación Cambio del estado gaseoso al estado líquido.

cone The reproductive structure of a gymnosperm. (340)
cono Estructura reproductora de una gimnosperma.

coniferous tree A tree that produces its seeds in cones and that has needle-shaped leaves coated in a waxy substance to reduce water loss. (470)
árbol conífero Árbol que produce sus semillas en piñones y que tiene hojas en forma de aguja y cubiertas por una sustancia cerosa que reduce la pérdida de agua.

conservation plowing Soil conservation method in which weeds and dead stalks from the previous year's crop are plowed into the ground. (501)
arado de conservación Método de conservación de la tierra en el que las plantas y los tallos muertos de la cosecha del año anterior se dejan en la tierra al ararla.

consumer An organism that obtains energy by feeding on other organisms. (450)
consumidor Organismo que obtiene energía al alimentarse de otros organismos.

continental drift The hypothesis that the continents slowly move across Earth's surface. (479)
deriva continental Hipótesis que sostiene que los continentes se desplazan lentamente sobre la superficie de la Tierra.

contour plowing Plowing fields along the curves of a slope to prevent soil loss. (501)
arado en contorno Arar los campos siguiendo las curvas de una pendiente para evitar la pérdida del suelo.

controlled experiment An experiment in which only one variable is manipulated at a time. (22)
experimento controlado Experimento en el cual sólo se manipula una variable a la vez.

convergent evolution The process by which unrelated organisms evolve similar characteristics. (109)
evolución convergente Proceso por el cual organismos no relacionados exhiben una evolución de características similares.

cotyledon A leaf produced by an embryo of a seed plant; sometimes stores food. (324)
cotiledón Hoja producida por el embrión de una planta fanerógama; a veces almacena alimentos.

courtship behavior The behavior in which males and females of the same species engage to prepare for mating. (393)
comportamiento de cortejo Comportamiento de los machos y las hembras de una especie en preparación del apareamiento.

critical night length The number of hours of darkness that determines whether or not a plant will flower. (347)
duración crítica de la noche El número de horas de oscuridad que determina si florecerá una planta o no.

crop rotation The planting of different crops in a field each year to maintain the soil's fertility. (501)
rotación de las cosechas Cultivo anual de cosechas diferentes en un campo para mantener la fertilidad del suelo.

cultural bias An outlook influenced by the beliefs, social forms, and traits of a group. (13)
prejuicio cultural Opinión influenciada por las creencias, costumbres sociales y características de un grupo.

cuticle The waxy, waterproof layer that covers the leaves and stems of most plants. (314)
cutícula Capa cerosa e impermeable que cubre las hojas y los tallos de la mayoría de las plantas.

GLOSSARY

cytokinesis The final stage of the cell cycle, in which the cell's cytoplasm divides, distributing the organelles into each of the two new daughter cells. (178)
citocinesis Última etapa del ciclo celular en la que se divide el citoplasma y se reparten los orgánulos entre las dos células hijas nuevas.

cytoplasm The thick fluid region of a cell located inside the cell membrane (in prokaryotes) or between the cell membrane and nucleus (in eukaryotes). (131)
citoplasma Región celular de líquido espeso ubicada dentro de la membrana celular (en las procariotas) o entre la membrana celular y el núcleo (en las eucariotas).

D

data Facts, figures, and other evidence gathered through observations. (23)
dato Hechos, cifras u otra evidencia reunida por medio de observaciones.

day-neutral plant A plant with a flowering cycle that is not sensitive to periods of light and dark. (347)
planta de día neutro Planta con un ciclo de floración que no es sensible a la luz o la oscuridad.

death rate The number of deaths per 1,000 individuals for a certain time period. (417)
tasa de mortalidad Número de muertes por 1,000 individuos durante un período de tiempo determinado.

deciduous tree A tree that sheds its leaves during a particular season and grows new ones each year. (469)
árbol caducifolio Árbol que pierde las hojas durante una estación específica y al que le salen hojas nuevas cada año.

decomposer An organism that gets energy by breaking down biotic wastes and dead organisms, and returns raw materials to the soil and water. (451)
descomponedor Organismo que obtiene energía al descomponer desechos bióticos y organismos muertos, y que devuelve materia prima al suelo y al agua.

deductive reasoning A way to explain things by starting with a general idea and then applying the idea to a specific observation. (15)
razonamiento deductivo Manera de explicar las cosas en la que se aplica una idea general a una observación específica.

density The measurement of how much mass of a substance is contained in a given volume. (44)
densidad Medida de la masa de una sustancia que tiene un volumen dado.

desert A dry region that on average receives less than 25 centimeters of precipitation per year. (465)
desierto Región seca en la que se registra un promedio menor de 25 centímetros de precipitación anual.

development The process of change that occurs during an organism's life to produce a more complex organism. (87)
desarrollo Proceso de cambio que ocurre durante la vida de un organismo, mediante el cual se crea un organismo más complejo.

dicot An angiosperm that has two seed leaves. (324)
dicotiledónea Angiosperma cuyas semillas tienen dos cotiledones.

diffusion The process by which molecules move from an area of higher concentration to an area of lower concentration. (146)
difusión Proceso por el cual las moléculas se mueven de un área de mayor concentración a otra de menor concentración.

dispersal The movement of organisms from one place to another. (480)
dispersión Traslado de los organismos de un lugar a otro.

DNA Deoxyribonucleic acid; the genetic material that carries information about an organism and is passed from parent to offspring. (142)
ADN Ácido desoxirribonucleico; material genético que lleva información sobre un organismo y que se transmite de padres a hijos.

DNA replication Before a cell divides, the process in which DNA copies itself. (228)
replicación del ADN Proceso en el que el ADN se duplica, antes de que la célula se divida.

dominant allele An allele whose trait always shows up in the organism when the allele is present. (193)
alelo dominante Alelo cuyo rasgo siempre se manifiesta en el organismo, cuando el alelo está presente.

dormancy A period of time when an organism's growth or activity stops. (348)
latencia Período de tiempo durante el cual se detiene el crecimiento o la actividad de un organismo.

double helix The shape of a DNA molecule. (142)
doble hélice Forma de una molécula de ADN.

E

echinoderm A radially symmetrical marine invertebrate that has an internal skeleton and a system of fluid-filled tubes. (379)
equinodermo Invertebrado marino de simetría radiada que tiene un esqueleto interno y un sistema de apéndices en forma de tubos llenos de líquido.

ecology The study of how organisms interact with each other and their environment. (415)
ecología Estudio de la forma en que los organismos interactúan entre sí y con su medio ambiente.

ecosystem The community of organisms that live in a particular area, along with their nonliving environment. (415)
ecosistema Comunidad de organismos que viven en un área específica, y el medio ambiente que los rodea.

ectotherm An animal whose body temperature is determined by the temperature of its environment. (383)
ectotermo Animal cuya temperatura corporal es determinada por la temperatura de su medio ambiente.

element A pure substance that cannot be broken down into other substances by chemical or physical means. (138)
elemento Sustancia que no se puede descomponer en otras sustancias por medios químicos o físicos.

embryo 1. The young organism that develops from a zygote. **2.** A developing human during the first eight weeks after fertilization has occurred. (332)
embrión 1. Organismo joven que se desarrolla a partir del cigoto. **2.** Un ser humano en desarrollo durante las primeras ocho semanas después de llevarse a cabo la fertilización.

emergent layer The tallest layer of the rain forest that receives the most sunlight. (467)
capa emergente Capa superior de la selva tropical, que recibe la mayor cantidad de luz solar.

emigration Movement of individuals out of a population's area. (418)
emigración Traslado de individuos fuera del área de una población.

endangered species A species in danger of becoming extinct in the near future. (507)
especie en peligro de extinción Especie que corre el riesgo de desaparecer en el futuro próximo.

endocytosis The process by which the cell membrane takes particles into the cell by changing shape and engulfing the particles. (149)
endocitosis Proceso en el que la membrana celular absorbe partículas al cambiar de forma y envolver las partículas.

endoplasmic reticulum An organelle that forms a maze of passageways in which proteins and other materials are carried from one part of the cell to another. (131)
retículo endoplasmático Orgánulo que forma un laberinto de conductos que llevan proteínas y otros materiales de una parte de la célula a otra.

endoskeleton An internal skeleton; structural support system within the body of an animal. (379)
endoesqueleto Esqueleto interno; sistema estructural de soporte dentro del cuerpo de un animal.

endotherm An animal whose body temperature is regulated by the internal heat the animal produces. (383)
endotermo Animal cuya temperatura corporal es regulada por el calor interno que produce.

energy pyramid A diagram that shows the amount of energy that moves from one feeding level to another in a food web. (454)
pirámide de energía Diagrama que muestra la cantidad de energía que fluye de un nivel de alimentación a otro en una red alimentaria.

enzyme 1. A type of protein that speeds up a chemical reaction in a living thing. **2.** A biological catalyst that lowers the activation energy of reactions in cells. (141)
enzima 1. Tipo de proteína que acelera una reacción química de un ser vivo. **2.** Catalizador biológico que disminuye la energía de activación de las reacciones celulares.

estimate An approximation of a number based on reasonable assumptions. (49)
estimación Aproximación de un número basada en conjeturas razonables.

estuary A kind of wetland formed where fresh water from rivers mixes with salty ocean water. (476)
estuario Tipo de pantanal que se forma donde el agua dulce de los ríos se junta con el agua salada del océano.

GLOSSARY

ethics The study of principles about what is right and wrong, fair and unfair. (12)
ética Estudio de los principios de qué es lo bueno y lo malo, lo justo y lo injusto.

eukaryote An organism whose cells contain a nucleus. (104)
eucariota Organismo cuyas células contienen un núcleo.

evaluating Comparing observations and data to reach a conclusion about them. (8)
evaluar Comparar observaciones y datos para llegar a una conclusión.

evaporation The process by which molecules at the surface of a liquid absorb enough energy to change to a gas. (457)
evaporación Proceso mediante el cual las moléculas en la superficie de un líquido absorben suficiente energía para pasar al estado gaseoso.

evolution Change over time; the process by which modern organisms have descended from ancient organisms. (106)
evolución Cambios a través del tiempo; proceso por el cual los organismos modernos se originaron a partir de organismos antiguos.

exocytosis The process by which the vacuole surrounding particles fuses with the cell membrane, forcing the contents out of the cell. (149)
exocitosis Proceso en el que la vacuola que envuelve partículas se funde con la membrana celular, expulsando así el contenido al exterior de la célula.

exoskeleton External skeleton; a tough, waterproof outer covering that protects, supports, and helps prevent evaporation of water from the body of many invertebrates. (378)
exoesqueleto Esqueleto exterior; una cobertura fuerte e impermeable que protege, soporta y ayuda a prevenir la evaporación del agua del cuerpo de muchos invertebrados.

exotic species Species that are carried to a new location by people. (480)
especies exóticas Especies que las personas trasladan a un nuevo lugar.

experimental bias A mistake in the design of an experiment that makes a particular result more likely. (13)
prejuicio experimental Error en el diseño de un experimento que aumenta la probabilidad de un resultado.

extinction The disappearance of all members of a species from Earth. (507)
extinción Desaparición de la Tierra de todos los miembros de una especie.

F

feedback Output that changes a system or allows the system to adjust itself. (62)
retroalimentación Salida que cambia un sistema o permite que éste se ajuste.

fermentation The process by which cells release energy by breaking down food molecules without using oxygen. (170)
fermentación Proceso en el que las células liberan energía al descomponer las moléculas de alimento sin usar oxígeno.

fertilization The process in sexual reproduction in which an egg cell and a sperm cell join to form a new cell. (191)
fertilización Proceso de la reproducción sexual en el que un óvulo y un espermatozoide se unen para formar una nueva célula.

field Any area outside of the laboratory. (72)
campo Cualquier área fuera del laboratorio.

fish A vertebrate whose body temperature is determined by the temperature of its environment, and that lives in the water and has fins. (385)
pez Vertebrado cuya temperatura corporal es determinada por la temperatura de su medio ambiente, que vive en el agua y que tiene aletas.

flower The reproductive structure of an angiosperm. (334)
flor Estructura reproductora de una angiosperma.

food chain A series of events in an ecosystem in which organisms transfer energy by eating and by being eaten. (452)
cadena alimentaria Serie de sucesos en un ecosistema por medio de los cuales los organismos transmiten energía al comer o al ser comidos por otros.

food web The pattern of overlapping feeding relationships or food chains among the various organisms in an ecosystem. (452)
red alimentaria Patrón de las relaciones de alimentación superpuestas o de cadenas alimentarias entre los diferentes organismos de un ecosistema.

fossil The preserved remains or traces of an organism that lived in the past. (283)
fósil Restos o vestigios conservados de un organismo que vivió en el pasado.

frond The leaf of a fern plant. (320)
fronda Hoja de un helecho.

fruit The ripened ovary and other structures of an angiosperm that enclose one or more seeds. (343)
fruto Ovario maduro y otras estructuras de una angiosperma que encierran una o más semillas.

G

gametophyte The stage in the life cycle of a plant in which the plant produces gametes, or sex cells. (336)
gametofito Etapa del ciclo vital de una planta en la que produce gametos, es decir, células sexuales.

gene A sequence of DNA that determines a trait and is passed from parent to offspring. (193)
gen Secuencia de ADN que determina un rasgo y que se pasa de los progenitores a los hijos.

gene therapy The process of changing a gene to treat a medical disease or disorder. An absent or faulty gene is replaced by a normal working gene. (267)
terapia genética Proceso que consiste en cambiar un gen para tratar una enfermedad o un trastorno médico. El gen ausente o defectuoso se cambia por un gen con función normal.

genetic disorder An abnormal condition that a person inherits through genes or chromosomes. (257)
desorden genético Condición anormal que hereda una persona a través de los genes o cromosomas.

genetic engineering The transfer of a gene from the DNA of one organism into another organism, in order to produce an organism with desired traits. (265)
ingeniería genética Transferencia de un gen desde el ADN de un organismo a otro, para producir un organismo con los rasgos deseados.

genetics The scientific study of heredity. (191)
genética Ciencia que estudia la herencia.

genome A complete set of genetic information that an organism carries in its DNA. (269)
genoma Toda la información genética que un organismo lleva en su ADN.

genotype An organism's genetic makeup, or allele combinations. (200)
genotipo Composición genética de un organismo, es decir, las combinaciones de los alelos.

genus A classification grouping that consists of a number of similar, closely related species. (96)
género Clase de agrupación que consiste de un número de especies similares y estrechamente relacionadas.

germination The sprouting of the embryo out of a seed; occurs when the embryo resumes its growth following dormancy. (333)
germinación Brotamiento del embrión a partir de la semilla; ocurre cuando el embrión reanuda su crecimiento tras el estado latente.

Golgi apparatus An organelle in a cell that receives proteins and other newly formed materials from the endoplasmic reticulum, packages them, and distributes them to other parts of the cell. (134)
aparato de Golgi Orgánulo de la célula que recibe, empaqueta y distribuye a otras partes de la célula las proteínas y otros materiales que se forman en el retículo endoplasmático.

gradualism Pattern of evolution characterized by the slow and steady accumulation of small genetic changes over long periods of time. (298)
gradualismo Evolución de una especie por medio de la acumulación lenta pero continua de cambios genéticos a través de largos períodos de tiempo.

graph A picture of information from a data table; shows the relationship between variables. (57)
gráfica Representación visual de la información de una tabla de datos; muestra la relación entre las variables.

grassland An area populated mostly by grasses and other nonwoody plants that gets 25 to 75 centimeters of rain each year. (468)
pradera Área poblada principalmente por hierbas y otras plantas no leñosas, y donde caen entre 25 y 75 centímetros de lluvia cada año.

gymnosperm A plant that produces seeds directly on the scales of cones—not enclosed by a protective fruit. (322)
gimnosperma Planta que produce semillas directamente sobre las escamas de los conos—sin estar encerradas en un fruto protector.

GLOSSARY

H

habitat An environment that provides the things a specific organism needs to live, grow, and reproduce. (411)
hábitat Medio que provee lo que un organismo específico necesita para vivir, crecer y reproducirse.

habitat destruction The loss of a natural habitat. (508)
destrucción del habitat Pérdida de un hábitat natural.

habitat fragmentation The breaking of a habitat into smaller, isolated pieces. (508)
fragmentación del hábitat Desintegración de un hábitat en porciones aisladas más pequeñas.

herbivore A consumer that obtains energy by eating only plants. (450)
herbívoro Consumidor que come sólo plantas para obtener energía.

heredity The passing of traits from parents to offspring. (190)
herencia Transmisión de rasgos de padres a hijos.

heterotroph An organism that cannot make its own food and gets food by consuming other living things. (91)
heterótrofo Organismo que no puede producir sus propios alimentos y que se alimenta al consumir otros seres vivos.

heterozygous Having two different alleles for a particular gene. (200)
heterocigoto Que tiene dos alelos distintos para un gen particular.

hibernation An animal's state of greatly reduced activity that occurs during the winter. (396)
hibernación Estado de gran reducción de la actividad de un animal que ocurre en el invierno.

homeostasis The condition in which an organism's internal environment is kept stable in spite of changes in the external environment. (93)
homeostasis Condición en la que el medio ambiente interno de un organismo se mantiene estable a pesar de cambios en el medio ambiente externo.

homologous structures Structures that are similar in different species and that have been inherited from a common ancestor. (294)
estructuras homólogas Estructuras parecidas de especies distintas y que se han heredado de un antepasado común.

homozygous Having two identical alleles for a particular gene. (200)
homocigoto Que tiene dos alelos idénticos para un gen particular.

hormone 1. A chemical that affects growth and development. **2.** The chemical produced by an endocrine gland. (346)
hormona 1. Sustancia química que afecta el crecimiento y el desarrollo. **2.** Sustancia química producida por una glándula endocrina.

host An organism that a parasite lives with, in, or on, and which provides a source of energy or a suitable environment for the parasite to live. (432)
huésped Organismo dentro del o sobre el cual vive un parásito y que provee una fuente de energía o un medio ambiente apropiado para la existencia del parásito.

hybrid An offspring of crosses that has two different alleles for a trait. (194)
híbrido Descendiente de cruces que tiene dos alelos distintos para un rasgo.

hybridization A selective breeding method that involves crossing different individuals to bring together the best traits from both parents. (264)
hibridación Técnica reproductiva en la que se cruzan individuos distintos para reunir los mejores rasgos de ambos progenitores.

hypothesis A possible explanation for a set of observations or answer to a scientific question; must be testable. (20)
hipótesis Explicación posible de un conjunto de observaciones o respuesta a una pregunta científica; se debe poder poner a prueba.

I

immigration Movement of individuals into a population's area. (418)
inmigración Movimiento de individuos al área de una población.

inbreeding A selective breeding method in which two individuals with similar sets of alleles are crossed. (264)
endogamia Técnica reproductiva en la que se cruzan dos individuos con conjuntos de alelos parecidos.

incomplete dominance A situation in which one allele is not completely dominant over another allele. (203)
dominancia incompleta Situación en la que un alelo no es completamente dominante sobre el otro.

inductive reasoning Using specific observations to make generalizations. (16)
razonamiento inductivo Usar observaciones específicas para hacer generalizaciones.

inferring The process of making an inference, an interpretation based on observations and prior knowledge. (6)
inferir Proceso de hacer una inferencia; interpretación basada en observaciones y conocimientos previos.

input Material, energy, or information that goes into a system. (62)
entrada Material, energía o informacion que se agrega a un sistema.

International System of Units (SI) A system of units used by scientists to measure the properties of matter. (39)
Sistema Internacional de Unidades (SI) Sistema de unidades que los científicos usan para medir las propiedades de la materia.

interphase The first stage of the cell cycle that takes place before cell division occurs, during which a cell grows and makes a copy of its DNA. (174)
interfase Primera etapa del ciclo celular que ocurre antes de la división celular y durante la cual la célula crece y duplica su ADN.

intertidal zone An area between the highest high-tide line on land and the point on the continental shelf exposed by the lowest low-tide line. (476)
zona intermareal Área entre el punto más alto de la marea alta y el punto más bajo de la marea baja.

invertebrate An animal without a backbone. (366)
invertebrado Animal sin columna vertebral.

K

karyotype A picture of all the human chromosomes in a cell grouped together in pairs and arranged in order of decreasing size. (260)
cariotipo Fotografía de todos los cromosomas humanos en una célula agrupados en pares y ordenados de los más grandes a los más pequeños.

keystone species A species that influences the survival of many other species in an ecosystem. (503)
especie clave Especie que tiene un impacto en la supervivencia de muchas otras especies de un ecosistema.

L

limiting factor An environmental factor that causes a population to decrease in size. (421)
factor limitante Factor ambiental que causa la disminución del tamaño de una población.

linear graph A line graph in which the data points yield a straight line. (58)
gráfica lineal Gráfica en la cual los puntos de los datos forman una línea recta.

lipid An energy-rich organic compound, such as a fat, oil, or wax, that is made of carbon, hydrogen, and oxygen. (141)
lípido Compuesto orgánico rico en energía, como una grasa, aceite o cera, formado por los elementos carbono, hidrógeno y oxígeno.

long-day plant A plant that flowers when the nights are shorter than the plant's critical night length. (347)
planta de día largo Planta que florece cuando la duración de la noche es más corta que la duración crítica.

lysosome A cell organelle which contains chemicals that break down large food particles into smaller ones and that can be used by the rest of the cell. (135)
lisosoma Orgánulo de una célula, que tiene sustancias químicas que convierten partículas grandes de alimentos en partículas más pequeñas que el resto de la célula puede utilizar.

M

making models The process of creating representations of complex objects or processes. (9)
hacer modelos Proceso de crear representaciones de objetos o procesos complejos.

mammal A vertebrate whose body temperature is regulated by its internal heat, and that has skin covered with hair or fur and glands that produce milk to feed its young. (389)
mamífero Vertebrado cuya temperatura corporal es regulada por su calor interno, cuya piel está cubierta de pelo o pelaje y que tiene glándulas que producen leche para alimentar a sus crías.

mammary gland An organ in female mammals that produces milk for the mammal's young. (389)
glándula mamaria Órgano de los mamíferos hembra que produce leche para alimentar a sus crías.

manipulated variable The one factor that a scientist changes during an experiment; also called independent variable. (21)
variable manipulada Único factor que el científico cambia durante un experimento; también llamada variable independiente.

marsupial A mammal whose young are born at an early stage of development, and which usually continue to develop in a pouch on their mother's body. (389)
marsupial Mamífero cuyas crías nacen en una etapa muy temprana del desarrollo, y que normalmente continúan el desarrollo en una bolsa del cuerpo de la madre.

mass A measure of how much matter is in an object. (41)
masa Medida de cuánta materia hay en un cuerpo.

mean The numerical average of a set of data. (53)
media Promedio numérico de un conjunto de datos.

median The middle number in a set of data. (53)
mediana Número del medio de un conjunto de datos.

meiosis The process that occurs in the formation of sex cells (sperm and egg) by which the number of chromosomes is reduced by half. (212)
meiosis Proceso durante la formación de las células sexuales (espermatozoide y óvulo) por el cual el número de cromosomas se reduce a la mitad.

meniscus The curved upper surface of a liquid in a column of liquid. (42)
menisco Superficie superior curva de un líquido en una columna de líquido.

messenger RNA Type of RNA that carries copies of instructions for the assembly of amino acids into proteins from DNA to ribosomes in the cytoplasm. (231)
ARN mensajero Tipo de ARN que lleva, del ADN a los ribosomas del citoplasma, copias de instrucciones para sintetizar a los aminoácidos en proteínas.

metabolism The combination of chemical reactions through which an organism builds up or breaks down materials. (86)
metabolismo Combinación de reacciones químicas mediante las cuales un organismo compone o descompone la materia.

metric system A system of measurement based on the number 10. (39)
sistema métrico Sistema de medidas basado en el número 10.

microscope An instrument that makes small objects look larger. (122)
microscopio Instrumento que permite que los objetos pequeños se vean más grandes.

migration The regular, seasonal journey of an animal from one environment to another and back again for the purpose of feeding or reproduction. (396)
migración Viaje estacional y regular, de ida y vuelta, que hace un animal de un medio ambiente a otro con el propósito de alimentarse y reproducirse.

mitochondria Rod-shaped organelles that convert energy in food molecules to energy the cell can use to carry out its functions. (131)
mitocondria Estructura celular con forma de bastón que transforma la energía de las moléculas de alimentos en energía que la célula puede usar para llevar a cabo sus funciones.

mitosis The second stage of the cell cycle during which the cell's nucleus divides into two new nuclei and one set of DNA is distributed into each daughter cell. (175)
mitosis Segunda etapa del ciclo celular, durante la cual se divide el núcleo de la célula en dos núcleos nuevos y el conjunto del ADN se reparte entre cada célula hija.

mode The number that appears most often in a list of numbers. (53)
moda Número que aparece con más frecuencia en una lista de números.

model A representation of a complex object or process, used to help people understand a concept that they cannot observe directly. (61)
modelo Representación de un objeto o proceso complejo que se usa para explicar un concepto que no se puede observar directamente.

mollusk An invertebrate with a soft, unsegmented body; most are protected by a hard outer shell. (377)
molusco Invertebrado con cuerpo blando y sin segmentos; la mayoría tienen una concha exterior dura que les sirve de protección.

monocot An angiosperm that has only one seed leaf. (324)
monocotiledónea Angiosperma cuyas semillas tienen un solo cotiledón.

monotreme A mammal that lays eggs. (389)
monotrema Mamífero que pone huevos.

multicellular Consisting of many cells. (136)
multicelular Que se compone de muchas células.

multiple alleles Three or more possible alleles of a gene that determine a trait. (204)
alelo múltiple Tres o más alelos posibles del gen que determina un rasgo.

mutation Any change in the DNA of a gene or a chromosome. (235)
mutación Cualquier cambio del ADN de un gen o cromosoma.

mutualism A type of symbiosis in which both species benefit from living together. (431)
mutualismo Tipo de relación simbiótica entre dos especies en la cual ambas especies se benefician de su convivencia.

N

natural resource Anything naturally occuring in the environment that humans use. (499)
recurso natural Cualquier elemento natural en el medio ambiente que el ser humano usa.

natural selection The process by which organisms that are best adapted to their environment are most likely to survive and reproduce. (288)
selección natural Proceso por el cual los organismos que se adaptan mejor a su ambiente tienen mayor probabilidad de sobrevivir y reproducirse.

neritic zone The area of the ocean that extends from the low-tide line out to the edge of the continental shelf. (476)
zona nerítica Área del océano que se extiende desde la línea de bajamar hasta el borde de la plataforma continental.

niche How an organism makes its living and interacts with the biotic and abiotic factors in its habitat. (426)
nicho Forma en que un organismo vive e interactúa con los factores bióticos y abióticos de su hábitat.

nitrogen bases Molecules that contain nitrogen and other elements. (225)
bases nitrogenadas Moléculas que contienen nitrógeno y otros elementos.

nitrogen fixation The process of changing free nitrogen gas into nitrogen compounds that plants can absorb and use. (460)
fijación del nitrógeno Proceso que consiste en transformar el gas de nitrógeno libre en compuestos de nitrógeno que las plantas pueden absorber y usar.

nonlinear graph A line graph in which the data points do not fall along a straight line. (58)
gráfica no lineal Gráfica lineal en la que los puntos de datos no forman una línea recta.

nonpoint source A widely spread source of pollution that is difficult to link to a specific point of origin. (494)
fuente dispersa Fuente muy extendida de contaminación que es difícil vincular a un punto de origen específico.

nonvascular plant A low-growing plant that lacks true vascular tissue for transporting materials. (316)
planta no vascular Planta de crecimiento lento que carece de tejido vascular verdadero para el transporte de materiales.

notochord A flexible rod that supports a chordate's back just below the nerve cord. (381)
notocordio Cilindro flexible que sostiene la columna de un cordado, debajo del cordón nervioso.

nucleic acid A very large organic molecule made of carbon, oxygen, hydrogen, nitrogen, and phosphorus, that contains the instructions cells need to carry out all the functions of life. (142)
ácido nucleico Molécula muy grande formada por carbono, oxígeno, hidrógeno, nitrógeno y fósforo, que porta las instrucciones necesarias para que las células realicen todas las funciones vitales.

nucleus **1.** In cells, a large oval organelle that contains the cell's genetic material in the form of DNA and controls many of the cell's activities. **2.** The central core of an atom which contains protons and neutrons. **3.** The solid core of a comet. (103)
núcleo **1.** En las células, orgánulo grande y ovalado que contiene el material genético de la célula en forma de ADN y que controla muchas de las funciones celulares. **2.** Parte central del átomo que contiene los protones y los neutrones. **3.** Centro sólido de un cometa.

O

objective **1.** A lens that gathers light from an object and forms a real image. **2.** Describes the act of decision-making or drawing conclusions based on available evidence. (14)
objetivo **1.** Lente que reúne la luz de un objeto y forma una imagen real. **2.** Describe el acto de tomar una decisión o llegar a una conclusión basándose en la evidencia disponible.

GLOSSARY

observing The process of using one or more of your senses to gather information. (5)
observar Proceso de usar uno o más de tus sentidos para reunir información.

omnivore A consumer that obtains energy by eating both plants and animals. (450)
omnívoro Consumidor que come plantas y animales para obtener energía.

organ A body structure that is composed of different kinds of tissues that work together. (137)
órgano Estructura del cuerpo compuesta de distintos tipos de tejidos que trabajan conjuntamente.

organ system A group of organs that work together to perform a major function. (137)
sistema de órganos Grupo de órganos que trabajan juntos para realizar una función importante.

organelle A tiny cell structure that carries out a specific function within the cell. (130)
orgánulo Estructura celular diminuta que realiza una función específica dentro de la célula.

organism A living thing. (85)
organismo Un ser vivo.

osmosis The diffusion of water molecules across a selectively permeable membrane. (147)
ósmosis Difusión de moléculas de agua a través de una membrana permeable selectiva.

output Material, energy, result, or product that comes out of a system. (62)
salida Material, energía, resultado o producto que un sistema produce.

ovary 1. A flower structure that encloses and protects ovules and seeds as they develop. **2.** Organ of the female reproductive system in which eggs and estrogen are produced. (335)
ovario 1. Estructura de una flor que encierra y protege a los óvulos y las semillas durante su desarrollo. **2.** Órgano del sistema reproductivo femenino en el que se producen los óvulos y el estrógeno.

ovule A plant structure in seed plants that produces the female gametophyte; contains an egg cell. (340)
óvulo Estructura vegetal de las plantas de semilla que produce el gametofito femenino; contiene una célula reproductora femenina.

P

parasite An organism that benefits by living with, on, or in a host in a parasitism interaction. (432)
parásito Organismo que se beneficia al vivir dentro de o sobre un huésped en una relación parasítica.

parasitism A type of symbiosis in which one organism lives with, on, or in a host and harms it. (432)
parasitismo Tipo de relación simbiótica en la cual un organismo vive con o en un huésped y le hace daño.

passive transport The movement of dissolved materials across a cell membrane without using cellular energy. (146)
transporte pasivo Movimiento de materiales a través de una membrana celular sin usar energía celular.

peat Compressed layers of dead sphagnum mosses that accumulate in bogs. (352)
turba Capas comprimidas de musgos esfagnáceos muertos que se acumulan en las marismas.

pedigree A chart that shows the presence or absence of a trait according to the relationships within a family across several generations. (259)
genealogía Diagrama que muestra la presencia o ausencia de un rasgo según las relaciones familiares a través de varias generaciones.

percent error A calculation used to determine how accurate, or close to the true value, an experimental value really is. (52)
error porcentual Cálculo usado para determinar cuán exacto, o cercano al valor verdadero, es realmente un valor experimental.

perennial A flowering plant that lives for more than two years. (337)
perenne Planta con flores que vive más de dos años.

permafrost Permanently frozen soil found in the tundra biome climate region. (471)
permagélido Suelo que está permanentemente congelado y que se encuentra en el bioma climático de la tundra.

personal bias An outlook influenced by a person's likes and dislikes. (13)
prejuicio personal Perspectiva influenciada por las preferencias de un individuo.

petal A colorful, leaflike structure of some flowers. (334)
pétalo Estructura de color brillante, similar a una hoja, que algunas flores poseen.

phenotype An organism's physical appearance, or visible traits. (200)
fenotipo Apariencia física, o rasgos visibles, de un organismo.

pheromone A chemical released by one animal that affects the behavior of another animal of the same species. (391)
feromona Sustancia química que produce un animal y que afecta el comportamiento de otro animal de la misma especie.

phloem The vascular tissue through which food moves in some plants. (319)
floema Tejido vascular de algunas plantas por el que circulan los alimentos.

photoperiodism A plant's response to seasonal changes in the length of night and day. (347)
fotoperiodicidad Respuesta de una planta a los cambios estacionales del día y de la noche.

photosynthesis The process by which plants and other autotrophs capture and use light energy to make food from carbon dioxide and water. (162)
fotosíntesis Proceso por el cual las plantas y otros autótrofos absorben la energía de la luz para producir alimentos a partir del dióxido de carbono y el agua.

pioneer species The first species to populate an area during succession. (435)
especies pioneras La primera especie que puebla un área durante la sucesión.

pistil The female reproductive part of a flower. (335)
pistilo Parte reproductora femenina de una flor.

placenta An organ in most pregnant mammals, including humans, that links the mother and the developing embryo and allows for the passage of materials between them. (389)
placenta Órgano de la mayoría de los mamíferos preñados, incluyendo a los seres humanos, que conecta a la madre con el embrión en desarrollo y que permite el intercambio de materiales.

placental mammal A mammal that develops inside its mother's body until its body systems can function independently. (389)
mamífero placentario Mamífero que se desarrolla dentro del cuerpo de la madre hasta que sus sistemas puedan funcionar por sí solos.

poaching Illegal killing or removal of wildlife from their habitats. (508)
caza ilegal Matanza o eliminación de la fauna silvestre de su hábitat.

point source A specific source of pollution that can be identified. (494)
fuente localizada Fuente específica de contaminación que puede identificarse.

pollen Tiny structure (male gametophyte) produced by seed plants that contain the cell that later becomes a sperm cell. (322)
polen Diminuta estructura (gametofito masculino) producida por las plantas de semilla que contiene la célula que más adelante se convertirá en un espermatozoide.

pollination The transfer of pollen from male reproductive structures to female reproductive structures in plants. (334)
polinización Transferencia del polen de las estructuras reproductoras masculinas de una planta a las estructuras reproductoras femeninas.

polygenic inheritance The inheritance of traits that are controlled by two or more genes, such as height in humans. (204)
herencia poligénica Herencia de los rasgos controlados por dos o más genes, como la altura en los seres humanos.

population All the members of one species living in the same area. (414)
población Todos los miembros de una especie que viven en el mismo lugar.

population density The number of individuals in an area of a specific size. (420)
densidad de población Número de individuos en un área de un tamaño específico.

precipitation Any form of water that falls from clouds and reaches Earth's surface as rain, snow, sleet, or hail. (457)
precipitación Cualquier forma del agua que cae de las nubes y llega a la superficie de la tierra como lluvia, nieve, aguanieve o granizo.

precision How close a group of measurements are to each other. (50)
precisión Cuán cerca se encuentran un grupo de medidas.

GLOSSARY

predation An interaction in which one organism kills another for food or nutrients. (428)
depredación Interacción en la cual un organismo mata a otro para alimentarse u obtener nutrientes de él.

predator The organism that does the killing in a predation interaction. (428)
depredador Organismo que mata durante la depredación.

predicting The process of forecasting what will happen in the future based on past experience or evidence. (7)
predecir Proceso de pronosticar lo que va a suceder en el futuro, basándose en evidencia o experiencias previas.

prey An organism that is killed and eaten by another organism in a predation interaction. (428)
presa Organismo que es consumido por otro organismo en el proceso de depredación.

primary succession The series of changes that occur in an area where no soil or organisms exist. (435)
sucesión primaria Serie de cambios que ocurren en un área donde no existe suelo ni organismos.

probability A number that describes how likely it is that a particular event will occur. (197)
probabilidad Número que describe cuán probable es que ocurra un suceso.

process A sequence of actions in a system. (62)
proceso Secuencia de acciones en un sistema.

producer An organism that can make its own food. (449)
productor Organismo que puede generar su propio alimento.

prokaryote A unicellular organism that lacks a nucleus and some other cell structures. (103)
procariota Organismo unicelular que carece de un núcleo y otras estructuras celulares.

protein Large organic molecule made of carbon, hydrogen, oxygen, nitrogen, and sometimes sulfur. (141)
proteína Molécula orgánica grande compuesta de carbono, hidrógeno, oxígeno, nitrógeno y, a veces, azufre.

punctuated equilibrium Pattern of evolution in which long stable periods are interrupted by brief periods of more rapid change. (299)
equilibrio puntual Patrón de la evolución en el que los períodos largos estables son interrumpidos por breves períodos de cambio rápido.

Punnett square A chart that shows all the possible combinations of alleles that can result from a genetic cross. (198)
cuadrado de Punnett Tabla que muestra todas las combinaciones posibles de los alelos que se pueden derivar de un cruce genético.

purebred An offspring of many generations that have the same form of a trait. (191)
raza pura Descendiente de varias generaciones que tienen los mismos rasgos.

Q

qualitative observation An observation that deals with characteristics that cannot be expressed in numbers. (5)
observación cualitativa Observación que se centra en las características que no se pueden expresar con números.

quantitative observation An observation that deals with a number or amount. (5)
observación cuantitativa Observación que se centra en un número o cantidad.

R

radial symmetry A body plan in which any number of imaginary lines that all pass through a central point divide the animal into two mirror images. (370)
simetría radiada Esquema del cuerpo en el que cualquier número de líneas imaginarias que atraviesan un punto central dividen a un animal en dos partes que son el reflejo la una de la otra.

rain forest A forest that receives at least 2 meters of rain per year, mostly occurring in the tropical wet climate zone. (466)
selva tropical Bosque donde caen al menos 2 metros de lluvia al año, principalmente en la zona climática tropical húmeda.

range The difference between the greatest value and the least value in a set of data. (53)
rango Diferencia entre el mayor y el menor valor de un conjunto de datos.

recessive allele An allele that is hidden whenever the dominant allele is present. (193)
alelo recesivo Alelo que no se manifiesta cuando el alelo dominante está presente.

replication The process by which a cell makes a copy of the DNA in its nucleus before cell division. (174)
replicación Proceso en el que la célula copia el ADN de su núcleo antes de la división celular.

reptile A vertebrate whose temperature is determined by the temperature of its environment, that has lungs and scaly skin, and that lays eggs on land. (387)
reptil Vertebrado cuya temperatura corporal es determinada por la temperatura de su medio ambiente, que tiene pulmones y piel escamosa y que pone huevos en la tierra.

responding variable The factor that changes as a result of changes to the manipulated, or independent, variable in an experiment; also called dependent variable. (21)
variable de respuesta Factor que cambia como resultado del cambio de la variable manipulada, o independiente, en un experimento; también llamada variable dependiente.

response An action or change in behavior that occurs as a result of a stimulus. (87)
respuesta Acción o cambio del comportamiento que ocurre como resultado de un estímulo.

rhizoid A thin, rootlike structure that anchors a moss and absorbs water and nutrients for the plant. (317)
rizoide Estructura fina parecida a una raíz que sujeta un musgo al suelo, y que absorbe el agua y los nutrientes para la planta.

ribosome A small grain-shaped organelle in the cytoplasm of a cell that produces proteins. (130)
ribosoma Orgánulo pequeño con forma de grano en el citoplasma de una célula que produce proteínas.

root cap A structure that covers the tip of a root, protecting the root from injury as the root grows through soil. (327)
cofia Estructura que cubre la punta de una raíz y la protege de cualquier daño mientras crece en la tierra.

S

safety symbols A sign used to alert you to possible sources of accidents in an investigation. (69)
símbolos de seguridad Señal de alerta sobre elementos que pueden causar accidentes durante una investigación.

savanna A grassland located close to the equator that may include shrubs and small trees and receives as much as 120 centimeters of rain per year. (468)
sabana Pradera que puede tener arbustos y árboles pequeños, ubicada cerca del ecuador y donde pueden caer hasta 120 centímetros de lluvia al año.

scavenger A carnivore that feeds on the bodies of dead or decaying organisms. (450)
carroñero Carnívoro que se alimenta de los restos de organismos muertos o en descomposición.

science A way of learning about the natural world through observations and logical reasoning; leads to a body of knowledge. (5)
ciencia Estudio del mundo natural a través de observaciones y del razonamiento lógico; conduce a un conjunto de conocimientos.

scientific inquiry The ongoing process of discovery in science; the diverse ways in which scientists study the natural world and propose explanations based on evidence they gather. (19)
indagación científica Proceso continuo de descubrimiento en la ciencia; diversidad de métodos con los que los científicos estudian el mundo natural y proponen explicaciones del mismo basadas en la evidencia que reúnen.

scientific law A statement that describes what scientists expect to happen every time under a particular set of conditions. (27)
ley científica Enunciado que describe lo que los científicos esperan que suceda cada vez que se da una serie de condiciones determinadas.

scientific theory A well-tested explanation for a wide range of observations or experimental results. (27)
teoría científica Explicación comprobada de una gran variedad de observaciones o resultados de experimentos.

secondary succession The series of changes that occur in an area where the ecosystem has been disturbed, but where soil and organisms still exist. (436)
sucesión secundaria Serie de cambios que ocurren en un área después de la perturbación de un ecosistema, pero donde todavía hay suelo y organismos.

seed The plant structure that contains a young plant and a food supply inside a protective covering. (322)
semilla Estructura vegetal que contiene una planta joven y una fuente alimenticia encerradas en una cubierta protectora.

GLOSSARY

selective breeding Method of breeding that allows only those organisms with desired traits to produce the next generation. (263)
cruce selectivo Técnica reproductiva por medio de la cual sólo los organismos con rasgos deseados producen la próxima generación.

selectively permeable A property of cell membranes that allows some substances to pass across it, while others cannot. (145)
permeabilidad selectiva Propiedad de las membranas celulares que permite el paso de algunas sustancias y no de otras.

sepal A leaflike structure that encloses and protects the bud of a flower. (334)
sépalo Estructura similar a una hoja que encierra y protege el capullo de una flor.

sex chromosomes A pair of chromosomes carrying genes that determine whether a person is male or female. (253)
cromosomas sexuales Par de cromosomas portadores de genes que determinan el sexo (masculino o femenino) de una persona.

sex-linked gene A gene that is carried on a sex (X or Y) chromosome. (254)
gen ligado al sexo Gen de un cromosoma sexual (X o Y).

sexual reproduction A reproductive process that involves two parents that combine their genetic material to produce a new organism which differs from both parents. (87)
reproducción sexual Proceso de reproducción que involucra a dos reproductores que combinan su material genético para producir un nuevo organismo que es distinto a los dos reproductores.

shared derived characteristic A characteristic or trait, such as fur, that the common ancestor of a group had and passed on to its descendants. (107)
característica derivada compartida Característica o rasgo, como el pelaje, del ancestro común de un grupo que éste pasa a sus descendientes.

short-day plant A plant that flowers when the nights are longer than the plant's critical night length. (347)
planta de día corto Planta que florece cuando la duración de la noche es más larga que la duración crítica.

significant figures All the digits in a measurement that have been measured exactly, plus one digit whose value has been estimated. (50)
cifras significativas En una medida, todos los dígitos que se han medido con exactitud, más un dígito cuyo valor se ha estimado.

skepticism An attitude of doubt. (12)
escepticismo Actitud de duda.

society A group of closely related animals of the same species that work together in a highly organized way for the benefit of the group. (395)
sociedad Grupo de animales de la misma especie y estrechamente vinculados que trabajan conjuntmente de manera organizada para el beneficio del grupo.

soil conservation The management of soil to limit its destruction. (501)
conservación del suelo Cuidado del suelo para limitar su destrucción.

species A group of similar organisms that can mate with each other and produce offspring that can also mate and reproduce. (96)
especie Grupo de organismos semejantes que pueden cruzarse y producir descendencia fértil.

spontaneous generation The mistaken idea that living things arise from nonliving sources. (88)
generación espontánea Idea equivocada de que los seres vivos surgen de fuentes inertes.

sporophyte The stage in the life cycle of a plant in which the plant produces spores. (336)
esporofito Etapa del ciclo vital de una planta en la que produce esporas.

stamen The male reproductive part of a flower. (334)
estambre Parte reproductora masculina de una flor.

stimulus Any change or signal in the environment that can make an organism react in some way. (87)
estímulo Cualquier cambio o señal del medio ambiente que puede causar una reacción en un organismo.

stoma Small opening on the underside of a leaf through which oxygen, water, and carbon dioxide can move (plural: stomata). (330)
estoma Pequeña abertura en la superficie inferior de la hoja a través de cual ocurre el intercambio de oxígeno, agua y dióxido de carbono.

subjective Describes the influence of personal feelings on a decision or conclusion. (14)
subjetivo Describe la influencia de sentimientos personales sobre una decisión o conclusión.

succession The series of predictable changes that occur in a community over time. (434)
sucesión Serie de cambios predecibles que ocurren en una comunidad a través del tiempo.

symbiosis Any relationship in which two species live closely together and that benefits at least one of the species. (431)
simbiosis Cualquier relación en la cual dos especies viven muy cerca y al menos una de ellas se beneficia.

system 1. A group of parts that work together as a whole. **2.** A group of related parts that work together to perform a function or produce a result. (62)
sistema 1. Partes de un grupo que trabajan en conjunto. 2. Grupo de partes relacionadas que trabajan conjuntamente para realizar una función o producir un resultado.

T

taxonomy The scientific study of how living things are classified. (95)
taxonomía Estudio científico de cómo se clasifican los seres vivos.

territory An area that is occupied and defended by an animal or group of animals. (392)
territorio Área ocupada y defendida por un animal o grupo de animales.

threatened species A species that could become endangered in the near future. (507)
especie amenazada Especie que puede llegar a estar en peligro de extinción en el futuro próximo.

tissue A group of similar cells that perform a specific function. (137)
tejido Grupo de células semejantes que realizan una función específica.

trait A specific characteristic that an organism can pass to its offspring through its genes. (190)
rasgo Característica específica que un organismo puede transmitir a sus descendientes a través de los genes.

transfer RNA Type of RNA in the cytoplasm that carries an amino acid to the ribosome during protein synthesis. (231)
ARN de transferencia Tipo de ARN del citoplasma que lleva un aminoácido al ribosoma durante la síntesis de proteínas.

transpiration The process by which water is lost through a plant's leaves. (331)
transpiración Proceso por el cual las hojas de una planta pierden agua.

tropism The response of a plant toward or away from a stimulus. (345)
tropismo Respuesta de una planta acercándose o apartándose del estímulo.

tumor A mass of rapidly dividing cells that can damage surrounding tissue. (238)
tumor Masa de células que se dividen rápidamente y que puede dañar los tejidos que la rodean.

tundra An extremely cold, dry biome climate region characterized by short, cool summers and bitterly cold winters. (471)
tundra Bioma de la región climática extremadamente fría y seca, que se caracteriza por veranos cortos y frescos e inviernos sumamente fríos.

U

understory A layer of shorter trees and vines that grows in the shade of a forest canopy. (467)
sotobosque Capa de árboles de poca altura y plantas trepadoras que crecen bajo la sombra del dosel de un bosque.

unicellular Made of a single cell. (86)
unicelular Compuesto por una sola célula.

V

vacuole A sac-like organelle that stores water, food, and other materials. (134)
vacuola Orgánulo en forma de bolsa que almacena agua, alimentos y otros materiales.

variable A factor that can change in an experiment. (21)
variable Factor que puede cambiar en un experimento.

variation Any difference between individuals of the same species. (289)
variación Cualquier diferencia entre individuos de la misma especie.

vascular plant A plant that has true vascular tissue for transporting materials. (319)
planta vascular Planta que tiene tejido vascular verdadero para el transporte de materiales.

vascular tissue The internal transporting tissue in some plants that is made up of tubelike structures that carry water, food, and minerals. (314)
tejido vascular Tejido interno de algunas plantas compuesto de estructuras tubulares que transportan agua, alimentos y minerales.

vertebrae The bones that make up the backbone of an organism. In humans, the 26 bones that make up the backbone. (382)
vértebras Huesos que componen la columna vertebral de un organismo. En los humanos, los 26 huesos que componen la columna vertebral.

vertebrate An animal with a backbone. (366)
vertebrado Animal con columna vertebral.

volume The amount of space that matter occupies. (42)
volumen Cantidad de espacio que ocupa la materia.

W

weight A measure of the force of gravity acting on an object. (41)
peso Medida de la fuerza de gravedad que actúa sobre un objeto.

X

xylem The vascular tissue through which water and minerals move in some plants. (319)
xilema Tejido vascular de algunas plantas por el que circulan agua y nutrientes.

Z

zygote A fertilized egg, produced by the joining of a sperm cell and an egg cell. (338)
cigoto Óvulo fertilizado, producido por la unión de un espermatozoide y un óvulo.

INDEX

Page numbers for key terms are printed in **boldface** type.

A

INDEX

Page numbers for key terms are printed in **boldface** type.

B

C

D

INDEX

Page numbers for key terms are printed in **boldface** type.

INDEX

Page numbers for key terms are printed in **boldface** type.

N

O

INDEX

Page numbers for key terms are printed in **boldface** type.

S

INDEX

Page numbers for key terms are printed in **boldface** type.

T

U

V

W

INDEX

Page numbers for key terms are printed in **boldface** type.

ACKNOWLEDGMENTS

Staff Credits

The people who made up the *Interactive Science* team—representing composition services, core design digital and multimedia production services, digital product development, editorial, editorial services, manufacturing, and production—are listed below:

Jan Van Aarsen, Samah Abadir, Ernie Albanese, Chris Anton, Zareh Artinian, Bridget Binstock, Suzanne Biron, Niki Birbilis, MJ Black, Nancy Bolsover, Stacy Boyd, Jim Brady, Katherine Bryant, Michael Burstein, Pradeep Byram, Jessica Chase, Jonathan Cheney, Arthur Ciccone, Allison Cook-Bellistri, Rebecca Cottingham, AnnMarie Coyne, Bob Craton, Chris Deliee, Paul Delsignore, Michael Di Maria, Diane Dougherty, Kristen Ellis, Kelly Engel, Theresa Eugenio, Amanda Ferguson, Jorgensen Fernandez, Kathryn Fobert, Alicia Franke, Louise Gachet, Julia Gecha, Mark Geyer, Steve Gobbell, Paula Gogan-Porter, Jeffrey Gong, Sandra Graff, Robert M. Graham, Adam Groffman, Lynette Haggard, Christian Henry, Karen Holtzman, Susan Hutchinson, Sharon Inglis, Marian Jones, Sumy Joy, Sheila Kanitsch, Courtenay Kelley, Chris Kennedy, Toby Klang, Greg Lam, Russ Lappa, Margaret LaRaia, Ben Leveillee, Thea Limpus, Charles Luey, Dotti Marshall, Kathy Martin, Robyn Matzke, John McClure, Mary Beth McDaniel, Krista McDonald, Tim McDonald, Rich McMahon, Cara McNally, Bernadette McQuilkin, Melinda Medina, Angelina Mendez, Maria Milczarek, Claudi Mimo, Mike Napieralski, Deborah Nicholls, Dave Nichols, William Oppenheimer, Jodi O'Rourke, Ameer Padshah, Lorie Park, Celio Pedrosa, Jonathan Penyack, Linda Zust Reddy, Jennifer Reichlin, Stephen Rider, Charlene Rimsa, Walter Rodriguez, Stephanie Rogers, Marcy Rose, Rashid Ross, Anne Rowsey, Logan Schmidt, Amanda Seldera, Laurel Smith, Nancy Smith, Ted Smykal, Emily Soltanoff, Cindy Strowman, Dee Sunday, Barry Tomack, Elizabeth Tustian, Patricia Valencia, Ana Sofia Villaveces, Stephanie Wallace, Amanda Watters, Christine Whitney, Brad Wiatr, Heidi Wilson, Heather Wright, Rachel Youdelman.

Illustrations

519 Stephen Durke.

Photographs

Every effort has been made to secure permission and provide appropriate credit for photographic material. The publisher deeply regrets any omission and pledges to correct errors called to its attention in subsequent editions.

Unless otherwise acknowledged, all photographs are the property of Pearson Education, Inc.

Photo locators denoted as follows: Top (T), Center (C), Bottom (B), Left (L), Right (R), Background (Bkgd)

Cover

Tom Vezo/Peter Arnold/PhotoLibrary Group, Inc.

Front Matter

i Caitlin Mirra/Shutterstock; **vi** (TR) NASA/NASA; **vii** (TR) DAN GURAVICH/Science Source; **viii** (TR) Kevin Schafer/Alamy; **ix** (TR) Nature Picture Library; **x** (TR) Ocean/Corbis; **xi** (TR) Blickwinkel/Schmidbauer/Alamy Images; **xiii** (TR) HALEY/SIPA/Newscom/NewsCom; **xiv** (TR) Mark Conlin/Alamy; **xv** (TR) Laurent Bouvet/Easy-Pix/AGE Fotostock, (TR) Tristan Lafranchis/Peter Arnold PhotoLibrary Group, Inc.; **xvi** (TR) pogona22/Fotolia; **xvii** (TR) Gary Bell/Corbis; **xviii** (TR) Marko König/Corbis; **xix** (TR) National Geographic Image Collection; **xxvi** (TC) iStockphoto; **xxviii** (TL) Arctic-Images/Corbis, (TR) John Cancalosi/Nature Picture Library; **xxix** (CR) AURORA, (BL) Thomas Deerinck, NCMIR/Science Source; **xxx** (TR) SuperStock; **xxxi** (TR) Jeffrey L. Rotman/Corbis, (CL) Mark Turner/Garden Picture Library/PhotoLibrary Group, Inc.

Chapter 1

1 (B) NASA/NASA; **3** Ken Seet/Corbis, (TL) National Geographic Image Collection; **4** (B) National Geographic Image Collection; **5** (BC) Nature Picture Library; **6** (TL) ©Manoj Shah/Getty Images, (BL) Anup Shah/Nature Picture Library; **7** (CC) Christoph Becker/Nature Picture Library; **8** (B) Kennan Ward/Corbis; **9** (TR) E.D. Torial/Alamy Images; **10** (B) Bortonia/iStockphoto, (B) Sarah Holmstrom/iStockphoto; **11** (BC) Karin Lau/iStockphoto, (BR) Kurt Lackovic/Alamy, (CC) Stephen Dalton/Photo Researchers, Inc.; **12** (T) Photo Network/Alamy Images; **13** (TCR) Gary Woodard/iStockphoto; **14** (B) Jon Helgason/iStockphoto, (CL) Ken Seet/Corbis; **15** (CR) Duncan Walker/iStockphoto, (B) Jon Helgason/iStockphoto, (BR) MBI/Alamy; **16** (B) Stephen Dorey Creative/Alamy; **17** (TR) Redmond Durrell/Alamy Images; **18** (BL) Sezione di Zoologia "La Specola"; **19** (BR) Andy Sands/Nature Picture Library; **21** (CR) Idamini/Alamy; **22** (TL) Idamini/Alamy; **23** (CR) Idamini/Alamy; **25** (B) Idamini/Alamy, (CR) U.S. Department of Energy Genome Program's Genome Management Information System; **26** (TR) D. Hurst/Alamy, (TCR) Don Carstens/Brand X Pictures/Jupiter Images; **27** (TR) Photodisc/Getty Images; **28** (BR) Idamini/Alamy, (TR) Nature Picture Library, (CL) Photo Network/Alamy Images; **29** (CL) Stockdale Studios; **30** (TR) image100/Corbis; **32** (BL) Academie des Sciences, Paris/Archives Charmet/Bridgeman Art Library; **33** (R) Tiago Estima/iStockphoto.

Chapter 2

34 (B) DAN GURAVICH/Science Source; **37** (R) Britvich/Dreamstime LLC, (TR) Chiyacat/Dreamstime LLC, (BL) SuperStock; **38** (TCR) Anthony Mercieca/Photo Researchers, Inc., (TR) Digital Vision/Alamy, (BC) Philip Dowell/©DK Images, (BCR) Shattil & Rozinski/Nature Picture Library; **43** (TR) Joe Traver/Time & Life Pictures/Getty Images; **44** (L) Terex/Dreamstime LLC, (TL) Britvich/Dreamstime LLC, (L) Chiyacat/Dreamstime LLC; **45** (B) Image Source/Jupiter Images; **48** (Bkgrd) Image Source/Getty Images, (CR) Pearson Education; **49** (BR) Kevin Fleming/Corbis; **51** (T) Hospitalera/Dreamstime LLC, (CL) Robert Manella/Comstock/Corbis; **52** (BL) Comstock/Thinkstock; **53** (CR) Frank Greenaway/©DK Images, (T) H. Lansdown/Alamy, (T) Reinhard Dirscherl/Ecoscene; **54** (B) Chris Johnson/Alamy Images; **55** (TR) NASA/Corbis; **56** (TR) Digital Vision/Alamy, (BC) Superclic/Alamy; **57** (CL) Miia Saastamoinen/Alamy Images; **58** (B) SuperStock; **60** (B) Joseph Sohm/Visions of America/Corbis; **61** (BL) Planetary Visions/©DK Images; **62** (R) Bryan Whitney/Photonica/Getty Images, (BL) Ilan Rosen/Alamy Images; **63** (TR) Harris Shiffman/Shutterstock, (T) Kevin Foy/Alamy Images; **64** (B) Stephen Frink Collection/Alamy Images; **66** (T) James Balog/AURORA; **68** (TR) Martin Shields/Alamy

Images, (B) William Philpott/AFP/Getty Images; **73** (TR) Lew Robertson/Alamy; **76** (BL) Bedo/Dreamstime LLC, (BCL) Dell/Dreamstime LLC, (BC) Pablo631/Dreamstime LLC; **78** (B) JPL/NASA/NASA; **79** (L) Andreas Gradin/Shutterstock.

Chapter 3

80 (Bkgrd) Kevin Schafer/Alamy; **81** (BR) Jane Allan/Fotolia; **83** (TCL) Joshua Haviv/Fotolia, (BCL) Eye of Science/Photo Researchers, Inc., (TL) Shutterstock; **84** (CR) ©George Steinmetz/Corbis; **85** (BL) Kjell Sandved/Oxford Scientific/PhotoLibrary Group, Inc., (TR) Matt Meadows/Peter Arnold/PhotoLibrary Group, Inc., (TL) Paroli Galperti/PhotoLibrary Group, Inc., (TC) Shutterstock; **86** (TR) Kerstin Hinze/Nature Picture Library, (TL) Photo Researchers, Inc., (BL) Science Photo Library RF/Photolibrary Group, Inc.; **87** (TR) ©John Kaprielian/Photo Researchers, Inc., (BL) Gentoo Multimedia/Fotolia; **88** (BL) Dan Duchars/PhotoLibrary Group, Inc., (TCL) Jürgen and Christine Sohns/Picture Press/PhotoLibrary Group, Inc.; **89** (B) Ian Thraves/Alamy; **91** (Bkgrd) Arco Images GmbH/Alamy; **92** (B) Jose Fuste Raga/Age Fotostock/PhotoLibrary Group, Inc., (TL) Pichugin Dmitry/Shutterstock; **93** (TL) Steve Byland/Shutterstock, (TL) Tony Campbell/Fotolia; **94** (BL) /©Chip Clark/Smithsonian Institution; **95** (BR) Ilian Animal/Alamy Images; **96** (T) Joshua Haviv/Fotolia, (BL) Eric Isselée/Shutterstock, (BR) Rod Williams/Nature Picture Library; **97** (TR) Alan Gleichman/Shutterstock; **98** (CL) FloridaStock/Shutterstock; **100** (CR) Stuart Wilson/Science Source; **101** (TL) Armando Frazao/iStockphoto, (TR) Eric Isselée/Shutterstock, (TCL) Hemera Technologies/Jupiter Images, (TC) JinYoung Lee/Shutterstock, (TCR) Joseph Calev/Shutterstock, (TC) Kim Taylor/Nature Picture Library; **102** (TR) alle/Fotolia; **103** (TCR) SciMAT/Photo Researchers, Inc., (BR) Eye of Science/Science Source; **104** (L) Eric V. Grave/Science Source, (BCR) Eye of Science/Photo Researchers, Inc., (Bkgrd) Ron Erwin/All Canada Photos/Corbis; **105** (CL) NICOLAS LARENTO/Fotolia; **106** (TR) Nature Picture Library; **108** (Bkgrd) Frans Lanting/Corbis, (CL) Photo courtesy of Research in Review, Florida State University: U. Treesucon, David Redfield Expedition. Used by permission, (BL) Tim Laman/Nature Picture Library; **109** (BL) Jasmina007/Shutterstock, (BL) Nick Garbutt/Nature Picture Library; **110** (BL) Eric V. Grave/Science Source, (BCR) Alan Gleichman/Shutterstock, (TR) Photo Researchers, Inc.; **112** (TCR) Virgin Galactic; **114** (Bkgrd) Alfred Wolf/Explorer/Photo Researchers, Inc.; **115** (BR) Rebecca Ellis/iStockphoto.

Chapter 4

116 (B) Nature Picture Library; **119** (BCL) iStockphoto, (BL) Michael Abbey/Photo Researchers, Inc., (TL) Perennou Nuridsany/Photo Researchers, Inc.; **120** (CR) Biophoto Associates/Photo Researchers, Inc.; **121** (Bkgrd) Nils-Johan Norenlind/AGE Fotostock; **122** (CL) Dr. Cecil H. Fox/Photo Researchers, Inc., (CL) Dr. Jeremy Burgess/Photo Researchers, Inc., (BCR) Science Museum, London/DK Images, (Inset) Steve Gschmeissner/Photo Researchers, Inc.; **123** (Inset) John Walsh/Photo Researchers, Inc., (Inset) M. I. Walker/Photo Researchers, Inc., (BCR) Perennou Nuridsany/Photo Researchers, Inc.; **124** (BR) ©DK Images, (CR) TheRocky41/Shutterstock, (BCR) Millard H. Sharp/Photo Researchers, Inc., (CL) Paul Taylor/Riser/Getty Images, (BCL) Wes Thompson/Corbis Yellow/Corbis; **126** (C) ©A. Syred/Photo Researchers, Inc.; **128** (Bkgrd) Dr. Torsten Wittmann/Photo Researchers, Inc.; **130** (CL) Alfred Paskieka/Photo Researchers, Inc., (BR) Bill Longcore/Photo Researchers, Inc.; **131** (CL) CNRI/Photo Researchers, Inc.; **134** (TL) Professors Pietro M. Motta & Tomonori Naguro/Photo Researchers, Inc.; **135** (TR) Biophoto Associates/Photo Researchers, Inc.; **136** (BL) Biophoto Associates/Photo Researchers, Inc., (BR) Thomas Deerinck, NCMIR/Science Source, (TR) Ed Reschke/Getty, (TL) Profs. P. Motta and S. Correr/Science Photo Library/Photo Researchers, Inc.; **138** (Bkgrd) Tierbild Okapia/Photo Researchers, Inc.; **139** (Bkgrd) Digital Vision/Getty Images; **140** (BL) David Murray/©DK Images, (BR) iStockphoto; **141** (TR) Tstarr/Shutterstock; **144** (BC) Michael Lamotte/Cole Group/Photodisc/Getty Images; **147** (TR, TCR) Perennou Nuridsany/Photo Researchers, Inc.; **149** (CR, CL, C) Michael Abbey/Photo Researchers, Inc.; **150** (TR) Science Museum, London/©DK Images; **152** (BCR) ©DK Images; **154** (BL) David M. Phillips/Photo Researchers, Inc., (Inset, Bkgrd) Kim Taylor and Jane Burton/Dorling/©DK Images; **155** (Inset) Martin Shields/Photo Researchers, Inc.

Chapter 5

156 (Bkgrd) Ocean/Corbis; **159** (B) Kent Wood/Getty, (BCL) Ed Reschke/Peter Arnold/PhotoLibrary Group, Inc., (TL) SuperStock, (TCL) Vincenzo Lombardo/Photodisc/Getty Images; **160** (CR) David Cook/blueshiftstudios/Alamy; **161** (BCL) AURORA, (Bkgrd) Robbert Koene/Getty Images, (BCR) SuperStock; **163** (Bkgrd) Rich Iwasaki/Getty Images; **165** (TR) NASA, (Bkgrd) Yuji Sakai/Digital Vision/Getty Images; **166** (TL) NASA, (Bkgrd) Pete Saloutos/Flirt/Corbis; **167** (TR) NASA; **168** (BC) NASA; **170** (Bkgrd) Vincenzo Lombardo/Photodisc/Getty Images; **171** (Bkgrd) Noah Clayton/Riser/Getty Images; **172** (C, Bkgrd) George Grall/National Geographic Image Collection; **173** (CR) Eric Bean/The Image Bank/Getty Images, (L) Helmut Gritscher/Peter Arnold/PhotoLibrary Group, Inc., (Inset) Michael Poliza/Getty; **174** (CR) NASA; **176** (TR, TCL, B) Ed Reschke/Peter Arnold/PhotoLibrary Group, Inc.; **177** (TC, CR, B) Ed Reschke/Peter Arnold/PhotoLibrary Group, Inc.; **178** (C) Kent Wood/Getty, (TCR) Dr. Gopal Murti/Photo Researchers, Inc.; **180** (TR, BR) Ed Reschke/Peter Arnold/PhotoLibrary Group, Inc.; **184** (CL) Andres Rodriguez/Alamy; **185** (Bkgrd) Thomas Deerinck, NCMIR/Photo Researchers, Inc.

Chapter 6

186 (C) SuperStock; **189** (BCL) Brand X Pictures/Jupiter Images, (BCL) Frank Krahmer/Getty Images, (TCL) iStockphoto; **190** (TC) Bettman/Corbis, (C) Maximilian Stock/Getty; **192** (CL) Andrea Jones/Alamy Images; **195** (TC) Herman Eisenbeiss/Photo Researchers, Inc., (Bkgrd) Monika Gniot/Shutterstock, (TCR) WildPictures/Alamy Images; **196** (Inset) J. Pat Carter/AP Images/©Associated Press, (Bkgrd) NOAA; **197** (CR) Brand X Pictures/Jupiter Images; **198** (Bkgrd) Monika Gniot/Shutterstock; **200** (R) Alexandra Grablewski/Jupiter Images; **201** (Bkgrd) Agg/Dreamstime LLC, (C) iStockphoto, (CR) Jomann/Dreamstime LLC; **202** (Bkgrd) Erik Rumbaugh/iStockphoto, (C) Joel Sartore/National Geographic/Getty Images; **203** (BR) ©DK Images, (BCL) Brand X Pictures/Jupiter Images, (BCR) CreativeAct-Animals Series/Alamy, (BCL) Frank Krahmer/Getty Images; **204** (TC) Geoff Dann/©DK Images, (TCR) Jay Brousseau/Stone/Getty Images, (TC) John Daniels/Ardea; **205** (BCR) Blickwinkel/Schmidbauer/Alamy Images, (C) Luis Carlos Torres/iStockphoto, (BC) Michael Melford/

National Geographic/Getty Images, (BR) Naile Goelbasi/Taxi/Getty Images, (BCL) Radius Images/Photolibrary Group, Inc., (B) Randy Faris/Spirit/Corbis, (BC) Stuart McClymont/Stone/Getty Images; **206** (BL, BCL) ©DK Images, (BC) Brand X Pictures/Jupiter Images, (BCL) CreativeAct-Animals Series/Alamy, (BC) Frank Krahmer/Getty Images, (BCL) Joel Sartore/National Geographic/Getty Images, (BCL) Radius Images/Photolibrary Group, Inc., (Bkgrd) Serg64/Shutterstock, (TCL) Stuart McClymont/Stone/Getty Images, (Bkgrd) Tomas Bercic/iStockphoto; **208** (BL) James King-Holmes/Science Source, (BR) Patrick Landmann/Science Source; **209** (BC) Cathlee/iStockphoto, (BL) Eric Isselée/iStockphoto, (C) Frank Greenaway/©DK Images, (BR) Jane Burton/©DK Images, (BR) proxyminder/iStockphoto; **214** (BL) Blickwinkel/Schmidbauer/Alamy Images; **218** (Bkgrd) We Shoot/Alamy Images; **219** (BR) Dorling Kindersley/©DK Images.

Chapter 7

220 (Bkgrd) David Doubilet/National Geographic/Getty Images; **223** (BCL) Christian Charisius/Reuters Media, (BL) Scott Camazine/Getty; **224** (T) Gerald C. Kelley/Photo Researchers, Inc., (BCR) Omikron/Photo Researchers, Inc., (CL) Science Source/Photo Researchers, Inc.; **226** (CL) Andrew Syred/Photo Researchers, Inc., (BR) Mark Evans/iStockphoto; **229** (TR) Dr. Gopal Murti/Science Photo Library/Photo Researchers, Inc.; **230** (CL) /©DK Images, (TR) Bedrock Studios/©DK Images; **234** (B) Peter Cade/Getty Images, (Inset) Russell Glenister/image100/Corbis; **236** (TL) ©Jim Stamates/Getty Images, (Inset) Christian Charisius/Reuters Media; **237** (BR) Andy Crawford/©DK Images, (CR) Scott Camazine/Getty; **244** (Bkgrd) D. Robert Franz/ImageState/Alamy Images, (BL) Denis Poroy/©Associated Press; **245** (C) Anthony Tueni/Alamy Images, (TL) Dave King/©DK Images, (Inset) Jamie Marshall/©DK Images.

Chapter 8

246 (Bkgrd) HALEY/SIPA/Newscom/NewsCom; **249** (TL) ©Department of Clinical Cytogenetics Addenbrookes Hospital/Science Photo Library/Photo Researchers, Inc., (TL) Addenbrookes Hospital/Photo Researchers, Inc., (TCL) Photo Researchers, Inc., (BCL) Splashnews/NewsCom, (BL) Yonhap, Choi Byung-kil/©Associated Press; **250** (CL) Pearson Education; **251** (BR) Timothey Kosachev/iStockphoto; **252** (TL) China Daily China Daily Information Corp-CDIC/Reuters Media; **253** (CR) ©Department of Clinical Cytogenetics Addenbrookes Hospital/Science Photo Library/Photo Researchers, Inc., (BC) Addenbrookes Hospital/Photo Researchers, Inc.; **254** (TR, BR) Jupiterimages/Brand X/Alamy/Alamy, (BC) Michael Newman/PhotoEdit, Inc.; **256** (BCL) John Long/iStockphoto, (BC) Lisa Svara/iStockphoto, (BL) Paul Cotney/iStockphoto; **257** (Bkgrd) Photo Researchers, Inc.; **259** (TCR) Nancy Hamilton/Photo Researchers, Inc.; **260** (CR, CL) Leonard Lessin/Science Source; **261** (TR) arlindo71/iStockphoto, (CR) Tomas Ovalle/The Fresno Bee/©Associated Press; **262** (BL) AFP/Stringer/Getty Images, (Bkgrd) Anke van Wyk/Shutterstock; **265** (BR) Splashnews/NewsCom; **267** (Bkgrd) Yonhap, Choi Byung-kil/©Associated Press; **268** (TC) PeJo/Shutterstock; **269** (TR) Andrey Prokhorov/iStockphoto, (CR) Laura Doss/Photolibrary Group, Inc.; **270** (BL) David Fairfield/Getty Images/Getty Images, (BCL) Kenneth C. Zirkel/iStockphoto; **272** (CR) Tomas Ovalle/The Fresno Bee/©Associated Press; **274** Leonard Lessin/Science Source; **276** (Bkgrd) Sam Ogden/Photo Researchers, Inc.; **277** (Bkgrd) Ed Reschke/Getty, (CR) Stocksearch/Alamy.

Chapter 9

278 Mark Conlin/Alamy; **280** (B) Xavi Arnau/iStockphoto; **282** (Inset) /©DK Images, (Bkgrd) Andreas Gross/Westend 61/Alamy Images, (TC) PoodlesRock/Corbis; **283** (BCR) Enzo & Paolo Ragazzini/Corbis, (T) Oyvind Martinsen/Alamy, (BCL) N. Reed of QED Images/Alamy, (BC) Wardene Weisser/Bruce Coleman Inc./Alamy Images; **284** (CR) Joe McDonald/Corbis, (BCL) Rosemary Calvert/Getty, (TL) Steve Bloom Images/Alamy; **286** (CL) GK Hart/Vikki Hart/Getty Images, (Bkgrd) Photo-Max/iStockphoto, (C) Steve Shott/©DK Images, (CR) Tracy Morgan/©DK Images; **287** (TR) Derrell Fowler, (TL) Georgette Douwma/Nature Picture Library, (TC) The Art of Animals.co.uk/PetStock Boys/Alamy Images; **290** (BL) Mark Conlin/getty; **291** (Bkgrd) Copyright ©2007 Maury Hatfield. All Rights Reserved; **292** (BL) Gordon Wiltsie/National Geographic Image Collection, (CR, BR) Model by Tyler Keillor/University of Chicago; **294** (BCR) /SuperStock, (BC) Ed Robinson/Design Pics/Corbis, (BCL) Winfried Wisniewski/Cusp/Corbis; **296** (TCR) Cook Islands Biodiversity, (C) /John T. Rotenberry; **297** (Bkgrd) kojihirano/Fotolia, (TCR) T. Leeson/Photo Researchers, Inc., (TCL) Thomas & Pat Leeson/Photo Researchers, Inc.; **300** (TR, TCR) Joe McDonald/Corbis, (TCR) T. Leeson/Photo Researchers, Inc., (BCR) Thomas & Pat Leeson/Photo Researchers, Inc.; **302** (TCR) S.Borisov/Shutterstock; **304** (TCL) Joshua Roper/Alamy.

Chapter 10

306 (Bkgrd) Laurent Bouvet/Easy-Pix/AGE Fotostock; **309** (TCL) Howard Rice/©DK Images, (BL) Nature Picture Library; **311** (B) Theodore Clutter/Science Source, (BR) Paul Paladin/iStockphoto; **312** (TL) Lusoimages/Shutterstock, (TCL) Perennou Nuridsany/Photo Researchers, Inc.; **314** (TCL) Kjell Sandved/Photo Researchers, Inc.; **316** (Inset) Garden Picture Library/Francesca Yorke/PhotoLibrary Group, Inc.; **317** (Inset) John Serrao/Photo Researchers, Inc., (Bkgrd) czamfir/Fotolia; **318** (TL) Adrian Davies/Nature Picture Library, (CL) Daniel Vega/Age fotostock/PhotoLibrary Group, Inc.; **319** (Inset) Dr. David T. Webb, (Bkgrd) Howard Rice/Garden Picture Library/PhotoLibrary Group, Inc.; **321** (C) Albert Aanensen/Nature Picture Library, (TCL) Philippe Clement/Nature Picture Library; **323** (TL) Christine M. Douglas/©DK Images, (BCL) Joanna Pecha/iStockphoto, (BL) M. Philip Kahl/Photo Researchers, Inc., (TC) Peter Anderson/©DK Images; **324** (BCR) Anna Subbotina/Shutterstock, (CL) Howard Rice/©DK Images, (TL) K. Kaplin/Shutterstock; **326** (CL) Fletcher & Baylis/Photo Researchers, Inc.; **327** (CR) Derek Croucher/Alamy Images, (C) Lynwood M. Chace/Photo Researchers, Inc.; **328** (C) Manfred Kage/Peter Arnold/PhotoLibrary Group, Inc., (TL) Peter Hestbaek/Shutterstock; **330** (Bkgrd) Pakhnyushcha/Shutterstock; **334** (BCL) Kim Taylor/Nature Picture Library, (BR, BL) Nature Picture Library, (BC) Niall Benvie/Nature Picture Library, (BR) Simon Williams/Nature Picture Library, (BCL) All Canada Photos/Alamy; **336** (Bkgrd) Ocean/Corbis; **338** (B) Ed Reschke/Peter Arnold/PhotoLibrary Group, Inc.; **339** (Bkgrd) Christine M. Douglas/©DK Images, (TR) Tristan Lafranchis/Peter Arnold/PhotoLibrary Group, Inc.; **340** (Bkgrd) Andrew Browne/Ecoscene/Corbis;

ACKNOWLEDGMENTS

341 (TCL) Trent Dietsche/Alamy, (TL), Breck P. Kent/Breck P. Kent Natural History Photography, (BL) David R. Frazier Photolibrary, Inc./Alamy; **342** (B) Nigel Cattlin/Alamy, (BL) Medio Images/Photodisc/PhotoLibrary Group, Inc.; **343** (Bkgrd) Nature Picture Library, (TC) Peter Chadwick/©DK Images, (CR, C) Peter Chapwick/©DK Images, (CR) Peter Chapwick/©DK Images; **344** (Bkgrd) Dr Kerry-Ann Nakrieko; **346** (TL) Maryann Frazier/Photo Researchers, Inc.; **347** (Bkgrd) Mark Turner/Garden Picture Library/PhotoLibrary Group, Inc.; **348** (TL) Carole Drake/Garden Picture Library/PhotoLibrary Group, Inc.; **350** (Bkgrd) Gary K. Smith/Nature Picture Library; **351** (Bkgrd) Albinger/AGE Fotostock; **352** (Bkgrd) Nature Picture Library; **353** (TR) Tom Mayes/Cal Sport Media/Zuma Press, Inc.; **354** (TC) Kjell Sandved/Photo Researchers, Inc., (BR) Nature Picture Library; **358** (TCL, BL) iStockphoto, (CL) sgame/iStockphoto, (BR) Susumu Nishinaga/Photo Researchers, Inc.; **359** (C) Bettmann/Corbis.

Chapter 11

360 (Bkgrd) age Fotostock 3/SuperStock; **363** (BCL) Andrew J. Martinez/Photo Researchers, Inc., (BL) Fritz Polking/Peter Arnold/PhotoLibrary Group, Inc., (TCL) Winelover/Fotolia, (TL) Nature Picture Library; **364** (Bkgrd) DLILLC/Corbis, (C) Nature Picture Library; **365** (BCL) Jason Edwards/National Geographic Image Collection, (CL) Pixtal/SuperStock, (C) Stock Connection, (BCR) Anthony Mercieca/Science Source; **367** (TR) Connie Coleman/Photographer's Choice/Getty Images, (TC) Don Hammond/Design Pics/Corbis, (TCR) Volodymyr Krasyuk/Fotolia, (TC) Keith Leighton/Alamy; **368** (Bkgrd) Comstock Images/Jupiter Images; **369** (BCR) Neil Fletcher/Oxford University/Museum of Natural History/©DK Images; **370** (BR) Bill Curtsinger/National Geographic Image Collection, (BCR) G. Mermet/Peter Arnold/PhotoLibrary Group, Inc., (BC) Getty Images, (TR) Winelover/Fotolia, (B) Photo Researchers, Inc.; **371** (TCR) B.A.E., Inc./Alamy, (Bkgrd, BCR) D. Hurst/Alamy, (BC) Image Source/SuperStock, (BCR) Photodisc/Alamy, (BCR) Tatiana Popova/iStockphoto; **372** (Bkgrd) ©Gray Hardel/Corbis, (Inset) Kaz Chiba/Stockbyte/Getty Images, (BCR) WaterFrame/Alamy; **373** (Bkgrd) Purestock/Getty Images; **374** (C) Daniel Aneshansley/Cornell University/Thomas Eisner; **375** (BCR) Michael DeFreitas Underwater/Alamy Images, (Bkgrd) WaterFrame/Alamy, (CL) Malcolm Ross/Alamy; **376** (CR) Steve Gschmeissner/Science Source, (BL) PHOTO FUN/Shutterstock, (BC) M.I. (Spike) Walker/Alamy Images, (Bkgrd) Tim Gainey/Alamy; **377** (BC) Andrew J. Martinez/Photo Researchers, Inc., (BR) David Fleetham/Mira, (BCL) Sebastian Duda/Shutterstock; **378** (Bkgrd) ©Grant Faint/Getty Images, (TCR) Dave King/©DK Images, (BCR) Dave King/DK Images, (TCR) Jupiterimages/Creatas/Alamy, (C) pogona22/Fotolia; **379** (Bkgd) ©Grant Faint/Getty Images, (C) WaterFrame/Alamy, (CR) NatureDiver/Shutterstock, (TR) Frans Lanting/Terra/Corbis, (CL) Kaz Chiba/Stockbyte/Getty Images; **380** (B) Tsuneo Nakamura/Volvox Inc/Alamy, (TL) Silver/Fotolia; **381** (BC) Heather Angel/Natural Visions; **382** (T) Dave King/©DK Images, (Bkgrd) David Peart/©DK Images; **383** (CR) Alan & Sandy Carey/Photo Researchers, Inc., (BCR) Christian Bauer/TIPS North America, (CR) Fritz Polking/Peter Arnold/PhotoLibrary Group, Inc., (BCR) John Cancalosi/AGE Fotostock; **384** (Bkgrd) Richard Cummins/Corbis; **385** (Inset) Heather Angel/Natural Visions/Alamy Images, (BL) Pavlo Vakhrushev/Fotolia, (Bkgrd) Stephen Frink/Stone/Getty Images, (CL) Marevision/Getty Images; **386** (TL) Arterra Picture Library/Alamy, (Bkgrd) Alex L. Fradkin/Stockbyte/Getty Images, (TCR) Nick Garbutt/Nature Picture Library; **387** (Inset) blickwinkel/Alamy, (TR) Karl Shone/©DK Images, (Bkgrd) Sarah Leen/National Geographic Image Collection; **388** (CL) Marvin Dembinsky Photo Associates/Alamy, (CR) Franco/Bonnard/Peter Arnold/PhotoLibrary Group, Inc., (TL) Hermann Brehm/Nature Picture Library, (Bkgrd) Shunsuke Yamamoto Photography/Getty Images; **389** (TR) Joe McDonald/Corbis, (CL) Nature Picture Library, (BC) Tom McHugh/Photo Researchers, Inc.; **390** (BL) Ron Cohn, koko, the Gorilla Foundation/NewsCom; **391** (B) PhotoStock-Israel/Science Source; **392** (BL) Linda Freshwaters Arndt/Photo Researchers, Inc., (Bkgrd) Mark Turner/PhotoLibrary Group, Inc.; **393** (TR) blickwinkel/Alamy, (TL) Robert Muth/Shutterstock, (Inset) Stan Osolinski/Corbis; **394** (Bkgrd) Doug Perrine/Alamy; **396** (BL) FLPA/SuperStock, (Bkgrd) Mark Carwardine/Nature Picture Library; **398** (TR) Doug Allan/Nature Picture Library, (Bkgrd) Kevin Schafer/age fotostock/PhotoLibrary Group, Inc., (BL) Kevin Maskell/Alamy; **399** (TR) T.J. Rich/Nature Picture Library; **400** (MR) Christian Bauer/TIPS North America, (ML) David Fleetham/Mira/Creative Eye, (BL) Ingo Arndt/Nature Picture Library, (TR) Photo Researchers; **402** (BCR) Photos/Jupiter Images; **403** (BCR) Geoff Brightling/Peter Minister, modelmaker/©DK Images, (BCR) Getty Images, (BCR) Jerry Young/©DK Images; **404** (CL) Bart Nedobre/Alamy Images; **405** (Bkgrd) Cornel Stefan Achirei/Alamy Images, (Bkgrd) Doug Steley /Alamy, (Inset) Ed Reschke/Peter Arnold/PhotoLibrary Group, Inc., (TR) Tom McHugh/Photo Researchers, Inc.

Chapter 12

406 (Bkgrd) Gary Bell/Corbis; **409** (BL) Christian Kosanetzky/Alamy, (BCL) Photoshot/AGE Fotostock, (CL) Tom Brakefield/Getty Images; **410** (BL) Dr. Jörn Köhler, (TCR) Frans Lanting/Corbis, (Bkgrd) Nick Garbutt/Nature Picture Library, (BR) Peter Arnold/PhotoLibrary Group, Inc.; **411** (BCR) Bruno Morandi/Corbis, (Inset) Tom Brakefield/Getty; **414** (B) Jason O. Watson/Alamy; **417** (CR) Chris Johns/National Geographic Image Collection; **418** (BC) Tom Brakefield/Getty Images; **419** (Bkgrd) Kim Taylor/Nature Picture Library; **421** (Bkgrd) Weatherstock/Peter Arnold/PhotoLibrary Group, Inc.; **422** (Bkgrd) ©Matt Brown/Corbis, (Bkgrd) Tim Mannakee/Corbis; **423** (TR) Taylor S. Kennedy/National Geographic Image Collection; **424** Alex Wild; **427** (BCL) Jim Zipp/Photo Researchers, Inc., (BL) Michael P. Gadomski/Photo Researchers, Inc., (CL) Glenn Bartley/Corbis; **428** (TR) Bill Curtsinger/National Geographic Image Collection, (BC) Christian Kosanetzky/Alamy, (BL) Klaas Lingbeek-van Kranen/Getty, (BCR) sndr/iStockphoto; **429** (CR) age Fotostock/SuperStock, (BCL) Ethan Daniels/Alamy Images, (BCL) Fabrice Bettex/Alamy Images, (TL) Jeff Hunter/Getty Images, (TR) Michael D. Kern/Nature Picture Library, (BR) Nature's Images/Photo Researchers, Inc.; **431** (BCL) Steve Byland/Fotolia, (BCR) Villiers Steyn/Shutterstock; **432** (BR)/Courtesy of USDA, Agricultural Research Service, (BCR) WaterFrame/Alamy, (CL) Jeff Foott/Getty Images; **433** (BR) Dietmar Nill/Nature Picture Library, (CR) Bruce Dale/Getty, (TR) Steve Jones/Corbis; **434** (Bkgrd) Ilene MacDonald/Alamy; **438** (CR) WaterFrame/Alamy; **442** (Bkgrd) Roger del Moral; **443** (BL) Chris Gomersall/Alamy Images, (TR) Dave & Les Jacobs/Blend Images/Getty Images.

Chapter 13

444 (Bkgrd) Marko König/Corbis; **447** (TL) /©DK Images, (BCL) Karen Huntt/Photographer's Choice/Getty Images; **448** (BC) Ian McAllister/All Canada Photos/PhotoLibrary Group, Inc.; **449** (B) Jerome Wexler/Photo Researchers, Inc., (Inset) Ted Kinsman/Photo Researchers, Inc.; **452** (Inset) ©DK Images, (Inset) iStockphoto; **453** (Inset) /©DK Images, (Inset) ©DK Images, (Inset) DK Images, (Inset) Frank Greenaway/©DK Images, (Inset) Geoff Brightling/©DK Images, (Inset) iStockphoto, (Inset) Jerry Young/©DK Images, (Inset) Judy Ledbetter/iStockphoto, (Inset) Nicholas Homrich/iStockphoto; **454** (Inset, BL, BC) ©DK Images, (BC) DK Images, (CC) GlobalP/iStockphoto; **456** (CL) Juniors Bildarchiv/Alamy; **458** (BL) Dr. Paul A. Zahl/Photo Researchers, Inc., (BL) Emma Firth/©DK Images; **465** (Inset) Floridapfe from S.Korea Kim in cherl/Getty, (Bkgrd) Karen Huntt/Photographer's Choice/Getty Images; **466** (BC) Peter Chadwick/©DK Images; **467** (C) Theo Allofs/Corbis; **468** (TC) Arco Images GmbH/Alamy Images, (TL) Juan-Carlos Munoz/Peter Arnold/PhotoLibrary Group, Inc., (TR) Peter Lillie/PhotoLibrary Group, Inc.; **469** (BR) Tim Shepard, Oxford Scientific Films/©DK Images; **470** (BL) ©Tom Brakefield/Corbis, (TL) Randy Green/Taxi/Getty Images; **471** (B) Foto Zihlmann/Fotolia; **472** (Bkgrd) blickwinkel/Alamy; **474** (TC) Sandy Felsenthal/Corbis; **475** (CL) PIER/Stone/Getty Images; **478** (B) Ken Findlay/©DK Images; **480** (CR) Geoff du Feu/Getty, (TL) Martin M. Bruce /SuperStock; **481** (Bkgrd) Inge Johnsson/Alamy Images; **482** (TCR) iStockphoto; **483** (CR) Cheerz/Dreamstime LLC; **486** (B) ©Masterfile Royalty-Free, (Bkgrd) Westend 61 GmbH/Alamy Images; **487** (Bkgrd) Brent Waltermire/Alamy Images, (Inset) Jupiter Images/Creatas/Alamy

Chapter 14

488 (Bkgrd) Stephen Dalton/Science Source; **491** (TCL, CL) Alamy, (BL) Exactostock/SuperStock, (TCL, L, C) Getty Images, (TL) Mark Bolton/Garden Picture Library/Photo Library Group, Inc., (BCL) Photodisc/Photolibrary Group, Inc., (TL) Susan Rayfield/Photo Researchers, Inc.; **492** (TC) Dr. Tony Brain/Photo Researchers, Inc., (C) Dr. Jeremy Burgess/ Photo Researchers, Inc., (B) Vinicius Ramalho Tupinamba/iStockphoto; **494** (BR) David R. Frazier Photolibrary, Inc./Alamy, (CR) Greg Gardner/iStockphoto; **495** (B) Arvydas Kniuk?ta/Shutterstock, (CR) Ruth Peterkin/Shutterstock, (TR) Larry Lee Photography/Alamy; **498** (C) Dorothea Lange/Corbis, (B) Margaret Bourke-White/Getty Images; **499** (B) Getty Images; **500** (CL) Alamy, (C) Dino Ferretti/ANSA/Corbis; **501** (TR) Dr. Jeremy Burgess/Photo Researchers, Inc., (BL) Exactostock/SuperStock, (TCR) Westend61 GmbH/Alamy; **502** (BCL) Jerome Whittingham/iStockphoto; **503** (BCR) arlindo 71/iStockphoto, (TCR) arlindo71/iStockphoto, (BL) Ocean/Corbis, (BC) kikkerdirk/Fotolia, (BC) PhotographerOlympus/iStockphoto; **505** (CR) kiamsoon/iStockphoto; **506** (BCR) mbongo/Fotolia; **507** (CR) National Tropical Botanical Garden; (CL) Betsy Gange/Hawaii Dept. of Land and Natural Resources/©Associated Press, (TR) Image Quest 3-D; **509** (BR) Jason Hahn Photography; (BC) Operation Migration, Inc., (TR) Kevin Schafer/Alamy, (CL) Markus Botzek/Bridge/Corbis, (BL) Kim Mitchell/Whooping Crane Eastern Partnership, (TC) James Caldwell/Alamy; **516** (B) Bettmann/Corbis, (CL) Ragnar Th Sigurdsson/Arctic Images/Alamy Images; **517** (TR) Colin Keates/Courtesy of the Natural History Museum, London/©DK Images, (TL) Dorling Kindersley/Getty Images, (B) Morton Beebe/Corbis, (BR) Nick Cobbing/Alamy Images, (T) Russell Sadur/©DK Images

Appendix

519 (R, L) Terry Whittaker/FLPA/PhotoLibrary Group, Inc.

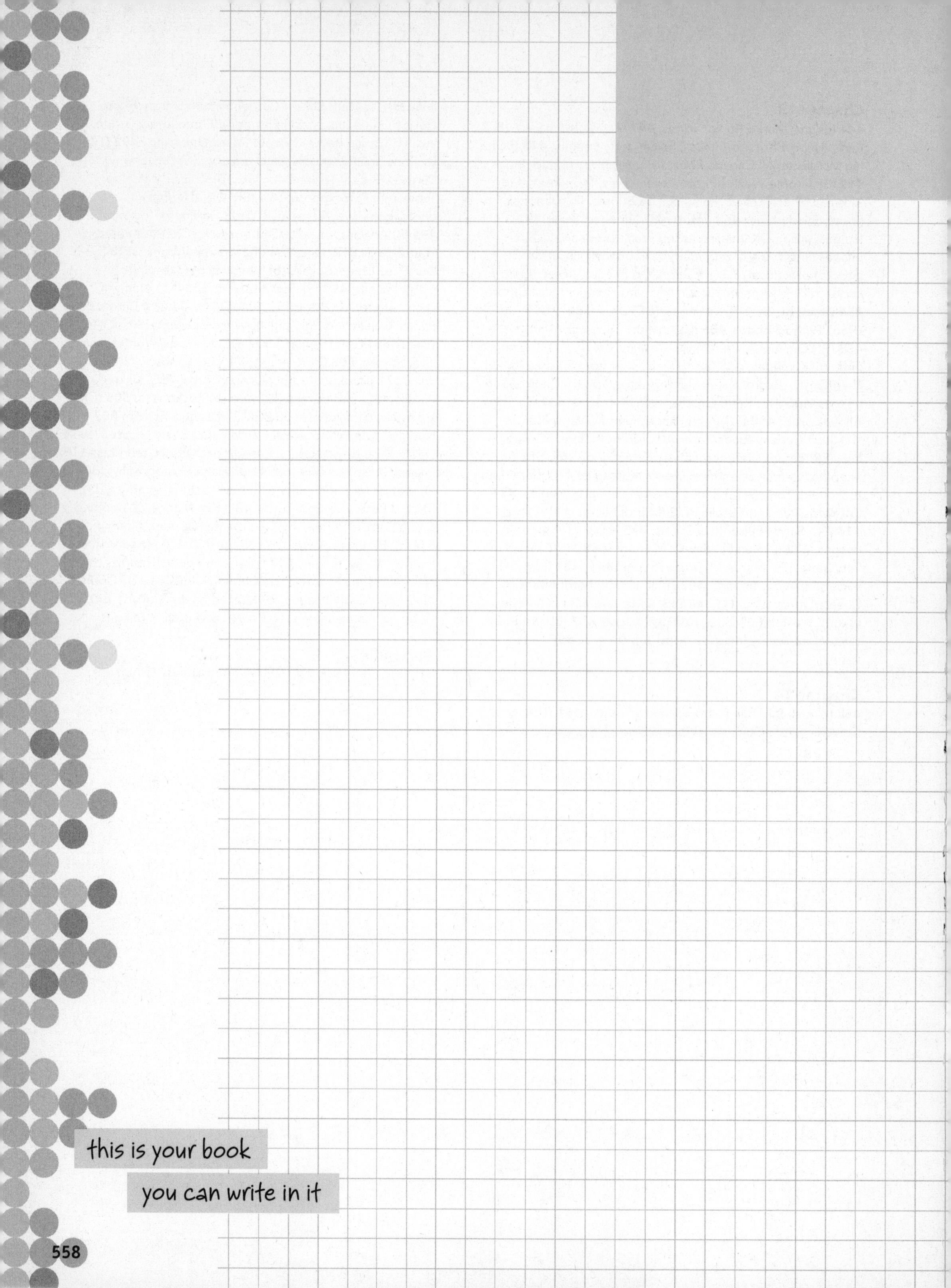
this is your book
you can write in it

take not

this space is yours—great for drawing diagrams and making no

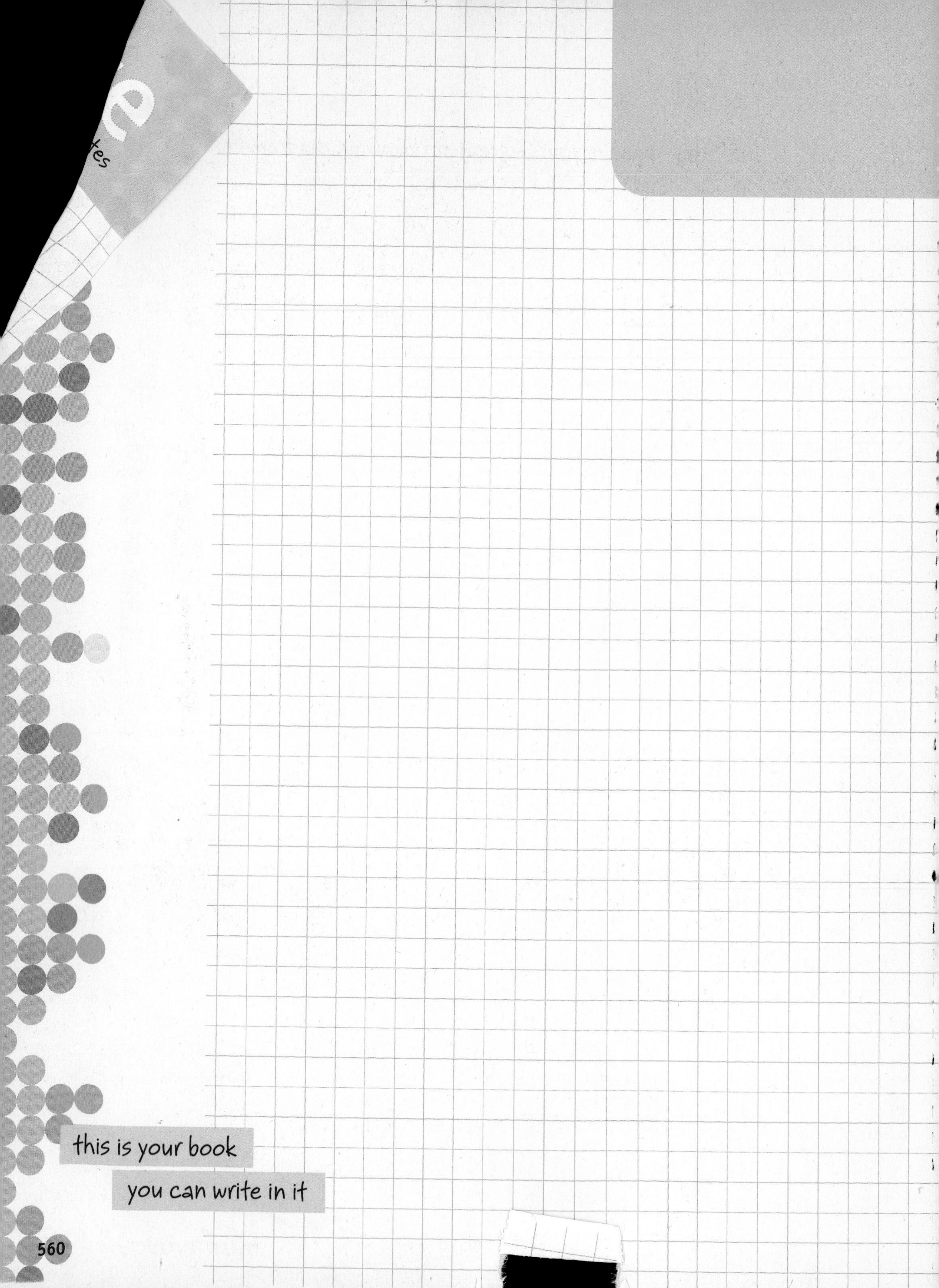
this is your book
you can write in it